INTEGRA

[For B.A. & B.Sc. Students]

SHANTI NARAYAN
Formerly, Dean of Colleges
University of Delhi, Delhi
(Formerly, Principal, Hans Raj College, Delhi)

Revised by
P.K. MITTAL
M.Sc., Ph.D.
Head of Mathematics Department
Govt. Post Graduate College
Rishikesh (Uttaranchal)

Revised Edition

S. CHAND
AN ISO 9001: 2000 COMPANY

2005
S. CHAND & COMPANY LTD.
RAM NAGAR, NEW DELHI-110 055

S. CHAND & COMPANY LTD.
(An ISO 9001 : 2000 Company)

Head Office : 7361, RAM NAGAR, NEW DELHI - 110 055
Phones : 23672080-81-82; Fax : 91-11-23677446
Shop at: **schandgroup.com**
E-mail: **schand@vsnl.com**

Branches:
- 1st Floor, Heritage, Near Gujarat Vidhyapeeth, Ashram Road, **Ahmedabad**-380 014. Ph. 27541965, 27542369..
- No. 6, Ahuja Chambers, 1st Cross, Kumara Krupa Road, **Bangalore**-560 001. Ph : 22268048, 22354008
- 152, Anna Salai, **Chennai**-600 002. Ph : 28460026
- S.C.O. 6, 7 & 8, Sector 9D, **Chandigarh**-160017, Ph-2749376, 2749377
- 1st Floor, Bhartia Tower, Badambadi, **Cuttack**-753 009, Ph-2332580; 2332581
- 1st Floor, 52-A, Rajpur Road, **Dehradun**-248 011. Ph : 2740889, 2740861
- Pan Bazar, **Guwahati**-781 001. Ph : 2522155
- Sultan Bazar, **Hyderabad**-500 195. Ph : 24651135, 24744815
- Mai Hiran Gate, **Jalandhar** - 144008 . Ph. 2401630
- 613-7, M.G. Road, Ernakulam, **Kochi**-682 035. Ph : 2381740
- 285/J, Bipin Bihari Ganguli Street, **Kolkata**-700 012. Ph : 22367459, 22373914
- Mahabeer Market, 25 Gwynne Road, Aminabad, **Lucknow**-226 018. Ph : 2226801, 2284815
- Blackie House, 103/5, Walchand Hirachand Marg , Opp. G.P.O., **Mumbai**-400 001. Ph : 22690881, 22610885
- 3, Gandhi Sagar East, **Nagpur**-440 002. Ph : 2723901
- 104, Citicentre Ashok, Govind Mitra Road, **Patna**-800 004. Ph : 2671366, 2302100

Marketing Offices :
- 238-A M.P. Nagar, Zone 1, **Bhopal** - 462 011. Ph : 5274723
- A-14 Janta Store Shopping Complex, University Marg, Bapu Nagar, **Jaipur** - 302 015, Phone : 0141-2709153

First Edition 1942
Subsequent Editions and Reprint 1947, 51, 55, 57, 59, 61, 63, 65, 67, 70, 72, 75, 79, 80, 81, 82, 83 (Twice), 84, 85, (Twice) 87, 88, 89, 91, 92, 93, 94, 96, 98, 99 (Twice), 2000, 2001, 2002, 2003, 2004
Tenth Revised edition 2005

ISBN : 81-219-0681-4

PRINTED IN INDIA

By Rajendra Ravindra Printers (Pvt.) Ltd., Ram Nagar, New Delhi-110 055 and published by S. Chand & Company Ltd., 7361, Ram Nagar, New Delhi-110 055

PREFACE TO THE TENTH EDITION

The book originally written, about 62 years ago, has during the intevening period been revised and reprinted several times. Due to the new U.G.C. Model syllabus and the demand of the students a thorough revision of the book was overdue. I very humbly took the challenge of revising a perfect work of Shri Shanti Narayan Ji and tried to meet the present demand, of those who always loved and liked the books of the famous Mathematician Shri Shanti Narayan Ji.

To meet out the changing trend in the course structure of different Indian Universities as per U.G.C. guide-lines, the book has been thoroughly revised and a large number of solved examples have been given in each topic to meet the present needs of the students. The following new chapters have been added in this present edition.

- Beta and Gamma Functions
- Convergence of Improper Integrals
- Differentiation under Integral Sign
- Multiple Integrals

The books, in the present, form, is a humble effort of make it more useful to the students and teachers. I owe my special gratitude to Sri Ravindra Kumar Gupta, M.D., S. Chand & Company Ltd., for giving me opportunity to revise the books of Late Shri Shanti Narayan, an eminent Indian Mathematician.

I expect to receive suggestions from the readers both from teachers as well as students for the improvement of the book, which will be highly appreciated.

Rishikesh   **P.K. MITTAL**
(Uttaranchal)

PREFACE TO THE FIRST EDITION

This book is intended to serve as a companion volume to my "Differential Calculus", and is designed to meet the requirements of the B.A. and B.Sc. students of our universities.

The book opens with a chapter on the definition of indefinite integrals based on the anti-derivative notion and proceeds to give the geometrical interpretation of definite integrals. A short and simple account of improper integrals has also been given in this chapter. The second chapter has been devoted to explaining the two methods of integration, *viz.* "Integration by substitution" and "Integration by parts". A systematic account of the integration of Algebraic rational function, Trigonometric functions and Algebraic irrational functions, has then been given in Chapters III, IV and V respectively. This division of the book into chapters according to the class of functions to be integrated, and, not according to the methods of integration, will greatly help in enabling the student to obtain mastery over the technique of integration. Then follows the application of integration to Quadrature, Rectification and Volumes and Surfaces of revolution. Next comes the exhibition of a definite integral as the limit of a sum. This exhibition is based on purely geometrical, rather than on purely analytical considerations. I have deliberately refrained from giving the analytical proof as the rigorous analytical proof is beyond the comprehension of the students at this stage and the proof usually given is unsatisfactory and thus misleading. No separate chapter has been devoted to reduction formulae and all such cases have been considered at their appropriate places. The last two chapters have been devoted to a short Elementary course on Differential Equations.

The book contains a large number of examples to illustrate the various types.

I am greatly indebted to Prof. Sita Ram Gupta, M.A., P.E.S. of the Government College, Lahore, who kindly went through a part of the manuscript and made some valuable suggestions. I am also deeply grateful to my friend and colleague Prof. Om Prakash, M.A., of the D.A.V. College Lahore and Prof. Ramji Dass Syal M.A., of the Dayanand Technical Institute, Lahore who have helped me in the preparation of this book.

I shall be thankful to those who suggest improvements or point some errors which might have escaped my notice.

Lahore,
Dec., 1942

Shanti Narayan

CONTENTS

1. Definitions   **1 – 21**

1.1.   Integral of a function   1
1.2.   The study of Integral Calculus   1
1.3.   Indefinite valuedness of Integration   2
1.4.   Table of Elementary Integrals.   3
1.5.   Two simple theorems   5
1.6.   Definite Integral   8
1.7.   Two important properties of definite integrals   10
1.8.   Geometrical interpretation of a definite integral   11
1.9.   Improper definite integrals   14

2. Methods of Integration   **22 – 77**

2.1.   Methods of Integration   22
2.2.   Integration by substitution   22
2.3.   Three inportant forms of integrals   28
2.4.   Six importnat integrals   38
2.5.   Integration by parts   48
2.6.   Sometimes both the methods of integration have to be
       applied in one and the same question.   59
2.7.   Definite Integrals   61
2.8.   Reduction formulae   66

3. Integration of Algebraic Rational Functions   **78 – 102**

3.1.   Integration of Rational function   78
3.2.   Case of non-repeated linear factors only in the denominator   82
3.3.   Case of non-repeated linear or repeated linear factors only
       in the denominator   84
3.4.   Case of linear or quadratie non-repeated factors only in the
       denominator   85
3.5.   Integration Reduction formula   89
3.6.   Integration of algebraic rational functions by substitution   93
3.7.   Integration of algebraic rational functions of e^n 96

4. Integration of Trigonomitric Functions   **103 – 164**

4.1.   Integration of $\sin^n x$ where n is a positive integer.   103
4.2.   Integration of $\cos^n x$ where n is a positive integer   107
4.3.   Integration of $\sin^p x \cos^q x$ where p, q are positive integers 112
4.4.   Integration of $\tan^n x$ and $\cot^n x$ where n is a positive integer 121
4.5.   Integration of $\sec^n x$ where n is a positive integer   125
4.6.   The integration of $\sin^p x \cos^q x$, when $p + q$ is a negative
       even integer.   127
4.7.   Integration of $R (\cos x, \sin x)$ 132
4.8.   To integrate (a cos x + b sin x) / (c cos x + d sin x).

4.9. Reduction formula for $\int \cos^m x \cos nx \, dx$. 145

5. Integration of Irrational Functions ... 165 – 212

5.1. Integration of rational function of x and a linear surd, $(ax + b)^{1/n}$, where n is some positive integer 165

5.2. To evaluate the integrals 108

5.3. Integration of

(i) $\dfrac{Ax + B}{\sqrt{ax^2 + bx + c}}$,   (ii) $(Ax + B)\sqrt{ax^2 + bx + c}$. 171

5.4. Reduction Formula for $\int \dfrac{x^n}{\sqrt{ax^2 + bx + c}} \, dx$, where n is a positive integer 175

5.5. To evaluate $\int \dfrac{dx}{(Ax + B)\sqrt{ax^2 + bx + c}}$. 179

5.6. To evaluate $\int \dfrac{dx}{(ax^2 + bx + c)\sqrt{Ax^2 + Bx + C}}$. 181

5.7. General Case. 183

5.8. Integration of irrational algebraic functions by trigonometric transformations 185

5.9. Integration of $x^m (a + bx^n)^p$. 188

5.10. Reduction Formula for $\int \dfrac{dx}{(x^2 + a^2)^n}$, n being a positive integer 190

5.11. Reduction Formula for $\int x^m (a + bx^n)^p \, dx$ where m, n, p are positive or negative integers or fractions 191

5.12. Reduction Formula for $\int (a^2 + x^2)^{n/2} \, dx$. 193

6. Definite Integrals ... 213 – 244

6.1. We have so far regarded integration as inverse of differentiation. The definite integral 213

6.2. Properties of Definite Integrals 213

6.3. Fundamental Theorem of Integral Calculus 227

6.4. Summation of series 232

7. Beta and Gamma Functions 245 – 272

7.1. Definitions 245

7.2. Properties of Beta and Gamma Functions 245

7.3. Transformations of Gamma Function 247

7.4. Some Important Deductions   250

7.5. Duplication Formula To prove that

$$\Gamma m \ \Gamma\left(m + \frac{1}{2}\right) = \frac{\sqrt{\pi}}{2^{2m-1}} \cdot \Gamma(2m).$$ 252

7.6. To find the value of $\Gamma\left(\dfrac{1}{n}\right) \Gamma\left(\dfrac{2}{n}\right) \Gamma\left(\dfrac{3}{n}\right) \ldots \Gamma\left(\dfrac{n-1}{n}\right)$, where n is a positive integer.

7.7. Evaluate the integrals

$$\int_0^\infty e^{-ax} \cos bx \cdot x^{m-1} \, dx \text{ and } \int_0^\infty e^{-ax} \sin bx \cdot x^{m-1} \, dx.$$ 266

8. Areas of Plane Regions   **... 275 – 319**

8.1. Area Enclosed by two curves   275

8.2. Quadrature of hyperbola   287

8.3. Sectorial Area   291

8.4. Area bounded by a closed curve   303

8.5. Simpson's rule for approximate evaluation of definite integrals and areas   310

9. Rectification Lengths of Plane Curves   **... 320 – 342**

9.1. Introduction   320

9.2. Cartesian Equations   320

9.3. Other Expressions for lengths of arcs   321

9.4. Intrinsic Equations of a Curve   331

9.5. Rectification of ellipse   338

10. Volumes and Surfaces of Revolution   **343 – 381**

10.1 Axis of revolution   343

10.2. Volumes and Surfaces of Revolution   342

10.3. Any axis of revolution   352

10.4. Area of the surface of the frustum of a cone   362

10.5. Surface of revolution   363

10.6. Theorems of Pappus   371

10.7. Surface of Revolution   372

11. Centre of Gravity. Moment of Inertia   **382 – 401**

11.1. Introduction   382

11.2. Centre of Gravity   382

11.3. Centre of gravity of a continuous distribution of matter383

11.4. Moment of Inertia   396

SOME MISCELLANEOUS TOPICS

12. Multiple Integrals   **405–468**

12.1 Multiple Integrals   405

12.2   Double Integral.   405

12.3   Applications of Double Integration   415

12.4   Change of order of Integration   424

12.5   Change of the variable in a multiple integral   438

12.6   Triple Integrals   448

12.7   Dritchlet's Theorem   433

13.   Convergence of Improper Integrals   468 – 509

13.1   Proper integrals   468

13.2   Improper integrals   468

13.3   Improper integrals of the first kind or infinite integrals   469

13.4.   Improper integrals of the second kind   470

13.5.   Convergence of improper integrals   471

13.6.   Test for convergence of improper integrals of the first kind   474

13.7.   Absolute convergence   486

13.8.   Tests of convergence of improper integrals of the second kind   490

14.   Differentiation Under Integral Sign   510 – 532

14.1.   Consider a continuous function $f(x, y)$ of two variables defined in a rectangle bounded by the lines $x = a, x = b; y = c, y = d$ 510

14.2.   Differentiation Under integrals sign in the cose of improper integrals   514

DIFFERENTIAL EQUATIONS

15.   Differential Equation of first order and first degree   535 – 597

15.1.A   Differential equation   535

15.2.   Number of arbitrary constants   538

15.3.   Equation of which the variables are separable   539

15.4.   Linear equations   543

15.5.   Equation reducible to the linear form   550

15.6.   Change of variables   558

15.7.   Homogeneous equations   562

15.8.   Equations reducible to the homogeneous form   569

15.9.   Exact differential equations   576

15.10.   Integrating factors   580

16.   Equations of the first order but not of the first degree   598 – 624

16.1.   In the discussion of equations of the first order which are not of the first degree, it is usual to denote dy/dx by p.   598

16.2.   Equations solvable for p 590

16.3.   Equations solvable for y 601

16.4.   Equations solvable for n 606

16.5.   Clairut's equation   610

16.6.   Geometrical meaning of a differential equation os the first order   613

16.7.   Singular solutions   614

17.   Trajectories of a Family of curves   625 –634
  17.1.   Definition   625
  17.2.   Cartesion coordinates   625
  17.3.   Polar coordinates   626
  17.4.   Self orthogonal families   627

18.   Linear equations   635–708
  18.1.   Linear differential equations   635
  18.2.   Linear differential equations with constant caefficiets   635
  18.3.   Operators   637
  18.4.   To prove that
          $(D - \alpha)\,(D - \beta)\,y \equiv (D - \beta)\,(D - \alpha)\,y,$
          α, β *being any constants whatsoever.*
  18.5.   To solve the differential equation
          $$\frac{d^n y}{dx^n} + a_1 \frac{d^{n-1}}{dx^{n-1}} + a_2 \frac{d^{n-2} y}{dx^{n-2}} + \ldots\ldots + a_{n-1} \frac{dy}{dx} + a_n y = 0.\quad 639$$
  18.6.   Inverse operators
  18.7.   To determine the particular integrals of
          $f\,(d)y = X$ 647
  18.8.   Rule for finding the particular integral when X is
          of the form e^{mm} 650
  18.9.   The following two sections will give us formulae which will be
          helpful in finding particular integrals of the differential equations
          of the form
          $f\,(D)\,y = e^{ax}\,V,\;\; f\,(D)\,y = xV,$
  18.10. Homogeneous linear equations   686
  18.11. Equations Reducible to Homogeneous form   696

16.7   Singular solutions   614
17.   Trajectories of a family of curves   625—634
17.1.   Definition   625
17.2.   Cartesian coordinates   625
17.3.   Polar coordinates   626
17.4.   Self orthogonal families   627
18.   Linear equations   635—708
18.1.   Linear differential equations   635
18.2.   Linear differential equations with constant coefficients   635
18.3.   Operators   637
18.4.   To prove that
18.5.   To solve the differential equation
18.6.   Inverse operators
18.7.   To determine the particular integrals of
18.8.   Rule for finding the particular integral when X is   647
        of the form e^{ax} 650
18.9.   The following two sections will give us formulae which will be helpful in finding particular integrals of the differential equations of the form
18.10.   Homogeneous linear equations   656
18.11.   Equations Reducible to Homogeneous form   690

1

Definitions

1
Definitions

TABLE OF STANDARD RESULTS

1.1. Integral of a function. Integrand. If the differential coefficient of a function $f(x)$ is $F(x)$, *i.e.*, if

$$\frac{d\,f(x)}{dx} = F(x),$$

we say that $f(x)$ is *an Integral* or a *Primitive* of $F(x)$ and, in symbols, write

$$\int F(x)\,dx = f(x).$$

For example,

$$\frac{d\sin x}{dx} = \cos x \;\Rightarrow\; \int \cos x\,dx = \sin x.$$

As another example, we see that

$$\frac{d\log x}{dx} = \frac{1}{x} \;\Rightarrow\; \int \frac{1}{x}\,dx = \log x.$$

The letter x in dx, denotes that the integration is to be performed with respect to the variable x.

The process of determining an integral of a function is called *Integration* and the function to be integrated is called *Integrand*.

Since integration and differentiation are inverse processes, we have

$$\frac{d}{dx}\left[\int f(x)\,dx\right] = f(x).$$

Ex. *Show that*

(i) $\int x\,dx = x^2/2.$ (ii) $\int \sin x\,dx = -\cos x + 2.$

(iii) $\int at^3\,dt = at^4/4.$ (iv) $\int (1/y)\,dy = \log y - 3.$

1.2. The study of Integral Calculus consists in developing techniques for the determination of integral of a given function. This subject finds extensive applications to Geometry, Natural and Social Sciences. In this book, we shall be concerned with applications in relation to the determination of Plane areas, Lengths of arcs and Volumes and Surfaces of solids of revolution, Centre of Gravity and Moment of Inertia.

Historically, the subject arose in connection with the determination of areas of plane regions and was based on the notion of the limit of a type of a sum when the number of terms in the sum tends to infinity and each term tends to zero. In fact, the name Integral Calculus has its origin in this process of summation and the words '*To integrate*' literally means '*To find the sum of*'. It is only afterwards that it was seen that the subject of Integration can also be viewed from the point of view of the Inverse of differentiation. We shall not develop the subject in the historical order and, as done above, start by defining Integration as the Inverse of differentiation. In Chapter 9, we shall consider the summation aspect of Integration also.

1.3. Indefinite valuedness of Integration. General Integral. Arbitrary Constant. If $f(x)$ is an integral of F (x), then $f(x) + c$ is also an integral of F (x); c being a constant whatsoever, for

$$\frac{d f(x)}{dx} = F(x) \implies \frac{d[f(x) + c]}{dx} = F(x).$$

Again, let $f(x)$, $\varphi(x)$ be two integrals of F (x) so that we have

$$f'(x) = \varphi'(x) = F(x).$$

*As the differential coefficients of the functions $f(x)$ and $\varphi(x)$ are equal, the functions differ by some constant, *i.e.*,

$$f(x) - \varphi(x) = c \iff f(x) = \varphi(x) + c,$$

where c is a constant.

From these considerations, we deduce that the *Integral of a function is not unique* and that if $f(x)$ be any one integral of F (x), then

(*i*) $f(x) + c$ is also its integral; c being any constant whatsoever ;

(*ii*) every integral of F (x) can be obtained from, $f(x) + c$, by giving some suitable value to c.

Thus if $f(x)$ be *any* one integral of F (x), then $f(x) + c$ is its *General integral*.

From this it follows that *any two integrals of the same function differ by a constant*.

The constant, c, is called *Constant of integration*. The constant of integration will generally be *omitted* and the symbol $\int$ F (x) dx will denote any one integral of F (x). But it must be remembered that the symbol $\int$ F (x) dx is *really infinite valued*.

It may happen that, by different methods of integration, we obtain different integrals of the same function, but it will always be seen that they differ from each other merely by a constant.

---

* Chapter IV of Author's *Differential Calculus*.

Ex. *Show that*

(i) $x^4 + c$ is the general integral of $4x^3$,

(ii) $\sin^{-1} x + c$ is the general integral of $1/\sqrt{1 - x^2}$,

(iii) $\sec x + c$ is the general integral of $\sec x \tan x$,

where, c denotes, an arbitrary constant.

1.4. Table of Elementary Integrals. We now give a table of elementary integrals based on the corresponding table of the differential coefficients of elementary functions.

$$* \int x^n \, dx = \frac{x^{n+1}}{n+1}, (n \neq -1) \qquad \frac{1}{n+1} \frac{d\,(x^{n+1})}{dx} = x^n.$$

$$\int \frac{1}{x} \, dx = \log x, \qquad \because \quad \frac{d\,(\log x)}{dx} = \frac{1}{x}.$$

$$\int e^x \, dx = e^x, \qquad \because \quad \frac{d\,(e^x)}{dx} = e^x.$$

$$\int a^x \, dx = \frac{a^x}{\log a}, \qquad \because \quad \frac{d\,(a^x / \log a)}{dx} = a^x.$$

$$\int \sin x \, dx = -\cos x, \qquad \because \quad \frac{d\,(-\cos x)}{dx} = \sin x.$$

$$\int \cos x \, dx = \sin x, \qquad \because \quad \frac{d\,(\sin x)}{dx} = \cos x.$$

$$\int \sec^2 x \, dx = \tan x, \qquad \because \quad \frac{d\,(\tan x)}{dx} = \sec^2 x.$$

$$\int \operatorname{cosec}^2 x \, dx = -\cot x, \qquad \because \quad \frac{d\,(-\cot x)}{dx} = \operatorname{cosec}^2 x.$$

$$\int \sec x \tan x \, dx = \sec x, \qquad \because \quad \frac{d\,(\sec x)}{dx} = \sec x \tan x.$$

$$\int \operatorname{cosec} x \cot x \, dx = -\operatorname{cosec} x, \qquad \because \quad \frac{d\,(-\operatorname{cosec} x)}{dx} = \cot x \operatorname{cosec} x.$$

$$\int \frac{1}{\sqrt{1 - x^2}} \, dx = \sin^{-1} x \qquad \because \quad \frac{d\,(\sin^{-1} x)}{dx} = \frac{1}{\sqrt{1 - x^2}}$$

$$\text{or} - \cos^{-1} x, \qquad \qquad = \frac{d\,(-\cos^{-1} x)}{dx}.$$

---

* When $n = -1$, we have $x^n = x^{-1} = 1/x$ whose integral is $\log x$.

$$\int \frac{1}{1+x^2}\, dx = \tan^{-1} x$$
$$\text{or} - \cot^{-1} x,$$

$$\therefore \frac{d\,(\tan^{-1} x)}{dx} = \frac{1}{1+x^2}$$

$$= \frac{d\,(-\cot^{-1} x)}{dx}.$$

$$\int \frac{1}{x\sqrt{x^2-1}}\, dx = \sec^{-1} x$$
$$\text{or} - \text{cosec}^{-1}\, x,$$

$$\frac{d\,(\sec^{-1} x)}{dx} = \frac{1}{x\sqrt{x^2-1}}$$

$$= \frac{d\,(-\text{cosec}^{-1} x)}{dx}.$$

$$\int \cosh x\, dx = \sinh x, \qquad \therefore \frac{d\,(\sinh x)}{dx} = \cosh x.$$

$$\int \sinh x\, dx = \cosh x, \qquad \therefore \frac{d\,(\cosh x)}{dx} = \sinh x.$$

It is important to notice that when $n \neq -1$, *the integral of x^n is obtained on increasing the index n by 1 and dividing by the increased index, n + 1.* Thus, for example,

$$\int x^{1/2}\, dx = \frac{x^{\frac{1}{2}+1}}{\frac{1}{2}+1} = \frac{2}{3} x^{3/2},$$

$$\int \frac{1}{x^2}\, dx = \int x^{-2}\, dx = \frac{x^{-2+1}}{-2+1} = -\frac{1}{x}.$$

Note 1. The result

$$\int \frac{dx}{x} = \log x,$$

requires some explanation. We know that $\log x$ is defined for positive values of x only and, therefore, in the statement $d\,(\log x)/dx = 1/x$ or, in its equivalent statement $\int (1/x)\, dx = \log x$, it is implied that x is positive.

Now, when x is negative, $-x$ is positive, and therefore $\log(-x)$ has a meaning. In this case, we have

$$\frac{d\,[\log(-x)]}{dx} = \frac{1}{-x} \times -1 = \frac{1}{x}.$$

Therefore

$$\int \frac{1}{x}\, dx = \log(-x), \text{ if } x \text{ is negative.}$$

Thus the integral of $1/x$ is $\log x$ or $\log(-x)$ according as x is positive or negative. Both these results are included in the single statement

$$\int \frac{1}{x}\,dx = \log|x|,$$

where $|x|$ denotes the absolute value of x.

Note 2. The inverse trigonometrical functions in the above table are single-valued functions as defined in Chapter II of the author's *Differential Calculus*. Thus

$$\sin^{-1}x,\ \tan^{-1}x,\ \cot^{-1}x,\ \csc^{-1}x$$

are the angles, lying between $-\pi/2$ and $\pi/2$, whose sine, tangent, cotangent and cosecant are x; also

$$\cos^{-1}x,\ \sec^{-1}x,$$

are the angles, lying between 0 and π whose cosine and secant are x.

Note 3. From the above table, we see that both $\sin^{-1}x$ and $-\cos^{-1}x$ are integrals of $1/\sqrt{1-x^2}$. From this we cannot deduce the equality of $\sin^{-1}x$ and $-\cos^{-1}x$. The only legitimate conclusion is that they differ by some constant.

In fact, from elementary trigonometry, we know that

$$\sin^{-1}x - (-\cos^{-1}x) = \sin^{-1}x + \cos^{-1}x = \frac{1}{2}\pi.$$

Ex. Write down the integrals of

(i) x^3,　　(ii) $\sqrt{x}$,　　(iii) $\sqrt[3]{x^2}$,　　(iv) $\sqrt{x^{-3}}$,

(v) 2^x,　　(vi) $(1/2)^x$,　　(vii) a^{2x},　　(viii) e^{3x}.

Ans.

(i) $\frac{1}{4}x^4$,　(ii) $\frac{2}{3}x^{3/2}$,　(iii) $\frac{3}{5}x^{5/3}$,　(iv) $-2x^{-1/2}$,

(v) $\frac{2^x}{\log 2}$,　(vi) $\frac{-(1/2)^x}{\log 2}$,　(vii) $\frac{a^{2x}}{2\log a}$,　(viii) $\frac{e^{3x}}{3}$.

1.5. Two simple theorems.

1.5.1. First Theorem.

$$\int a f(x)\,dx = a \int f(x)\,dx. \qquad \text{...(A)}$$

i.e., the integral of the product of a constant and a function is equal to the product of the constant and the integral of the function.

The proof will follow from the corresponding theorem of Differential Calculus which states that the derivative of the product of a constant and a function is equal to the product of a constant and the derivative of the function.

Differentiating the right hand side of (A), we obtain

$$\frac{d}{dx}\left[a \int f(x)\, dx \right] = a \frac{d}{dx} \int f(x)\, dx = a\, f(x),$$

$$\Rightarrow \qquad \int a f(x)\, dx = a \int f(x)\, dx.$$

Second Theorem.

$$\int [f(x) \pm F(x)]\, dx = \int f(x)\, dx \pm \int F(x)\, dx. \qquad \qquad ...(B)$$

i.e., the integral of the sum or difference of two functions is equal to the sum or difference of their integrals.

The proof will follow from the corresponding theorem of Differential Calculus which states that the derivative of the sum or difference of two functions is equal to the sum or difference of their derivatives.

Differentiating the right-hand side of (B), we obtain

$$\frac{d}{dx}\left[\int f(x)\, dx \pm \int F(x)\, dx \right] = \frac{d}{dx} \int f(x)\, dx \pm \frac{d}{dx} \int F(x)\, dx$$

$$= f(x) \pm F(x)$$

$$\Rightarrow \qquad \int [f(x) \pm F(x)]\, dx = \int f(x)\, dx \pm \int F(x)\, dx.$$

The theorem can easily be generalised to the case of the algebraic sum of a *finite* number of functions so that we have

$$\int [f_1(x) \pm f_2(x) \pm f_3(x) \pm ..... \pm f_n(x)]\, dx$$

$$= \int f_1(x)\, dx \pm \int f_2(x)\, dx \pm ..... \pm \int f_n(x)\, dx.$$

Note. The two theorems prove useful when the integrand can be decomposed into the sum of a number of functions whose integrals are known. In fact this *decomposition of an integrand into the sum of a number of functions with known integrals* constitutes an important technique of integration as will be seen later on.

EXAMPLES

1. $\displaystyle \int 3x^3\, dx = 3 \int x^3\, dx = \frac{3x^4}{4}$

2. $\displaystyle \int (a_0 + a_1 x + a_2 x^2 + ... + a_n x^n)\, dx$

$$= \int a_0\, dx + \int a_1 x\, dx + \int a_2 x^2\, dx + ... + \int a_n x^n\, dx$$

$$= a_0 \int 1\, dx + a_1 \int x\, dx + a_2 \int x^2\, dx + ... + a_n \int x^n\, dx$$

$$= a_0 x + a_1 \frac{x^2}{2} + a_2 \frac{x^3}{3} + ... + a_n \frac{x^{n+1}}{n+1}$$

3. $\int \left(\cos x + \dfrac{2}{x} - e^x \right) dx = \int \cos x \, dx + 2 \int \dfrac{1}{x} \, dx - \int e^x \, dx$

$$= \sin x + 2 \log x - e^x$$

4. $\int \dfrac{3 - 5x^2 + 7x^4 - 9x^6}{x^6} \, dx = \int \left(\dfrac{3}{x^6} - \dfrac{5}{x^4} + \dfrac{7}{x^2} - 9 \right) dx$

$$= \int \dfrac{3}{x^6} \, dx - \int \dfrac{5}{x^4} \, dx + \int \dfrac{7}{x^2} \, dx - \int 9 \, dx$$

$$= -\dfrac{3}{5x^5} + \dfrac{5}{3x^3} - \dfrac{7}{x} - 9x$$

$$= \dfrac{-9 + 25x^2 - 105x^4 - 135x^6}{15x^5}$$

5. $\int \dfrac{x^2}{1 + x^2} \, dx = \int \dfrac{(x^2 + 1) - 1}{x^2 + 1} \, dx$

$$= \int \left(1 - \dfrac{1}{x^2 + 1} \right) dx$$

$$= \int 1 \, dx - \int \dfrac{1}{x^2 + 1} \, dx = x - \tan^{-1} x$$

6. $\int \dfrac{x^4}{x^2 + 1} \, dx = \int \dfrac{x^4 - 1 + 1}{x^2 + 1} \, dx = \int \left(x^2 - 1 + \dfrac{1}{x^2 + 1} \right) dx$

$$= \dfrac{x^3}{3} - x + \tan^{-1} x$$

7. $\int \dfrac{\sin^3 x + \cos^3 x}{\sin^2 x \cos^2 x} \, dx = \int \dfrac{\sin^3 x}{\sin^2 x \cos^2 x} \, dx + \int \dfrac{\cos^3 x}{\sin^2 x \cos^2 x} \, dx$

$$= \int \tan x \sec x \, dx + \int \cot x \, \text{cosec} \, x \, dx$$

$$= \sec x - \text{cosec} \, x$$

9. $\int (1 - \cos 2x) \, dx = \int \sqrt{2 \sin^2 x} \, dx = \int \sqrt{2} \sin x \, dx$

$$= \sqrt{2} \int \sin x \, dx = -\sqrt{2} \cos x$$

EXERCISES

Integrate the following functions :

1. $x^{1/3} + x^{1/2} + x^{3/5}$.

2. $(x^2 + 2x + 3) / x^4$.

3. $\dfrac{(1 + 2x)^3}{x^4}$.

4. $\dfrac{2x^4 + 3}{x^2 + 1}$.

5. $\dfrac{x^2-1}{x^2+1}$.

6. $\dfrac{\left(\sqrt{x}+\sqrt[3]{x^2}\right)^2}{x}$.

7. $\dfrac{x^4+x^2+1}{2\,(x^2+1)}$.

8. $\dfrac{x^6-1}{x^2+1}$.

9. $5\cos x-3\sin x-\dfrac{2}{\cos^2 x}$.

10. $\dfrac{5\cos^3 x+7\sin^3 x}{2\sin^2 x\cos^2 x}$.

11. $\dfrac{\cos 2x}{\cos^2 x\sin^2 x}$.

12. $\sec^2 x\,\operatorname{cosec}^2 x$.

13. $\dfrac{3\cos x-4}{\sin^2 x}$.

14. $\dfrac{1+2\sin x}{\cos^2 x}$.

15. $\tan^2 x$.

16. $\cot^2 x$.

17. $(\tan x+\cot x)^2$.

18. $(1-\cos 2x)/(1+\cos 2x)$.

19. $\sqrt{1+\sin 2x}$.

20. $\sqrt{1+\cos 2x}$.

ANSWERS

1. $\dfrac{3}{4}x^{4/3}+\dfrac{2}{3}x^{3/2}+\dfrac{5}{8}x^{8/5}$.

2. $-(x^2+x+1)/x^3$.

3. $-(1+9x-36x^2)/3x^3+8\log x$.

4. $\dfrac{1}{6}(x^3-2x)+5\tan^{-1}x$.

5. $x-2\tan^{-1}x$.

6. $x+\dfrac{3}{4}x^{4/3}+\dfrac{12}{7}x^{7/6}$.

7. $\dfrac{1}{6}(x^3+3\tan^{-1}x)$.

8. $\dfrac{1}{5}x^5-\dfrac{1}{3}x^2+x-2\tan^{-1}x$.

9. $5\sin x-3\cos x-2\tan x$.

10. $\dfrac{7}{2}\sec x-\dfrac{5}{2}\operatorname{cosec} x$.

11. $-\sec x\,\operatorname{cosec} x$.

12. $-2\cot 2x$.

13. $-4\cot x+3\operatorname{cosec} x$.

14. $\tan x+2\sec x$.

15. $\tan x-x$.

16. $-\cot x-x$.

17. $-2\cot 2x$.

18. $\tan x-x$.

19. $-\cos x+\sin x$.

20. $\sqrt{2}\cos x$.

1.6. Definite Integral. In geometrical and other applications of Integral Calculus, it becomes necessary to find the difference in the values of an integral of a function $f(x)$ for two assigned values of the independent variable x, say, a, b. This difference is called the *Definite integral of $f(x)$* over the interval $[a,\ b]$ and is denoted by

$$\int_a^b f(x)\,dx.$$

Thus

$$\int_a^b f(x)\,dx = F(b) - F(a).$$

where $F(x)$ is an integral of $f(x)$.

The difference $[F(b) - F(a)]$ is sometimes denoted as

$$\left| F(x) \right|_a^b.$$

Thus if $F(x)$ is an integral of $f(x)$, we write

$$\int_a^b f(x)\,dx = \left| F(x) \right|_a^b = F(b) - F(a).$$

The number, a, is called the *Lower limit* and the number, b, the *Upper limit* of integration.

It should be seen that the *value of a definite integral is unique and is independent of the particular integral which we may employ to calculate it.* Considering $F(x) + c$ instead of $F(x)$, we obtain

$$\int_a^b f(x)\,dx = \left| F(x) + c \right|_a^b = \{F(b) + c\} - \{F(a) + c\}$$

$$= F(b) - F(a),$$

so that the arbitrary constant, c, disappears in the process and we get the same value as on considering $F(x)$.

EXAMPLES

1. $\displaystyle\int_1^2 x\,dx = \left| \frac{x^2}{2} \right|_1^2 = \frac{2^2}{2} - \frac{1^2}{2} = \frac{3}{2}.$

2. $\displaystyle\int_0^1 \frac{1}{1 + x^2}\,dx = \left| \tan^{-1} x \right|_0^1 = \tan^{-1} 1 - \tan^{-1} 0$

$$= \frac{\pi}{4} - 0 = \frac{\pi}{4}.$$

3. $\displaystyle\int_0^{\pi/2} \sin x\,dx = \left[-\cos x \right]_0^{\pi/2} = -\cos\frac{\pi}{2} + \cos 0 = 1.$

EXERCISES

Evaluate the following definite integrals :

1. $\displaystyle\int_0^2 x^3\,dx.$

2. $\displaystyle\int_0^2 (2x + 3x^2)\,dx.$

3. $\displaystyle\int_0^{1/2} \frac{1}{\sqrt{1-x^2}}\,dx.$ **4.** $\displaystyle\int_1^2 \frac{1}{x}\,dx.$

5. $\displaystyle\int_a^b e^x\,dx.$ **6.** $\displaystyle\int_0^1 x^4(1+x)^3\,dx.$

7. $\displaystyle\int_0^{\pi/2} \cos x\,dx.$ **8.** $\displaystyle\int_0^{\pi/4} \sec^2 x\,dx.$

9. $\displaystyle\int_0^2 \frac{x^4+1}{x^2+1}\,dx.$ **10.** $\displaystyle\int_0^{\pi/3} \frac{2+3\sin x}{\cos^2 x}\,dx.$

11. $\displaystyle\int_{-1}^{+1} \cosh x\,dx.$ **12.** $\displaystyle\int_0^1 \sqrt{1+\cosh 2x}\,dx.$

ANSWERS

1. 4. **2.** 12. **3.** $\pi/6.$

4. log 2. **5.** $e^b - e^a.$ **6.** $\dfrac{35!}{280}.$

7. 1. **8.** 1. **9.** $2/3 + 2\tan^{-1} 2.$

10. $2\sqrt{3}+3.$ **11.** $(e^2-1)/e.$ **12.** 2 sinh 1.

1.7. Two important properties of definite integrals.

(i) $\displaystyle\int_a^b f(x)\,dx = -\int_b^a f(x)\,dx,$

(ii) $\displaystyle\int_a^b f(x)\,dx = \int_a^c f(x)\,dx + \int_c^b f(x)\,dx,$

where c, is a point inside or outside the interval [a, b].

The proofs are quite simple.

Let F (x) be an integral of $f(x)$, so that we have

$$\int_b^a f(x)\,dx = \mathrm{F}(b) - \mathrm{F}(a).$$

(i) We have

$$\int_b^a f(x)\,dx = \big|\,\mathrm{F}(x)\,\big|_b^a = \mathrm{F}(a) - \mathrm{F}(b)$$

$$= -[\mathrm{F}(b) - \mathrm{F}(a)]$$

$$= -\int_{a}^{b} f(x)\,dx.$$

Hence the first result.

(ii) Now,

$$\begin{cases} \int_{a}^{c} f(x)\,dx = \big| F(x) \big|_{a}^{c} = F(c) - F(a). \\[3mm] \int_{c}^{b} f(x)\,dx = \big| F(x) \big|_{c}^{b} = F(b) - F(c). \end{cases}$$

$$\Rightarrow \qquad \int_{a}^{c} f(x)\,dx + \int_{c}^{b} f(x)\,dx$$

$$= [F(c) - F(a)] + [F(b) - F(c)]$$

$$= F(b) - F(a) = \int_{a}^{b} f(x)\,dx.$$

Hence the second result.

1.8. Geometrical interpretation of a definite integral.

To show that the definite integral

$$\int_{a}^{b} f(x)\,dx$$

denotes the area bounded by the curve $y = f(x)$, the axis of x, and the two ordinates $x = a$ and $x = b$.

Let $y = f(x)$ be the equation of a curve referred to two rectangular axes. Let, A, denote the area bounded by the curve, the axis of x, a fixed ordinate AG, (OA = a), and a variable ordinate MP.

Let OM = x so that

$$MP = y = f(x).$$

The area A, depends on the position of the ordinate MP whose abscissa is x, and is, therefore, a function of x.

We take a point Q $(x + \Delta x, y + \Delta y)$ on the curve which lies so near P that, as a point moves along the curve from P to Q, its ordinate either *constantly* increases (Fig. 1) or constantly decreases (Fig. 2).

We have

$$ON = x + \Delta x, \ NQ = y + \Delta y, \ MN = \Delta x.$$

The increment ΔA in A, consequent to the change Δx in x, is the area of the region MNQPM.

The area Δ A of the figure MNQPM lies between the area $(y + \Delta y) \Delta x$ and $y \Delta x$ of the two rectangles QM, PN.

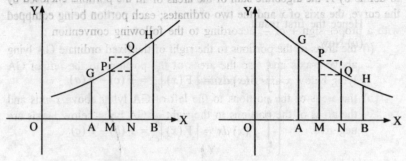

Fig. 1   **Fig. 2**

For figure 1, we have

$$(y + \Delta y) \Delta x > \Delta A > y \Delta x$$

$$\Rightarrow \qquad (y + \Delta y) > \frac{\Delta A}{\Delta x} > y \qquad \qquad ...(i)$$

Let Q $\to$ P so that $\Delta x \to 0$. Then from (i), we obtain

$$\frac{d A}{dx} = y = f(x).$$

For figure 2, we have

$$y \Delta x > \Delta A > (y + \Delta y) \Delta x$$

$$\Rightarrow \qquad y > \frac{\Delta A}{\Delta x} > (y + \Delta y),$$

so that, for this case also, we obtain in the limit

$$\frac{d A}{dx} = y = f(x).$$

Let BH be the ordinate $x = b$. We have

$$\int_a^b f(x)\,dx = \int_a^b \frac{d A}{dx}\,dx$$

$$= \Big| A \Big|_a^b$$

$$= \text{the value of A for } x \text{ equal to } b$$

$$= \text{the value of A for } x \text{ equal to } a$$

$$= \text{area of the region GABHGA} - 0$$

$$= \text{area of the region GABHGA},$$

which is the area bounded by the curve $y = f(x)$, x-axis and the two ordinates $x = a$, $x = b$.

Note. The definition of the area-function, A, as given above, is not complete. To adequately define A so as to cover all possible cases, we agree to define by A the algebraic sum of the areas of all the portions enclosed by the curve, the axis of x and the two ordinates; each portion being equipped with a proper sign + or −, according to the following convention :

(*i*) the areas of the portions to the right of the fixed ordinate GA lying above x-axis and also the areas of the portions to the left of GA lying below x-axis are positive;

(*ii*) the areas of the portions to the left of GA lying above x-axis and the areas of the portions to the right of GA lying below x-axis are negative.

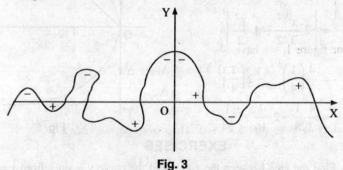

Fig. 3

It is easy to show that with these conventions as to the meaning of the areas A, the result of § 1.8 holds whatever be the portion of the variable ordinate MP relative to GA.

EXAMPLES

1. *Find by integration the area of the triangle the equations of whose sides are $y = x$, $y = 0$ and $x = 2$; also verify your result by elementary geometry.*

The area, in question, is enclosed by the curve $y = x$, the axis of x and the two ordinates $x = 0$ and $x = 2$. Therefore, the required area

$$= \int_0^2 y\, dx = \int_0^2 x\, dx$$

$$= \left| \frac{x^2}{2} \right|_0^2 = 2.$$

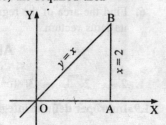

Fig. 4

Also, by elementary geometry, the area of the triangle

$$= \frac{1}{2} OA \cdot AB = \frac{1}{2} \cdot 2 \cdot 2 = 2.$$

Hence the verification.

2. *Find the area of the region bounded by the parabola* $y^2 = 4x$ *and the line* $y = 4x$.

The equations to the parabola and the straight line are $y^2 = 4x$ and $y = 4x$.

Their points of intersection are $(0, 0)$, $\left(\dfrac{1}{4}, 1\right)$.

Therefore the required area

$$= \int_{0}^{1/4} (\sqrt{4x} - 4x)\, dx$$

$$= \left| 2 \cdot \frac{x^{3/2}}{3/2} - 4 \cdot \frac{x^2}{2} \right|_{0}^{1/4}$$

$$= \frac{4}{3}\left(\frac{1}{4}\right)^{3/2} - 2\left(\frac{1}{4}\right)^{2}$$

$$= \frac{4}{3} \cdot \frac{1}{8} - 2 \cdot \frac{1}{16} = \frac{1}{24}.$$

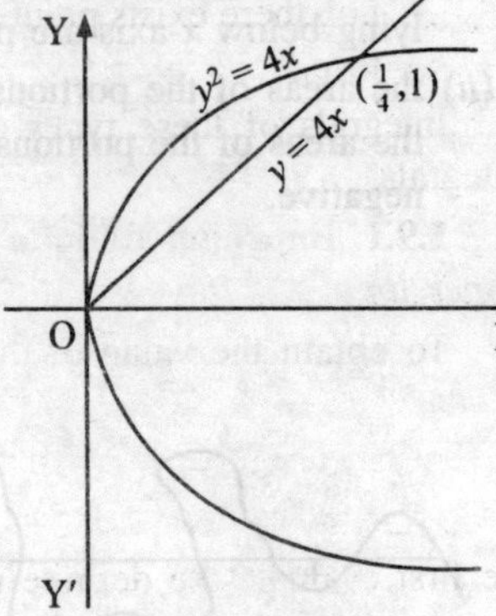

Fig. 5

EXERCISES

1. Find the area between the x-axis and the curve $y = \sin x$ from $x = 0$ to $x = \pi$.

2. Find the area enclosed by the curve $y = \sec^2 x$; x-axis, y-axis and the ordinate $x = \pi / 4$.

3. Find the area enclosed by the curve $y = e^x$, x-axis and the two ordinates $x = -1$, $x = 1$.

4. Trace the curves $y = \sin x$, $y = \cos x$ as x varies from 0 to $\pi / 2$ and find the area of the region enclosed by them and the axis of x.

5. Show that the area of the region enclosed by the hyperbola $xy = 1$, x-axis and the two ordinates $x = 1$, $x = 2$ is $\log 2$.

6. Find the area of the region bounded by the parabola $y^2 = 4ax$ and its latus rectum.

ANSWERS

1. 2.   **2.** 1.   **3.** $(e^2 - 1) / e$.   **4.** $2 - \sqrt{2}$.   **6.** $\dfrac{8}{3} a^2$.

1.9. Improper definite integrals. In the definition of the definite integral

$$\int_{a}^{b} f(x)\, dx$$

and its geometrical interpretation, it is understood that

(*i*) both the limits *a*, *b* are finite, and

(*ii*) $f(x)$ is continuous in $[a, b]$.

We now generalise the definition so as to include the case of definite integrals for which either

(*i*) *a* or *b* or both are infinite, or

(*ii*) for which $f(x)$ becomes infinite at some point of the interval $[a, b]$, *i.e.*, there exists point *c* of $[a, b]$ such that $f(x)$ tends to ∞ as *x* tends to *c*.

Integrals of these types are called *Generalised*, *Improper* or *Infinite* integrals.

1.9.1. Improper definite integrals of the first type. *Suppose that the upper limit b is* ∞.

To obtain the value of the integral

$$\int_a^\infty f(x)\, dx,$$

we first evaluate the definite integral

$$\int_a^t f(x)\, dx,$$

where *t* is a number $> a$. We then examine the limit of the definite integral whose value, of course, depends upon '*t*' as $t \to \infty$.

This limit, if it exists finitely, is defined to be the value of the symbol

$$\int_a^\infty f(x)\, dx.$$

In case the limit does not exist finitely, we cannot assign any meaning to

$$\int_a^\infty f(x)\, dx$$

and we, then, say this infinite integral does not exist.

ILLUSTRATIONS

1. To evaluate

$$\int_0^\infty \frac{1}{1+x^2}\, dx,$$

we first calculate the integral

$$\int_0^t \frac{1}{1+x^2}\, dx.$$

We have

$$\int_0^t \frac{1}{1+x^2} \, dx = \left| \tan^{-1} x \right|_0^t = \tan^{-1} t - \tan^{-1} 0 = \tan^{-1} t$$

$$\Rightarrow \quad \lim_{t \to \infty} \int_0^t \frac{1}{1+x^2} \, dx = \lim_{t \to \infty} \tan^{-1} t = \frac{\pi}{2}$$

$$\Rightarrow \quad \int_0^\infty \frac{1}{1+x^2} \, dx = \frac{\pi}{2}.$$

2. To evaluate

$$\int_1^\infty \frac{1}{\sqrt{x}} \, dx,$$

we first calculate the integral

$$\int_1^t \frac{dx}{\sqrt{x}}.$$

We have

$$\int_1^t \frac{dx}{\sqrt{x}} = \left| 2\sqrt{x} \right|_1^t = 2\sqrt{t} - 2$$

which $\to +\infty$ as $t \to \infty$.

Thus, we see that the infinite integral $\displaystyle\int_1^\infty \frac{1}{\sqrt{x}} \, dx$ does not exist.

1.9.2. *Now suppose that the lower limit is* $-\infty$. *To obtain*

$$\int_{-\infty}^b f(x) \, dx,$$

we first evaluate

$$\int_t^b f(x) \, dx.$$

The limit of this integral, as $t \to -\infty$, if it exists finitely, is to be the value of the integral

$$\int_{-\infty}^b f(x) \, dx.$$

1.9.3. *To examine and evaluate, if possible, the infinite integral*

$$\int_{-\infty}^{\infty} f(x)\, dx,$$

we examine the two integrals

$$\int_{-\infty}^{a} f(x)\, dx \text{ and } \int_{a}^{\infty} f(x)\, dx,$$

and then, if these two latter integrals exist finitely, we write

$$\int_{-\infty}^{\infty} f(x)\, dx = \int_{-\infty}^{a} f(x)\, dx + \int_{a}^{\infty} f(x)\, dx.$$

Ex. 1. *Evaluate the following improper integrals :*

(*i*) $\int_{1}^{\infty} \dfrac{1}{x^2}\, dx,$ (*ii*) $\int_{4}^{\infty} \dfrac{dx}{\sqrt[2]{x^3}},$ (*iii*) $\int_{-\infty}^{-1} \dfrac{dx}{x^4},$ (*iv*) $\int_{-\infty}^{+\infty} \dfrac{1}{1+x^2}\, dx.$

Ans. (*i*) 1, (*ii*) 1, (*iii*) $\dfrac{1}{3}$, (*iv*) π.

Ex. 2. *Show that the improper integrals*

$$\int_{1}^{\infty} \dfrac{1}{\sqrt{x}}\, dx \text{ and } \int_{1}^{\infty} \dfrac{1}{x}\, dx$$

do not exist.

Ex. 3. *Find the area bounded by the curve $y = 1 / x^2$, the axis of x and the ordinate $x = 1$.*

In this case the region whose area is required extends to infinity so that, in the ordinary sense, we cannot speak of its area. A meaning may, however, be assigned to it by means of passage to the limit as follows.

Let OA = a.

We take a *variable* ordinate MP where OM = t and consider the area of the finite region GAMPG. If this area tends to a finite limit as the ordinate MP recedes to infinity, then this limit is said to be the area of the infinite region under consideration.

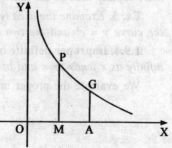

Fig. 6

Thus we have

$$\text{Area GAMPG} = \int_1^t y\, dx = \int_1^t \frac{1}{x^2}\, dx$$

$$= -\left|\frac{1}{x}\right|_1^t = -\frac{1}{t} + 1$$

which $\to 1$ as $t \to \infty$.

Thus the infinite region has a finite area which is equal to 1. When we say that the area of the infinite region is 1, we mean that the area of the region GAMPG can be made as near, 1, as we like by taking MP sufficiently far off.

Ex. 4. *Examine the area bounded by the curve* $y = 1/\sqrt{x}$, *x-axis and the ordinate* $x = 1$.

Let $OM = t$, $OA = 1$.

$$\text{Area GAMPG} = \int_1^t \frac{1}{\sqrt{x}}\, dx$$

$$= \left| 2\sqrt{x} \right|_1^t$$

$$= 2(\sqrt{t} - 1),$$

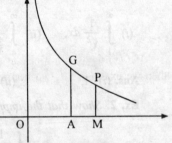

Fig. 7

which $\to \infty$ as $t \to \infty$ so that the areas of the infinite region in this case is not finite.

This means that the area of the region GAMPG can be made as large as we like by taking MP sufficiently far off.

Note. The fact that the area of the infinite region in Ex. 3 is finite, whereas that of the infinite region in Ex. 4 is infinite, is intuitively explained by the fact that in the former case the curve approaches the X-axis much more rapidly than in the latter.

Ex. 5. *Examine the area lying in the second quadrant and bounded by the curve* $y = e^x$ *and the two coordinate axes.*

1.9.4. Improper definite integrals of the second type. *Let* $f(x)$ *tend to infinity as x tends to* ∞ *and at no other point. Let h be a positive number.*

We evaluate the proper integral

$$\int_{a+h}^b f(x)\, dx$$

whose value is a function of h. If this function of h tends to a finite limit as h tends to 0, then this finite limit is defined to be the value of the improper integral

$$\int_a^b f(x)\, dx.$$

In case the limit does not exist finitely, then

$$\int_a^b f(x)\, dx$$

has no meaning.

Similarly, if $f(x)$ tends to infinity as $x \to b$ and for no other point, we examine the limit of the proper integral

$$\int_a^{b-h} f(x)\, dx,$$

as h tends to 0. This limit, if it exists finitely, is defined to be the value of

$$\int_a^b f(x)\, dx.$$

If $f(x)$ tends to infinity at some point $x = c$ within the interval $[a, b]$, then we examine the two improper integrals

$$\int_a^c f(x)\, dx \text{ and } \int_c^b f(x)\, dx$$

and if they both exist finitely, we write

$$\int_a^b f(x)\, dx = \int_a^c f(x)\, dx + \int_c^b f(x)\, dx.$$

Ex. 1. *Examine the improper integral*

$$\int_0^1 \frac{1}{\sqrt{1-x^2}}\, dx.$$

The integrand $\dfrac{1}{\sqrt{1-x^2}}$ tends to infinity as x tends to 1. To examine the value of the integral, we evaluate

$$\int_0^{1-h} \frac{1}{\sqrt{1-x^2}}\, dx.$$

We have

$$\int_0^{1-h} \frac{1}{\sqrt{1-x^2}}\, dx = \left| \sin^{-1} x \right|_0^{1-h}$$

$$= \sin^{-1}(1-h) - \sin^{-1}0$$

$$= \sin^{-1}(1-h).$$

$$\Rightarrow \quad \lim_{h \to 0} \int_0^{1-h} \frac{1}{\sqrt{1-x^2}}\, dx = \lim_{h \to 0} \sin^{-1}(1-h) = \sin^{-1}1 = \frac{\pi}{2}$$

$$\Rightarrow \quad \int_0^1 \frac{1}{\sqrt{1-x^2}}\, dx = \frac{\pi}{2}.$$

Ex. 2. *Examine the area bounded by the curve,* $y = 1/\sqrt{x}$, *Y-axis and the ordinate* $x = 1$.

Here the region extends to infinity and we proceed as in Ex. 3 of § 1.93.

Let OA = 1.

We take an ordinate MP whose abscissa is h and examine the limit of the area of the region MPGAM as the ordinate MP tends towards Y-axis, *i.e.*, as $h \to 0$. The area of the region

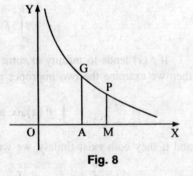

Fig. 8

$$\text{MPGAM} = \int_h^1 y\, dx$$

$$= \int_h^1 \frac{1}{\sqrt{x}}\, dx$$

$$= \left| \; 2\sqrt{x} \; \right|_h^1 = 2 - 2\sqrt{h},$$

which $\to$ the finite limit 2, as $h \to 0$.

Thus in this case we say that the area of the infinite region under consideration is 2.

Ex. 3. *Examine the improper integrals*

$$(i) \quad \int_0^1 \frac{1}{\sqrt[3]{x}}\, dx, \qquad\qquad (ii) \quad \int_0^1 \frac{1}{x^2}\, dx.$$

Ex. 4. *Show that the area of the region bounded by the curve* $y = 1/x^4$, *Y-axis and the ordinate* $x = 2$ *is not finite.*

Ans. (*i*) 3/2,   (*ii*) Does not exist.

OBJECTIVE QUESTIONS

For each of the following questions, four alternatives are given for the answer. Only one of them is correct. Choose the correct alternative.

1. One value of $\int f'(x)\, dx$ is

(a) $f'(x)$ (b) $\dfrac{f(x)^2}{2}$

(c) $f(x)$ (d) None of these.

2. If $\int f(x)\, dx = g(x)$ and also $\int f(x)\, dx = h(x)$, then

(a) $h(x) + g(x)$ = constant   (b) $g(x)\, h(x)$ = constant

(c) $g(x) - h(x)$ = constant   (d) $g(x) = h(x)$.

3. $\int e^{-\log x}\, dx$ is equal to

(a) $- e^{-\log x}$ (b) $- x e^{-\log x}$

(c) $\log |x|$ (d) None of these.

4. If n is an odd positive integer, then $\int |x^n|\, dx$ is equal to

(a) $\left| \dfrac{x^{n+1}}{n+1} \right|$ (b) $\dfrac{x^{n+1}}{n+1}$

(c) $\dfrac{|x^n|x}{n+1}$ (d) None of these.

ANSWERS

1. (c)   **2.** (c)   **3.** (c)   **4.** (c)

2

Methods of Integration

INTEGRATION BY SUBSTITUTION AND INTEGRATION BY PARTS

2.1. Methods of Integration. The following are the four principal methods of Integration :

(I) *Decomposition of the given integrand as a sum of integrands with known integrals.*

(II) *Integration by substitution.*

(III) *Integration by parts.*

(IV) *Integration by successive reduction.*

The first method of integration which depends upon the two theorems proved in § 1.5, page 5, has already been illustrated in the preceding chapter. It will be seen in Chapter 3 that this method of integration is very largely employed for the integration of algebraic rational functions.

The other methods will be taken up in this chapter. It will be seen that the method of *Integrating by parts* is essentially a method by successive reduction for, with its help, we are enabled to express the integral of a product of two functions in terms of another whose evaluation may be simpler. The method of integration by successive reduction is thus also only a development of the method of integration by parts.

In the present chapter, we shall be laying emphasis mainly on the different *methods* of integration and in the following three chapters we shall consider the various *Classes of functions* and indicate the method of integrating functions belonging to any given class.

Note. The process of integration is largely of a tentative nature and is not so systematic as that of differentiation. In general, experience is the best guide for suggesting the quickest and the simplest method for integrating a given function.

2.2. Integration by Substitution. This method consists in expressing the integral $\int f(x)\, dx$, where x is the independent variable, in terms of another integral where some other variable, say t, is the independent variable; x and t being connected by some suitable relation $x = \phi(t)$.

It leads to the result
$$\int f(x)\ dx = \int f[\phi(t)]\ \phi'(t)\ dt,$$
which is proved as follows :

Let $\qquad v = \int f(x)\ dx \implies \dfrac{dv}{dx} = f(x).$

We have
$$\frac{dv}{dt} = \frac{dv}{dx}\cdot\frac{dx}{dt} = f(x)\cdot\frac{dx}{dt}.$$

$$\implies \qquad v = \int f(x)\frac{dx}{dt}\ dt = \int f[\phi(t)]\ \phi'(t)\ dt \text{ for } x = \phi(t).$$

Thus we have shown that

the integral of a function f (x) with respect to x is equal to the integral of, f (x) (dx/dt) with respect to t.

Here x is to be replaced by $\phi(t)$.

This method proves useful only when a relation $x = \phi_{-}(t)$ can be so selected that the new integrand $f(x)\ (dx/dt)$ is of a form whose integral is known.

An Important Note. It may be noted that in the result
$$\int f(x)\ dx = \int f[\phi(t)]\ \phi'(t)\ dt$$
dx has been replaced by $\phi'(t)\ dt$ and this equality can be obtained from $dx/dt = \phi'(t)$, *by supposing* that dx and dt are separate quantities. This supposition greatly simplifies the presentation of the process of integration by substitution. [Refer Ex. 3, on next page].

The logical justification for this supposition is not required here, for it has only been *formally* introduced for the sake of convenience.

EXAMPLES

1. *Integrate* $e^x \sin e^x$.

We put $e^x = t \implies e^x \dfrac{dx}{dt} = 1 \implies \dfrac{dx}{dt} = \dfrac{1}{e^x}.$

$$\therefore \quad \int e^x \sin e^x\ dx = \int (e^x \sin e^x)\frac{dx}{dt}\ dt$$
$$= \int (e^x \sin e^x)\frac{1}{e^x}\ dt$$
$$= \int \sin t\ dt = -\cos t$$
$$= -\cos e^x.$$

2. *Integrate* $\cos^3 x \sin x$.

We put $\cos x = t \implies -\sin x \dfrac{dx}{dt} = 1 \implies \dfrac{dx}{dt} = \dfrac{-1}{\sin x}.$

$$\therefore \int \cos^3 x \sin x \, dx = \int \cos^3 x \sin x \cdot \frac{dx}{dt} \, dt$$

$$= \int \cos^3 x \sin x \cdot \frac{-1}{\sin x} \, dt$$

$$= \int -t^3 \, dt = -\frac{t^4}{4}$$

$$= -\frac{1}{4} \cos^4 x.$$

3. Evaluate $\int \frac{x^5}{1 + x^{12}} \, dx$.

We put $x^6 = t \implies 6x^5 \frac{dx}{dt} = 1 \implies 6x^5 \, dx = dt$.

$$\therefore \int \frac{x^5}{1 + x^{12}} \, dx = \int \frac{dt}{6(1 + t^2)} = \frac{1}{6} \tan^{-1} t$$

$$= \frac{1}{6} \tan^{-1} x^6.$$

4. Evaluate $\int \frac{dx}{x^{1/2} + x^{1/3}}$.

$$I = \int \frac{dx}{x^{1/2} + x^{1/3}} = \int \frac{dx}{x^{1/3}(1 + x^{1/6})}$$

Put $x = y^6$, then $dx = 6y^5 \, dy$.

$$\therefore \quad I = \int \frac{6y^5 \, dy}{y^2(1 + y)} = 6\int \left[y^2 - y + 1 - \frac{1}{1 + y} \right] dy$$

$$= 6\left[\frac{1}{3} y^3 - \frac{1}{2} y^2 + y - \log(1 + y) \right] + c$$

$$= 2\sqrt{x} - 3x^{1/3} + 6x^{1/6} - 6 \log(1 + x^{1/6}) + c.$$

5. *Integrate* : $\sin x \cos x (2 \sin x + 3 \cos x)$.

$$I = \int \sin x \cos x (2 \sin x + 3 \cos x) \, dx$$

$$= 2\int \sin^2 x \cos x \, dx + 3\int \sin x \cos^2 x \, dx$$

Substitute $\sin x = y$ in the first integral and $\cos x = t$ in the second integral, we get

$$I = 2\int y^2 \, dy - 3\int t^2 \, dt = \frac{2}{3} y^3 - t^3 + c$$

$$= \frac{2}{3} \sin^3 x - \cos^3 x + c.$$

6. *Evaluate :* $\int \dfrac{x \sin^{-1}(x^2)}{\sqrt{1-x^4}}\,dx.$

Substitute $\sin^{-1}(x^2) = y \Rightarrow \dfrac{2x\,dx}{\sqrt{1-x^4}} = dy.$

Then, we have

$$I = \int \frac{1}{2}\,y\,dy = \frac{1}{4}y^2 + c = \frac{1}{4}[\sin^{-1}(x^2)]^2 + c.$$

7. *Evaluate :* $\int \dfrac{\cos x - \sin x}{\cos x + \sin x}\,dx.$

Substitute $\cos x + \sin x = y \Rightarrow (-\sin x + \cos x)\,dx = dy.$
Then, we have

$$I = \int \frac{dy}{y} = \log y + c = \log(\cos x + \sin x) + c.$$

8. *Evaluate :* $\int \dfrac{dx}{a^2 \sin^2 x + b^2 \cos^2 x}$

Write the integral as :

$$I = \int \frac{dx}{\cos^2 x\,(b^2 + a^2 \tan^2 x)} = \int \frac{\sec^2 x\,dx}{b^2 + a^2 \tan^2 x}$$

Put $a \tan x = by \Rightarrow a \sec^2 x\,dx = b\,dy.$
Then, the given integral becomes

$$I = \int \frac{(b/a)\,dy}{b^2(1+y^2)} = \frac{1}{ab}\int \frac{dy}{1+y^2}$$

$$= \frac{1}{ab}\tan^{-1} y + c = \frac{1}{ab}\tan^{-1}\left(\frac{a}{b}\tan x\right) + c.$$

9. *Evaluate :* $\int \dfrac{e^{\sqrt{x}} \cos(e^{\sqrt{x}})\,dx}{\sqrt{x}}.$

Substituting $e^{\sqrt{x}} = y$, we get $\dfrac{1}{2\sqrt{x}}e^{\sqrt{x}}\,dx = dy.$

We have

$$I = \int 2 \cos y\,dy = 2 \sin y + c$$

$$= 2 \sin(e^{\sqrt{x}}) + c.$$

10. *Integrate* $\sqrt{(e^x - 1)}$, *w.r.t.* $x.$

Let $I = \int \sqrt{(e^x - 1)}\,dx.$

Let $e^x - 1 = t^2$, we get $e^x \, dx = 2t \, dt$

$\Rightarrow \ (1 + t^2) \, dx = 2t \, dt \ \Rightarrow \ dx = \dfrac{2t}{1 + t^2} \, dt.$

Then

$$I = \int \sqrt{t^2} \cdot \left(\frac{2t}{1 + t^2} \right) dt = 2 \int \frac{t^2}{1 + t^2} \, dt$$

$$= 2 \int \left(1 - \frac{1}{1 + t^2} \right) dt$$

$$= 2 \, (t - \tan^{-1} t) + c$$

$$= 2 \left[\sqrt{(e^x - 1)} - \tan^{-1} \left(\sqrt{e^x - 1} \right) \right] + c.$$

11. *Evaluate* : $\displaystyle\int \frac{dx}{x^2 \, (x^4 + 1)^{3/4}}.$

We have

$$I = \int \frac{dx}{x^2 \cdot x^3 \, [1 + (1/x^4)]^{3/4}}$$

$$= \int \frac{dx}{x^5 \, [1 + (1/x^4)]^{3/4}}$$

Substituting $1 + \dfrac{1}{x^4} = t$, we get $- \dfrac{4}{x^5} \, dx = dy.$

We have

$$I = - \int \frac{dy/4}{y^{3/4}} = - \frac{1}{4} \cdot \left[\frac{y^{1/4}}{1/4} \right] + c$$

$$= - y^{1/4} + c = - \frac{1}{x} (x^4 + 1)^{1/4} + c.$$

12. *Evaluate* : $\displaystyle\int \frac{\sin 2x}{p \cos^2 x + q \sin^2 x} \, dx.$

We have

$$I = \int \frac{\sin 2x}{p \cos^2 x + q \sin^2 x} \, dx = \int \frac{2 \sin x \cos x \, dx}{p + (q - p) \sin^2 x}$$

Substituting $\sin^2 x = y$, we have $2 \sin x \cos x \, dx = dy.$
The integral simplifies to

$$I = \int \frac{dy}{p + (q - p) y} = \frac{1}{(q - p)} \log | \, p + (q - p) \, y \, | + c$$

$$= \frac{1}{(q - p)} \log | \, p + (q - p) \sin^2 x \, | + c.$$

EXERCISES

Find the integrals of the following functions :

1. (i) $e^x \cos e^x$, (ii) $2xe^{x^2}$, (iii) $x^3 e^{x^4}$,

(iv) $e^{\tan t} \sec^2 t$, (v) $e^{\log x}/x$, (vi) $\dfrac{e^{\tan^{-1} x}}{1 + x^2}$,

(vii) $\dfrac{e^{\sin^{-1} x}}{\sqrt{1 - x^2}}$, (viii) $\dfrac{e^{\sqrt{x}}}{3\sqrt{x}}$, (ix) $\dfrac{e^x (1 + x)}{\cos^2 (xe^x)}$.

2. (i) $\sin^2 x \cos x$, (ii) $\sqrt[3]{\sin x \cos x}$, (iii) $\sin x \cos x$,

(iv) $3 \sin x \sec^4 x$.

3. (i) $\dfrac{\cos x}{1 + \sin^2 x}$, (ii) $\dfrac{\tan^2 x \sec^2 x}{1 + \tan^6 x}$, (iii) $\dfrac{2}{x [1 + (\log x)^2]}$,

(iv) $\dfrac{3e^{2x}}{1 + e^{4x}}$, (v) $\dfrac{2x}{1 + x^4}$, (vi) $\dfrac{x^5}{1 + x^{12}}$,

(vii) $\dfrac{2x^3}{1 + x^8}$, (viii) $\dfrac{1}{e^x + e^{-x}}$.

4. (i) $\dfrac{\cos x}{(1 + \sin x)^2}$, (ii) $\dfrac{\sec^2 x}{(1 + \tan x)^3}$, (iii) $\dfrac{(1 - \log x)^2}{x}$.

5. (i) $4x^3 \operatorname{cosec}^2 (x^4)$, (ii) $x^4 \sec^2 (x^5)$, (iii) $x^3 \sin x^4$,

(iv) $\cos \sqrt{x} / \sqrt{x}$, (v) $e^x \sec^2 (e^x)$.

6. (i) $\dfrac{\cos (\log x)}{x}$, (ii) $\dfrac{\sec^2 (\log x)}{x}$, (iii) $\dfrac{\sin (2 + 3 \log x)}{x}$,

(iv) $e^x \tan (e^x) \sec (e^x)$.

7. (i) $\dfrac{2x}{\sqrt{1 - x^4}}$, (ii) $\dfrac{x^2}{\sqrt{1 - x^6}}$,

(iii) $\dfrac{2}{\sqrt{[2 - (2x + 3)^2]}}$, (iv) $\dfrac{\sec^2 x}{\sqrt{1 - \tan^2 x}}$.

8. (i) $\dfrac{x^2 \tan^{-1} x^3}{1 + x^6}$, (ii) $\dfrac{2x \sin^{-1} x^2}{\sqrt{1 - x^4}}$, (iii) $\dfrac{\tan \sqrt{x} \sec^2 \sqrt{x}}{\sqrt{x}}$.

ANSWERS

1. (i) $\sin e^x$ (ii) e^{x^2} (iii) $\dfrac{1}{4} e^{x^3}$

(iv) $e^{\tan t}$ (v) x (vi) $e^{\tan^{-1} x}$

(vii) $e^{\sin^{-1} x}$ $(viii)$ $\dfrac{2}{3} e^{\sqrt{x}}$ (ix) $\tan(xe^x)$

2. (i) $\dfrac{1}{3} \sin^3 x$ (ii) $\dfrac{3}{4} \sin^{4/3} x$ (iii) $-\dfrac{1}{4} \cos 2x$

   (iv) $\sec^3 x.$

3. (i) $\tan^{-1}(\sin x)$ (ii) $\dfrac{1}{3} \tan^{-1}(\tan^3 x)$ (iii) $2 \tan^{-1}(\log x)$

   (iv) $\dfrac{3}{2} \tan^{-1}(e^{2x})$ (v) $\tan^{-1} x^2$ (vi) $\dfrac{1}{6} \tan^{-1} x^5$

   (vii) $\dfrac{1}{2} \tan^{-1} x^4$ $(viii)$ $\tan^{-1}(e^x)$

4. (i) $-1/(1 + \sin x)$ (ii) $-\dfrac{1}{2}(1 + \tan x)^2$ (iii) $-\dfrac{1}{3}(1 - \log x)^3$

5. (i) $-\cot x^4$ (ii) $\dfrac{1}{5} \tan x^5$ (iii) $-\dfrac{1}{4} \cos x^4$

   (iv) $2 \sin \sqrt{x}$ (v) $\tan e^x$

6. (i) $\sin(\log x)$ (ii) $\tan(\log x)$

   (iii) $-\dfrac{1}{3} \cos(2 + 3 \log x)$ (iv) $\sec e^x$

7. (i) $\sin^{-1} x^2$ (ii) $\dfrac{1}{3} \sin^{-1} x^3$

   (iii) $\sin^{-1}[(2x + 3)/\sqrt{2}]$ (iv) $\sin^{-1}(\tan x)$

8. (i) $\dfrac{1}{6}(\tan^{-1} x^3)^2$ (ii) $\dfrac{1}{2}(\sin^{-1} x^2)^2$ (iii) $(\tan \sqrt{x})^2.$

2.3. Three important forms of integrals

2.3.1. $\displaystyle \int \dfrac{f'(x)}{f(x)}\, dx = \log f(x).$

We put $f(x) = t \Rightarrow f'(x)\, dx = dt.$

$\therefore \quad \displaystyle \int \dfrac{f'(x)}{f(x)}\, dx = \int \dfrac{dt}{t} = \log t = \log f(x).$

Thus we see that

the integral of a fraction whose numerator is the derivative of its denominator is equal to the logarithm of the denominator.

ILLUSTRATIONS

(1) $\displaystyle \int \dfrac{3x^2}{1 + x^3}\, dx = \log(1 + x^3)$, for the numerator $3x^2$ is the derivative

of the denominator $1 + x^3$.

(2) $\int \dfrac{e^x}{1+e^x}\, dx = \log (1+e^x).$

2.3.1.1. Integrals of tan x, cot x, sec x, cosec x.

The result given above enables us to obtain the integrals of tan x, cot x, sec x and cosec x as shown below :

(I) $\int \tan x\, dx = \int \dfrac{\sec x \tan x}{\sec x}\, dx = \log \sec x.$

$$\int \tan x\, dx = \log \sec x.$$

(II) $\int \cot x\, dx = \int \dfrac{\cos x}{\sin x}\, dx = \log \sin x.$

$$\int \cot x\, dx = \log \sin x.$$

(III) $\int \sec x\, dx = \int \dfrac{\sec x\,(\sec x + \tan x)}{\sec x + \tan x}\, dx$

$$= \log (\sec x + \tan x),$$

for the numerator, $\sec^2 x + \sec x \tan x$, is the derivative of the denominator $\sec x + \tan x$.

To put the result in another form, we write

$$\sec x + \tan x = \frac{1 + \sin x}{\cos x}$$

and employ the results

$$\sin x = \frac{2 \tan (x/2)}{1 + \tan^2 (x/2)}, \quad \cos x = \frac{1 - \tan^2 (x/2)}{1 + \tan^2 (x/2)},$$

so that we obtain

$$\sec x + \tan x = \frac{1 + \tan (x/2)}{1 - \tan (x/2)} = \tan\left(\frac{\pi}{4} + \frac{x}{2}\right).$$

Thus $\qquad\displaystyle \int \sec x\, dx = \log \tan \left(\frac{\pi}{4} + \frac{x}{2}\right).$

(IV) $\int \cosec x\, dx = \int \dfrac{\cosec x\,(\cosec x - \cot x)}{\cosec x - \cot x}\, dx$

$$= \log (\cosec x - \cot x).$$

As in III above, we have

$$\cosec x - \cot x = \frac{1 - \cos x}{\sin x} = \frac{1 - \dfrac{1 - \tan^2 (x/2)}{1 + \tan^2 (x/2)}}{\dfrac{2 \tan^2 (x/2)}{1 + \tan^2 (x/2)}} = \tan \frac{x}{2}.$$

Thus $$\int \operatorname{cosec} x \, dx = \log \tan \frac{x}{2}.$$

EXAMPLES

1. *Evaluate the integral* $\displaystyle\int \frac{\sin x}{\sin (x + a)} \, dx.$

Let $x + a = y \implies dx = dy.$

Substituting in the given integral, we get

$$I = \int \frac{\sin (y - a) \, dy}{\sin y} = \int \frac{\sin y \cos a - \cos y \sin a}{\sin y} \, dy$$

$$= \cos a \int dy - \sin a \int \cot y \, dy$$

$$= (\cos a) \, y - (\sin a) \log \sin y + c$$

$$= (\cos a) \, (x + a) - (\sin a) \log \{\sin (x + a)\} + c.$$

2. *Evaluate* : $\displaystyle\int \frac{dx}{\cos (x + a) \cos (x + b)}.$

Let

$$I = \int \frac{dx}{\cos (x + a) \cos (x + b)}$$

$$= \frac{1}{\sin (a - b)} \int \frac{\sin (a - b)}{\cos (x + a) \cos (x + b)} \, dx$$

$$= \frac{1}{\sin (a - b)} \int \frac{\sin [(x + a) - (x + b)]}{\cos (x + a) \cos (x + b)} \, dx$$

$$= \frac{1}{\sin (a - b)} \int \frac{\sin (x + a) \cos (x + b) - \cos (x + a) \sin (x + b)}{\cos (x + a) \cos (x + b)} \, dx$$

$$= \frac{1}{\sin (a - b)} \int [\tan (x + a) - \tan (x + b)] \, dx$$

$$= \frac{1}{\sin (a - b)} [\log \{\sec (x + a)\} - \log \{\sec (x + b)\}] + c$$

$$= \frac{1}{\sin (a - b)} \log \left[\frac{\sec (x + a)}{\sec (x + b)} \right] + c.$$

3. *Evaluate* : $\displaystyle\int \frac{dx}{x \cos^2 (1 + \log x)}.$

Substituting $1 + \log x = y$, we get $\dfrac{dx}{x} = dy.$

We have

$$I = \int \frac{dy}{\cos^2 y} = \int \sec^2 y \, dy = \tan y + c$$

$$= \tan (1 + \log x) + c.$$

4. *Evaluate :* $\int e^x \, \mathrm{cosec} \, x \, (1 - \cot x) \, dx.$

Substituting $e^x \, \mathrm{cosec} \, x = y$, we get

$$(e^x \, \mathrm{cosec} \, x - e^x \, \mathrm{cosec} \, x \cot x) \, dx = dy$$

$$\Rightarrow \qquad e^x \, \mathrm{cosec} \, x \, (1 - \cot x) \, dx = dy.$$

We have

$$I = \int dy = y + c = e^x \, \mathrm{cosec} \, x + c.$$

5. *Evaluate :* $\int \sqrt{\{1 + 2 \tan x \, (\tan x + \sec x)\}} \, dx.$

We have

$$\tan x + \sec x = \frac{1 + \sin x}{\cos x}$$

$$\Rightarrow \quad 1 + 2 \tan x \, (\tan x + \sec x) = 1 + \frac{2 \sin x \, (1 + \sin x)}{\cos^2 x}$$

$$= \frac{\cos^2 x + 2 \sin x + 2 \sin^2 x}{\cos^2 x}$$

$$= \frac{1 + 2 \sin x + \sin^2 x}{\cos^2 x}$$

$$= \frac{(1 + \sin x)^2}{\cos^2 x}.$$

Therefore,

$$I = \int \frac{1 + \sin x}{\cos x} \, dx = \int (\sec x + \tan x) \, dx$$

$$= \log (\sec x + \tan x) + \log \sec x + c$$

$$= \log \{\sec x \, (\sec x + \tan x)\} + c$$

$$= \log \left(\frac{1 + \sin x}{\cos^2 x} \right) + c = - \log (1 - \sin x) + c.$$

EXERCISES

1. Integrate the following :

(i) $\dfrac{x^2}{1+x^3}$,   (ii) $\dfrac{2x+1}{x^2+x+1}$,

(iii) $\dfrac{1}{\sqrt{1-x^2}\,\sin^{-1}x}$,   (iv) $\dfrac{1}{(1+x^2)\tan^{-1}x}$,   (v) $\tanh x$,

(vi) $\coth x$,   (vii) $\dfrac{\cos x}{a+b\sin x}$,   (viii) $\dfrac{\cot x}{\log\sin x}$,

(ix) $\dfrac{\sec^2 x}{1+\tan x}$,   (x) $\dfrac{\csc^2 x}{1+\cot x}$,   (xi) $\dfrac{1}{x\log x}$,

(xii) $\dfrac{x^{e-1}+e^{x-1}}{x^e+e^x}$,   (xiii) $\dfrac{ax^{n-1}}{bx^n+c}$,   (xiv) $\dfrac{1}{\sqrt{x}+x}$,

(xv) $\dfrac{1}{x\log x\,[\log(\log x)]}$,   (xvi) $\dfrac{\sin 2x}{a\cos^2 x+b\sin^2 x}$,

(xvii) $\dfrac{1-\tan x}{1+\tan x}$,   (xviii) $\dfrac{\cos 2x}{(\sin x+\cos x)^2}$,

(xix) $\dfrac{\sec x\,\csc x}{\log(\tan x)}$.

2. Integrate the following functions by changing the independent variable :

(i) $e^x\tan(e^x)$,   (ii) $x^2\tan x^3$,   (iii) $\cos x\cot(\sin x)$,

(iv) $\dfrac{\cot(\log x)}{x}$,   (v) $\dfrac{\tan(\sin^{-1}x)}{\sqrt{1-x^2}}$,   (vi) $\dfrac{\cot\sqrt{x}}{\sqrt{x}}$,

(vii) $\cot(2x+3)$,   (viii) $\tan(3x+4)$,   (ix) $e^x\cot(e^x)$.

3. Integrate

(i) $\sec(\tan x)\sec^2 x$,   (ii) $x^{n-1}\csc x^n$,

(iii) $\sec(ax+b)$,   (iv) $\csc(ax+b)$,

(v) $\csc(\csc x)\cot x\csc x$,   (vi) $\dfrac{\csc(\tan^{-1}x)}{1+x^2}$.

4. Evaluate

$$\int \frac{dx}{\sin(x-a)\sin(x-b)}.$$

ANSWERS

1. (i) $\dfrac{1}{3}\log(1+x^3)$ (ii) $\log(x^2+x+1)$

(iii) $\log\sin^{-1}x$ (iv) $\log\tan^{-1}x$

(v) log cosh x (vi) log sinh x

(vii) $(1/b)$ log $(a + b \sin x)$ (viii) log log (sin x)

(ix) log $(1 + \tan x)$ (x) $-$ log $(1 + \cot x)$

(xi) log log x (xii) $(1/e)$ log $(x^e + e^x)$

(xiii) (a/nb) log $(bx^n + c)$ (xiv) 2 log $(1 + \sqrt{x})$

(xv) log [log (log x)]   (xvi) $[1/b - a)]$ log $(a \cos^2 x + b \sin^2 x)$

(xvii) log (sin x + cos x)   (xviii) log (sin x + cos x)

(xix) log [log (tan x)]

2.   (i) log (sec e^x)   (ii) $\dfrac{1}{3}$ log (sec x^3)   (iii) log [sin (sin x)]

     (iv) log [sin (log x)]   (v) log sec (sin^{-1} x) (vi) 2 log (sin $\sqrt{x}$)

     (vii) $\dfrac{1}{2}$ log [sin $(2x + 3)$]

     (viii) $\dfrac{1}{3}$ log [sec $(3x + 4)$]   (ix) $\dfrac{1}{2}$ log (sin e^x)

3.   (i) $\log\left[\tan\left(\dfrac{\pi}{4} + \dfrac{1}{2}\tan x\right)\right]$ (ii) $\left(\dfrac{1}{n}\right)\log\left[\tan\left(\dfrac{1}{2}x^n\right)\right]$

     (iii) $\left(\dfrac{1}{a}\right)\log\tan\left[\dfrac{1}{4}\pi + \dfrac{1}{2}(ax + b)\right]$ (iv) $\left(\dfrac{1}{a}\right)\log\left(\dfrac{ax + b}{2}\right)$

     (v) $-\log\tan\left(\dfrac{1}{2}\operatorname{cosec} x\right)$ (vi) $\log\tan\left(\dfrac{1}{2}\tan^{-1}x\right)$

4. $\dfrac{1}{\sin(a - b)}\log\dfrac{\sin(x - a)}{\sin(x - b)}$

2.3.2. $\displaystyle\int [f(x)]^n\, f'(x)\, dx = \dfrac{[f(x)]^{n+1}}{n+1}$, when $n \neq -1$.

We put $f(x) = t \Rightarrow f'(x)\, dx = dt$.

$$\therefore \quad \int [f(x)]^n\, f'(x)\, dx = \int t^n\, dt = \dfrac{t^{n+1}}{n+1}, \text{ for } n \neq -1$$

$$= \dfrac{[f(x)]^{n+1}}{n+1}.$$

It should be noticed that the integrand consists of the product of a power of a function $f(x)$ and the derivative $f'(x)$ of $f(x)$. The integral then is obtained on increasing the index by unity and dividing by the increased index.

The case of $n = -1$ corresponds to that of the preceding subsection 2.3.1.

ILLUSTRATION

Evaluate

$$\int \sin^4 x \cos x \, dx$$

Taking $f(x) = \sin x$, we see that the given integral is of the form

$$\int [f(x)]^4 \, f'(x) \, dx$$

so that

$$\int \sin^4 x \cos x \, dx = \frac{\sin^{4+1} x}{4+1} = \frac{1}{5} \sin^5 x.$$

EXERCISES

1. Integrate the following :

(i) $\sqrt{\sin x} \cos x,$

(ii) $\tan^4 x \sec^2 x,$

(iii) $\operatorname{cosec}^2 x \sqrt{\cot x},$

(iv) $\dfrac{(\tan^{-1} x)^3}{1+x^2},$

(v) $\dfrac{1}{(\tan^{-1} x)^2 \, (1+x^2)},$

(vi) $\dfrac{\sin^{-1} x}{\sqrt{1-x^2}},$

(vii) $\dfrac{1}{\sqrt{\sin^{-1} x} \, \sqrt{1-x^2}},$

(viii) $\dfrac{x}{\sqrt{1-x^2}},$

(ix) $\dfrac{x}{\sqrt[3]{x^2+1}},$

(x) $x\sqrt{x^2+1},$

(xi) $e^x \sqrt{1+e^x},$

(xii) $\sin^3 x \cos x,$

(xiii) $\dfrac{2x+3}{\sqrt{x^2+3x-4}},$

(xiv) $\dfrac{(x+1)(x+\log x)^2}{2x},$

(xv) $\dfrac{1}{x(1+\log x)^3},$

(xvi) $\dfrac{\log x}{x},$

(xvii) $\sqrt{(2+\sec^2 x) \sec^2 x \tan x},$

(xviii) $(e^x + e^{-x})(e^x - e^{-x}),$

(xix) $\sec x \log (\sec x + \tan x).$

ANSWERS

1. (i) $\dfrac{2}{3}(\sin x)^{3/2}$

(ii) $\dfrac{1}{5}\tan^5 x$

(iii) $-\dfrac{2}{3}\cot^{2/3} x$

(iv) $\dfrac{1}{4}(\tan^{-1} x)^4$

(v) $\dfrac{-1}{\tan^{-1} x}$

(vi) $\dfrac{1}{2}(\sin^{-1} x)^2$

(vii) $2\sqrt{\sin^{-1}x}$ (viii) $-\sqrt{1-x^2}$ (ix) $\dfrac{3}{4}(1+x^2)^{2/3}$

(x) $\dfrac{1}{3}(1+x^2)^{3/2}$ (xi) $\dfrac{2}{3}(1+e^x)^{3/2}$ (xii) $\dfrac{1}{4}\sin^4 x$

(xiii) $2\sqrt{x^2+3x-4}$ (xiv) $\dfrac{1}{6}(x+\log x)^3$ (xv) $-\dfrac{1}{2}(1+\log x)^2$

(xvi) $\dfrac{1}{2}(\log x)^2$ (xvii) $\dfrac{1}{3}(2+\sec^2 x)^{3/2}$ (xviii) $\dfrac{1}{2}(e^x - e^{-x})^2$

(xix) $\dfrac{1}{2}[\log(\sec x + \tan x)]^2$

2.3.3. $\displaystyle\int f'(ax+b)\,dx = \dfrac{f(ax+b)}{a}.$

We put $ax + b = t \Rightarrow a\,dx = dt \Rightarrow dx = dt/a$.

$$\therefore \quad \int f(ax+b)\,dx = \int f'(t)\cdot\frac{dt}{a}$$

$$= \frac{1}{a}\int f'(t)\,dt$$

$$= \frac{1}{a}\cdot f(t) = \frac{1}{a}f(ax+b).$$

Thus the integral of a function of $(ax + b)$ is of the same form as the integral of the same function of x divided by a, which is the coefficient of x.

EXAMPLES

1. (i) The integral of $\cos x$ is $\sin x \Rightarrow$ the integral of $\cos(ax+b)$ is

$\dfrac{1}{a}\sin(ax+b).$

(ii) The integral of x^3 is $\dfrac{x^4}{4} \Rightarrow$ the integral of $(2x+3)^3$ is $\dfrac{(2x+3)^4}{4\cdot 2}$

$$= \frac{(2x+3)^4}{8}.$$

2. Integrate (i) $\sin^2 x$, (ii) $\sin^3 x$, (iii) $\cos x \cos 2x$.

(i) We know that

$$\cos 2x = 1 - 2\sin^2 x$$

$$\therefore \qquad \sin^2 x = \frac{1}{2}(1 - \cos 2x)$$

$$\therefore \qquad \int \sin^2 x\,dx = \frac{1}{2}\int(1 - \cos 2x)\,dx$$

$$= \frac{1}{2}\left[\int 1\,dx - \int \cos 2x\,dx\right]$$

$$= \frac{1}{2}\left(x - \frac{\sin 2x}{2}\right)$$

$$= \frac{1}{2}(x - \sin x \cos x).$$

(*ii*) We know that

$$\sin 3x = 3 \sin x - 4 \sin^3 x$$

$$\therefore \qquad \sin^3 x = \frac{1}{4}(3 \sin x - \sin^3 x)$$

$$\therefore \qquad \int \sin^3 x \, dx = \frac{1}{4}\left[\int 3 \sin x \, dx - \int \sin 3x \, dx\right]$$

$$= \frac{1}{4}\left(-3 \cos x + \frac{\cos 3x}{3}\right)$$

$$= \frac{1}{12}(\cos 3x - 9 \cos x).$$

(*iii*) We know that

$$\cos x \cos 2x = \frac{1}{2}(\cos 3x + \cos x)$$

$$\therefore \int \cos x \cos 2x \, dx = \frac{1}{2}\left[\int \cos 3x \, dx + \int \cos x \, dx\right]$$

$$= \frac{1}{2}\left(\frac{\sin 3x}{3} + \sin x\right)$$

$$= \frac{\sin 3x + 3 \sin x}{6}.$$

3. *Integrate* $\dfrac{1}{a \sin x + b \cos x}$.

We find two numbers r and α such that

$$a = r \cos \alpha, \ b = r \sin \alpha.$$

From these, squaring and adding, we obtain

$$r = \sqrt{a^2 + b^2},$$

and on dividing one by the other, we obtain

$$\tan \alpha = b/a \text{ or } \alpha = \tan^{-1}(b/a)$$

$$\therefore \qquad a \sin x + b \cos x = r(\sin x \cos \alpha + \cos x \sin \alpha)$$

$$= r \sin (x + \alpha),$$

$$\therefore \qquad \int \frac{dx}{a \sin x + b \cos x} = \frac{1}{r}\int \frac{dx}{\sin (x + \alpha)}$$

$$= \frac{1}{r} \int \csc(x + \alpha)\, dx$$

$$= \frac{1}{r} \log \tan\left(\frac{x + \alpha}{2}\right),$$

where $r = \sqrt{a^2 + b^2}$, $\alpha = \tan^{-1}(b/a)$.

EXERCISES

1. Integrate :

(i) $\cos^2 x$, (ii) $\cos^3 x$, (iii) $\sin 4x \cos 2x$,

(iv) $\sin 5x \sin 3x$, (v) $\cos x \cos 2x \cos 3x$.

2. Integrate :

(i) $\sin^4 x$, (ii) $\cos^4 x$.

3. Integrate :

(i) $1/(ax + b)$, (ii) $\sec^2(2x + 3)$, (iii) $\cot(4x + 5)$,

(iv) $\cos\left(\frac{x}{2}\right)$, (v) $\sec^2\left(\frac{x}{2}\right)\csc^2\left(\frac{x}{2}\right)$,

(vi) $\dfrac{1}{1 + \cos x}$, (vii) $\sqrt{1 - \cos x}$, (viii) $\sqrt{1 + \sin x}$,

(ix) $\sqrt{1 + \cos x}$, (x) $\sqrt{1 - \sin x}$, (xi) $\sec(ax + b)$,

(xii) $\csc(ax + b)$, (xiii) $\dfrac{1}{3\sin x + 4\cos x}$, (xiv) $\dfrac{1}{5\cos x - 12\sin x}$.

ANSWERS

1. (i) $(1/2)(x + \sin x \cos x)$ (ii) $(1/12)(9\sin x + \sin 3x)$

(iii) $(-1/12)(\cos 6x + 3\cos 2x)$ (iv) $(1/16)(4\sin 2x - \sin 8x)$

(v) $(1/48)(12x + 6\sin 2x + 3\sin 4x + 2\sin 6x)$

2. (i) $(1/32)(12x - 8\sin 2x + \sin 4x)$

(ii) $(1/32)(12x + 8\sin 2x + \sin 4x)$

3. (i) $(1/a)\log(ax + b)$ (ii) $(1/2)\tan(2x + 3)$

(iii) $\frac{1}{4}\log\sin(4x + 5)$ (iv) $2\sin\frac{1}{2}x$

(v) $-4\cot x$ (vi) $\tan\frac{1}{2}x$

(vii) $-2\sqrt{2}\cos\frac{x}{2}$ (viii) $2\left(\sin\frac{1}{2}x - \cos\frac{1}{2}x\right)$

(ix) $2\sqrt{2}\,\sin\dfrac{1}{2}x$ (x) $2\left(\sin\dfrac{1}{2}x+\cos\dfrac{1}{2}x\right)$

(xi) $(1/a)\log\tan\left[\dfrac{1}{2}(ax+b)+\dfrac{1}{4}\pi\right]$ (xii) $(1/a)\log\tan\left(\dfrac{ax+b}{2}\right)$

(xiii) $(1/5)\log\tan\left[\dfrac{1}{2}\{x+\tan^{-1}(4/3)\}\right]$

(xiv) $(1/18)\log\tan\left[\dfrac{1}{2}\{x+\tan^{-1}(12/5)\}+\dfrac{1}{4}\pi\right]$

2.4. Six important integrals. We now obtain the integrals of

(i) $\dfrac{1}{\sqrt{a^2-x^2}}$,   (ii) $\dfrac{1}{\sqrt{a^2+x^2}}$,   (iii) $\dfrac{1}{\sqrt{x^2-a^2}}$,

(iv) $\sqrt{a^2-x^2}$,   (v) $\sqrt{a^2+x^2}$,   (vi) $\sqrt{x^2-a^2}$.

(i) *To evaluate* $\displaystyle\int\dfrac{1}{\sqrt{a^2-x^2}}\,dx.$

Put $x=a\sin\theta\;\Rightarrow\;dx=a\cos\theta\,d\theta.$

Also $a^2-x^2=a^2(1-\sin^2\theta)=a^2\cos^2\theta.$

$\therefore\displaystyle\int\dfrac{1}{\sqrt{a^2-x^2}}\,dx=\int\dfrac{1}{a\cos\theta}\cdot a\cos\theta\,d\theta$

$$=\int1\cdot d\theta=\theta=\sin^{-1}\dfrac{x}{a}.$$

(ii) *To evaluate* $\displaystyle\int\dfrac{1}{\sqrt{a^2+x^2}}\,dx.$

Put $x=a\sinh\theta\;\Rightarrow\;dx=a\cosh\theta\,d\theta.$

Also $a^2+x^2=a^2(1+\sinh^2\theta)=a^2\cosh^2\theta.$

$\therefore\displaystyle\int\dfrac{1}{\sqrt{a^2+x^2}}\,dx=\int\dfrac{1}{a\cosh\theta}\cdot a\cosh\theta\,d\theta$

$$=\int1\cdot d\theta$$

$$=\theta=\sinh^{-1}\dfrac{x}{a}$$

$$=\log\dfrac{x+\sqrt{x^2+a^2}}{a}.$$

(iii) *To evaluate* $\displaystyle\int\dfrac{1}{\sqrt{x^2-a^2}}\,dx.$

Put $x=a\cosh\theta\;\Rightarrow\;dx=a\sinh\theta\,d\theta.$

Also $\quad x^2 - a^2 = a^2 (\cosh^2 \theta - 1) = a^2 \sinh^2 \theta.$

$$\therefore \quad \int \frac{1}{\sqrt{x^2 - a^2}}\, dx = \int \frac{1}{a \sinh \theta} \cdot a \sinh \theta \, d\theta$$

$$= \int 1 \cdot d\theta$$

$$= \theta = \cosh^{-1} \frac{x}{a}$$

$$= \log \frac{x + \sqrt{x^2 - a^2}}{a}.$$

(iv) To evaluate $\int \sqrt{(a^2 - x^2)}\, dx.$

Putting $x = a \sin \theta$, we get

$$\int \sqrt{a^2 - x^2}\, dx = \int a^2 \cos^2 \theta \, d\theta$$

$$= \frac{a^2}{2} \int (\cos 2\theta + 1)\, d\theta$$

$$= \frac{a^2}{2} \left(\frac{\sin 2\theta}{2} + \theta \right)$$

$$= \frac{a^2}{2} (\sin \theta \cos \theta + \theta)$$

$$= \frac{a^2}{2} \left[\sin \theta \sqrt{1 - \sin^2 \theta} + \theta \right]$$

$$= \frac{a^2}{2} \left[\frac{x}{a} \sqrt{1 - \frac{x^2}{a^2}} + \sin^{-1} \frac{x}{a} \right]$$

$$= \frac{x \sqrt{a^2 - x^2}}{2} + \frac{a^2}{2} \sin^{-1} \frac{x}{a}.$$

(v) To evaluate $\int \sqrt{a^2 + x^2}\, dx.$

Put $x = a \sinh \theta \implies dx = a \cosh \theta \, d\theta.$

$$\therefore \quad \int \sqrt{a^2 + x^2}\, dx = \int a^2 \cosh^2 \theta \, d\theta$$

We know that

and $\quad \begin{cases} \cosh 2\theta = \cosh^2 \theta + \sinh^2 \theta \\ \qquad\quad 1 = \cosh^2 \theta - \sinh^2 \theta. \end{cases}$

$$\implies \quad \frac{1 + \cosh 2\theta}{2} = \cosh^2 \theta.$$

$$\therefore \quad \int \sqrt{a^2 + x^2}\ dx = \frac{a^2}{2} \int (\cosh 2\theta + 1)\ d\theta$$

$$= \frac{a^2}{2} \left(\frac{\sinh 2\theta}{2} + \theta \right)$$

$$= \frac{a^2}{2} \left(\sinh \theta \cosh \theta + \theta \right)$$

$$= \frac{a^2}{2} \left[\sinh \theta \sqrt{1 + \sinh^2 \theta} + \theta \right]$$

$$= \frac{a^2}{2} \left[\frac{x}{2} \sqrt{1 + \frac{x^2}{a^2}} + \sinh^{-1} \frac{x}{a} \right]$$

$$= \frac{x \sqrt{a^2 + x^2}}{2} + \frac{a^2}{2} \sinh^{-1} \frac{x}{a}$$

$$= \frac{x \sqrt{a^2 + x^2}}{2} + \frac{a^2}{2} \log \frac{x + \sqrt{x^2 + a^2}}{a}.$$

(*vi*) *To evaluate* $\int \sqrt{x^2 - a^2}\ dx$.

Put $x = a \cosh \theta \implies dx = a \sinh \theta\ d\theta$.

$$\therefore \quad \int \sqrt{x^2 - a^2}\ dx = \int a^2 \sinh^2 \theta\ d\theta.$$

We know that

and $\qquad \begin{cases} \cosh 2\theta = \cosh^2 \theta + \sinh^2 \theta \\ 1 = \cosh^2 \theta - \sinh^2 \theta. \end{cases}$

$$\implies \qquad \frac{\cosh 2\theta - 1}{2} = \sinh^2 \theta.$$

$$\therefore \quad \int \sqrt{x^2 - a^2}\ dx = \frac{a^2}{2} \int (\cosh 2\theta - 1)\ d\theta$$

$$= \frac{a^2}{2} \left(\frac{\sinh 2\theta}{2} - \theta \right)$$

$$= \frac{a^2}{2} \left(\sinh \theta \cosh \theta - \theta \right)$$

$$= \frac{a^2}{2} \left[\sqrt{\cosh^2 \theta - 1}\ \cosh \theta - \theta \right]$$

$$= \frac{a^2}{2} \left[\frac{x}{a} \sqrt{\frac{x^2}{a^2} - 1} - \cosh^{-1} \frac{x}{a} \right]$$

$$= \frac{x \sqrt{x^2 - a^2}}{2} - \frac{a^2}{2} \cosh^{-1} \frac{x}{a}$$

$$= \frac{x \sqrt{x^2 - a^2}}{2} - \frac{a^2}{2} \log \frac{x + \sqrt{x^2 - a^2}}{a}.$$

We have thus obtained the following *six* results :

$$\int \frac{1}{\sqrt{a^2 - x^2}} \, dx = \sin^{-1} \frac{x}{a}.$$

$$\int \sqrt{a^2 - x^2} \, dx = \frac{x \sqrt{a^2 - x^2}}{2} + \frac{a^2}{2} \sin^{-1} \frac{x}{a}.$$

$$\int \frac{1}{\sqrt{a^2 - x^2}} \, dx = \sinh^{-1} \frac{x}{a}.$$

$$\int \sqrt{a^2 + x^2} \, dx = \frac{x \sqrt{a^2 + x^2}}{2} + \frac{a^2}{2} \sinh^{-1} \frac{x}{a}.$$

$$\int \frac{1}{\sqrt{x^2 - a^2}} \, dx = \cosh^{-1} \frac{x}{a}.$$

$$\int \sqrt{x^2 - a^2} \, dx = \frac{x \sqrt{x^2 - a^2}}{2} - \frac{a^2}{2} \cosh^{-1} \frac{x}{a}.$$

The *minus* sign in the last case should be specially noted.

EXAMPLES

1. *Integrate*

(i) $\dfrac{1}{\sqrt{[a^2 - (bx + c)^2]}}$,

(ii) $\dfrac{1}{\sqrt{[a^2 + (bx + c)^2]}}$,

(iii) $\dfrac{1}{\sqrt{[(bx + c)^2 - a^2]}}$.

We have, (Refer § 2.4),

$$\int \frac{dx}{\sqrt{[a^2 - (bx + c)^2]}} = \frac{1}{b} \sin^{-1} \frac{bx + c}{a}.$$

$$\int \frac{dx}{\sqrt{[a^2 + (bx + c)^2]}} = \frac{1}{b} \sinh^{-1} \frac{bx + c}{a}.$$

$$\int \frac{dx}{\sqrt{[(bx + c)^2 - a^2]}} = \frac{1}{b} \cosh^{-1} \frac{bx + c}{a}.$$

2. *Integrate*

(i) $\dfrac{1}{\sqrt{x^2 + 2x + 2}}$,   (ii) $\dfrac{1}{\sqrt{x^2 + 4x + 2}}$,

(iii) $\dfrac{1}{\sqrt{-2x^2 + 3x + 4}}$.

(*i*) We have

$$(x^2 + 2x + 2) = [(x + 1)^2 + 1^2]$$

$$\Rightarrow \quad \int \frac{1}{\sqrt{x^2 + 2x + 2}}\, dx = \int \frac{dx}{\sqrt{[(x + 1)^2 + 1^2]}}$$

$$= \sinh^{-1}(x + 1).$$

(*ii*) $(x^2 + 4x + 2) = (x + 2)^2 - (\sqrt{2})^2$

$$\Rightarrow \quad \int \frac{1}{\sqrt{x^2 + 4x + 2}}\, dx = \int \frac{dx}{\sqrt{[(x + 2)^2 - (\sqrt{2})^2]}}$$

$$= \cosh^{-1}\frac{x + 2}{\sqrt{2}}.$$

(*iii*) We have

$$-2x^2 + 3x + 4 = -2\left[x^2 - \frac{3}{2}x - 2\right]$$

$$= -2\left[\left(x - \frac{3}{4}\right)^2 - \left(\frac{\sqrt{41}}{4}\right)^2\right]$$

$$= 2\left[\left(\frac{\sqrt{41}}{4}\right)^2 - \left(x - \frac{3}{4}\right)^2\right].$$

$$\Rightarrow \quad \int \frac{1}{\sqrt{-2x^2 + 3x + 4}}\, dx = \frac{1}{\sqrt{2}} \int \frac{dx}{\sqrt{\left(\frac{\sqrt{41}}{4}\right)^2 - \left(x - \frac{3}{4}\right)^2}}$$

$$= \frac{1}{\sqrt{2}} \sin^{-1} \frac{x - \dfrac{3}{4}}{\dfrac{\sqrt{41}}{4}} = \frac{1}{\sqrt{2}} \sin^{-1} \frac{4x - 3}{\sqrt{41}}.$$

3. *Integrate* :

(i) $\dfrac{1}{x^4 + a^2}$,   (ii) $\dfrac{2x^2}{x^4 + a^2}$.

(i) $\quad I = \displaystyle\int \frac{dx}{x^4 + a^2} = \frac{1}{2a} \int \frac{(x^2 + a) - (x^2 - a)}{x^4 + a^2} \, dx$

$\quad = \dfrac{1}{2a} \displaystyle\int \frac{x^2 + a}{x^4 + a^2} \, dx - \frac{1}{2a} \int \frac{x^2 - a}{x^4 + a^2} \, dx$

$\quad = \dfrac{1}{2a} (I_1 - I_2).$

We have

$$I_1 = \int \frac{x^2 + a}{x^4 + a^2} \, dx = \int \frac{1 + \dfrac{a}{x^2}}{x^2 + \dfrac{a^2}{x^2}} \, dx$$

$$= \int \frac{1 + \dfrac{a}{x^2}}{\left(x - \dfrac{a}{x}\right)^2 + 2a} \, dx.$$

Let $x - \dfrac{a}{x} = y$. Then, $\left(1 + \dfrac{a}{x^2}\right) dx = dy.$

Substituting in the integral, we get

$$I_1 = \int \frac{dy}{y^2 + 2a} = \frac{1}{\sqrt{2a}} \tan^{-1}\left(\frac{y}{\sqrt{2a}}\right) + C_1$$

$$= \frac{1}{\sqrt{2a}} \tan^{-1}\left(\frac{x^2 - a}{x\sqrt{2a}}\right) + C_1.$$

Similarly, we write

$$I_2 = \int \frac{x^2 - a}{x^4 + a^2} \, dx = \int \frac{1 - \dfrac{a}{x^2}}{x^2 + \dfrac{a^2}{x^2}} \, dx$$

$$= \int \frac{1 - \dfrac{a}{x^2}}{\left(x + \dfrac{a}{x}\right)^2 - 2a} \, dx.$$

Substitute $x + \dfrac{a}{x} = y$. Then, $\left(1 - \dfrac{a}{x^2}\right) dx = dy.$

The integral reduces to

$$I_2 = \int \frac{dy}{y^2 - 2a} = \frac{1}{2\sqrt{2a}} \log\left(\frac{y - \sqrt{2a}}{y + \sqrt{2a}}\right) + C_2$$

$$= \frac{1}{2\sqrt{2a}} \log \left(\frac{x^2 - \sqrt{2a}\,x + a}{x^2 + \sqrt{2a}\,x + a} \right) + C_2.$$

Hence, we obtain

$$I = \frac{1}{2a\sqrt{2a}} \left[\tan^{-1} \left(\frac{x^2 - a}{x\sqrt{2a}} \right) - \frac{1}{2} \log \left(\frac{x^2 - \sqrt{2a}\,x + a}{x^2 + \sqrt{2a}\,x + a} \right) \right] + C$$

where $C = (C_1 - C_2)/2$ is another arbitrary constant.

(ii) $I = \displaystyle\int \frac{2x^2}{x^4 + a^2}\, dx = \int \frac{(x^2 + a) + (x^2 - a)}{x^4 + a^2}\, dx$

$$= \int \frac{x^2 + a}{x^4 + a^2}\, dx + \int \frac{x^2 - a}{x^4 + a^2}\, dx$$

$$= I_1 + I_2.$$

Using the results from (i), we obtain

$$I = \frac{1}{\sqrt{2a}} \left[\tan^{-1} \left(\frac{x^2 - a}{x\sqrt{2a}} \right) + \frac{1}{2} \log \left(\frac{x^2 - \sqrt{2a}\,x + a}{x^2 + \sqrt{2a}\,x + a} \right) \right] + C.$$

4. *Evaluate* :

(i) $\displaystyle\int \frac{x\, dx}{(9 - x^2)^{3/2}},$ (ii) $\displaystyle\int \frac{\sin (2x) \cos (2x)\, dx}{\sqrt{9 - \cos^4 (2x)}}.$

(i) Substitute $x = 3 \sin \theta$, $dx = 3 \cos \theta\, d\theta$, we get

$$I = \int \frac{9 \sin \theta \cos \theta\, d\theta}{27 \cos^3 \theta} = \frac{1}{3} \int \sec \theta \tan \theta\, d\theta$$

$$= \frac{1}{3} \sec \theta + C = \frac{1}{3\sqrt{1 - \sin^2 \theta}} + C$$

$$= \frac{1}{\sqrt{(9 - x^2)}} + C.$$

(ii) Substitute $\cos^2 (2x) = y$, then, we get $4 \sin 2x \cos 2x\, dx = - dy$. The integral becomes

$$I = -\frac{1}{4} \frac{dy}{\sqrt{9 - y^2}} = -\frac{1}{4} \sin^{-1} \left(\frac{y}{3} \right) + C$$

$$= -\frac{1}{4} \sin^{-1} \left[\frac{1}{3} \cos^2 (2x) \right] + C.$$

5. *Evaluate* : $\displaystyle\int \frac{dx}{\sqrt{2x + x^2}}.$

We have $2x - x^2 = 1 - (1 - 2x + x^2) = 1 - (1 - x)^2$ and

$$I = \int \frac{dx}{\sqrt{1 - (1 - x)^2}} = -\int \frac{dy}{\sqrt{1 - y^2}}, \text{ where } 1 - x = y$$

$$= -\sin^{-1} y + C = -\sin^{-1}(1 - x) + C.$$

6. *Evaluate* :

(i) $\displaystyle\int \frac{dx}{\sqrt{7 - 6x - x^2}},$
(ii) $\displaystyle\int \frac{x^4 \, dx}{x^2 - x + 1},$

(iii) $\displaystyle\int \frac{x \, dx}{x^4 - x^2 + 1}.$

(i) $\displaystyle I = \int \frac{dx}{\sqrt{7 - 6x - x^2}} = \int \frac{dx}{\sqrt{16 - (x - 3)^2}}.$

Let $x + 3 = 4y$. Then, $dx = 4 \, dy$. We get

$$I = \int \frac{4 \, dy}{4\sqrt{1 - y^2}} = \sin^{-1}(y) + C$$

$$= \sin^{-1}\left(\frac{x + 3}{4}\right) + C.$$

(ii) $\displaystyle I = \int \frac{x^4 \, dx}{x^2 - x + 1} = \int \left[x^2 + x - \frac{x}{x^2 - x + 1} \right] dx$

$$= \int (x^2 + x) \, dx - \int \frac{x \, dx}{x^2 - x + 1} = I_1 - I_2.$$

We have

$$I_1 = \int (x^2 + x) \, dx = \frac{1}{3} x^3 + \frac{1}{2} x^2 + C_1,$$

and $\displaystyle I_2 = \int \frac{x \, dx}{x^2 - x + 1}.$

Write $x = A(2x - 1) + B.$

Comparing coefficients on both sides, we get $2A = 1$ and $B - A = 0$. Hence, $A = B = 1/2$.

We can write

$$I_2 = \frac{1}{2} \int \frac{(2x - 1) \, dx}{x^2 - x + 1} + \frac{1}{2} \int \frac{dx}{x^2 - x + 1}$$

$$= \frac{1}{2} \log(x^2 - x + 1) + \frac{1}{2} \int \frac{dx}{(x - 1/2)^2 + (\sqrt{3}/2)^2}$$

$$= \frac{1}{2} \log (x^2 - x + 1) + \frac{1}{2}\left(\frac{2}{\sqrt{3}}\right) \tan^{-1}\left(\frac{x - 1/2}{\sqrt{3}/2}\right) + C_2$$

$$= \frac{1}{2} \log (x^2 - x + 1) + \frac{1}{\sqrt{3}} \tan^{-1}\left(\frac{2x - 1}{\sqrt{3}}\right) + C_2.$$

Hence we get

$$I = \frac{1}{3} x^3 + \frac{1}{2} x^2 - \frac{1}{2} \log (x^2 - x + 1) - \frac{1}{\sqrt{3}} \tan^{-1}\left(\frac{2x - 1}{\sqrt{3}}\right) + C.$$

(iii) $I = \int \dfrac{x\, dx}{x^4 - x^2 + 1}$.

Substitute $x^2 = y$. Then $2x\, dx = dy$. The integral reduces to

$$I = \frac{1}{2} \int \frac{dy}{y^2 - y + 1} = \frac{1}{2} \int \frac{dy}{(y - 1/2)^2 + (\sqrt{3}/2)^2}$$

$$= \frac{1}{\sqrt{3}} \tan^{-1}\left(\frac{2y - 1}{\sqrt{3}}\right) + C$$

$$= \frac{1}{\sqrt{3}} \tan^{-1}\left(\frac{2x^2 - 1}{\sqrt{3}}\right) + C.$$

7. Evaluate the following integrals :

(i) $\displaystyle\int \sqrt{\frac{1 + x}{1 - x}}\, dx,$ (ii) $\displaystyle\int \frac{dx}{\sqrt{x\,(1 - 2x)}}.$

(i) $I = \displaystyle\int \sqrt{\frac{1 + x}{1 - x}}\, dx = \int \frac{1 + x}{\sqrt{1 - x^2}}\, dx$

$$= \int \frac{dx}{\sqrt{1 - x^2}} + \int \frac{x\, dx}{\sqrt{1 - x^2}}$$

$$= \sin^{-1} x + I_1 + C.$$

In I_1, substitute $1 - x^2 = t^2$, we get $-2x\, dx = 2t\, dt$ or $x\, dx = -t\, dt$. We have

$$I_1 = -\int \frac{t\, dt}{\sqrt{t^2}} = -\int dt = -t$$

$$= -\sqrt{1 - x^2}$$

$\therefore\quad I = \sin^{-1} x - \sqrt{1 - x^2} + C.$

(ii) $I = \displaystyle\int \frac{dx}{\sqrt{x\,(1 - 2x)}}$

$$= \frac{1}{\sqrt{2}} \int \frac{dx}{\sqrt{(x/2) - x^2}}$$

$$= \frac{1}{\sqrt{2}} \int \frac{dx}{\sqrt{(1/16) - [x - (1/16)]^2}}.$$

Substituting $x - (1/4) = y$, we get $dx = dy$.

$$I = \frac{1}{\sqrt{2}} \int \frac{dy}{\sqrt{(1/16) - y^2}} = \frac{1}{\sqrt{2}} \sin^{-1}\left(\frac{y}{1/4}\right) + C$$

$$= \frac{1}{\sqrt{2}} \sin^{-1}[4\{x - (1/4)\}] + C$$

$$= \frac{1}{\sqrt{2}} \sin^{-1}(4x - 1) + C.$$

EXERCISES

1. Integrate :

(i) $\dfrac{1}{\sqrt{2x^2 + 3x + 4}}$,   (ii) $\dfrac{1}{\sqrt{3x^2 + 4x + 1}}$,   (iii) $\dfrac{2}{\sqrt{x^2 + x + 1}}$.

2. Integrate :

(i) $\sqrt{1 - x^2}$,   (ii) $\sqrt{1 + x^2}$,   (iii) $\sqrt{x^2 - 1}$.

3. Integrate :

(i) $\sqrt{2x^2 + 3x + 4}$,   (ii) $\sqrt{3x^2 + 4x + 1}$,

(iii) $\sqrt{-2x^2 + 3x + 4}$.

4. Integrate :

(i) $\dfrac{x^2}{\sqrt{(x^2 + 1)^2}}$,   (ii) $\dfrac{2x^2}{\sqrt{x^2 - 1}}$,   (iii) $\dfrac{2x + 3}{\sqrt{x^2 + 1}}$,

(iv) $(x + 2)\sqrt{x^2 + 1}$,   (v) $(2x + 4)\sqrt{2x^2 + 3x + 1}$,

(vi) $\dfrac{2x + 5}{\sqrt{x^2 - 2x + 2}}$.

5. Integrate :

(i) $\dfrac{x^2}{\sqrt{x^6 + 2x^3 + 2}}$,   (ii) $\dfrac{x^3}{\sqrt{x^8 + 1}}$,

(iii) $\dfrac{\cos x}{\sqrt{2\sin^2 x + 3\sin x + 4}}$.

ANSWERS

1. (i) $\left(\dfrac{1}{\sqrt{2}}\right)\sinh^{-1}\dfrac{4x+3}{\sqrt{23}}$ (ii) $\left(\dfrac{1}{\sqrt{3}}\right)\cosh^{-1}(3x+2)$

(iii) $\sinh^{-1}[(2x+1)/\sqrt{3}]$

2. (i) $\dfrac{1}{2}x\sqrt{1-x^2}+\dfrac{1}{2}\sin^{-1}x$ (ii) $\dfrac{1}{2}x\sqrt{x^2+1}+\dfrac{1}{2}\sinh^{-1}x$

(iii) $\dfrac{1}{2}x\sqrt{x^2-1}-\dfrac{1}{2}\cosh^{-1}x$

3. (i) $\dfrac{1}{8}(4x+3)\sqrt{2x^2+3x+4}+\dfrac{23}{32}\sqrt{2}\sinh^{-1}\left[\dfrac{4x+3}{\sqrt{23}}\right]$

(ii) $\dfrac{1}{6}(3x+2)\sqrt{3x^2+4x+1}-\dfrac{1}{18}\sqrt{3}\cosh^{-1}(3x+2)$

(iii) $\dfrac{1}{8}(4x-3)\sqrt{-2x^2+3x+4}+\dfrac{41}{32}\sqrt{2}\sin^{-1}\left[\dfrac{4x-3}{\sqrt{41}}\right]$

4. (i) $\dfrac{1}{2}x\sqrt{x^2+1}-\dfrac{1}{2}\sinh^{-1}x$ (ii) $x\sqrt{x^2-1}+\cosh^{-1}x$

(iii) $2\sqrt{x^2+1}+3\sinh^{-1}x$

(iv) $\dfrac{1}{3}\sqrt{(x^2+1)(x^2+3x+1)}+\sinh^{-1}x$

(v) $\dfrac{1}{48}\sqrt{(2x^2+3x+1)(32x^2+108x+61)}-\dfrac{5\sqrt{2}}{64}\cosh^{-1}(4x+3)$

(vi) $2\sqrt{x^2-2x+2}+7\sinh^{-1}(x-1)$

5. (i) $\dfrac{1}{3}\sinh^{-1}(x^3+1)$ (ii) $\dfrac{1}{4}\sinh^{-1}x^4$

(iii) $\dfrac{1}{\sqrt{2}}\sinh^{-1}\dfrac{4\sin x+3}{\sqrt{23}}$

2.5. Integration by parts

If u, v be two functions of x, we have

$$\frac{d(uv)}{dx}=u\frac{dv}{dx}+v\frac{du}{dx}.$$

Integrating both sides, we get

$$uv=\int u\frac{dv}{dx}dx+\int v\frac{du}{dx}dx$$

$$\Rightarrow\qquad \int u\frac{dv}{dx}dx=uv-\int v\frac{du}{dx}dx. \qquad\qquad ...(1)$$

Let

$$u = f(x) \text{ and } \frac{dv}{dx} = \phi(x).$$

Therefore

$$\frac{du}{dx} = f'(x) \text{ and } v = \int \phi(x)\,dx.$$

The statement (1) may now be rewritten as

$$\int f(x)\,\phi(x)\,dx = f(x)\int \phi(x)\,dx - \int \left[\int \phi(x)\,dx\right]\cdot f'(x)\,dx.$$

In words, this formula states that

The integral of the product of two functions

= **first function × integral of second**

– **integral of (diff. coefficient of first × integral of second).**

EXAMPLES

1. *Evaluate* $\int xe^x\,dx.$

Let

$$x = f(x),\ e^x = \phi(x).$$

$$\therefore \quad \int xe^x\,dx = x\cdot e^x - \int e^x\cdot 1\,dx = xe^x - e^x.$$

Note. Suppose we take

$$f(x) = e^x,\ \phi(x) = x$$

$$\therefore \quad \int xe^x\,dx = \frac{1}{2}x^2 e^x - \frac{1}{2}\int x^2 e^x\,dx,$$

so that the given integral $\int xe^x\,dx$ is reduced to a comparatively more

complicated integral $\int x^2 e^x\,dx$; the index of x having increased.

Thus a proper choice of the order of factors is sometimes necessary.

2. *Evaluate* $\int x^2 \cos x\,dx.$

We take $f(x) = x^2,\ \phi(x) = \cos x.$

$$\therefore \quad \int x^2 \cos x\,dx = x^2\cdot \sin x - \int 2x \sin x\,dx.$$

[To evaluate $\int x \sin x\,dx$, we have again to apply the rule of integration

by parts.]

$$= x^2 \sin x - 2\left[x(-\cos x) - \int(-\cos x)\,dx\right]$$

$$= x^2 \sin x + 2x \cos x - 2 \sin x$$

$$= (x^2 - 2)\sin x + 2x \cos x.$$

We thus see that the *rule of integration by parts may have to be repeated several times.*

3. *Evaluate* $\int cos^{-1} x \, dx.$

Here *we take unity as one factor.* We have

$$\int cos^{-1} x \, dx = \int cos^{-1} x \cdot 1 \, dx$$

$$= cos^{-1} x \cdot x - \int \frac{-1}{\sqrt{1-x^2}} x \, dx$$

$$= x cos^{-1} x - \frac{1}{2} \int (1-x^2)^{-\frac{1}{2}} (-2x) \, dx$$

$$= x cos^{-1} x - \frac{1}{2} \cdot \frac{(1-x^2)^{-\frac{1}{2}+1}}{-\frac{1}{2}+1}$$

$$= x cos^{-1} x - \sqrt{1-x^2}$$

$$\therefore \int cos^{-1} x \, dx = x cos^{-1} x - \sqrt{1-x^2}.$$

4. *Evaluate* $\int log(x + 1) \, dx.$

Take $log(x + 1)$ as the first function and 1 as the second function. Integrating by parts, we get

$$I = x log(x + 1) - \int \frac{x \, dx}{x + 1}$$

$$= x log(x + 1) - \int \frac{(x + 1 - 1) \, dx}{x + 1}$$

$$= x log(x + 1) - \int dx + \int \frac{dx}{x + 1}$$

$$= x log(x + 1) - x + log(x + 1) + C$$

$$= (x + 1) log(x + 1) - x + C.$$

5. *Integrate* $cos \sqrt{x}$ *with respect to x.*

Substitute $x = t^2$, we get $dx = 2t \, dt$. Then

$$I = \int cos \sqrt{x} \, dx = 2 \int t \, cos \, t \, dt.$$

Take t as the first function and $cos \, t$ as the second function. Integrating by parts, we get

$$I = 2 \left[t \sin t - \int \sin t \, dt \right] = 2 [t \sin t + cos \, t] + C$$

$$= 2 [\sqrt{x} \sin \sqrt{x} + cos \sqrt{x}] + C.$$

6. *Evaluate* : $\int \sin(\log x)\, dx.$

Substituting $\log x = t$, we get $\dfrac{1}{x}\, dx = dt$ or $dx = x\, dt = e^t\, dt.$

$$I = \int \sin(\log x)\, dx = \int e^t \sin t\, dt.$$

Taking $\sin t$ as the second function and integrating by parts, we get

$$I = e^t\,(-\cos t) - \int (-\cos t)\, e^t\, dt$$

$$= -e^t \cos t + \int e^t \cos t\, dt.$$

Integrating again by parts, we get

$$I = -e^t \cos t + e^t \sin t - \int e^t \sin t\, dt$$

$$= e^t\,(\sin t - \cos t) - I + C_1$$

or $\qquad 2I = e^t\,(\sin t - \cos t) + C_1$

$\therefore \quad I = \dfrac{1}{2}\, e^t\,(\sin t - \cos t) + \dfrac{C_1}{2}$

$$= \dfrac{1}{2}\, x\,[\sin(\log x) - \cos(\log x)] + C$$

where $C = C_1/2.$

7. *Evaluate* : $\int x\,(\log x)^2\, dx.$

$$I = \int x\,(\log x)^2\, dx.$$

Integrating by parts, taking $(\log x)^2$ as first function, we get

$$I = \dfrac{x^2}{2}\,(\log x)^2 - \int \dfrac{x^2}{2}\left[2\,(\log x)\left(\dfrac{1}{x}\right)\right] dx$$

$$= \dfrac{x^2}{2}\,(\log x)^2 - \int x \log x\, dx.$$

Again integrating by parts, taking $\log x$ as first function, we have

$$I = \dfrac{x^2}{2}\,(\log x)^2 - \left[\dfrac{x^2}{2}\,\log x - \int \dfrac{1}{2}\,x^2\cdot\left(\dfrac{1}{x}\right) dx\right]$$

$$= \dfrac{x^2}{2}\,(\log x)^2 - \dfrac{x^2}{2}\,\log x + \dfrac{1}{2}\int x\, dx$$

$$= \dfrac{x^2}{2}\,(\log x)^2 - \dfrac{x^2}{2}\,\log x + \dfrac{1}{4}\,x^2 + C.$$

8. *Evaluate* $\int \sec^3 x \, dx$.

$$I = \int \sec^3 x \, dx = \int \sec^2 x \sec x \, dx.$$

Taking $\sec x$ as first part and integrating by parts, we get

$$I = \sec x \tan x - \int \tan x \, (\sec x \tan x) \, dx$$

$$= \sec x \tan x - \int \sec x \tan^2 x \, dx$$

$$= \sec x \tan x - \int \sec x \, (\sec^2 x - 1) \, dx$$

$$= \sec x \tan x - \int \sec^3 x \, dx + \int \sec x \, dx$$

$$= \sec x \tan x - I + \log (\sec x + \tan x) + C_1.$$

$$\therefore \quad 2I = \sec x \tan x + \log (\sec x + \tan x) + C_1$$

or $\qquad I = \dfrac{1}{2} [\sec x \tan x + \log (\sec x + \tan x)] + C.$

9. *Evaluate* : $\int (cos^{-1} x)^2 \, dx$.

$$I = \int (cos^{-1} x)^2 \, dx.$$

Taking $(\cos^{-1} x)^2$ as first and 1 as second part and integrating by parts, we get

$$I = x \, (\cos^{-1} x)^2 - \int x \left[2 \, (\cos^{-1} x) \left(\frac{-1}{\sqrt{1 - x^2}} \right) \right] dx$$

$$= x \, (\cos^{-1} x)^2 + \int \frac{2x}{\sqrt{1 - x^2}} \cos^{-1} x \, dx$$

$$= x \, (\cos^{-1} x)^2 + I_1$$

where $\quad I_1 = \int \dfrac{2x}{\sqrt{1 - x^2}} \cos^{-1} x \, dx.$

Integrate it taking $\cos^{-1} x$ as first part and $\dfrac{2x}{\sqrt{1 - x^2}}$ as second part,

since $\int \dfrac{2x \, dx}{\sqrt{1 - x^2}} = -2 \sqrt{1 - x^2}$, we obtain on integrating by parts

$$I_1 = -2 \sqrt{1 - x^2} \cos^{-1} x - \int \left(-2 \sqrt{1 - x^2} \right) \left(- \frac{1}{\sqrt{1 - x^2}} \right) dx$$

$$= -2\sqrt{1-x^2}\ \cos^{-1} x - 2x + C.$$

$$\therefore \quad I = x\,(\cos^{-1} x)^2 - 2\sqrt{1-x^2}\ \cos^{-1} x - 2x + C.$$

EXERCISES

Integrate the following functions :

1. (i) $x^2 e^x$,   (ii) $x^3 e^x$,   (iii) $x \sinh x$.

2. (i) $\log x$,   (ii) $x \log x$,   (iii) $x^2 \log x$,   (iv) $x^n \log x$.

3. (i) $x (\log x)^2$,   (ii) $(x \log x)^3$,   (iii) $\sqrt{x}\,(\log x)^2$.

4. (i) $\tan^{-1} x$,   (ii) $x \tan^{-1} x$,   (iii) $\cot^{-1} x$,   (iv) $x \cot^{-1} x$,
   (v) $x^3 \tan^{-1} x$.

5. (i) $\sin^{-1} x$,   (ii) $x \sin^{-1} x$,   (iii) $\sec^{-1} x$,   (iv) $x \sec^{-1} x$.

6. (i) $x \cos x$,   (ii) $x^2 \sin x$,   (iii) $x^3 \cos x$,   (iv) $x^2 \sin^2 x$,
   (v) $x^2 \sin x \cos x$,   (vi) $x \cos x \cos 2x$,
   (vii) $x \sin x \sec^3 x$,   (viii) $x \cos^3 x \sin x$.

7. (i) $\dfrac{x}{\sin^2 x}$,   (ii) $\dfrac{x}{\cos^2 x}$,   (iii) $x \log (1 + x)$.

ANSWERS

1. (i) $(x^2 - 2x + 2)\, e^x$.   (ii) $(x^3 - 3x^2 + 6x - 6)\, e^x$.
   (iii) $x \cosh x - \sinh x$.

2. (i) $x \log (x/e)$.   (ii) $\dfrac{1}{4} x^2 \log (x^2/e)$.

   (iii) $\dfrac{1}{4} x^3 \log (x^3/e)$.   (iv) $[x^{n+1}/(n+1)^2] \log (x^{n+1}/e)$.

3. (i) $\dfrac{1}{4} x^2 [2 (\log x)^2 - 2 \log x + 1]$.

   (ii) $\dfrac{1}{128} x^4 [32 (\log x)^3 - 24 (\log x)^2 + 12 \log x - 3]$.

   (iii) $\dfrac{1}{27} [18 (\log x)^2 - 24 \log x + 16]\, x^{3/2}$.

4. (i) $x \tan^{-1} x - \log \sqrt{x^2 + 1}$.   (ii) $\dfrac{1}{2} (x^2 + 1) \tan^{-1} x - \dfrac{1}{2} x$.

   (iii) $x \cot^{-1} x + \log \sqrt{x^2 + 1}$.   (iv) $\dfrac{1}{2} (x^2 + 1) \cot^{-1} x + \dfrac{1}{2} x$.

5. (i) $x \sin^{-1} x + \sqrt{1 - x^2}$.

   (ii) $\dfrac{1}{4} (2x^2 - 1) \sin^{-1} x + \dfrac{1}{4} x \sqrt{1 - x^2}$.

   (iii) $x \sec^{-1} x - \cosh^{-1} x$.   (iv) $\dfrac{1}{2} [x^2 \sec^{-1} x - \sqrt{x^2 - 1}]$.

6. (*i*) $x \sin x + \cos x$.   (*ii*) $-x^2 \cos x + 2 (x \sin x + \cos x)$.

(*iii*) $(x^3 - 6x) \sin x + 3 (x^2 - 2) \cos x$.

(*iv*) $\dfrac{1}{6} x^3 + \dfrac{1}{8} (1 - 2x^2) \sin 2x - \dfrac{1}{4} x \cos 2x$.

(*v*) $\dfrac{1}{8} (1 - 2x^2) \cos 2x + \dfrac{1}{4} x \sin 2x$.

(*vi*) $\dfrac{1}{81} (3x \sin 3x + \cos 3x + \dfrac{1}{2} x \sin x + \cos x)$.

(*vii*) $\dfrac{1}{2} (x \sec^2 x - \tan x)$.

(*viii*) $-\dfrac{1}{4} x \cos^4 x + \dfrac{1}{128} (12x + 8 \sin 2x + \sin 4x)$.

7. (*i*) $-x \cot x + \log \sin x$.   (*ii*) $x \tan x - \log \sec x$.

(*iii*) $\dfrac{1}{2} (x^2 - 1) \log (1 + x) - \dfrac{1}{4} (x^2 - 2x)$.

2.5.1. To evaluate the integral

$$\int e^x [f(x) + f'(x)] \, dx.$$

Integrating by parts, we have

$$\int e^x f(x) \, dx = e^x f(x) - \int e^x f'(x) \, dx$$

$$\Rightarrow \quad \int e^x [f(x) + f'(x)] \, dx = e^x f(x).$$

This form of integral is quite important.

EXAMPLES

1. *Evaluate the following integrals* :

(*i*) $\displaystyle\int \dfrac{xe^x}{(x+1)^2} \, dx,$ (*ii*) $\displaystyle\int e^x \dfrac{1 - \sin x}{1 - \cos x} \, dx.$

We have

(*i*) $\displaystyle\int \dfrac{xe^x}{(x+1)^2} \, dx = \int \dfrac{x + 1 - 1}{(x+1)^2} e^x \, dx,$

$$= \int \left[\dfrac{1}{x+1} - \dfrac{1}{(x+1)^2} \right] e^x \, dx.$$

Taking $f(x) = \dfrac{1}{x+1}$ so that $f'(x) = -\dfrac{1}{(x+1)^2}$ we see that the function to be integrated is of the form

$$e^x [f(x) + f'(x)]$$

and accordingly, the integral is

$$= e^x f(x) = \frac{e^x}{x+1}.$$

We may also, however, proceed independently as follows :

Integrating $\int \dfrac{1}{x+1} e^x \, dx$ by parts, we get

$$\int \frac{1}{x+1} \cdot e^x \, dx = \frac{1}{x+1} \cdot e^x - \int -\frac{1}{(x+1)^2} e^x \, dx.$$

$$\Rightarrow \int \left[\frac{1}{x+1} - \frac{1}{(x+1)^2}\right] e^x \, dx = \frac{1}{x+1} e^x.$$

(ii) Now, $e^x \left(\dfrac{1-\sin x}{1-\cos x}\right) = e^x \left\{\dfrac{1 - 2\sin \dfrac{x}{2}\cos \dfrac{x}{2}}{2\sin^2 \dfrac{x}{2}}\right\}$

$$= e^x \left\{\frac{1}{2}\operatorname{cosec}^2 \frac{x}{2} - \cot \frac{x}{2}\right\}$$

so that $f(x) = \cot \dfrac{x}{2}$. We see that the integrand is of the form

$$e^x [f(x) + f'(x)].$$

Integrating $e^x \cot \dfrac{x}{2}$ by parts, we obtain

$$\int e^x \cot \frac{x}{2} \, dx = e^x \cot \frac{x}{2} - \int -\frac{1}{2}\operatorname{cosec}^2 x \, dx$$

$$\therefore \quad \int e^x \left(\cot \frac{x}{2} - \frac{1}{2}\operatorname{cosec}^2 \frac{x}{2}\right) dx = e^x \cot \frac{x}{2}$$

$$\therefore \quad \int e^x \left(\frac{1}{2}\operatorname{cosec}^2 \frac{x}{2} - \cot \frac{x}{2}\right) dx = -e^x \cot \frac{x}{2}.$$

EXERCISES

1. Integrate the following functions :

(i) $\dfrac{1+x}{(2+x)^2} e^x$,

(ii) $\dfrac{1+\sin x}{1+\cos x} e^x$,

(iii) $\dfrac{1+x \log x}{x} e^x$,

(iv) $\dfrac{2+\sin 2x}{1+\cos 2x} e^x$,

(v) $\dfrac{2-\sin 2x}{1-\cos 2x} e^x$,

(vi) $\dfrac{1+\sin 2x}{1+\cos 2x} e^{2x}$,

(vii) $\dfrac{\sqrt{1-\sin x}}{1+\cos x}\, e^{-\frac{1}{2}x}$,   (viii) $\dfrac{(x^2+1)}{(x+1)^2}\, e^x$,

(ix) $e^x\,(\tan x - \log \cos x)$.

ANSWERS

1. (i) $\dfrac{e^x}{(2+x)}$.   (ii) $e^x \tan \dfrac{x}{2}$.   (iii) $e^x \log x$.

(iv) $e^x \tan x$.   (v) $-e^x \cot x$.   (vi) $\dfrac{1}{2} e^{2x} \tan x$.

(vii) $e^{-\frac{1}{2}x} \sec \dfrac{1}{2} x$.   (viii) $(x-1)\dfrac{e^x}{(x+1)}$.   (ix) $e^x \log \sec x$.

2.5.2. Integrals of

(i) $e^{ax} \cos (bx + c)$ (ii) $e^{ax} \sin (bx + c)$.

Applying the rule of integration by parts, we obtain

$$\int e^{ax} \cos (bx + c)\, dx$$

$$= \frac{e^{ax}}{a} \cos (bx + c) - \int -\frac{e^{ax}}{a} \cdot b \sin (bx + c)\, dx$$

$$= \frac{e^{ax}}{a} \cos (bx + c) + \frac{b}{a} \int e^{ax} \sin (bx + c)\, dx. \qquad ...(1)$$

Similarly we have

$$\int e^{ax} \sin (bx + c)\, dx$$

$$= \frac{e^{ax}}{a} \sin (bx + c) - \int \frac{e^{ax}}{a} \cdot b \cos (bx + c)\, dx$$

$$= \frac{e^{ax}}{a} \sin (bx + c) - \frac{b}{a} \int e^{ax} \cos (bx + c)\, dx. \qquad ...(2)$$

If the value of $\int e^{ax} \cos (bx + c)\, dx$ be required, we substitute the R.H.S. of (2) for the last term of (1) and if the value of $\int e^{ax} \sin (bx + c)\, dx$ be required, we substitute the R.H.S. of (1) for the last term of (2). In the former case we get

$$\int e^{ax} \cos (bx + c)\, dx$$

$$= \frac{e^{ax}}{a} \cos (bx + c) + \frac{b}{a^2} e^{ax} \sin (bx + c)$$

$$- \frac{b^2}{a^2} \int e^{ax} \cos (bx + c)\, dx$$

$$\Rightarrow \left(1 + \frac{b^2}{a^2}\right)\int e^{ax} \cos(bx + c)\, dx$$

$$= e^{ax} \frac{a\cos(bx + c) + b\sin(bx + c)}{a^2},$$

$$\Rightarrow \int e^{ax} \cos(bx + c)\, dx = e^{ax} \frac{a\cos(bx + c) + b\sin(bx + c)}{a^2 + b^2}.$$

Similarly we have

$$\int e^{ax} \sin(bx + c)\, dx = e^{ax} \frac{a\sin(bx + c) - b\cos(bx + c)}{a^2 + b^2}.$$

To put the results in another form, we determine two numbers r and α such that

$$a = r\cos\alpha \text{ and } b = r\sin\alpha.$$

These give

$$r = \sqrt{a^2 + b^2}, \ \alpha = \tan^{-1}(b/a).$$

$$\therefore \int e^{ax} \cos(bx + c)\, dx = e^{ax} \frac{r\cos(bx + c - \alpha)}{a^2 + b^2}$$

$$= e^{ax} \frac{\cos\left(bx + c - \tan^{-1}\dfrac{b}{a}\right)}{\sqrt{a^2 + b^2}}.$$

Similarly

$$\int e^{ax} \sin(bx + c)\, dx = e^{ax} \frac{\sin\left(bx + c - \tan^{-1}\dfrac{b}{a}\right)}{\sqrt{a^2 + b^2}}.$$

EXAMPLES

1. *Evaluate*

(i) $\displaystyle\int e^{3x} \sin 4x\, dx,$ (ii) $\displaystyle\int e^{4x} \cos 2x \cos 4x\, dx,$

(iii) $\displaystyle\int x e^{2x} \cos x\, dx.$

(i) From the formula proved above in § 2.5.2, we get

$$\int e^{3x} \sin 4x\, dx = \frac{e^{3x}}{\sqrt{3^2 + 4^2}} \sin\left(4x - \tan^{-1}\frac{4}{3}\right)$$

$$= \frac{e^{3x}}{5} \sin\left(4x - \tan^{-1}\frac{4}{3}\right).$$

(*ii*) Now, $\cos 2x \cos 4x = \dfrac{1}{2}(2 \cos 2x \cos 4x)$

$$= \dfrac{1}{2}(\cos 6x + \cos 2x).$$

$$\therefore \int e^{4x} \cos 2x \cos 4x \, dx$$

$$= \dfrac{1}{2}\int e^{4x} \cdot \cos 6x \, dx + \dfrac{1}{2}\int e^{4x} \cdot \cos 2x \, dx$$

$$= \dfrac{1}{2} \cdot \dfrac{e^{4x}}{\sqrt{4^2 + 6^2}} \cos\left(6x - \tan^{-1}\dfrac{6}{4}\right)$$

$$+ \dfrac{1}{2} \cdot \dfrac{e^{4x}}{\sqrt{4^2 + 2^2}} \cos\left(2x - \tan^{-1}\dfrac{2}{4}\right)$$

$$= \dfrac{e^{4x}}{2}\left[\dfrac{1}{\sqrt{52}}\cos\left(6x - \tan^{-1}\dfrac{3}{2}\right) + \dfrac{1}{\sqrt{20}}\cos\left(2x - \tan^{-1}\dfrac{1}{2}\right)\right].$$

(*iii*) To evaluate $\int xe^{2x}\cos x \, dx$, we apply the rule of integration by parts. Taking x and $e^{2x}\cos x$ as two factors, we have

$$\int xe^{2x}\cos x \, dx$$

$$= x \cdot \dfrac{e^{2x}}{\sqrt{5}}\cos\left(x - \tan^{-1}\dfrac{1}{2}\right) - \int 1 \cdot \dfrac{e^{2x}}{\sqrt{5}}\cos\left(x - \tan^{-1}\dfrac{1}{2}\right) dx.$$

Again,

$$\int e^{2x}\cos\left(x - \tan^{-1}\dfrac{1}{2}\right) dx = \dfrac{e^{2x}}{\sqrt{5}}\cos\left(x - 2\tan^{-1}\dfrac{1}{2}\right)$$

$$\therefore \int xe^{2x}\cos x \, dx$$

$$= e^{2x}\left[\dfrac{x}{\sqrt{5}}\cos\left(x - \tan^{-1}\dfrac{1}{2}\right) - \dfrac{1}{5}\cos\left(x - 2\tan^{-1}\dfrac{1}{2}\right)\right].$$

EXERCISES

1. Evaluate the following integrals :

(*i*) $\displaystyle\int e^{4x}\cos 5x \, dx$,   (*ii*) $\displaystyle\int e^{x}\cos^2 x \, dx$,

(*iii*) $\displaystyle\int e^{2x}\cos^2 x \, dx$,   (*iv*) $\displaystyle\int e^{x}\sin x \sin 2x \sin 3x \, dx$,

(*v*) $\displaystyle\int x^2 e^{x}\sin x \, dx$,   (*vi*) $\displaystyle\int \sinh 2x \sin 2x \, dx$.

2. Integrate

(*i*) $\cos(\log x)$,   (*ii*) $x\sin(2\log x)$,   (*iii*) $x^2 \sin(a\log x)$.

ANSWERS

1. *(i)* $\sqrt{\dfrac{1}{41}}\, e^{4x} \cos\left(5x - \tan^{-1}\dfrac{5}{4}\right).$

(ii) $\dfrac{1}{2} e^x + \dfrac{1}{2}\sqrt{\dfrac{1}{5}}\, e^x \cos(2x - \tan^{-1} 2).$

(iii) $\dfrac{1}{4} e^{2x} \left[\dfrac{3}{\sqrt{5}} \cos\left(x - \tan^{-1}\dfrac{1}{2}\right) + \dfrac{1}{\sqrt{13}} \cos\left(3x - \tan^{-1}\dfrac{3}{2}\right) \right].$

(iv) $\dfrac{1}{4} e^x \left[\sqrt{\dfrac{1}{5}} \sin(2x - \tan^{-1} 2) - \sqrt{\dfrac{1}{37}} \sin(6x - \tan^{-1} 6) \right.$

$$\left. + \sqrt{\dfrac{1}{17}} \sin(4x - \tan^{-1} 4) \right].$$

(v) $\sqrt{\dfrac{1}{2}}\, e^x \left[x^2 \sin\left(x - \dfrac{1}{4}\pi\right) + \sin\left(x - \dfrac{3}{4}\pi\right) \right] + x e^x \cos x.$

(vi) $\dfrac{1}{4}(\cosh 2x \sin 2x - \sinh 2x \cos 2x).$

2. *(i)* $\sqrt{\dfrac{1}{2}} \cdot x \cos\left(\log x - \dfrac{1}{4}\pi\right).$ *(ii)* $\sqrt{\dfrac{1}{8}}\, x^2 \sin\left(2\log x - \dfrac{1}{4}\pi\right).$

(iii) $\dfrac{x^4}{\sqrt{16 + a^2}} \sin\left(a \log x - \tan^{-1}\dfrac{a}{4}\right).$

2.6. Sometimes both the methods of integration have to be applied in one and the same question. We will illustrate the procedure by two examples.

EXAMPLES

1. *Evaluate* $\displaystyle\int \dfrac{x \sin^{-1} x}{\sqrt{1 - x^2}}\, dx.$

We put

$$x = \sin\theta \;\Rightarrow\; dx = \cos\theta\, d\theta.$$

$$\therefore \quad \int \dfrac{x \sin^{-1} x}{\sqrt{1 - x^2}}\, dx = \int \dfrac{\sin\theta \cdot \theta}{\cos\theta} \cos\theta\, d\theta = \int \theta \sin\theta\, d\theta.$$

To evaluate $\int \theta \sin\theta\, d\theta$, we apply the rule of integration by parts and obtain

$$\int \theta \sin\theta\, d\theta = (-\theta\cos\theta) - \int -\cos\theta \cdot 1\, d\theta$$

$$= -\theta\cos\theta + \int \cos\theta\, d\theta = -\theta\cos\theta + \sin\theta.$$

$$\therefore \quad \int \frac{x \sin^{-1} x}{\sqrt{1 - x^2}}\, dx = -\theta \cos\theta + \sin\theta$$

$$= -\sqrt{1 - x^2}\, \sin^{-1} x + x.$$

2. *Integrate* $\tan^{-1} \sqrt{\dfrac{1 - x}{1 + x}}$.

We put

$$x = \cos\theta \implies dx = -\sin\theta\, d\theta.$$

Also

$$\tan^{-1} \sqrt{\frac{1 - x}{1 + x}} = \tan^{-1} \sqrt{\frac{1 - \cos\theta}{1 + \cos\theta}}$$

$$= \tan^{-1} \sqrt{\frac{2 \sin^2 (\theta/2)}{2 \cos^2 (\theta/2)}}$$

$$= \tan^{-1} \left(\tan\frac{\theta}{2} \right) = \frac{\theta}{2}.$$

$$\therefore \quad \int \tan^{-1} \sqrt{\frac{1 - x}{1 + x}}\, dx = \int \frac{\theta}{2} (-\sin\theta)\, d\theta$$

$$= -\frac{1}{2} \int \theta \sin\theta\, d\theta$$

$$= -\frac{1}{2} (-\theta \cos\theta + \sin\theta)$$

$$= -\frac{1}{2} \left[-x \cos^{-1} x + \sqrt{1 - x^2} \right].$$

EXERCISES

Integrate the following :

1. $x^5 \tan^{-1} x^2$.

2. $x \tan^{-1} x / (1 + x^2)^{3/2}$.

3. $x^5 \cos x^2$.

4. $\tan^{-1} [2x / (1 - x^2)]$.

5. $\dfrac{e^{m \tan^{-1} x}}{(1 + x^2)^{3/2}}$.

6. $\dfrac{e^{m \tan^{-1} x}}{(1 + x^2)^2}$.

7. $\dfrac{x e^{m \sin^{-1} x}}{\sqrt{1 - x^2}}$.

8. $\dfrac{x^2 e^{m \sin^{-1} x}}{\sqrt{1 - x^2}}$.

ANSWERS

1. $\frac{1}{6}[(x^6+1)\tan^{-1}x^3 - x^3]$. **2.** $(x - \tan^{-1}x)/\sqrt{1+x^2}$.

3. $\frac{1}{2}(x^4 - 2)\sin x^2 + x^2\cos x^2$. **4.** $2x\tan^{-1}x - \log(1+x^2)$.

5. $\dfrac{e^{m\theta}}{\sqrt{m^2+1}}\cos(\theta - \cot^{-1}m)$, where $\theta = \tan^{-1}x$.

6. $\dfrac{e^{m\theta}}{2}\left[\dfrac{1}{m} + \dfrac{1}{\sqrt{m^2+1}}\cos\left(2\theta - \tan^{-1}\dfrac{2}{m}\right)\right]$, where $\theta = \tan^{-1}x$.

7. $\dfrac{e^{m\theta}}{\sqrt{m^2+1}}\sin(\theta - \cot^{-1}m)$, where $\theta = \sin^{-1}x$.

8. $\dfrac{e^{m\theta}}{2}\left[\dfrac{1}{m} - \dfrac{1}{\sqrt{m^2+4}}\cos\left(2\theta - \tan^{-1}\dfrac{2}{m}\right)\right]$, where $\theta = \sin^{-1}x$.

2.7. Definite Integrals. The application of the methods of integrating by substitution and of integrating by parts for evaluating definite integrals shall be illustrated by means of examples.

The validity of the procedure will be seen to be quite apparent.

When the variable x in a definite integral

$$\int_a^b f(x)\,dx$$

is changed, we usually change the limits also; the new limits being the values of the new variable which correspond to the values a and b of x.

EXAMPLES

1. *Evaluate* $\displaystyle\int_0^{\pi/2} \frac{\cos x}{1+\sin^2 x}\,dx$.

We put

$$\sin x = t \;\Rightarrow\; \cos x\,dx = dt \qquad\qquad \text{...(1)}$$

From (1), we see that

$$x = 0 \;\Rightarrow\; t = 0 \quad\text{and}\quad x = \frac{\pi}{2} \;\Rightarrow\; t = 1.$$

Thus 0 and 1 are the limits for the new variable t. We have

$$\int_0^{\pi/2} \frac{\cos x}{1 + \sin^2 x}\, dx = \int_0^1 \frac{dt}{1 + t^2} = \left| \tan^{-1} t \right|_0^1$$

$$= \tan^{-1} t - \tan^{-1} 0 = \frac{\pi}{4}.$$

2. *Evaluate* $\displaystyle\int_0^1 x^2 e^{2x}\, dx$.

Integrating by parts, we have

$$\int x^2 e^{2x}\, dx = \frac{x^2 e^x}{2} - \int \frac{2x}{2}\cdot e^{2x}\, dx = \frac{x^2 e^{2x}}{2} - \int x e^{2x}\, dx.$$

$$\Rightarrow \int_0^1 x^2 e^{2x}\, dx = \left| \frac{x^2 e^{2x}}{2} \right|_0^1 - \int_0^1 x e^{2x}\, dx$$

$$= \frac{e^2}{2} - \int_0^1 x e^{2x}\, dx.$$

Again,

$$\int x e^{2x}\, dx = \frac{x e^{2x}}{2} - \int \frac{e^{2x}}{2}\, dx$$

$$= \frac{x e^{2x}}{2} - \frac{e^{2x}}{4}.$$

$$\Rightarrow \int_0^1 x e^{2x}\, dx = \left| \frac{x e^{2x}}{2} \right|_0^1 - \left| \frac{e^{2x}}{4} \right|_0^1$$

$$= \frac{e^2}{4} + \frac{1}{4}.$$

$$\therefore \int_0^1 x^2 e^{2x}\, dx = \frac{e^2}{2} - \left(\frac{e^2}{4} + \frac{1}{4} \right) = \frac{e^2 - 1}{4}.$$

3. *Prove that*

$$\int_0^{\sqrt{1/2}} \frac{\sin^{-1} x\, dx}{(1 - x^2)^{3/2}} = \frac{\pi}{4} - \frac{1}{2} \log 2.$$

We put

$$x = \sin \theta \;\Rightarrow\; dx = \cos \theta\, d\theta \qquad\qquad ...(1)$$

From (1), we see that

$$\theta = 0 \text{ when } x = 0 \text{ and } \theta = \frac{1}{4}\pi \text{ when } x = \sqrt{\frac{1}{2}}.$$

Thus the given integral

$$= \int_0^{\pi/4} \theta \sec^2 \theta \, d\theta.$$

Integrating by parts, we obtain

$$\int \theta \sec^2 \theta \, d\theta = \theta \tan \theta - \int 1 \cdot \tan \theta \, d\theta$$

$$= \theta \tan \theta - \log \sec \theta$$

$$\therefore \int_0^{\pi/4} \theta \sec^2 \theta \, d\theta = \Big| \theta \tan \theta - \log \sec \theta \Big|_0^{\pi/4}$$

$$= \frac{\pi}{4} \cdot 1 - \log \sqrt{2} = \frac{\pi}{4} - \frac{1}{2} \log 2.$$

EXERCISES

1. Evaluate the following integrals :

(i) $\displaystyle\int_0^1 \frac{2x}{1+x^2} \, dx,$ (ii) $\displaystyle\int_0^{\pi/2} \cos^2 t \, dt,$ (iii) $\displaystyle\int_0^1 \frac{(\tan^{-1} x)^2}{1+x^2} \, dx,$

(iv) $\displaystyle\int_0^{\pi/3} \sin^3 t \cos t \, dt,$ (v) $\displaystyle\int_0^{\pi/2} \sin^3 t \, dt,$ (vi) $\displaystyle\int_0^1 \frac{\sqrt{\tan^{-1} x}}{1+x^2} \, dx,$

(vii) $\displaystyle\int_0^{\pi} x \cos x \, dx,$ (viii) $\displaystyle\int_0^{\pi} x \sin^{-1} x \, dx,$ (ix) $\displaystyle\int_0^1 x \tan^{-1} x^2 \, dx,$

(x) $\displaystyle\int_{1/4}^{1/2} \frac{dx}{\sqrt{x - x^2}}.$

2. Prove that

$$\int_0^1 x \, (\tan^{-1} x)^2 \, dx = \frac{\pi}{4} \left(\frac{\pi}{4} - 1 \right) + \frac{1}{2} \log 2.$$

ANSWERS

1. (i) $\log 2.$ (ii) $\pi/4.$ (iii) $\pi^3/192.$ (iv) $1/4.$
   (v) $2/3.$ (vi) $\pi^{3/2}/12.$ (vii) $-2.$ (viii) $\pi/8.$
   (ix) $(\pi - 2)/4.$ (x) $\pi/6.$

2.7.1. Improper Definite Integrals. *While calculating improper definite integrals, we often need the following limits :

$$(i) \quad \lim_{x \to \infty} \frac{x^n}{e^x} = 0, \quad (ii) \quad \lim_{x \to \infty} \frac{\log x}{x^n} = 0, \quad (iii) \quad \lim_{x \to 0} (x^n \log x) = 0,$$

n being a positive number.

EXAMPLES

1. *Evaluate*

$$\int_0^1 \log x \, dx.$$

We know that $\log x \to -\infty$ as $x \to 0$ so that here we are concerned with an improper integral.

We firstly evaluate

$$\int_h^1 \log x \, dx.$$

We have

$$\int_h^1 \log x \, dx = \int_h^1 1 \cdot \log x \, dx$$

$$= \left| x \log x \right|_h^1 - \int_h^1 1 \cdot dx$$

$$= \left| x \log x \right|_h^1 - \left| x \right|_h^1$$

$$= -h \log h - (1 - h), \text{ for } \log 1 = 0.$$

As $h \to 0$, $h \log h \to 0$ and, therefore, the right hand side $\to -1$.

Thus $\int_0^1 \log x \, dx$ exists finitely and is equal to -1.

2. *Show that, a being positive,*

$$\int_0^\infty e^{-ax} \cos bx \, dx = \frac{a}{a^2 + b^2} \int_0^\infty e^{-ax} \sin bx \, dx = \frac{b}{a^2 + b^2}.$$

We write

$$I = \int_0^\infty e^{-ax} \cos bx \, dx, \quad J = \int_0^\infty e^{-ax} \sin bx \, dx.$$

---

* These results have been proved in Chapter XIII of the Author's *Differential Calculus*.

Let x be a positive number. Integrating by parts, we have

$$\int\limits_0^x e^{-ax} \cos bx \, dx = \left| e^{-ax} \frac{\sin bx}{b} \right|_0^x + \frac{a}{b} \int\limits_0^x e^{-ax} \sin bx \, dx \qquad ...(1)$$

Now

$$\left| e^{-ax} \frac{\sin bx}{b} \right|_0^x = \frac{\sin bx}{be^{ax}} - 0 = \frac{\sin bx}{be^{ax}},$$

which tends to 0 as $x \to \infty$, for $1/e^{ax} \to 0$ and $\sin bx$ remains numerically less than 1.

Thus letting $x \to \infty$, we obtain, from (1)

$$I = \frac{a}{b} J. \qquad ...(2)$$

Again, we have

$$\int\limits_0^x e^{-ax} \sin bx \, dx = \left| -e^{-ax} \frac{\cos bx}{b} \right|_0^x - \frac{a}{b} \int\limits_0^x e^{-ax} \cos bx \, dx \qquad ...(3)$$

Now

$$\left| -e^{-ax} \frac{\cos bx}{b} \right|_0^x = -\frac{\cos bx}{be^{ax}} + \frac{1}{b},$$

which tends to $1/b$ as $x \to \infty$.

Therefore, letting $x \to \infty$, we obtain, from (3)

$$J = \frac{1}{b} - \frac{a}{b} I. \qquad ...(4)$$

Solving (2) and (4) for I and J, we obtain

$$I = \frac{a}{a^2 + b^2}, \quad J = \frac{b}{a^2 + b^2}.$$

EXERCISES

Evaluate the following improper integrals :

(i) $\displaystyle\int\limits_0^1 \frac{\sin^{-1} x}{\sqrt{1-x^2}} \, dx,$

(ii) $\displaystyle\int\limits_0^\infty x^2 e^{-x} \, dx,$

(iii) $\displaystyle\int\limits_0^\infty x^3 e^{-x} \, dx,$

(iv) $\displaystyle\int\limits_0^1 x \log x \, dx,$

(v) $\displaystyle\int\limits_0^\infty \frac{\log x}{x^2} \, dx,$

(vi) $\displaystyle\int\limits_1^\infty \frac{\log x}{x^3} \, dx,$

(vii) $\displaystyle\int\limits_0^a \frac{dx}{\sqrt{ax - x^2}},$

(viii) $\displaystyle\int\limits_0^a \sqrt{\frac{a-x}{x}} \, dx,$

(ix) $\displaystyle\int\limits_{-\infty}^{+\infty} \frac{e^x}{1+e^{2x}} \, dx,$

(x) $\displaystyle\int_0^\infty e^{-ax} \sin nx\, dx,\ (a > 0),$

(xi) $\displaystyle\int_0^\infty e^{-2x} \sin x \sin 3x\, dx,$ $\qquad\qquad$ (xii) $\displaystyle\int_{-\infty}^0 e^x \sin x\, dx.$

ANSWERS

(i) $\pi^2/8$. $\qquad$ (ii) 2. $\qquad\qquad$ (iii) 6. $\qquad\qquad$ (iv) $-1/4$.

(v) 1. $\qquad\quad$ (vi) $1/4$. $\qquad\qquad$ (vii) π. $\qquad\qquad$ $(viii)$ $a\pi/2$.

(ix) $\pi/2$. $\qquad$ (x) $n/(a^2 + n^2)$. $\quad$ (xi) $3/40$. $\qquad$ (xii) $-1/2$.

2.8. Reduction Formulae. In the general sense of the term, any formula which expresses an integral in terms of another which is simpler, is a reduction formula for the first integral. The common practice is, however, to confine the use of the term to cases in which the integral is a member of a class of functions and the formula expresses the integral of the general member of the class in terms of one or two integrals of the same class. The successive application of the reduction formula enables us to express the integral of the general member of the class of functions in terms of that of simplest member of the class.

The reduction formulae are *generally obtained by applying the rule of integration by parts.*

A large number of reduction formulae will be obtained in the following chapters. Here we will consider some illustrative cases only.

EXAMPLES

1. *Establish a reduction formula for* $\int x^n e^{ax}\, dx$ *and apply it to evaluate* $\int x^3 e^{ax}\, dx$.

Integrating by parts, we have

$$\int x^n e^{ax}\, dx = x^n \cdot \frac{e^{ax}}{a} - \frac{n}{a} \int x^{n-1} e^{ax}\, dx,$$

which is the required reduction formula.

Putting $n = 3, 2, 1$ successively in it, we obtain

$$\int x^3 e^{ax}\, dx = \frac{x^3 e^{ax}}{a} - \frac{3}{a} \int x^2 e^{ax}\, dx \qquad\qquad ...(i)$$

$$\int x^2 e^{ax}\, dx = \frac{x^2 e^{ax}}{a} - \frac{2}{a} \int x e^{ax}\, dx \qquad\qquad ...(ii)$$

$$\int x e^{ax}\, dx = \frac{x e^{ax}}{a} - \frac{1}{a} \int e^{ax}\, dx$$

$$= \frac{x e^{ax}}{a} - \frac{e^{ax}}{a^2}. \qquad\qquad ...(iii)$$

From (ii) and (iii), we get

$$\int x^2 e^{ax}\, dx = \frac{x^2 e^{ax}}{a} - \frac{2xe^{ax}}{a^2} + \frac{2e^{ax}}{a^3}. \qquad \ldots(iv)$$

Again from (i) and (iv), we obtain

$$\int x^3 e^{ax}\, dx = \frac{x^3 e^{ax}}{a} - \frac{3x^2 e^{ax}}{a^2} + \frac{6xe^{ax}}{a^3} - \frac{6e^{ax}}{a^4}$$

$$= \frac{e^{ax}}{a^4}(a^3 x^3 - 3a^2 x^2 + 6ax - 6).$$

2. *Obtain a reduction formula for* $\int x^m \sin nx\, dx$.

We have, integrating by parts,

$$\int x^m \sin nx\, dx = -\frac{x^m \cos nx}{n} + \frac{m}{n}\int x^{m-1}\cos nx\, dx \qquad \ldots(i)$$

Again,

$$\int x^{m-1}\cos nx\, dx = \frac{x^{m-1}\sin nx}{n} - \frac{m-1}{n}\int x^{m-2}\sin nx\, dx \qquad \ldots(ii)$$

Substituting this value in (i), we get

$$\int x^m \sin nx\, dx = -\frac{x^m \cos nx}{n} + \frac{mx^{m-1}\sin nx}{n^2}$$

$$-\frac{m(m-1)}{n^2}\int x^{m-2}\sin nx\, dx,$$

which is the required reduction formula.

3. *Obtain a reduction formula for* $\int x^n e^{-x}\, dx$ *and hence show that the improper integral*

$$\int_0^\infty x^n e^{-x}\, dx = n!,$$

where n is any positive integer.

Integrating by parts, we have

$$\int_0^t x^n e^{-x}\, dx = \left| -x^n e^{-x} \right|_0^t + n\int_0^t x^{n-1}e^{-x}\, dx$$

$$= -t^n e^{-t} + n\int_0^t x^{n-1}e^{-x}\, dx.$$

Now $\quad \lim_{t \to \infty}(-t^n e^{-t}) = \lim_{t \to \infty}\left(\frac{t^n}{e^t}\right) = 0.$

$$\therefore \int_0^\infty x^n e^{-x}\, dx = \int_0^\infty x^{n-1} e^{-x}\, dx.$$

Denoting $\int_0^\infty x^n e^{-x}\, dx$ by I_n, we write

$$I_n = n I_{n-1}.$$

Changing n to $n-1$, $n-2$, ..., 2, 1, we get

$$I_{n-1} = (n-1)\, I_{n-2},$$

$$I_{n-2} = (n-2)\, I_{n-3},$$

$$I_{n-3} = (n-3)\, I_{n-4},$$

....
....

$$I_1 = 1 \cdot I_0 = I_0.$$

From these we obtain

$$I_n = n! \cdot I_0.$$

Now

$$I_0 = \int_0^\infty e^{-x}\, dx = \lim_{t \to \infty} \left[\int_0^t e^{-x}\, dx \right]$$

$$= \lim_{t \to \infty} (-e^{-t} + 1) = 1$$

$$\therefore \quad I_n = n!.$$

4. *Obtain a reduction formula for $\int x^m (\log x)^n\, dx$ and apply it to evaluate $\int_0^1 x^4 (\log x)^3\, dx$.*

Integrating by parts, we have

$$\int x^m (\log x)^n\, dx$$

$$= \frac{x^{m+1}}{m+1} (\log x)^n - \frac{n}{m+1} \int x^{m+1} (\log x)^{n-1} \cdot \frac{1}{x}\, dx$$

$$= \frac{x^{m+1}}{m+1} (\log x)^n - \frac{n}{m+1} \int x^m (\log x)^{n-1}\, dx,$$

as the required reduction formula.

Putting $m = 4$, we get

$$\int x^4 (\log x)^n\, dx = \frac{x^5}{5} (\log x)^n - \frac{n}{5} \int x^4 (\log x)^{n-1}\, dx.$$

Putting $n = 3, 2, 1$ successively, we get

$$\int x^4 (\log x)^3 \, dx = \frac{x^5}{5} (\log x)^3 - \frac{3}{5} \int x^4 (\log x)^2 \, dx \qquad ...(i)$$

$$\int x^4 (\log x)^2 \, dx = \frac{x^5}{5} (\log x)^2 - \frac{2}{5} \int x^4 \log x \, dx \qquad ...(ii)$$

$$\int x^4 \log x \, dx = \frac{x^5}{5} \log x - \frac{1}{5} \int x^4 \, dx$$

$$= \frac{x^5}{5} \log x - \frac{x^5}{25}.$$

From these, we obtain

$$\int x^4 (\log x)^3 \, dx = \frac{x^5}{5} (\log x)^3 - \frac{3x^5}{25} (\log x)^2$$

$$+ \frac{6x^5}{125} \log x - \frac{6}{625} x^5.$$

$$\Rightarrow \int_0^1 x^4 (\log x)^3 \, dx = \left| \frac{x^5}{5} (\log x)^3 - \frac{3x^5}{25} (\log x)^2 \right.$$

$$\left. + \frac{6x^5}{125} \log x - \frac{6}{625} x^5 \right|_0^1.$$

When $x \to 0$, $x^5 (\log x)^3$, $x^5 (\log x)^2$, $x^5 \log x$ all $\to 0$.

$$\therefore \quad \int_0^1 x^4 (\log x)^3 \, dx = -\frac{6}{625}.$$

5. *Obtain a reduction formula for* $\displaystyle\int \frac{x^n}{(\log x)^m} \, dx.$

(Rohilkhand, 1998)

We have

$$\int \frac{x^n}{(\log x)^m} \, dx = \int x^{n+1} \left[\frac{1}{(\log x)^m} \cdot \frac{1}{x} \right] dx.$$

Integrating by parts, taking x^{n+1} as the first function, we have

$$\int \frac{x^n}{(\log x)^m} \, dx = x^{n+1} \cdot \frac{(\log x)^{-m+1}}{-m+1} - \int (n+1) x^n \frac{(\log x)^{-m+1}}{-m+1} \, dx$$

$$= -\frac{x^{n+1}}{(m-1)(\log x)^{m-1}} + \frac{n+1}{m-1} \int \frac{x^n}{(\log x)^{m-1}} \, dx.$$

6. *If m and n are positive integers and* $f(m, n) = \int_0^1 x^{n-1} (\log x)^m \, dx$,

prove $f(m, n) = -\dfrac{m}{n} f(m-1, n)$.

Deduce that $f(m, n) = (-1)^m \dfrac{m!}{n^{m+1}}$.

Integrating by parts, taking x^{n-1} as the second function, we have

$$f(m, n) = \int_0^1 x^{n-1} (\log x)^m \, dx$$

$$= \left[(\log x)^m \cdot \frac{x^n}{n} \right]_0^1 - \int_0^1 n (\log x)^{m-1} \cdot \frac{1}{x} \cdot \frac{x^n}{n} \, dx$$

$$= 0 - \frac{m}{n} \int_0^1 x^{n-1} (\log x)^{m-1} \, dx$$

since $\lim_{x \to 0} x^n (\log x)^m = \lim_{x \to 0} \dfrac{(\log x)^m}{x^{-n}} = 0$ (by Hospital's Rule)

$$\therefore \quad f(m, n) = -\frac{m}{n} f(m-1, n) \qquad\qquad\qquad ...(i)$$

Use the reduction formula (i) successively, we get

$$f(m, n) = \left(-\frac{m}{n} \right) \left(-\frac{m-1}{n} \right) \left(-\frac{m-2}{n} \right) ..... \left(-\frac{1}{n} \right) \int_0^1 x^{n-1} \, dx$$

$$= (-1)^m \frac{m(m-1)(m-2).....1}{n^m} \left[\frac{x^n}{n} \right]_0^1$$

$$= (-1)^m \frac{m!}{n^{m+1}}.$$

7. *If* $I_n = \int_0^{\pi/2} x^n \sin(2p+1) x \, dx$, *prove that* $I_n + \dfrac{n(n-1)}{(2p+1)^2} I_{n-2}$

$= (-1)^p \dfrac{n}{(2p+2)^2} \left(\dfrac{\pi}{2} \right)^{n-2}$, *n and p being positive integers.*

We have

$$I_n = \int_0^{\pi/2} x^n \sin(2p+1) x \, dx$$

$$= \left[\frac{x^n \cos(2p+1)x}{(2p+1)} \right]_0^{\pi/2} + \frac{n}{(2p+1)} \int_0^{\pi/2} x^{n-1} \cos(2p+1)\, dx$$

$$= \frac{n}{(2p+1)^2} \left[x^{n-1} \sin(2p+1)x \right]_0^{\pi/2}$$

$$- \frac{n(n-1)}{(2p+1)^2} \int_0^{\pi/2} x^{n-2} \sin(2p+1)x\, dx$$

or $\quad I_n = \dfrac{n}{(2p+1)^2} (-1)^n \left(\dfrac{\pi}{2} \right)^{n-1} - \dfrac{n(n-1)}{(2p+1)^2} \dfrac{\pi}{2}$

as $\sin(2p+1)x$ when $x = \dfrac{\pi}{2}$ is $\sin(2p+1)\dfrac{\pi}{2}$

or $\quad \sin\left(p\pi + \dfrac{\pi}{2} \right)$ or $\sin p\pi \cos \dfrac{\pi}{2} + \cos p\pi \sin \dfrac{\pi}{2}$

i.e., $\quad \cos p\pi$ or $(-1)^p$.

8. *Find reduction formulae for $\int x \sin^n x \, dx$ and $\int x \cos^n x \, dx$.*

(*Vikram, 1995; Ravishanker, 1998*)

We have

$$I_n = \int x \sin^n x \, dx = \int x \sin^{n-1} x \cdot \sin x \, dx$$

$$= (x \sin^{n-1} x)(-\cos x) - \int (-\cos x) \{ x(n-1)\sin^{n-2} x \cos x$$

$$+ \sin^{n-1} x \} \, dx$$

$$= -x \sin^{n-1} x \cos x + (n-1) \int x \sin^{n-2} x \cos^2 x \, dx$$

$$+ \int \sin^{n-1} x \cos x \, dx$$

$$= -x \sin^{n-1} x \cos x + (n-1) \int x \sin^{n-2} x (1 - \sin^2 x) \, dx$$

$$+ \frac{\sin^n x}{n}$$

$$= -x \sin^{n-1} x \cos x + (n-1) \int x \sin^{n-2} x \, dx$$

$$- (n-1) \int x \sin^n x \, dx + \frac{\sin^n x}{n}$$

$$= -x \sin^{n-1} x \cos x + (n-1) I_{n-2} - (n-1) I_n + \frac{\sin^n x}{n}$$

$$\therefore \quad I_n (1 + n - 1) = -x \sin^{n-1} x \cos x + \frac{\sin^n x}{n} + (n-1) I_{n-2}$$

$$\therefore \quad I_n = -\frac{x \sin^{n-1} x \cos x}{x} + \frac{\sin^n x}{n^2} + \frac{n-1}{n} I_{n-2}.$$

Similarly, we can derive reduction formula for $\int x \cos^n x \, dx$.

$$I_n = \frac{x \cos^{n-1} x \sin x}{n} + \frac{\cos^n x}{n^2} + \frac{n-1}{n} I_{n-2}.$$

9. *If* $U_n = \displaystyle\int_0^{\pi/2} \theta \sin^n \theta \, d\theta$ *and* $n > 1$, *prove that* $U_n = \dfrac{1}{n^2} + \dfrac{n-1}{n} U_{n-2}.$

Deduce that $U_5 = \dfrac{149}{225}.$ *(Rohilkhand, 2000; Rewa, 1994, 97)*

We have

$$U_n = \int_0^{\pi/2} \theta \sin^n \theta \, d\theta = \int_0^{\pi/2} (\theta \sin^{n-1} \theta) \sin \theta \, d\theta$$

$$= \left[\theta \sin^{n-1} \theta \, (-\cos \theta) \right]_0^{\pi/2} - \int_0^{\pi/2} [\sin^{n-1} \theta$$

$$+ \theta \cdot (n-1) \sin^{n-2} \theta \cos \theta] (-\cos \theta) \, d\theta$$

$$= 0 + \int_0^{\pi/2} \sin^{n-1} \theta \cos \theta \, d\theta + (n-1) \int_0^{\pi/2} \theta \cdot \sin^{n-2} \theta \, (1 - \sin^2 \theta) \, d\theta$$

$$= \left[\frac{\sin^n \theta}{n} \right]_0^{\pi/2} + (n-1) \int_0^{\pi/2} \theta \sin^{n-2} \theta \, (1 - \sin^2 \theta) \, d\theta$$

$$= \frac{1}{n} + (n-1) U_{n-2} - (n-1) U_n$$

or $U_n = \dfrac{1}{n^2} + \dfrac{n-1}{n} U_{n-2}$ ...(1)

Putting $n = 5$ and 3 successively in (1), we get

$$U_5 = \frac{1}{25} + \frac{4}{5} U_3 \quad \text{and} \quad U_3 = \frac{1}{9} + \frac{2}{3} U_1.$$

But $U_1 = \displaystyle\int_0^{\pi/2} \theta \sin \theta \, d\theta$

$$= \left[\theta \, (-\cos \theta) \right]_0^{\pi/2} - \int_0^{\pi/2} 1 \cdot (-\cos \theta) \, d\theta$$

$$= 0 + \left[\sin \theta \right]_0^{\pi/2} = 1.$$

$$\therefore \quad U_5 = \frac{1}{25} + \frac{4}{5}\left(\frac{1}{9} + \frac{2}{3}\right) = \frac{149}{225}.$$

EXERCISES

1. Obtain a reduction formula for $\int x^m \cos nx \, dx$ and apply it to evaluate $\int x^3 \cos 3x \, dx$.

2. If

$$u_n = \int_0^{\pi/2} x^n \sin x \, dx \text{ and } n > 1,$$

prove that

$$u_n + n(n-1) u_{n-2} = n\left(\frac{\pi}{2}\right)^{n-1}$$

(*Rohilkhand, 1995, 99; Indore, 1995S; Rewa, 1996, 99; Sagar, 1999; Ravishanker, 1998*)

3. Show that

$$\int x^m (1-x)^{n-1} \, dx = \frac{x^{m+1}(1-x)^{n-1}}{m+n} + \frac{n-1}{m+1} \int x^m (1-x)^{n-2} \, dx.$$

Hence deduce that

$$\int_0^1 x^m (1-x)^{n-1} \, dx = \frac{(n-1)! \, m!}{m+n},$$

m, n being positive integers.

4. If m and n are positive integers, prove that

$$\int_0^1 x^{m-1} (1-x)^{n-1} \, dx = \int_0^1 x^{n-1} (1-x)^{m-1} \, dx$$

$$= \frac{1 \cdot 2 \cdot 3 \dots (m-1)}{n(n+1)(n+2) \dots (n+m-1)}.$$

ANSWERS

1. $\int x^m \cos nx \, dx = x^{m-1} \dfrac{nx \sin nx + m \cos nx}{n^2}$

$$- \frac{m(m-1)}{n^2} \int x^{m-2} \cos nx \, dx.$$

$$\int x^3 \cos 3x \, dx = \frac{1}{27}(9x^2 - 2) \cos 3x + \frac{1}{9}(3x^3 - 2x) \sin 3x.$$

EXERCISES ON CHAPTER II

1. Prove that if m and n are unequal integers

$$\int_0^\pi \sin mx \sin nx \, dx = 0, \quad \int_0^\pi \sin^2 mx \, dx = \frac{\pi}{2}.$$

2. Evaluate $\int e^x (x - 2)(2x + 3) \, dx$.

3. Evaluate $\int x^3 \log(1 + x^2) \, dx$.

4. Prove that if n is an integer > 1,

$$\int_0^\infty \frac{dx}{[x + \sqrt{1 + x^2}\,]^n} = \frac{n}{n^2 - 1}.$$

(Put $x = \sinh \theta$)

5. Evaluate $\displaystyle \int \frac{\cos^{-1} x}{x^3} \, dx.$

6. Evaluate $\displaystyle \int \frac{\sin(\log x)}{x^3} \, dx.$

7. Show that

(i) $\displaystyle \int \frac{x}{1 + \cos x} \, dx = x \tan \frac{1}{2} x + 2 \log \cos \frac{1}{2} x.$

(ii) $\displaystyle \int \frac{x}{1 - \cos x} \, dx = - x \cot \frac{1}{2} x + 2 \log \sin \frac{1}{2} x.$

(iii) $\displaystyle \int \frac{x}{1 + \sin x} \, dx = - x \tan \frac{1}{2} \left(\frac{1}{2} \pi - x \right)$

$$+ 2 \log \cos \frac{1}{2} \left(\frac{1}{2} \pi - x \right).$$

(iv) $\displaystyle \int \frac{x}{1 - \sin x} \, dx = x \cot \frac{1}{2} \left(\frac{1}{2} \pi - x \right) + 2 \log \sin \frac{1}{2} \left(\frac{1}{2} \pi - x \right).$

8. Show that $\displaystyle \int_a^b \frac{\log x}{x} \, dx = \frac{1}{2} \log \left(\frac{b}{a} \right) \cdot \log(ab).$

9. Evaluate $\displaystyle \int_\alpha^\beta \left[\log \log x + \frac{1}{(\log x)^2} \right] dx.$

10. Evaluate the following integrals :

(i) $\displaystyle \int \frac{\cos 2x}{\cos x} \, dx,$ (ii) $\displaystyle \int \frac{x - \sin x}{1 - \cos x} \, dx,$ (iii) $\displaystyle \int \sec^3 x \, dx.$

11. Evaluate

(i) $\displaystyle\int x^2 \tan^{-1} x \, dx,$

(ii) $\displaystyle\int x^8 \tan^{-1} x^3 \, dx,$

(iii) $\displaystyle\int \frac{(1-x)\, e^x \, dx}{x^2},$

(iv) $\displaystyle\int (\sin x + \cos x)\, e^x \, dx,$

(v) $\displaystyle\int_0^1 \frac{x^3 \sin^{-1} x}{\sqrt{1-x^2}}\, dx,$

(vi) $\displaystyle\int_0^\infty \frac{x\,(\tan^{-1} x)^2}{(1+x^2)^{3/2}}\, dx,$

(vii) $\displaystyle\int_0^\pi x e^{2x} \sin x \, dx,$

(viii) $\displaystyle\int_0^1 x^2 e^x \sin \pi x \, dx.$

12. Integrate

(i) $\displaystyle\frac{1}{\sqrt{x+a}+\sqrt{x+b}},$

(ii) $\displaystyle\frac{\sqrt{a^2-x^2}}{x},$

(iii) $\log [\, x + \sqrt{x^2 + a^2}\,],$

(iv) $x \log [\, x + \sqrt{x^2 + a^2}\,].$

13. Integrate

(i) $\displaystyle\sqrt{\frac{x}{a+x}},$

(ii) $\displaystyle\frac{\sin x}{\sin (x-a)},$

(iii) $\displaystyle\sqrt{\frac{x+a}{x}},$

(iv) $\displaystyle\tan^{-1} \frac{3x - x^3}{1 - 3x^2}.$

ANSWERS

2. $(2x^2 - 5x - 1)\, e^x.$

3. $\dfrac{1}{4}(x^4 - 1) \log (1 + x^2) - \dfrac{1}{8}(x^4 - 2x^2).$

5. $[\, x \sqrt{1 - x^2} - \cos^{-1} x\,]/ 2x^2.$

6. $- [2 \sin (\log x) + \cos (\log x)]/ 5x^2.$

9. $\beta \log (\log \beta) - \alpha \log (\log \alpha) - [\beta (\log \beta)^{-1} - \alpha (\log \alpha)^{-1}].$

10. (i) $2 \sin x - \log \tan \left(\dfrac{1}{2} x + \dfrac{1}{4}\pi\right).$

(ii) $- x \cot \left(\dfrac{1}{2} x\right).$

(iii) $\dfrac{1}{2} \tan x \sec x + \dfrac{1}{2} \log \tan \left(\dfrac{1}{2} x + \dfrac{1}{4}\pi\right).$

11. (i) $\dfrac{1}{3} x^3 \tan^{-1} x + \dfrac{1}{6}[\log (x^2 + 1) - x^2].$

(ii) $\dfrac{1}{9} x^9 \tan^{-1} x^3 + \dfrac{1}{18}[\log (x^6 + 1) - x^6].$

(iii) $- e^x / x.$ (iv) $e^x \sin x.$ (v) $\dfrac{7}{9}.$ (vi) $(\pi - 2).$

(vii) $\dfrac{1}{25}\left(5\pi - 4e^{2\pi} - \dfrac{4}{25}\right).$

(viii) $\pi \left[e \left(\pi^4 - 4\pi^2 + 3 \right) - 2\pi^2 + 6 \right] / (1 + \pi^2)^3.$

12. (i) $\dfrac{2}{3(a-b)}[(x+a)^{3/2} - (x+b)^{3/2}].$

(ii) $\sqrt{a^2 - x^2} + a \log \dfrac{a - \sqrt{a^2 - x^2}}{x}.$

(iii) $x \log [x + \sqrt{a^2 + x^2}] - \sqrt{a^2 + x^2}.$

(iv) $\dfrac{1}{2} x^2 \log [x + \sqrt{a^2 + x^2}] - \dfrac{1}{4}[x\sqrt{a^2 + x^2} - a^2 \sinh^{-1}(x/a)].$

13. (i) $(a + x) \tan^{-1} \sqrt{x/a} - \sqrt{ax}.$

(ii) $\sin a \log \sin (x - a) + (x - a) \cos a.$

(iii) $a \tan \theta \sec \theta + a \log \tan \left(\dfrac{1}{2}\theta + \dfrac{1}{4}\pi \right),$ where $x = a \tan^2 \theta.$

(iv) $3x \tan^{-1} x - \dfrac{3}{2} \log (1 + x^2).$

OBJECTIVE QUESTIONS

For each of the following questions, four alternatives are given for the answer. Only one of them is correct. Choose the correct alternative.

1. If $\int g(x)\,dx = f(x),$ then $\int f(x)\,g(x)\,dx$ is equal to

   (a) $\log |f(x)|$ (b) $\dfrac{1}{2}[g(x)]^2$

   (c) $\dfrac{1}{2}[f(x)]^2$ (d) None of these.

2. If $\int g(x)\,dx = g(x),$ then $\int f(x)\,g(x)[f(x) + 2f'(x)]\,dx$ is equal to

   (a) $f(x)\,g(x)$ (b) $f^2(x)\,g(x)$

   (c) $[f(x) - f'(x)]\,g(x)$ (d) $f^2(x)\,g'(x).$

3. $\int \dfrac{e^{-x}}{1+e^x}\,dx$ is equal to

   (a) $e^x + \log (1 + e^x) + c$ (b) $e^{-x} + \log (1 + e^x) + c$

   (c) $- e^{-x} + \log (1 + e^{-x}) + c$ (d) None of these.

4. If $\dfrac{d}{dx}[f(x)] = g(x)$, then $\displaystyle\int_a^b f(x)\, g(x)\, dx$ is equal to

   (a) $f(b) - f(a)$

   (b) $\dfrac{1}{2}[\{f(b)\}^2 - \{f(a)\}^2]$

   (c) $g(b) - g(a)$

   (d) $\dfrac{1}{2}[\{g(b)\}^2 - \{g(a)\}^2]$.

5. If $u_n = \displaystyle\int_0^{\pi/2} x^n \sin x\, dx$ and $n > 1$, then $u_n + n(n-1)\, u_{n-2}$ is equal to

   (a) $n(2/\pi)^{n-1}$

   (b) $n(\pi/2)^{n-1}$

   (c) $n\pi^n$

   (d) None of these.

6. If $U_n = \displaystyle\int_0^{\pi/2} \theta \sin^n \theta\, d\theta$ and $n > 1$, then $U_n - \dfrac{n-1}{n} U_{n-2}$ is equal to

   (a) $\dfrac{1}{n}$

   (b) $\dfrac{1}{n^2}$

   (c) n^2

   (d) None of these.

7. If m and n are positive integers and $f(m, n) = \displaystyle\int_0^1 x^{n-1} (\log x)^m\, dx$,

   then $f(m, n)$ is equal to

   (a) 0

   (b) $\dfrac{n!}{m^{n+1}}$

   (c) $(-1)^m \dfrac{m!}{n^{m+1}}$

   (d) $(-1)^n \dfrac{n!}{m^{n+1}}$.

ANSWERS

1. (c)   2. (b)   3. (c)   4. (b)
5. (b)   6. (b)   7. (c)

3

Integration of Algebraic Rational Functions

3.1. In this chapter we shall be concerned with the integration of rational functions $f(x) / \varphi(x)$, where $f(x)$ and $\varphi(x)$ are polynomials, say

$$f(x) = a_0 x^m + a_1 x^{m-1} + \ldots + a_{m-1} x + a_m,$$
$$\varphi(x) = b_0 x^n + b_1 x^{n-1} + \ldots + b_{n-1} x + b_n.$$

We can assume that the degree m of the numerator $f(x)$ is smaller than the degree n of the denominator. For, otherwise, we may divide the numerator by the denominator, till we get a remainder whose degree is smaller than that of the denominator. Thus we have

$$\frac{f(x)}{\varphi(x)} = Q(x) + \frac{R(x)}{\varphi(x)},$$

where the polynomial $Q(x)$ is the quotient and the polynomial $R(x)$ is the remainder obtained on dividing $f(x)$ by $\varphi(x)$, the degree of $R(x)$ being smaller than that of $\varphi(x)$.

The part $Q(x)$ which is a polynomial can be at once integrated term by term.

We will now see how the integration of $R(x) / \varphi(x)$ can be effected, the degree of $R(x)$ being smaller than that of $\varphi(x)$.

From Algebra, we know that every polynomial $\varphi(x)$ can be resolved into real factors of the first and second degree so that we may write

$$\varphi(x) = A (a_1 x + b_1)^{p_1} (a_2 x + b_2)^{p_2} \ldots$$
$$\times (A_1 x^2 + 2B_1 x + C_1)^{q_1} (A_2 x^2 + 2B_2 x + C_2)^{q_2}.$$

Here $p_1, p_2, p_3, \ldots$; $q_1, q_2, q_3, \ldots$ are positive integers denoting the number of times each factor is repeated.

Also, some or all of $p_1, p_2, p_3, \ldots$ and of $q_1, q_2, q_3, \ldots$ may be unity. Thus, we have four types of factors of the denominator $\varphi(x)$:

    (*i*) *Linear non-repeated.*   (*ii*) *Linear repeated.*

    (*iii*) *Quadratic non-repeated.*   (*iv*) *Quadratic repeated.*

From the theory of partial fractions, we know that $R(x) / \varphi(x)$ can be decomposed into the sum of a number of fractions such that

(i) to a linear non-repeated factor, $(ax + b)$, corresponds a partial fraction of the form

$$\frac{L}{ax+b};$$

(ii) to a linear repeated factor, $(ax + b)^p$, corresponds a sum of p fractions of the form

$$\frac{L_1}{(ax+b)} + \frac{L_2}{(ax+b)^2} + \ldots\ldots + \frac{L_p}{(ax+b)^p};$$

(iii) to a quadratic non-repeated factor, $(Ax^2 + 2Bx + C)$, which cannot be further resolved into real linear factors, corresponds a fraction of the form

$$\frac{Lx + M}{Ax^2 + 2Bx + C};$$

(iv) to a quadratic repeated factor, $(Ax^2 + 2Bx + C)^q$, corresponds a sum of q fractions of the form

$$\frac{L_1 x + M_1}{(Ax^2 + 2Bx + C)} + \frac{L_2 x + M_2}{(Ax^2 + 2Bx + C)^2} + \ldots\ldots + \frac{L_q x + M_q}{(Ax^2 + 2Bx + C)^q}.$$

The method of determining the constants L and M etc. is explained in books on Elementary Algebra which give an account of partial fractions.

Thus to be able to complete the integration of an algebraic rational function, we have to learn to integrate fractions of the types

(i) $\dfrac{L}{ax+b}$,   (ii) $\dfrac{L}{(ax+b)^r}$,

(iii) $\dfrac{Lx+M}{Ax^2 + 2Bx + C}$,   ($iv$) $\dfrac{Lx+M}{(Ax^2 + 2Bx + C)^r}$.

We consider these types one by one :

(i) $\displaystyle\int \frac{L}{ax+b}\,dx = \frac{L}{a}\log(ax+b).$

(ii) $\displaystyle\int \frac{L}{(ax+b)^r}\,dx = \frac{L}{a(1-r)} \cdot \frac{1}{(ax+b)^{r-1}},$ for $r \neq 1.$

(iii) *To integrate*

$$(Lx + M) / (Ax^2 + 2Bx + C),$$

we determine two constants λ, μ such that

$$Lx + M \equiv \lambda(2Ax + 2B) + \mu \qquad\qquad \ldots(i)$$

the co-factor, $2Ax + 2B$, of λ being the derivative of the denominator $Ax^2 + 2Bx + C$. From (1), we have

$$L = 2A\lambda, \quad M = 2B\lambda + \mu.$$

$$\Rightarrow \quad \lambda = \frac{L}{2A}, \; \mu = \frac{AM - BL}{A}.$$

$$\therefore \quad \int \frac{Lx + M}{Ax^2 + 2Bx + C} dx$$

$$= \lambda \int \frac{2Ax + 2B}{Ax^2 + 2Bx + C} dx + \mu \int \frac{dx}{Ax^2 + 2Bx + C}$$

$$= \lambda \log (Ax^2 + 2Bx + C) + \mu \int \frac{dx}{Ax^2 + 2Bx + C}.$$

Again,

$$\int \frac{dx}{Ax^2 + 2Bx + C} = \frac{1}{A} \int \frac{dx}{x^2 + \frac{2B}{A} x + \frac{C}{A}}$$

$$= \frac{1}{A} \int \frac{dx}{\left(x + \frac{B}{A} \right)^2 + \left(\frac{\sqrt{AC - B^2}}{A} \right)^2}.$$

We assume that $AC - B^2$ is positive, for otherwise $Ax^2 + 2Bx + C = 0$ would have real roots and $Ax^2 + 2Bx + C$ would be capable of being expressed as the product of real linear factors.

$$\therefore \quad \int \frac{dx}{Ax^2 + 2Bx + C} = \frac{1}{\sqrt{AC - B^2}} \tan^{-1} \frac{Ax + B}{\sqrt{AC - B^2}}.$$

Thus we have completed the integration of

$$(Lx + M) / (Ax^2 + 2Bx + C).$$

Note. The integral of $1 / (x^2 + a^2)$ is $(1 / a) \tan^{-1} (x / a)$.

(*iv*) The method for integrating fractions of the type

$$\frac{Lx + M}{(Ax^2 + 2Bx + C)^r}$$

will be given in § 3.5 on page 89.

EXAMPLES

1. *Evaluate* $\displaystyle \int \frac{dx}{x^2 + 2x + 2}$.

$$I = \int \frac{dx}{x^2 + 2x + 2} = \int \frac{dx}{(x + 1)^2 + 1}.$$

Let $x + 1 = y$. Then $dx = dy$. We get

$$I = \int \frac{dy}{y^2 + 1} = \tan^{-1}(y) + c$$

$$= \tan^{-1}(x+1) + c.$$

2. *Evaluate* : $\int \frac{(x+7)\,dx}{x^2 + 4x + 13}$.

$$I = \int \frac{(x+7)\,dx}{x^2 + 4x + 13}.$$

Write $x + 7 = \lambda(2x+4) + \mu$.

Comparing coefficients on both sides, we get

$$2\lambda = 1 \text{ and } 4\lambda + \mu = 7.$$

$$\Rightarrow \quad \lambda = \frac{1}{2} \text{ and } \mu = 5. \text{ We have}$$

$$I = \frac{1}{2}\int \frac{(2x+4)\,dx}{x^2 + 4x + 13} + 5\int \frac{dx}{x^2 + 4x + 13}$$

$$= \frac{1}{2}\log(x^2 + 4x + 13) + 5I_1 + c.$$

Now, $I_1 = \int \frac{dx}{x^2 + 4x + 13} = \int \frac{dx}{(x+2)^2 + 9}$.

Substituting $x + 2 = 3y$. Then, $dx = 3\,dy$, we get

$$I_1 = \frac{1}{3}\int \frac{dy}{y^2 + 1} = \frac{1}{3}\tan^{-1} y = \frac{1}{3}\tan^{-1}\left(\frac{x+2}{3}\right).$$

Hence, we obtain

$$I = \frac{1}{2}\log(x^2 + 4x + 13) + \frac{5}{3}\tan^{-1}\left(\frac{x+2}{3}\right) + c.$$

EXERCISES

1. *Evaluate*

(i) $\int \frac{dx}{3x - 4}$, (ii) $\int \frac{dx}{5 - 2x}$, (iii) $\int \frac{2\,dx}{3 - 2x}$.

2. *Evaluate*

(i) $\int \frac{dx}{(2x-3)^3}$, (ii) $\int \frac{dx}{(5+3x)^2}$, (iii) $\int \frac{dx}{(3-2x)^4}$.

3. *Evaluate*

(i) $\int \frac{dx}{x^2 + 3x + 4}$, (ii) $\int \frac{(x+2)\,dx}{x^2 + 2x + 3}$, (iii) $\int \frac{(2x-3)\,dx}{3x^2 + 4x + 5}$.

4. Show that

$$\int_0^1 \frac{(4x^2 + 3)\,dx}{8x^2 + 4x + 5} = \frac{1}{2} - \frac{1}{8}\log\frac{17}{5} + \frac{1}{6}\tan^{-1}\frac{6}{7}.$$

ANSWERS

1. (i) $\frac{1}{3}\log(3x - 4)$.   (ii) $-\frac{1}{2}\log(5 - 2x)$.   (iii) $-\log(3 - 2x)$.

2. (i) $-\frac{1}{4}\cdot\frac{1}{(2x - 3)^2}$.   (ii) $-\frac{1}{3}\cdot\frac{1}{5 + 3x}$.   (iii) $\frac{1}{6}\cdot\frac{1}{(3 - 2x)^3}$.

3. (i) $\frac{2}{\sqrt{7}}\tan^{-1}\left(\frac{2x + 3}{\sqrt{7}}\right)$.

(ii) $\frac{1}{2}\log(x^2 + 2x + 3) + \sqrt{\frac{1}{3}}\tan^{-1}\left(\frac{x + 1}{\sqrt{2}}\right)$.

(iii) $\frac{1}{3}\log(3x^2 + 4x + 5) - \frac{13}{3\sqrt{11}}\tan^{-1}\left(\frac{3x + 2}{\sqrt{11}}\right)$.

3.2. Case of non-repeated linear factors only in the denominator.

EXAMPLE

Evaluate $\displaystyle\int \frac{x^2 + 5x + 41}{(x + 3)(x - 1)(2x - 1)}\,dx$.

We have

$$\frac{x^2 + 5x + 41}{(x + 3)(x - 1)(2x - 1)} = \frac{A}{x + 3} + \frac{B}{x - 1} + \frac{C}{2x - 1}.$$

$$\Rightarrow\ x^2 + 5x + 41 = A(x - 1)(2x - 1) + B(x + 3)(2x - 1)$$
$$+ C(x + 3)(x - 1).$$

Putting $x = -3,\ 1,\ 1/2$ respectively, we get

$$A = \frac{5}{4},\ B = \frac{47}{4},\ C = -25.$$

$$\therefore\ \int \frac{x^2 + 5x + 41}{(x + 3)(x - 1)(2x - 1)}\,dx$$

$$= \frac{5}{4}\int \frac{dx}{x + 3} + \frac{47}{4}\int \frac{dx}{x - 1} - 25\int \frac{dx}{2x - 1}$$

$$= \frac{5}{4}\log(x + 3) + \frac{47}{4}\log(x - 1) - \frac{25}{2}\log(2x - 1).$$

EXERCISES

1. *Evaluate*

(i) $\int \dfrac{dx}{x^2-1}$,

(ii) $\int \dfrac{x^2+1}{x^2-1}\,dx$,

(iii) $\int \dfrac{dx}{(x+1)(x+2)(x+3)}$,

(iv) $\int \dfrac{(2x-3)\,dx}{(x^2-1)(2x+3)}$,

(v) $\int \dfrac{(x-1)(x-2)(x-3)}{(x+1)(x+2)(x+3)}\,dx$,

(vi) $\int \dfrac{x^2\,dx}{(x+1)(x-2)(x+3)}$,

(vii) $\int \dfrac{x^2\,dx}{(x+1)(x+2)(x+3)}$,

(viii) $\int \dfrac{x^3+3}{x^3-3x}\,dx$,

(ix) $\int \dfrac{(x^2+1)\,dx}{(x^2-1)(x^2-4)}$,

(x) $\int \dfrac{x^5\,dx}{x^3-2x^2-5x+6}$,

(xi) $\int_{2}^{3} \dfrac{(x^2+1)}{(2x+1)(x^2-1)}\,dx$,

(xii) $\int_{0}^{1} \dfrac{dx}{x^2+2x\cos\alpha+1}$,

$$(0 \le \alpha < \pi).$$

ANSWERS

1. (i) $\dfrac{1}{2}\log[(x-1)/(x+1)]$.

(ii) $x + \log[(x-1)/(x+1)]$.

(iii) $\dfrac{1}{2}\log[(x+1)(x+3)/(x+2)^2]$.

(iv) $\dfrac{5}{2}\log(x+1) - \dfrac{1}{10}\log(x-1) - \dfrac{12}{5}\log(2x+3)$.

(v) $x + 12\log[(x+2)^3/(x+1)(x+3)^5]$.

(vi) $\dfrac{9}{10}\log(x+3) + \dfrac{4}{15}\log(x-2) - \dfrac{1}{6}\log(1+x)$.

(vii) $\dfrac{1}{2}\log(x+1) - 4\log(x+2) + \dfrac{9}{2}\log(x+3)$.

(viii) $x - \log x + \dfrac{1}{2}(1+\sqrt3)\log(x-\sqrt3) + \dfrac{1}{2}(1-\sqrt3)\log(x+\sqrt3)$.

(ix) $\dfrac{5}{12}\log[(x-2)/(x+2)] - \dfrac{1}{3}\log[(x-1)/(x+1)]$.

(x) $\dfrac{1}{3}x^3 + x^2 + 9x - \dfrac{1}{6}\log(x-1) - \dfrac{82}{15}\log(x+2)$

$$+ \dfrac{243}{10}\log(x-3).$$

(*xi*) $+ \log 3 - \dfrac{5}{6} \log \dfrac{7}{5} + \dfrac{7}{3} \log 2.$

(*xii*) $\dfrac{\alpha}{2} \sin \alpha,$ if $\alpha \neq 0;\ \dfrac{1}{2}$ if $\alpha = 0.$

3.3. Case of non-repeated linear or repeated linear factors only in the denominator.

EXAMPLE

Evaluate $\displaystyle \int \frac{1}{x^3 (x-1)^2 (x+1)}\, dx.$

We suppose

$$\frac{1}{x^3 (x-1)^2 (x+1)} = \frac{A}{x} + \frac{B}{x^2} + \frac{C}{x^3} + \frac{D}{x-1} + \frac{E}{(x-1)^2} + \frac{F}{x+1}.$$

$$\therefore\ \ 1 \equiv Ax^2 (x-1)^2 (x+1) + Bx (x-1)^2 (x+1) + C (x-1)^2 (x+1)$$
$$+ Dx^3 (x-1)(x+1) + Ex^3 (x+1) + Fx^3 (x-1)^2 \ ...(1)$$

Putting $x = 0, -1$, we get

$$C = 1,\ E = \frac{1}{2},\ F = -\frac{1}{4}.$$

To obtain A, B, D we equate the coefficients of x^5, x^4, x^3 on both sides of (*i*) and get

$$0 = A + D + F,$$
$$0 = -A + B + E + 2F,$$
$$0 = -A - B + C - D + E + F.$$

Solving these equations we obtain

$$A = 2,\ B = 1,\ D = -\frac{7}{4}.$$

$$\therefore\ \ \int \frac{1}{x^3 (x-1)^2 (x+1)}\, dx$$

$$= 2 \log x - \frac{1}{x} - \frac{1}{2x^2} - \frac{7}{4} \log (x-1) - \frac{1}{2(x-1)} - \frac{1}{4} \log (x+1).$$

EXERCISES

1. Integrate the following functions :

(*i*) $\dfrac{x^2 + x + 1}{(x+1)^2 (x+2)},$

(*ii*) $\dfrac{x+1}{(x-1)^2 (x+2)^2},$

(*iii*) $\dfrac{x^2 + 1}{(x+2)^3 (x-1)},$

(*iv*) $\dfrac{x^3 + 2}{(x-1)(x-2)^3},$

(v) $\dfrac{x^3 - 4x^2 + 5x - 2}{x^3 + 4x^2 + 5x + 2}$,

(vi) $\dfrac{(1 + x)^3}{(1 - x)^3}$,

(vii) $\dfrac{57x^3 - 25x^2 + 9x - 1}{(x - 1)^2 (2x - 1) (5x - 1)}$.

2. Evaluate the following definite integrals :

(i) $\displaystyle\int_0^{1/2} \dfrac{dx}{(1 - x^2)^2}$,

(ii) $\displaystyle\int_0^{\infty} \dfrac{dx}{(1 + x)^3 (2 + x)}$.

ANSWERS

1. (i) $-\dfrac{1}{x + 1} + \log \dfrac{(x + 2)^3}{(x + 1)^2}$.

(ii) $\dfrac{1}{27} \log \dfrac{x + 2}{x - 1} - \dfrac{2}{9} \cdot \dfrac{1}{x - 1} + \dfrac{1}{9} \cdot \dfrac{1}{x + 2}$.

(iii) $\dfrac{2}{27} \log \dfrac{x - 1}{x + 2} - \dfrac{7}{9} \cdot \dfrac{1}{x + 2} + \dfrac{5}{6} \cdot \dfrac{1}{(x + 2)^2}$.

(iv) $4 \log (x - 2) - 3 \log (x - 1) - \dfrac{2}{x - 2} - \dfrac{5}{(x - 2)^2}$.

(v) $x + 12 (x + 1)^{-1} + 28 \log (x + 1) - 36 \log (x + 2)$.

(vi) $- x - 12 (1 - x)^{-1} + 4 (1 - x)^{-2} - 6 \log (1 - x)$.

(vii) $- 10 (x - 1)^{-1} + (35 / 6) \log (2x - 1) - (2 / 15) \log (5x - 1)$.

2. (i) $(1 / 12) \log (27e^4)$.

(ii) $(1 / 2) \log (4 / e)$.

3.4. Case of linear or quadratic non-repeated factors only in the denominator.

EXAMPLE

Evaluate $\displaystyle\int \dfrac{dx}{(x - 1)^2 (x - 2) (x^2 + 4)}$.

We suppose

$$\dfrac{1}{(x - 1)^2 (x - 2) (x^2 + 4)} \equiv \dfrac{A}{x - 1} + \dfrac{B}{(x - 1)^2} + \dfrac{C}{x - 2} + \dfrac{Dx + E}{x^2 + 4}$$

$\Rightarrow$ $1 \equiv A (x - 1) (x - 2) (x^2 + 4) + B (x - 2) (x^2 + 4)$
$+ C (x - 1)^2 (x^2 + 4) + (Dx + E) (x - 1)^2 (x - 2)$.

Putting $x = 1, 2$, we get

$$B = - \dfrac{1}{5} \text{ and } C = \dfrac{1}{8}.$$

To find A, D, E, we equate the coefficients of x^4, x^3, x^2, so that we get

$$A + C + D = 0,$$
$$-3A + B - 2C - 2D + E = 0,$$
$$6A - 2B + 5C + 4D - 2E = 0.$$

Solving these equations, we get

$$A = -3/25, \quad D = -1/200, \quad E = 7/100.$$

$$\therefore \int \frac{1}{(x-1)^2 (x-2)(x^2+4)} \, dx = -\frac{3}{25} \int \frac{dx}{x-1} - \frac{1}{5} \int \frac{dx}{(x-1)^2}$$

$$+ \frac{1}{8} \int \frac{dx}{x-2} - \frac{1}{400} \int \frac{2x}{x^2+4} \, dx + \frac{7}{100} \int \frac{dx}{x^2+4}$$

$$= -\frac{3}{25} \log(x-1) + \frac{1}{5(x-1)} + \frac{1}{8} \log(x-2)$$

$$- \frac{1}{400} \log(x^2+4) + \frac{7}{200} \tan^{-1} \frac{x}{2}.$$

EXERCISES

1. Evaluate

(i) $\displaystyle \int \frac{x^3}{x^2+1} \, dx,$

(ii) $\displaystyle \int \frac{x^4}{(x^2-1)(x^2+4)} \, dx,$

(iii) $\displaystyle \int \frac{x}{1+x^3} \, dx,$

(iv) $\displaystyle \int \frac{x^5}{(x^2+1)(x-4)} \, dx,$

(v) $\displaystyle \int \frac{x^2+1}{x^3+1} \, dx,$

(vi) $\displaystyle \int \frac{x^2+6x-25}{(x^2+4x)^2-25} \, dx,$

(vii) $\displaystyle \int \frac{dx}{(x+1)^2(x^2+1)},$

(viii) $\displaystyle \int \frac{dx}{1-x^6},$

(ix) $\displaystyle \int \frac{(x+a)\,dx}{x^2(x-a)(x^2+a^2)},$

(x) $\displaystyle \int \frac{x\,dx}{(x+1)^3(x^2+1)},$

(xi) $\displaystyle \int \frac{dx}{(x-1)^2(x^2+4)},$

(xii) $\displaystyle \int \frac{x\,dx}{x^3+x^2+x+1},$

(xiii) $\displaystyle \int \frac{x^3\,dx}{x^4+3x^2+2}.$

2. Evaluate the following definite integrals :

(i) $\displaystyle \int_1^\infty \frac{dx}{(x+1)^2(x^2+1)},$

(ii) $\displaystyle \int_0^2 \frac{4-x}{x(x^2-2x+2)} \, dx.$

ANSWERS

1. (i) $\frac{1}{2} x^2 - \frac{1}{2} \log (x^2 + 1)$.

(ii) $x + \frac{1}{10} \log [(x - 1)/(x + 1)] - \frac{8}{5} \tan^{-1} (x/2)$.

(iii) $\frac{1}{6} \log (x^2 - x + 1) - \frac{1}{3} \log (x + 1) + \sqrt{\frac{1}{3}} \tan^{-1} [(2x - 1)/\sqrt{3}]$.

(iv) $\frac{1}{3} x^3 + 2x^2 + 15x + \frac{1024}{17} \log (x - 4) + \frac{2}{17} \log (x^2 + 1)$

$$+ \frac{1}{17} \tan^{-1} x.$$

(v) $\frac{2}{3} \log (x + 1) + \frac{1}{6} \log (x^2 - x + 1) + \sqrt{\frac{1}{3}} \tan^{-1} [(2x - 1)/\sqrt{3}]$.

(vi) $\frac{1}{2} \log (x + 5) - \frac{3}{10} \log (x - 1) - \frac{1}{10} \log (x^2 + 4x + 5)$

$$+ \frac{17}{5} \tan^{-1} (x + 2).$$

(vii) $\frac{1}{2} \log (x + 1) - \frac{1}{4} \log (x^2 + 1) - \frac{1}{2} (x + 1)^2$.

(viii) $\frac{1}{6} \log \frac{x + 1}{1 - x} + \frac{1}{12} \log \frac{x^2 + x + 1}{x^2 - x + 1}$

$$+ \frac{1}{2\sqrt{3}} \left(\tan^{-1} \frac{2x + 1}{\sqrt{3}} + \tan^{-1} \frac{2x - 1}{\sqrt{3}} \right).$$

(ix) $\frac{1}{a^3} \log \frac{(x - a) \sqrt{x^2 + a^2}}{x^2} + \frac{1}{a^2 x}$.

(x) $\frac{1}{4} \log (x + 1) - \frac{1}{8} \log (x^2 + 1) + \frac{1}{4} \tan^{-1} x + \frac{1}{4} (x + 1)^{-2}$.

(xi) $-\frac{2}{25} \log (x - 1) - \frac{1}{5 (x - 1)} + \frac{1}{25} \log (x^2 + 4) - \frac{3}{50} \tan^{-1} \frac{x}{2}$.

(xii) $\frac{1}{2} \log \frac{\sqrt{x^2 + 1}}{x + 1} + \frac{1}{2} \tan^{-1} x$.

(xiii) $\log (x^2 + 2) - \frac{1}{2} \log (x^2 + 1)$.

2. (i) $\frac{1}{2}$.   (ii) $\frac{1}{4} \pi + \log 2$.

3.4.1. Case of the integrand consisting of even powers of x only.

EXAMPLES

Integrate

$$\frac{(x^2 + 1)(x^2 + 2)}{(x^2 + 3)(x^2 + 4)}.$$

We note that the fraction is a function of x^2. On this account its decomposition into partial fractions is more conveniently effected by putting $x^2 = y$. We have

$$\frac{(x^2 + 1)(x^2 + 2)}{(x^2 + 3)(x^2 + 4)} = \frac{(y+1)(y+2)}{(y+3)(y+4)}$$

$$= 1 + \frac{(y+1)(y+2)}{(y+3)(y+4)} - 1$$

$$= 1 + \frac{(y+1)(y+2) - (y+3)(y+4)}{(y+3)(y+4)}.$$

Let

$$\frac{(y+1)(y+2) - (y+3)(y+4)}{(y+3)(y+4)} = \frac{A}{y+3} + \frac{B}{y+4}.$$

$\Rightarrow$ $(y+1)(y+2) - (y+3)(y+4) = A(y+4) + B(y+3).$

Putting $y = -3$ and $y = -4$ on both the sides, we get

$$A = 2, B = -6.$$

$$\therefore \quad \frac{(x^2+1)(x^2+2)}{(x^2+3)(x^2+4)} = 1 + \frac{2}{y+3} - \frac{6}{y+4}$$

$$= 1 + \frac{2}{x^2+3} - \frac{6}{x^2+4}$$

$$\Rightarrow \quad \int \frac{(x^2+1)(x^2+2)}{(x^2+3)(x^2+4)}\,dx = x + \frac{x}{\sqrt{3}}\tan^{-1}\frac{x}{\sqrt{3}} - 3\tan^{-1}\frac{x}{2}.$$

EXERCISES

1. Evaluate the following integrals :

(i) $\displaystyle\int \frac{x^2}{(x^2+a^2)(x^2+b^2)}\,dx,$

(ii) $\displaystyle\int \frac{x^2}{x^4 + x^2 - 2}\,dx.$

2. Evaluate

$$\int \frac{\cos^2\theta}{\cos^2\theta + 4\sin^2\theta}\,d\theta.$$

ANSWERS

1. (i) $\dfrac{1}{(a^2-b^2)}\left(a\tan^{-1}\dfrac{x}{a}-b\tan^{-1}\dfrac{x}{b}\right)$.

(ii) $(1/6)\log[(x-1)/(x+1)]+(\sqrt{2}/3)\tan^{-1}(x/\sqrt{2})$.

2. $-\dfrac{1}{3}\tan^{-1}(\tan\theta)-\dfrac{2}{3}\tan^{-1}(2\tan\theta)$.

3.5. Integration of

$$\frac{Lx+M}{(Ax^2+2Bx+C)^n},$$

where n is a positive integer different from 1.

To evaluate

$$\int\frac{(Lx+M)\,dx}{(Ax^2+2Bx+C)^n}$$

we determine two constants λ and μ, such that

$$Lx+M=\lambda(2Ax+2B)+\mu,\qquad\text{[Refer § 3.1]}$$

where the co-factor $2Ax+2B$ of λ is the derivative of $Ax^2+2Bx+C$.

We thus have

$$\int\frac{Lx+M}{(Ax^2+2Bx+C)^n}\,dx$$

$$=\lambda\int\frac{2Ax+2B}{(Ax^2+2Bx+C)^n}\,dx+\mu\int\frac{dx}{(Ax^2+2Bx+C)^n}$$

$$=\frac{\lambda}{(1-n)}\cdot\frac{1}{(Ax^2+2Bx+C)^{n-1}}+\mu\int\frac{dx}{(Ax^2+2Bx+C)^n}.$$

To evaluate the integral

$$\int\frac{dx}{(Ax^2+2Bx+C)^n}$$

we obtain a reduction formula, we write

$$Ax^2+2Bx+C=A\left[\left(x+\frac{B}{A}\right)^2+\left(\frac{\sqrt{AC-B^2}}{A}\right)^2\right]$$

$$=A\left[\left(x+\frac{B}{A}\right)^2+k^2\right],$$

where, for the sake of simplicity, we have written

$$\sqrt{AC-B^2}/A=k.$$

Also, putting $x + B/A = y$, we get

$$\int \frac{dx}{(Ax^2 + 2Bx + C)^n} = \frac{1}{A^n} \int \frac{dy}{(y^2 + k^2)^n}.$$

The integral

$$\int \frac{dy}{(y^2 + k^2)^n}$$

is evaluated with the help of a *reduction formula* which is obtained in the following section.

3.5.1. Reduction Formula for

$$\int \frac{1}{(y^2 + k^2)^n} \, dy.$$

To obtain the required reduction formula, we write

$$\int \frac{dy}{(y^2 + k^2)^n} = \int 1 \cdot \frac{1}{(y^2 + k^2)^n} \, dy,$$

and apply the rule of integration by parts. Thus, we have

$$\int \frac{dy}{(y^2 + k^2)^n} = \frac{y}{(y^2 + k^2)^n} - \int y \cdot (-n)(y^2 + k^2)^{-n-1} \cdot 2y \, dy$$

$$= \frac{y}{(y^2 + k^2)^n} + 2n \int \frac{y}{(y^2 + k^2)^{n+1}} \, dy$$

$$= \frac{y}{(y^2 + k^2)^n} + 2n \int \frac{y^2 + k^2 - k^2}{(y^2 + k^2)^{n+1}} \, dy$$

$$= \frac{y}{(y^2 + k^2)^n} + 2n \int \frac{dy}{(y^2 + k^2)^n}$$

$$\qquad\qquad - 2nk^2 \int \frac{dy}{(y^2 + k^2)^{n+1}}.$$

$$\therefore \quad 2nk^2 \int \frac{dy}{(y^2 + k^2)^{n+1}} = \frac{y}{(y^2 + k^2)^n} + (2n-1) \int \frac{dy}{(y^2 + k^2)^n},$$

$$\Rightarrow \int \frac{dy}{(y^2 + k^2)^{n+1}} = \frac{y}{2nk^2 (y^2 + k^2)^n} + \frac{2n-1}{2nk^2} \int \frac{dy}{(y^2 + k^2)^n}.$$

Changing n to $n-1$, we get

$$\int \frac{dy}{(y^2 + k^2)^n} = \frac{y}{2(n-1)k^2 (y^2 + k^2)^{n-1}} + \frac{2n-3}{2(n-1)k^2} \int \frac{dy}{(y^2 + k^2)^{n-1}}$$

which is the required reduction formula. With its help, we can integrate the given integral by successive reduction.

EXAMPLE

Evaluate $\displaystyle\int \frac{dx}{(x^2+1)^4}$.

Changing k to 1 and y to x in the reduction formula on page 90, we get

$$\int \frac{dx}{(x^2+1)^n} = \frac{x}{2(n-1)(x^2+1)^{n-1}} + \frac{2n-3}{2(n-1)} \int \frac{dx}{(x^2+1)^{n-1}}.$$

Changing n to 4, 3, 2, successively, we get

$$\int \frac{dx}{(x^2+1)^4} = \frac{x}{6(x^2+1)^3} + \frac{5}{6} \int \frac{dx}{(x^2+1)^3},$$

$$\int \frac{dx}{(x^2+1)^3} = \frac{x}{4(x^2+1)^2} + \frac{3}{4} \int \frac{dx}{(x^2+1)^2},$$

$$\int \frac{dx}{(x^2+1)^2} = \frac{x}{2(x^2+1)} + \frac{1}{2} \int \frac{dx}{x^2+1},$$

$$= \frac{x}{2(x^2+1)} + \frac{1}{2} \tan^{-1} x.$$

From this system of equalities, we get

$$\int \frac{dx}{(x^2+1)^4} = \frac{x}{6(x^2+1)^3} + \frac{5x}{24(x^2+1)^2} + \frac{5x}{16(x^2+1)} + \frac{5}{16} \tan^{-1} x.$$

Note. The integral

$$\int \frac{dy}{(y^2+1)^2}$$

can also be evaluated by the substitution $y = \tan\theta$, so that we make no use of the reduction formula. We have

$$\int \frac{dy}{(y^2+1)^2} = \int \frac{\sec^2\theta\, d\theta}{\sec^4\theta} = \int \cos^2\theta\, d\theta$$

$$= \frac{1}{2} \int (1 + \cos 2\theta)\, d\theta$$

$$= \frac{1}{2}(\theta + \sin\theta\cos\theta)$$

$$= \frac{1}{2}\left(\tan^{-1} y + \frac{y}{y^2+1}\right)$$

which agrees with the result obtained above with the help of the reduction formula.

EXERCISES

1. Evaluate the following integrals :

(i) $\displaystyle\int \frac{2x-3}{(x^2+x+1)^2}\,dx,$

(ii) $\displaystyle\int \frac{x+2}{(x+1)(x^2+1)^2}\,dx,$

(iii) $\displaystyle\int \frac{x^3-x^2-1}{(x^2+1)^2(x^2-1)}\,dx,$

(iv) $\displaystyle\int \frac{x^2+1}{(x^2-1)(x^2+2)^2}\,dx,$

(v) $\displaystyle\int \frac{x(2x^2-x+5)}{(x^2+2x+2)^2}\,dx,$

(vi) $\displaystyle\int \frac{x^2-21}{(x^2-2x+6)^3}\,dx,$

(vii) $\displaystyle\int \frac{x^2-2}{(x^2+2)^3}\,dx,$

(viii) $\displaystyle\int_{-\infty}^{+\infty} \frac{x^2}{(x^2+1)^2(x^2+2)^2}\,dx.$

2. Show that

$$\int_0^\infty \frac{dx}{(x^2+1)^n} = \frac{2n-3}{2n-2}\int_0^\infty \frac{dx}{(x^2+1)^{n-1}},$$

and deduce that

$$\int_0^\infty \frac{dx}{(1+x^2)^3} = \frac{\pi}{2}\cdot\frac{1\cdot3\cdot5\cdot7}{2\cdot4\cdot6\cdot8}.$$

ANSWERS

1. (i) $-\dfrac{1}{x^2+x+1} - \dfrac{16}{3\sqrt{3}}\tan^{-1}\dfrac{2x+1}{\sqrt{3}} - \dfrac{4}{3}\cdot\dfrac{2x+1}{x^2+x+1}.$

(ii) $\dfrac{1+3x}{4(1+x^2)} + \tan^{-1}x + \dfrac{1}{8}\log\dfrac{(x+1)^2}{x^2+1}.$

(iii) $-\dfrac{1}{4}\cdot\dfrac{1}{x^2+1} + \dfrac{1}{2}\tan^{-1}x + \dfrac{1}{8}\log\dfrac{(x+1)^3}{(x^2+1)(x-1)}.$

(iv) $\dfrac{1}{12}\cdot\dfrac{x}{2+x^2} - \dfrac{5\sqrt{2}}{72}\tan^{-1}\dfrac{x}{\sqrt{2}} + \dfrac{1}{9}\log\dfrac{x-1}{x+1}.$

(v) $\log(x^2+2x+2) - \dfrac{15}{2}\tan^{-1}(x+1) - \dfrac{11}{2(x^2+2x+2)}$

$\qquad\qquad - \dfrac{x+1}{2(x^2+2x+2)}.$

(vi) $-\dfrac{11x-11}{40(x^2-2x+6)} - \dfrac{5(x-1)+2}{4(x^2-2x+6)^2} - \dfrac{11\sqrt{5}}{200}\tan^{-1}\dfrac{x-1}{\sqrt{5}}.$

$(vii) \quad -\dfrac{x}{8\,(x^2+2)} - \dfrac{x}{2\,(x^2+2)^2} - \dfrac{\sqrt{2}}{16}\tan^{-1}\dfrac{x}{\sqrt{2}}.$

$(viii) \quad \dfrac{(10-7\sqrt{2})\,\pi}{4}.$

3.6. Integration of algebraic rational functions by substitution. The process of integrating an algebraic rational function can sometimes be shortened by the use of a suitable substitution.

EXAMPLES

1. *Evaluate* $\displaystyle\int \dfrac{dx}{x\,(x^2+1)^3}.$

The denominator consists of a repeated quadratic factor.

Putting $x^2 + 1 = y$, we get

$$\int \dfrac{dx}{x\,(x^2+1)^3} = \int \dfrac{dy}{2y^3\,(y-1)}.$$

In this new integrand we have linear factors in the denominator.

Let

$$\dfrac{1}{y^3\,(y-1)} = \dfrac{A}{y} + \dfrac{B}{y^2} + \dfrac{C}{y^3} + \dfrac{D}{y-1}.$$

$\Rightarrow \quad 1 = Ay^2\,(y-1) + By\,(y-1) + C\,(y-1) + Dy^3.$

Putting $y = 0$ and 1, we get

$$C = -1,\ D = 1.$$

Equating the coefficients of y^3 and y^2, we get

$$0 = A + D,$$
$$0 = -A + B,$$

$\Rightarrow \qquad\qquad A = -1,\ B = -1.$

$\therefore \quad \displaystyle\int \dfrac{dy}{y^3\,(y-1)} = -\log y + \dfrac{1}{y} + \dfrac{1}{2y^2} + \log\,(y-1),$

where $y = x^2 + 1$.

The process may now be easily completed.

Note. It is easy to see that the process of splitting up into partial fractions the integrand which is obtained after substitution is shorter than the one for so splitting up the given integrand.

2. *Evaluate* $\displaystyle\int_0^\infty \dfrac{dx}{(x^2+1)^2}.$

Putting $x = \tan\theta$, we get

$$\int \frac{dx}{\left(x^2+1\right)^2} = \int \cos^2 \theta \, d\theta$$

$$= \frac{1}{2} \int (1 + \cos 2\theta) \, d\theta$$

$$= \frac{1}{2}\left(\theta + \frac{\sin 2\theta}{2}\right) = \frac{1}{2}\left(\theta + \sin \theta \cos \theta\right).$$

Also as θ varies from 0 to $\pi/2$, x varies from 0 to ∞. Therefore the limits for θ are 0 and $\pi/2$.

$$\therefore \quad \int_0^\infty \frac{dx}{\left(x^2+1\right)^2} = \frac{1}{2}\left| \theta + \sin \theta \cos \theta \right|_0^{\pi/2} = \frac{\pi}{4}.$$

3. Evaluate $\displaystyle \int \frac{1+x^2}{1+x^4} \, dx.$

We write

$$\frac{1+x^2}{1+x^4} = \frac{1/x^2 + 1}{1/x^2 + x^2} = \frac{1 + 1/x^2}{\left(x - 1/x\right)^2 + 2}.$$

Put $x - \dfrac{1}{x} = y$ so that $\left(1 + \dfrac{1}{x^2}\right) dx = dy.$

$$\int \frac{1+x^2}{1+x^4} \, dx = \int \frac{dy}{y^2 + 2} = \frac{1}{\sqrt{2}} \tan^{-1} \frac{y}{\sqrt{2}}$$

$$= \frac{1}{\sqrt{2}} \tan^{-1} \frac{x - 1/x}{\sqrt{2}} = \frac{1}{\sqrt{2}} \tan^{-1} \frac{x^2 - 1}{\sqrt{2}\,x}.$$

4. Evaluate $\displaystyle \int \frac{x^2 - 1}{1 + x^4} \, dx.$

Now

$$\int \frac{x^2 - 1}{1 + x^4} \, dx = \int \frac{1 - 1/x^2}{1/x^2 + x^2} \, dx = \int \frac{(1 - 1/x^2)}{(x + 1/x)^2 - 2} \, dx.$$

Put $x + \dfrac{1}{x} = y$ so that $\left(1 - \dfrac{1}{x^2}\right) dx = dy.$

$$\therefore \quad I = \int \frac{dy}{y^2 - 2} = \frac{1}{2\sqrt{2}} \int \left(\frac{1}{y - \sqrt{2}} - \frac{1}{y + \sqrt{2}}\right) dy$$

$$= \frac{1}{2\sqrt{2}} \log \frac{y - \sqrt{2}}{y + \sqrt{2}} = \frac{1}{2\sqrt{2}} \log \frac{x^2 - \sqrt{2}\,x + 1}{x^2 + \sqrt{2}\,x + 1}.$$

EXERCISES

1. Evaluate the integrals of the following functions :

(i) $\dfrac{x}{x^4 + x^2 + 1}$,

(ii) $\dfrac{2x}{(x^2 + 1)(x^2 + 3)}$,

(iii) $\dfrac{x^3}{(x^2 + 1)^4}$,

(iv) $\dfrac{1}{x(x^2 + 1)(x^2 + 2)^2}$,

(v) $\dfrac{1}{x(x^5 + 1)}$,

(vi) $\dfrac{1}{x(x^4 - 1)^2}$,

(vii) $\dfrac{1}{x(1 + x^n)}$.

2. Evaluate :

(i) $\displaystyle\int \dfrac{dx}{x^4 + 1}$,

(ii) $\displaystyle\int_0^\infty \dfrac{x^2}{1 + x^4}\, dx$,

(iii) $\displaystyle\int \dfrac{x^2 + 1}{x^4 + x^2 + 1}\, dx$,

(iv) $\displaystyle\int \dfrac{dx}{x^4 + x^2 + 1}$,

(v) $\displaystyle\int \dfrac{x^2 + 3x + 1}{x^4 - x^2 + 1}\, dx$,

(vi) $\displaystyle\int_0^{\pi/4} \sqrt{\tan x}\, dx$,

(vii) $\displaystyle\int \sqrt{\cot x}\, dx$.

3. Evaluate

$$\int \dfrac{x^3}{(x^2 + 1)^3}\, dx,$$

by the substitutions (a) $x = \tan \theta$, (b) $x^2 + 1 = u$, and show that the results you obtain by the two methods are in accordance.

ANSWERS

1. (i) $\dfrac{1}{\sqrt{3}} \tan^{-1} \dfrac{2x^2 + 1}{\sqrt{3}}$.

(ii) $\dfrac{1}{2} \log \dfrac{x^2 + 1}{x^2 + 3}$.

(iii) $-\dfrac{3x^2 + 1}{12(x^2 + 1)^3}$.

(iv) $\dfrac{1}{8} \log \dfrac{x^2(x^2 + 2)^3}{(x^2 + 1)^4} - \dfrac{1}{4(x^2 + 2)}$.

(v) $\dfrac{1}{5} \log \dfrac{x^5}{x^5 + 1}$.

(vi) $\dfrac{1}{4} \log \dfrac{x^4}{x^4 - 1} - \dfrac{1}{4(x^4 - 1)}$.

(vii) $\dfrac{1}{n} \log \dfrac{x^n}{1 + x^n}$.

2. (i) $\dfrac{1}{2\sqrt{2}}\tan^{-1}\dfrac{x^2-1}{\sqrt{2}\,x}-\dfrac{1}{4\sqrt{2}}\log\dfrac{x^2-\sqrt{2}\,x+1}{x^2+\sqrt{2}\,x+1}.$

(ii) $\dfrac{\pi}{2\sqrt{2}}.$ (iii) $\dfrac{1}{\sqrt{3}}\tan^{-1}\dfrac{x^2-1}{\sqrt{3}\,x}.$

(iv) $\dfrac{1}{2\sqrt{3}}\tan^{-1}\dfrac{x^2-1}{\sqrt{3}\,x}-\dfrac{1}{4}\log\dfrac{x^2-x+1}{x^2+x+1}.$

(v) $\tan^{-1}\dfrac{x^2-1}{x}+\sqrt{3}\tan^{-1}\dfrac{2x^2-1}{\sqrt{3}}.$

(vi) $\dfrac{1}{2}\sqrt{2}\log(\sqrt{2}-1)+\dfrac{1}{4}\sqrt{2}\,\pi.$

(vii) $\dfrac{1}{2\sqrt{2}}\log\dfrac{t^2+\sqrt{2}\,t+1}{t^2-\sqrt{2}\,t+1}-\dfrac{1}{\sqrt{2}}\tan^{-1}\dfrac{t^2-1}{\sqrt{2}\,t}$ where $t=\sqrt{\cot x}.$

3.7. Integration of algebraic rational functions of e^x. An integral of a rational function of e^x is transformed into an integral of a rational function of t by means of the substitution $e^x=t$ as is illustrated below.

EXAMPLES

1. *Evaluate* $\displaystyle\int\dfrac{4e^x+6e^{-x}}{9e^x-4e^{-x}}\,dx.$

We put $e^x=t$, so that $e^x\,dx=dt$.

$$\therefore\ \int\dfrac{4e^x+6e^{-x}}{9e^x-4e^{-x}}\,dx=\int\dfrac{4t+6/t}{9t-4/t}\cdot\dfrac{dt}{t}$$

$$=\int\dfrac{4t^2+6}{t(9t^2-4)}\,dt$$

$$=-\dfrac{3}{2}\int\dfrac{dt}{t}+\dfrac{35}{12}\int\dfrac{dt}{3t-2}+\dfrac{35}{12}\int\dfrac{dt}{3t+2}$$

$$=-\dfrac{3}{2}\log t+\dfrac{35}{36}\log(3t-2)+\dfrac{35}{36}\log(3t+2)$$

$$=-\dfrac{3}{2}\log t+\dfrac{35}{36}\log(9t^2-4)$$

$$=-\dfrac{3}{2}x+\dfrac{35}{36}\log(9e^{2x}-4).$$

2. *Evaluate* $\displaystyle\int_0^\infty \operatorname{sech} x\,dx.$

Now,

$$\int \text{sech } x \, dx = \int \frac{2}{e^x + e^{-x}} \, dx = \int \frac{2e^x}{1 + e^{2x}} \, dx.$$

Putting $e^x = y$, we see that

$$\int \text{sech } x \, dx = \int \frac{2 \, dy}{1 + y^2} = 2 \tan^{-1} y = 2 \tan^{-1} e^x$$

$$\therefore \quad \int_0^\infty \text{sech } x \, dx = \left| 2 \tan^{-1} (e^x) \right|_0^\infty$$

$$= 2 \left[\frac{\pi}{2} - \frac{\pi}{4} \right] = \frac{\pi}{2},$$

for $\quad \lim_{x \to \infty} (\tan^{-1} e^x) = \frac{\pi}{2}.$

EXERCISES

1. Evaluate

(i) $\displaystyle \int \frac{dx}{e^x + e^{2x}},$

(ii) $\displaystyle \int \frac{dx}{(e^x - 1)^2},$

(iii) $\displaystyle \int \frac{dx}{(1 + e^x)(1 + e^{-x})},$

(iv) $\displaystyle \int_0^\infty \frac{e^{-x}}{(e^x - 1)^2} \, dx,$

(v) $\displaystyle \int_1^\infty \text{cosech } x \, dx,$

(vi) $\displaystyle \int \frac{dx}{1 + \cosh x}.$

ANSWERS

1. (i) $\log (1 + e^{-x}) - e^{-x}.$

(ii) $(1 - e^x)^{-1} - \log (1 - e^{-x}).$

(iii) $-\dfrac{1}{1 + e^x}.$

(iv) $2 \log \dfrac{e - 1}{e} + \dfrac{2e - 1}{e^2 - e}.$

(v) $\log [(e + 1) / (e - 1)].$

(vi) $\tanh \dfrac{1}{2} x.$

EXERCISES ON CHAPTER III

Integrate the following functions :

1. (i) $\dfrac{2x^3 + 7x^2 + 4x + 2}{2x + 3},$

(ii) $\dfrac{3x^3 - 4x^2 + 5x - 6}{x^2 + x - 6},$

(iii) $\dfrac{x^2 - 3x + 3}{x^3 - 4x^2 - 7x + 10},$

(iv) $\dfrac{17x^2 - x - 26}{(x^2 - 1)(x^2 - 4)},$

2. (i) $\dfrac{3x^2 - 5x + 4}{x^3 - 2x^2 + 3x + 6}$,

(ii) $\dfrac{1}{(2 + x^2)(1 - x^2)}$,

(iii) $\dfrac{x^2 - 3x}{x^4 - 1}$,

(iv) $\dfrac{2x^2 - x + 3}{x^3 + 1}$,

3. (i) $\dfrac{x^3 + 1}{x^4 - 3x^3 + 3x^2 - x}$,

(ii) $\dfrac{(x^2 + 1)(x^2 + 2)(x^2 + 3)}{(x^2 + 4)(x^2 + 5)(x^2 + 6)}$,

(iii) $\dfrac{1}{x^6 + 1}$,

(iv) $\dfrac{3x^2 + x - 2}{(x + 1)^3(x^2 + 1)}$,

4. (i) $\dfrac{x^5}{x^3 - 1}$,

(ii) $\dfrac{1}{x(x^2 + a^2)^2}$,

(iii) $\dfrac{1}{x^{13}(x^6 - 1)}$,

(iv) $\dfrac{1}{(x - 1)^3(x^3 + 1)}$,

5. (i) $\dfrac{1}{x(x - 1)^2(x^2 + 1)}$,

(ii) $\dfrac{x^2 + 2}{(x^2 + 1)^2}$,

(iii) $\dfrac{2x + 1}{(x^2 + 1)^3}$,

(iv) $\dfrac{2x}{(1 + x)(1 + x^2)^2}$,

(v) $\dfrac{1}{(x^2 - a^2)(x^2 + a^2)^2}$,

(vi) $\dfrac{3x + 4}{(2x^2 - x + 2)^2}$.

6. Evaluate $\displaystyle\int_0^1 \dfrac{24t^3}{(1 + t^2)^4}\, dt.$

7. Show that $\displaystyle\int_1^\infty \dfrac{(x^2 + 3)\, dx}{x^6(x^2 + 1)} = \dfrac{1}{30}(58 - 15\pi).$

8. Show that

$$\int_0^\infty \dfrac{x^2\, dx}{(x^2 + a^2)(x^2 + b^2)(x^2 + c^2)} = \dfrac{\pi}{2(a + b)(b + c)(c + a)}.$$

9. Show that $\displaystyle\int_0^1 \dfrac{1 - x^2}{1 + x^2 + x^4}\, dx = \dfrac{1}{2}\log 3.$

10. Integrate :

(i) $\dfrac{\log(x^2 + a^2)}{x^2}$,

(ii) $x \log(x^3 + 1)$,

(iii) $e^x \log(e^{2x} + 5e^x + 6)$,

(iv) $\dfrac{\tan^{-1} x}{(1 + x)^2}$.

ANSWERS

1. (i) $\dfrac{1}{3}(x^3 + 3x^2 - 3x) + \dfrac{5}{2}\log(2x+3)$.

   (ii) $\dfrac{1}{2}(3x^2 - 14x) + \dfrac{138}{5}\log(x+3) + \dfrac{12}{5}\log(x-2)$.

   (iii) $\dfrac{13}{21}\log(x+2) + \dfrac{13}{28}\log(x-5) - \dfrac{1}{12}\log(x-1)$.

   (iv) $\dfrac{1}{3}\log[(x-1)^5(x-2)^{10}/(x+1)^4(x+2)^{11}]$.

2. (i) $\dfrac{6}{5}\log(x+1) + \dfrac{9}{10}\log(x^2 - 3x + 6) - \dfrac{1}{\sqrt{15}}\tan^{-1}\dfrac{(2x-3)}{\sqrt{15}}$.

   (ii) $\dfrac{1}{3\sqrt{2}}\tan^{-1}(x/\sqrt{2}) + \dfrac{1}{6}[\log(1+x) - \log(1-x)]$.

   (iii) $\dfrac{1}{2}\tan^{-1}x + \dfrac{3}{4}\log(x^2+1) - \dfrac{1}{2}\log(x-1) - \log(x+1)$.

   (iv) $2\log(x+1) + (2/\sqrt{3})\tan^{-1}[(2x-1)/\sqrt{3}]$.

3. (i) $\log(x-1)^2 - \log x - x/(x-1)^2$.

   (ii) $x - \dfrac{3}{2}\tan^{-1}\dfrac{x}{2} + \dfrac{24}{\sqrt{5}}\tan^{-1}\dfrac{x}{\sqrt{5}} - \dfrac{30}{\sqrt{6}}\tan^{-1}\dfrac{x}{\sqrt{6}}$.

   (iii) $\dfrac{1}{3}\tan^{-1}x - \dfrac{1}{4\sqrt{3}}\log\dfrac{x^2 - \sqrt{3}x + 1}{x^2 + \sqrt{3}x + 1} + \dfrac{1}{6}\tan^{-1}\dfrac{x^2-1}{x}$.

   (iv) $\dfrac{1}{2}\log\dfrac{x^2+1}{(x+1)^2} + \dfrac{3}{2}\tan^{-1}x + \dfrac{5}{2(x+1)}$.

4. (i) $\dfrac{1}{3}x^3 + \dfrac{1}{3}\log(x^3 - 1)$.

   (ii) $\dfrac{1}{2a^2}\cdot\dfrac{1}{x^2 + a^2} - \dfrac{1}{2a^4}\log\dfrac{x^2 + a^2}{x^2}$.

   (iii) $\dfrac{1}{3}\left[\log\{(x^6 - 1)/x^6\} + x^{-6} + \dfrac{1}{2}x^{-12}\right]$.

   (iv) $\dfrac{3}{8}\log(x-1) - \dfrac{1}{24}\log(x+1) - \dfrac{1}{6}\log(x^2 - x + 1)$

   $\qquad + (\sqrt{3}/3)\tan^{-1}[(2x-1)/\sqrt{3}] + \dfrac{1}{4}(5x-4)/(x-1)^2$.

5. (i) $\log[x/(x-1)] + \dfrac{1}{2}\tan^{-1}x - \dfrac{1}{2}(x-1)^{-1}$.

   (ii) $\dfrac{3}{2}\tan^{-1}x + \dfrac{1}{2}x/(1+x^2)$.

(iii) $\dfrac{x-2}{4(x^2+1)^2} + \dfrac{3x}{8(x^2+1)} + \dfrac{3}{8}\tan^{-1}x.$

(iv) $\dfrac{1}{2}\dfrac{x-1}{x^2+1} + \dfrac{1}{4}\log\dfrac{x^2+1}{(x+1)^2}.$

(v) $\dfrac{1}{8a^5}\log - \dfrac{x-a}{x+a}\dfrac{1}{2a^5}\tan^{-1}\dfrac{x}{a} + \dfrac{1}{4a^4}\cdot\dfrac{x}{x^2+a^2}.$

(vi) $\dfrac{19x-16}{15(2x^2-x+2)} + \dfrac{38\sqrt{15}}{225}\tan^{-1}\dfrac{4x-1}{\sqrt{15}}.$

6. 1.

10. (i) $\dfrac{2}{a}\tan^{-1}\dfrac{x}{a} - \dfrac{1}{x}\log(x^2+a^2).$

(ii) $\dfrac{1}{2}x^2\log(x^3+1) - \dfrac{1}{2}\log(x+1) + \dfrac{1}{4}\log(x^2-x+1)$

$$+ \sqrt{3/2}\tan^{-1}[(2x-1)/\sqrt{3}] - \dfrac{3}{4}x^3.$$

(iii) $e^x\log(e^{2x}+5e^x+6) + 2\log(e^x+2) + 3\log(e^x+3) - 2e^x.$

(iv) $\dfrac{(x-1)\tan^{-1}x}{2(x+1)} + \log\sqrt{\dfrac{1+x}{\sqrt{1+x^2}}}.$

OBJECTIVE QUESTIONS

For each of the following questions, four alternatives are given for the answer. Only one of them is correct. Choose the correct alternative.

1. The value of $\displaystyle\int\dfrac{dx}{e^x+1}$ is

(a) $\log(e^x-1)+c$ (b) $\log(e^x+1)+c$

(c) $x-\log(e^x+1)+c$ (d) None of these.

2. Given that

$$\int_0^\infty \dfrac{x^2\,dx}{(x^2+a^2)(x^2+b^2)(x^2+c^2)} = \dfrac{\pi}{2(a+b)(b+c)(c+a)},$$

then the value of $\displaystyle\int_0^\infty \dfrac{dx}{(x^2+4)(x^2+9)}$ is

(a) $\pi/60$ (b) $\pi/20$ (c) $\pi/40$ (d) $\pi/80$.

3. $\int e^x[\phi(x)+\phi'(x)]\,dx$ is equal to

(a) $\int e^x\phi'(x)\,dx$ (b) $e^x\phi(x)+c$

(c) $e^x\phi'(x)+c$ (d) None of these.

4. $\int \dfrac{e^{2x}+1}{e^{2x}-1}\,dx\ (x \in R_0) =$

   (a) $\log(e^x - e^{-x}) + c$ (b) $\log(e^x + e^{-x}) + c$

   (c) $\log |e^x - e^{-x}| + c$ (d) None of these.

5. $\int \dfrac{(x-1)\,dx}{(x-2)(x-3)}$ is equal to

   (a) $\log[(x-3)^2/(x-2)]$ (b) $\log[(x-3)/(x-2)^2]$

   (c) $\log[(x-2)/(x-3)]$ (d) None of these.

6. $\int \dfrac{(1-x)\,e^x}{x^2}\,dx =$

   (a) $\dfrac{e^x}{x}$ (b) $-\dfrac{e^x}{x}$ (c) $\dfrac{e^x}{x^2}$ (d) None of these.

7. $\int \dfrac{dx}{x^2+x+1}$ is equal to

   (a) $\dfrac{1}{2} \log \left| \dfrac{x-1}{x+1} \right|$ (b) $-\dfrac{1}{\sqrt{2}} \log \left| \dfrac{x-\sqrt{2}}{x+\sqrt{2}} \right|$

   (c) $\dfrac{2}{\sqrt{3}} \tan^{-1}\left(\dfrac{2x+1}{3} \right)$ (d) None of these.

8. $\int_{0}^{1} \dfrac{x^5}{1+x^4}\,dx =$

   (a) $(\pi-4)/8$ (b) $(4-\pi)/8$ (c) $(\pi-4)/4$ (d) $(4-\pi)/4$.

9. $\int \dfrac{x^3-7x+6}{x^2+3x}\,dx =$

   (a) $\dfrac{1}{2}x^2 - 3x + 2\log x$ (b) $\dfrac{1}{2}x^2 + 3x + 2\log x$

   (c) $\dfrac{1}{2}x^2 - 3x - 2\log x$ (d) None of these.

10. $\int \dfrac{x^4+x^2+1}{x^2-x+1}\,dx =$

   (a) $\dfrac{1}{3}x^3 + \dfrac{1}{2}x^2 + x$ (b) $\dfrac{1}{3}x^3 - \dfrac{1}{2}x^2 + x$

   (c) $\dfrac{1}{3}x^3 + \dfrac{1}{2}x^2 - x$ (d) None of these.

11. $\int \dfrac{2x^2+3}{(x^2-1)(x^2+4)}\,dx = a\log\left(\dfrac{x+1}{x-1}\right) + b\tan^{-1}\dfrac{x}{2}$, then (a, b) is

(a) $\left(-\dfrac{1}{2}, \dfrac{1}{2}\right)$ 　　　　(b) $\left(\dfrac{1}{2}, \dfrac{1}{2}\right)$

(c) $(-1, 1)$ 　　　　(d) $(1, -1)$.

ANSWERS

1. (c)　　　2. (a)　　　3. (b)　　　4. (c)
5. (a)　　　6. (b)　　　7. (c)　　　8. (c)
9. (a)　　　10. (a)　　　11. (b)

4

Integration of
Trigonometric Functions

4.1. Integration of $\sin^n x$ where n is a positive integer.

When n is a positive integer, odd or even, the function $\sin^n x$ may be integrated with the help of a reduction formula. If, however, n is an odd positive integer, the function can be more easily integrated by means of the substitution $\cos x = t$ so that the reduction formula may only be employed when n is an even positive integer.

Let n be an odd positive integer, say $2k + 1$, where k is a positive integer.

We put $\cos x = t$ so that $-\sin x\, dx = dt$.

$$\therefore \quad \int \sin^n x\, dx = \int \sin^{2k+1} x\, dx$$

$$= \int \sin^{2k} x \sin x\, dx$$

$$= -\int (1 - \cos^2 x)^k (-\sin x)\, dx = -\int (1 - t^2)^k\, dt.$$

Since k is a positive integer, the integrand $(1 - t^2)^k$ can, by the Binomial theorem, be expanded as a sum of $(k + 1)$ terms each of which may be easily integrated.

Reduction Formula for $\int \sin^n x\, dx$.

We write

$$\int \sin^n x\, dx = \int \sin x \cdot \sin^{n-1} x\, dx.$$

Integrating by parts, we get

$$\int \sin^n x\, dx = -\cos x \sin^{-1} x$$

$$\qquad\qquad - \int (-\cos x)(n-1)\sin^{n-2} x \cos x\, dx$$

$$= -\cos x \sin^{n-1} x + (n-1)\int \sin^{n-2} x (1 - \sin^2 x)\, dx$$

$$= -\cos x \sin^{n-1} x + (n-1)\int \sin^{n-2} x\, dx$$

$$\qquad\qquad - (n-1)\int \sin^n x\, dx.$$

Transposing $(n-1)\int \sin^n x\, dx$, we get

$$n \int \sin^n x\, dx = -\cos x \sin^{-1} x + (n-1)\int \sin^{n-2} x\, dx,$$

$$\Rightarrow \quad \int \sin^n x\, dx = \frac{-\cos x \sin^{n-1} x}{n} + \frac{n-1}{n}\int \sin^{n-2} x\, dx \quad ...(A)$$

which is the required reduction formula.

(Jiwaji, 1995; Bhopal, 2000; Sagar, 1999;
Vikram, 2001; Rohilkhand, 1995)

103

This formula which connects the integrals

$$\int \sin^n x \, dx \quad \text{and} \quad \int \sin^{n-2} x \, dx$$

enables us to successively integrate any positive integral power of sin x, odd or even. But it need be applied only when, n, is even.

EXAMPLES

Integrate

   (*i*) $\sin^3 x$ (*ii*) $\sin^4 x$.

(*i*) The index, 3, being odd, we proceed by substitution.

We put cos $x = t$, so that

$$\int \sin^3 x \, dx = -\int (1 - t^2) \, dt$$

$$= -\left(t - \frac{t^2}{3} \right)$$

$$= -\left(\cos x - \frac{\cos^3 x}{3} \right)$$

$$= -\cos x + \frac{1}{3} \cos^3 x.$$

(*ii*) The index, 4, being even, we employ the reduction formula. To integrate $\sin^4 x$, we first obtain the reduction formula (A). Putting $n = 4, 2$ successively in the reduction formula, we obtain

$$\int \sin^4 x \, dx = -\frac{\cos x \sin^3 x}{4} + \frac{3}{4} \int \sin^2 x \, dx \qquad ...(i)$$

$$\int \sin^2 x \, dx = -\frac{\cos x \sin x}{2} + \frac{1}{2} \int \sin^0 x \, dx$$

$$= -\frac{\cos x \sin x}{2} + \frac{1}{2} x \qquad ...(ii)$$

From (*i*) and (*ii*), we obtain

$$\int \sin^4 x = -\frac{\cos x \sin^3 x}{4} - \frac{3}{8} \cos x \sin x + \frac{3}{8} x.$$

EXERCISES

Evaluate :

1. (*i*) $\int \sin^2 x \, dx$,   (*ii*) $\int \sin^5 x \, dx$,   (*iii*) $\int \sin^6 x \, dx$.

2. (*i*) $\int_0^{\pi/2} \sin^7 x \, dx$,   (*ii*) $\int_0^{\pi/2} \sin^8 x \, dx$,   (*iii*) $\int_0^{\pi/2} \sin^9 x \, dx$.

ANSWERS

1. (i) $\dfrac{1}{2}(x - \sin x \cos x)$.   (ii) $-\left[\cos x - \dfrac{1}{3}\cos^3 x + \dfrac{1}{5}\cos^5 x\right]$.

(iii) $\dfrac{1}{6}\cos x \sin^5 x - \dfrac{5}{24}\cos x \sin^3 x - \dfrac{5}{16}\cos x \sin x + \dfrac{5}{16}x$.

2. (i) $16/35$.   (ii) $35\pi/256$.   (iii) $128/315$.

4.1.1. Evaluation of the definite integral

$$\int_0^{\pi/2} \sin^n x\, dx,$$

where, n, is a positive integer.   *(Ravishankar, 1997; Sagar, 1994, 99)*

Firstly, we obtain the reduction formula (A), *viz.*,

$$\int \sin^n x\, dx = -\frac{\cos x \cdot \sin^{n-1} x}{n} + \frac{n-1}{n}\int \sin^{n-2} x\, dx.$$

This gives

$$\int_0^{\pi/2} \sin^n x\, dx = \left| -\frac{\cos x \cdot \sin^{n-1} x}{n} \right|_0^{\pi/2} + \frac{n-1}{n}\int_0^{\pi/2} \sin^{n-2} x\, dx$$

$$= 0 + \frac{n-1}{n}\int_0^{\pi/2} \sin^{n-2} x\, dx.$$

Writing I_n for $\displaystyle\int_0^{\pi/2} \sin^n x\, dx$, we obtain the connection formula

$$I_n = \frac{n-1}{n} I_{n-2}.$$ *(Jiwaji, 1994)*

With the help of this formula, we will successively connect I_{n-2} with I_{n-4}, I_{n-4} with I_{n-6} etc., and finally, I_3 with I_1 or I_2 with I_0, according as n is odd or even. Thus we have

$$I_n = \frac{n-1}{n} I_{n-2},$$

$$I_{n-2} = \frac{n-3}{n-2} I_{n-4},$$

$$I_{n-4} = \frac{n-5}{n-4} I_{n-6},$$

....
....

$$\begin{cases} I_3 = \dfrac{2}{3} I_1, & \text{if } n \text{ is odd,} \\[2mm] I_2 = \dfrac{1}{2} I_0, & \text{if } n \text{ is even.} \end{cases}$$

From these, we get

$$I_n = \begin{cases} \dfrac{n-1}{n} \cdot \dfrac{n-3}{n-2} \cdot \dfrac{n-5}{n-4} \ldots \dfrac{2}{3} I_1, & \text{when } n \text{ is odd,} \\[3mm] \dfrac{n-1}{n} \cdot \dfrac{n-3}{n-2} \cdot \dfrac{n-5}{n-4} \ldots \dfrac{1}{2} I_0, & \text{when } n \text{ is even.} \end{cases}$$

Now,

$$I_1 = \int_0^{\pi/2} \sin x\, dx = \big| -\cos x \big|_0^{\pi/2} = 1,$$

$$I_0 = \int_0^{\pi/2} \sin^0 x\, dx = \int_0^{\pi/2} 1 \cdot dx = \frac{\pi}{2}.$$

$$\therefore \quad I_n = \begin{cases} \dfrac{n-1}{n} \cdot \dfrac{n-3}{n-2} \cdot \dfrac{n-5}{n-4} \ldots \dfrac{2}{3}, & \textbf{when } \boldsymbol{n} \textbf{ is odd.} \\[3mm] \dfrac{n-1}{n} \cdot \dfrac{n-3}{n-2} \cdot \dfrac{n-5}{n-4} \ldots \dfrac{1}{2} \cdot \dfrac{\pi}{2}, & \textbf{when } \boldsymbol{n} \textbf{ is even.} \end{cases}$$

EXAMPLE

Evaluate :

(i) $\displaystyle\int_0^{\pi/2} \sin^7 x\, dx,$ (ii) $\displaystyle\int_0^{\pi/2} \sin^8 x\, dx.$

We have

$$\int_0^{\pi/2} \sin^7 x\, dx = \frac{6}{7} \cdot \frac{4}{5} \cdot \frac{2}{3} = \frac{16}{35},$$

$$\int_0^{\pi/2} \sin^8 x\, dx = \frac{7}{8} \cdot \frac{5}{6} \cdot \frac{3}{4} \cdot \frac{1}{2} \cdot \frac{\pi}{2} = \frac{35\pi}{256}.$$

EXERCISES

1. Evaluate :

(i) $\displaystyle\int_0^{\pi/2} \sin^5 x\, dx,$ (ii) $\displaystyle\int_0^{\pi/2} \sin^6 x\, dx,$ (iii) $\displaystyle\int_0^{\pi/2} \sin^{10} x\, dx.$

2. Evaluate :

$$\text{(i)} \int_0^{\pi/4} \sin^4 2x\, dx, \qquad \text{(ii)} \int_0^{\pi/6} \sin^6 3x\, dx, \qquad \text{(iii)} \int_0^{\pi} \sin^5\left(\frac{1}{2}\, x\right) dx.$$

3. Evaluate :

$$\text{(i)} \int_0^{\pi} \frac{\sin^4 \theta\, d\theta}{(1 + \cos \theta)^2}, \qquad \text{(ii)} \int_0^{\pi} \sin^2 \theta \, \frac{\sqrt{1 - \cos \theta}}{1 + \cos \theta}\, d\theta.$$

ANSWERS

1. (i) $8/15$.   (ii) $5\pi/32$.   (iii) $63\pi/512$.

2. (i) $3\pi/32$.   (ii) $5\pi/96$.   (iii) $16/25$.

3. (i) $3\pi/2$.   (ii) $8\sqrt{2}/3$.

4.2. Integration of $\cos^n x$ where n is a positive integer. When n is a positive integer, the function $\cos^n x$ may be integrated with the help of a reduction formula. If, however, n is an *odd* positive integer, the function can be more easily integrated by means of the substitution $\sin x = t$.

Let n be an odd positive integer, say $2k + 1$, where k is a positive integer.

We put $\sin x = t \Rightarrow \cos x\, dx = dt$.

We have

$$\int \cos^n x\, dx = \int \cos^{2k+1} x\, dx$$

$$= \int \cos^{2k} x \cdot \cos x\, dx$$

$$= \int (1 - \sin^2 x)^k \cdot \cos x\, dx = \int (1 - t^2)^k\, dt,$$

which may be easily evaluated by expanding $(1 - t^2)^k$ by the Binomial theorem.

Reduction formula for $\int \cos^n x\, dx$.

We write

$$\int \cos^n x\, dx = \int \cos x \cdot \cos^{n-1} x\, dx,$$

so that, on integrating by parts, we obtain

$$\int \cos^n x\, dx = \sin x \cdot \cos^{n-1} x - \int \sin x \cdot (n-1) \cos^{n-2} x \cdot (- \sin x)\, dx$$

$$= \sin x \cdot \cos^{n-1} x + (n-1) \int \cos^{n-2} x\, (1 - \cos^2 x)\, dx$$

$$= \sin x \cdot \cos^{n-1} x + (n-1) \int \cos^{n-2} x\, dx - (n-1) \int \cos^n x\, dx$$

$$\Rightarrow n \int \cos^n x\, dx = \sin x\, \cos^{n-1} x + (n-1) \int \cos^{n-2} x\, dx,$$

$$\Rightarrow \int \cos^n x\, dx = \frac{\sin x \cdot \cos^{n-1} x}{n} + \frac{n-1}{n} \int \cos^{n-2} x\, dx \qquad \text{...(B)}$$

is the required reduction formula.   *(Jabalpur, 1998; Rohilkhand, 1993)*

4.2.1. Evaluation of the definite integral

$$\int_0^{\pi/2} \cos^n x \, dx.$$

As in § 4.1.1, we can show that

$$\int_0^{\pi/2} \cos^n x \, dx = \begin{cases} \dfrac{n-1}{n} \cdot \dfrac{n-3}{n-2} \cdot \dfrac{n-5}{n-4} \cdots \dfrac{2}{3}, & \text{when } n \text{ is odd.} \\[2ex] \dfrac{n-1}{n} \cdot \dfrac{n-3}{n-2} \cdot \dfrac{n-5}{n-4} \cdots \dfrac{1}{2} \cdot \dfrac{\pi}{2}, & \text{when } n \text{ is even.} \end{cases}$$

On comparing the values of

$$\int_0^{\pi/2} \cos^n x \, dx \text{ and } \int_0^{\pi/2} \sin^n x \, dx,$$

we see that

$$\int_0^{\pi/2} \cos^n x \, dx = \int_0^{\pi/2} \sin^n x \, dx,$$

for every value of n.

This result is also capable of a direct proof on putting

$$x = \frac{1}{2}\pi - y.$$

EXERCISES

Write down the values of

(i) $\displaystyle\int_0^{\pi/2} \cos^7 x \, dx,$ (ii) $\displaystyle\int_0^{\pi/2} \cos^8 x \, dx,$ (iii) $\displaystyle\int_0^{\pi/4} \cos^6 2t \, dt.$

ANSWERS

(i) $16/35.$ (ii) $35\pi/256.$ (iii) $5\pi/64.$

Cor. *The values of the definite integrals*

$$\int_0^{\pi/2} \sin^n x \, dx \text{ and } \int_0^{\pi/2} \cos^n x \, dx$$

enable us at once to obtain the values of the following definite integrals,

(i) $\displaystyle\int_0^1 \frac{x^n}{\sqrt{1-x^2}} \, dx,$ (ii) $\displaystyle\int_0^\infty \frac{1}{(1+x^2)^n} \, dx,$ (iii) $\displaystyle\int_0^\infty \frac{dx}{(1+x^2)^{n+1/2}},$

where n is a positive integer.

(*i*) We put $x = \sin \theta$ and note that $\theta = 0$ when $x = 0$ and $\theta = \pi/2$ when $x = 1$, so that limits of the new variable θ are 0 and $\pi/2$. Making this substitution, we get

$$\int_0^1 \frac{x^n}{\sqrt{1-x^2}}\, dx = \int_0^{\pi/2} \frac{\sin^n \theta \cos \theta\, d\theta}{\cos \theta} = \int_0^{\pi/2} \sin^n \theta\, d\theta.$$

(*ii*) We put $x = \tan \theta$ and note that $\theta = 0$ when $x = 0$ and $\theta \to \pi/2$ when $x \to \infty$, so that the limits of the new variable θ are 0 and $\pi/2$. Making this substitution, we get

$$\int_0^\infty \frac{dx}{(1+x^2)^n} = \int_0^{\pi/2} \frac{\sec^2 \theta\, d\theta}{\sec^{2n} \theta} = \int_0^{\pi/2} \cos^{2n-2} \theta\, d\theta.$$

(*iii*) Putting $x = \tan \theta$, we see that

$$\int_0^\infty \frac{dx}{(1+x^2)^{n+1/2}} = \int_0^{\pi/2} \frac{\sec^2 \theta\, d\theta}{\sec^{2n+1} \theta} = \int_0^{\pi/2} \cos^{2n-1} \theta\, d\theta.$$

EXAMPLES

1. *Evaluate* $\displaystyle\int_0^a \frac{x^4\, dx}{\sqrt{a^2 - x^2}}.$

(Sagar, 1998; Bilaspur, 1998; Jabalpur, 2000)

Substituting $x = a \sin \theta$, $dx = a \cos \theta\, d\theta$, we get

$$I = \int_0^{\pi/2} \frac{a^5 \sin^4 \theta \cdot \cos \theta\, d\theta}{\sqrt{a^2 - a^2 \sin^2 \theta}}$$

$$= a^4 \int_0^{\pi/2} \sin^4 \theta\, d\theta$$

$$= a^4 \cdot \frac{3}{4} \cdot \frac{1}{2} \cdot \frac{\pi}{2} = \frac{3\pi a^4}{16}.$$

2. *Find the values of*

(*i*) $\displaystyle\int_0^3 \sqrt{\left(\frac{x^3}{3-x}\right)}\, dx,$ (*ii*) $\displaystyle\int_0^\infty \frac{dx}{(1+x^2)^4}.$

(*i*) Put $x = 3 \sin^2 \theta$, so that $dx = 6 \sin \theta \cos \theta\, d\theta$.

$$\therefore \quad \int_0^3 \sqrt{\left(\frac{x^3}{3-x}\right)}\, dx = \int_0^{\pi/2} \sqrt{\left\{\frac{27 \sin^6 \theta}{3(1 - \sin^2 \theta)}\right\}} \cdot 6 \sin \theta \cos \theta\, d\theta$$

$$= 18 \int\limits_0^{\pi/2} \frac{\sin^3 \theta}{\cos \theta} \cdot \sin \theta \cos \theta \, d\theta$$

$$= 18 \int\limits_0^{\pi/2} \sin^4 \theta \, d\theta$$

$$= 18 \cdot \frac{3}{4} \cdot \frac{1}{2} \cdot \frac{\pi}{2} = \frac{27\pi}{8}.$$

(*ii*) Put $x = \tan \theta$, so that $dx = \sec^2 \theta \, d\theta$.

$$\therefore \quad \int\limits_0^\infty \frac{dx}{(1 + x^2)^4} = \int\limits_0^{\pi/2} \frac{\sec^2 \theta \, d\theta}{(1 + \tan^2 \theta)^4}$$

$$= \int\limits_0^{\pi/2} \frac{\sec^2 \theta \, d\theta}{\sec^8 \theta} = \int\limits_0^{\pi/2} \cos^6 \theta \, d\theta$$

$$= \frac{5}{6} \cdot \frac{3}{4} \cdot \frac{1}{2} \cdot \frac{\pi}{2} = \frac{5\pi}{32}.$$

3. *Evaluate* $\int\limits_0^{\pi/4} (\cos 2\theta)^{3/2} \cos \theta \, d\theta.$

Here $\int\limits_0^{\pi/4} (1 - 2 \sin^2 \theta)^{3/2} \cos \theta \, d\theta.$

Now, put $\sqrt{2} \sin \theta = \sin t$, so that

$$\cos \theta \, d\theta = \frac{1}{\sqrt{2}} \cos t \, dt$$

and when $\theta = 0$, then $t = 0$ and when $\theta = \pi/4$, then $\sin t = \sqrt{2} \sin \frac{\pi}{4} = 1$.

$$\therefore \quad t = \pi/2.$$

Hence

$$\int\limits_0^{\pi/4} (\cos 2\theta)^{3/2} \cos \theta \, d\theta = \int\limits_0^{\pi/4} (1 - \sin^2 \theta)^{3/2} \frac{1}{\sqrt{2}} \cos \theta \, d\theta$$

$$= \frac{1}{\sqrt{2}} \int\limits_0^{\pi/2} \cos^4 \theta \, dt$$

$$= \frac{1}{\sqrt{2}} \cdot \frac{3}{4} \cdot \frac{1}{2} \cdot \frac{\pi}{2} = \frac{3\pi}{16\sqrt{2}}.$$

4. *If* $I_n = \int\limits_0^a (a^2 - x^2)^n \, dx$, *and* $n = 0$, *prove that*

$$I_n = \frac{2na^2}{2n+1} I_{n-1}.$$

(Bilaspur, 1996, 98; Indore, 1996, 98, 99, 2001; Jabalpur, 1998; Ravishankar, 1996, 98; Ujjain, 2000; Sagar, 2000; Rewa, 2000)

We have

$$I_n = \int\limits_0^a (a^2 - x^2)^n \, dx.$$

Put $x = a \sin \theta \Rightarrow dx = a \cos \theta \, d\theta$, we get

$$I_n = \int\limits_0^{\pi/2} (a^2 - a^2 \sin^2 \theta)^n (a \cos \theta) \, d\theta$$

$$= a^{2n+1} \int\limits_0^{\pi/2} \cos^{2n+1} \theta \, d\theta$$

$$= a^{2n+1} \left[\left[\frac{\cos^{2n} \theta \sin \theta}{2n+1} \right]_0^{\pi/2} + \frac{2n}{2n+1} \int\limits_0^{\pi/2} \cos^{2n-1} \theta \, d\theta \right]$$

$$= \frac{2n}{2n+1} a^{2n+1} \int\limits_0^{\pi/2} \cos^{2n-1} \theta \, d\theta$$

$$= \frac{2na^2}{2n+1} \left[a^{2n-1} \int\limits_0^{\pi/2} \cos^{2n-1} \theta \, d\theta \right]$$

$$= \frac{2na^2}{2n+1} I_{n-1}.$$

EXERCISES

Evaluate the following definite integrals :

1. $\int\limits_0^1 \dfrac{x^5}{\sqrt{1-x^2}} \, dx.$

2. $\int\limits_0^1 \dfrac{x^6}{\sqrt{1-x^2}} \, dx.$

3. $\int\limits_0^\infty \dfrac{1}{(1+x^2)^5} \, dx.$

4. $\int\limits_0^\infty \dfrac{1}{(1+x^2)^{7/2}} \, dx.$

5. $\displaystyle\int_0^1 \frac{x^2\,(2-x^2)}{\sqrt{1+x^2}}\,dx.$

6. $\displaystyle\int_0^1 x^2\,(1-x^2)^{3/2}\,dx.$

7. $\displaystyle\int_0^a x^2\,(a^2-x^2)^{9/2}\,dx.$

8. $\displaystyle\int_0^a x^4\,\sqrt{a^2-x^2}\,dx.$

9. $\displaystyle\int_0^a \frac{x^4}{\sqrt{a^2-x^2}}\,dx.$

10. $\displaystyle\int_0^1 \frac{x^7}{\sqrt{1-x^4}}\,dx.$

11. $\displaystyle\int_0^1 x^5\,\sqrt{\frac{1+x^2}{1-x^2}}\,dx.$

12. $\displaystyle\int_0^\infty \frac{x^2}{\sqrt{(1+x^6)^7}}\,dx.$

13. $\displaystyle\int_0^1 x^5\,\sin^{-1} x\,dx.$

14. $\displaystyle\int_0^1 x^6\,\sin^{-1} x\,dx.$

ANSWERS

1. $\dfrac{8}{15}.$ **2.** $\dfrac{5\pi}{32}.$ **3.** $\dfrac{35\pi}{256}.$ **4.** $\dfrac{8}{15}.$

5. $\dfrac{5\pi}{16}.$ **6.** $\dfrac{\pi}{32}.$ **7.** $\dfrac{21\pi}{2048}a^{12}.$ **8.** $\dfrac{\pi}{32}a^6.$

9. $\dfrac{3\pi}{16}a^4.$ **10.** $\dfrac{1}{3}.$ **11.** $\dfrac{3\pi+8}{24}.$ **12.** $\dfrac{8}{45}.$

13. $\dfrac{11\pi}{192}.$ **14.** $\dfrac{\pi}{14}-\dfrac{16}{245}.$

4.3. Integration of $\sin^p x \cos^q x$ where p, q are positive integers.

This can be integrated by the substitution $\cos x = t$ or $\sin x = t$ in case p is odd or q is odd. In case, however, p, q are *both* even, the integration is accomplished with the help of a reduction formula.

Let p be odd, say $2k + 1$. Putting $\cos x = t$, we get

$$\int \sin^{2k+1} x \cos^q x\,dx = -\int (1-t^2)^k\,t^q\,dt,$$

which may be evaluated on expanding $(1-t^2)^k$ by the Binomial theorem.

It may similarly be shown that the function can be integrated by the substitution $\sin x = t$, if q is odd.

In case p, q are both odd, we may proceed either way.

Reduction Formula for $\int \sin^p x \cos^q x\,dx$.   (*Jabalpur, 1996*)

We write

$$\int \sin^p x \cos^q x\,dx = \int \sin^{p-1} x\,(\sin x \cos^q x)\,dx$$

and apply the rule of integration by parts to obtain

$\int \sin^p x \cos^q x \, dx$

$$= -\frac{\cos^{q+1} x}{q+1} \sin^{p-1} x + \int \frac{\cos^{q+i} x}{q+1} \cdot (p-1) \sin^{p-2} x \cos x \, dx$$

$$= -\frac{\cos^{q+1} x \sin^{p-1} x}{q+1} + \frac{p-1}{q+1} \int \sin^{p-2} x \cos^q x \, (1 - \sin^2 x) \, dx$$

$$= -\frac{\cos^{q+1} x \sin^{p-1} x}{q+1} + \frac{p-1}{q+1} \int \sin^{p-2} x \cos^q x \, dx$$

$$- \frac{p-1}{q+1} \int \sin^p x \cos^q x \, dx.$$

Transposing

$$\frac{p-1}{q+1} \int \sin^p x \cos^q x \, dx,$$

to the left hand side and dividing by

$$1 + (p-1)/(q+1), \ i.e., \ (p+q)/(q+1);$$

we obtain

$$\int \sin^p x \cos^q x \, dx = -\frac{\cos^{q+1} x \sin^{p-1} x}{p+q}$$

$$+ \frac{p-1}{p+q} \int \sin^{p-2} x \cos^q x \, dx, \quad ...(C)$$

which is the required reduction formula.

It may be similarly shown that

$$\int \sin^p x \cos^q x \, dx = \frac{\sin^{p+1} x \cos^{q-1} x}{p+q}$$

$$+ \frac{q-1}{p+q} \int \sin^p x \cos^{q-2} x \, dx. \quad (Ravishankar, \ 1997S)$$

Note. The substitution $\cos x = t$ proves effective when p is an odd positive integer even if q is not an integer.

EXAMPLES

1. *Evaluate* $\int \sin^3 x \cos^2 x \, dx.$

We have

$$I = \int \sin^3 x \cos^2 x \, dx = \int \sin^2 x \cos^2 x \sin x \, dx$$

$$= \int (1 - \cos^2 x) \cos^2 x \sin x \, dx.$$

Put $\cos x = t \Rightarrow -\sin x\, dx = dt$, then

$$I = -\int (1-t^2)\, t^2\, dt = -\int t^2\, dt + \int t^4\, dt$$

$$= -\frac{1}{3}t^3 + \frac{1}{5}t^5 = -\frac{1}{3}\cos^3 x + \frac{1}{5}\cos^5 x.$$

2. *Connect the integrals* $\int \sin^m x \cos^n x\, dx$ *and* $\int \sin^{m-2} x \cos^n x\, dx$.

(Jabalpur, 2001)

$$I = \int \sin^m x \cos^n x\, dx = \int \sin^{m-1} x \cos^n x \sin x\, dx.$$

Integrating by parts, we get

$$I = -\frac{\sin^{m-1} x \cos^{n+1} x}{m+1} + \frac{m-1}{m+n} \int \sin^{m-2} x \cos^n x\, dx$$

or $\qquad \displaystyle\int \sin^m x \cos^n x\, dx = -\frac{\sin^{m-1} x \cos^{n+1} x}{m+1}$

$$+ \frac{m-1}{m+n} \int \sin^{m-2} x \cos^n x\, dx.$$

3. *Evaluate* $\displaystyle\int \frac{\sin^4 x}{\cos^2 x}\, dx$.

We shall connect $\displaystyle\int \sin^4 x \cos^{-2} x\, dx$ with $\displaystyle\int \sin^2 x\, dx$.

Let $P = \sin^3 x \cos^{-1} x$

$$\therefore \quad \frac{dP}{dx} = 3 \sin^2 x + \sin^3 x \cos^{-2} x \sin x$$

$$= 3 \sin^2 x + \sin^4 x \cos^{-2} x.$$

Integrate both sides w.r.t. x,

$$P = 3 \int \sin^2 x\, dx + \int \sin^4 x \cos^{-2} x\, dx$$

$$\Rightarrow \quad \int \frac{\sin^4 x}{\cos^2 x}\, dx = \frac{\sin^3 x}{\cos x} - \frac{3}{2} \int 2 \sin^2 x\, dx$$

$$= \frac{\sin^3 x}{\cos x} - \frac{3}{2} \int (1 - \cos 2x)\, dx$$

$$= \frac{\sin^3 x}{\cos x} - \frac{3}{2}\left(x - \frac{\sin 2x}{2}\right)$$

$$= \frac{\sin^3 x}{\cos x} + \frac{3}{2} \sin x \cos x - \frac{3}{2} x.$$

EXERCISES

1. Integrate

(i) $\sin^3 x \cos^4 x$,   (ii) $\sin^4 x \cos^2 x$,   (iii) $\tan^3 x \sec^3 x$.

2. Evaluate $\displaystyle\int_0^{\pi/2} \sin^{3/2} x \cos^3 x\, dx$.

3. Show that $\displaystyle\int_0^{\pi/2} \sqrt{\sin\theta}\,\cos^5\theta\,d\theta = \frac{64}{231}$.

4. Show that

(i) $\displaystyle\int \frac{\sin^5 x}{\cos^4 x}\, dx = \frac{1}{3\cos^3 x} - \frac{2}{\cos x} - \cos x.$

(ii) $\displaystyle\int \frac{\cos^5 x}{\sin x}\, dx = \frac{\sin^4 x}{4} - \sin^2 x + \log\sin x.$

5. Show that

$$\int \frac{\sin^6 x}{\cos x}\, dx = -\frac{\sin^5 x}{5} - \frac{\sin^3 x}{3} - \sin x + \log\tan\left(\frac{\pi}{4} + \frac{x}{2}\right).$$

6. Evaluate the following integrals :

(i) $\int \sin^2 x \cos^2 x\, dx$,   (ii) $\int \sin^2 x \cos^4 x\, dx$,

(iii) $\int \sin^4 x \cos^4 x\, dx$,   (iv) $\int \sin^2 x \cos^6 x\, dx$.

ANSWERS

1. (i) $\dfrac{1}{7}\cos^7 x - \dfrac{1}{5}\sin^5 x.$ (ii) $\dfrac{1}{5}\sin^5 x - \dfrac{1}{7}\sin^7 x.$

(iii) $\dfrac{1}{5}\sec^5 x - \dfrac{1}{3}\sec^3 x.$

2. $\dfrac{8}{45}$.

6. (i) $-\dfrac{1}{4}\sin x \cos^3 x + \dfrac{1}{8}(x + \sin x \cos x).$

(ii) $\dfrac{1}{6}\cos^3 x \sin^3 x + \dfrac{1}{8}\sin^3 x \cos x + \dfrac{1}{16}(x - \sin x \cos x).$

(iii) $-\dfrac{1}{8}\cos^5 x \sin^3 x - \dfrac{1}{16}\cos^5 x \sin x + \dfrac{1}{64}\sin x \cos^3 x$

$$+ \dfrac{3}{128}(x + \sin x \cos x).$$

(iv) $\dfrac{1}{8}\sin^3 x \cos^5 x + \dfrac{5}{48}\sin^3 x \cos^3 x + \dfrac{5}{64}\sin^3 x \cos x$

$$+ \dfrac{5}{128}(x - \sin x \cos x).$$

4.3.1. Evaluation of the definite integral

$$\int_0^{\pi/2} \sin^p x \cos^q x \, dx,$$

where p, q are positive integers.

We write

$$I_{p,\,q} = \int_0^{\pi/2} \sin^p x \cos^q x \, dx.$$

From the reduction formula (C) § 4.3, we obtain

$$\int_0^{\pi/2} \sin^p x \cos^q x \, dx = - \left| \frac{\cos^{q+1} x \sin^{p-1} x}{p+q} \right|_0^{\pi/2}$$

$$+ \frac{p-1}{p+q} \int_0^{\pi/2} \sin^{p-2} x \cos^q x \, dx$$

$$= \frac{p-1}{p+q} \int_0^{\pi/2} \sin^{p-2} x \cos^q x \, dx.$$

In terms of our notation, we have

$$I_{p,\,q} = \frac{p-1}{p+q} \cdot I_{p-2,\,q}.$$

From this we get, changing p to $p - 2$, $p - 4$, and so on,

$$I_{p-2,\,q} = \frac{p-3}{p+q-2} \cdot I_{p-4,\,q},$$

$$I_{p-4,\,q} = \frac{p-5}{p+q-4} \cdot I_{p-6,\,q},$$

....

....

Finally,

$$\begin{cases} I_{3,\,q} = \dfrac{2}{3+q} \cdot I_{1,\,q}, & \text{when } p \text{ is odd,} \\[2mm] I_{2,\,q} = \dfrac{1}{2+q} \cdot I_{0,\,q}, & \text{when } p \text{ is even.} \end{cases}$$

Thus

$$I_{p,\,q} = \begin{cases} \dfrac{p-1}{p+q} \cdot \dfrac{p-3}{p+q-2} \, \cdots \, \dfrac{2}{3+q} \cdot I_{1,\,q}, & \text{when } p \text{ is odd,} \\[3mm] \dfrac{p-1}{p+q} \cdot \dfrac{p-3}{p+q-2} \, \cdots \, \dfrac{1}{2+q} \cdot I_{0,\,q}, & \text{when } p \text{ is even.} \end{cases}$$

Now

$$I_{1,\,q} = \int_0^{\pi/2} \sin x \cos^q x \, dx = - \left| \frac{\cos^{q+1} x}{q+1} \right|_0^{\pi/2} = \frac{1}{q+1},$$

$$I_{0,\,q} = \int_0^{\pi/2} \sin^0 x \cos^q x \, dx = \int_0^{\pi/2} \cos^q x \, dx,$$

which has been evaluated in § 4.2.1.

Thus *when p is odd, we have*

$$I_{p,\,q} = \frac{p-1}{p+q} \cdot \frac{p-3}{p+q-2} \cdots \frac{2}{3+q} \cdot \frac{1}{q+1}$$

where q may be odd or even.

When p is even and q is odd.

$$I_{p,\,q} = \frac{p-1}{p+q} \cdot \frac{p-3}{p+q-2} \cdot \frac{p-5}{p+q-4} \cdots \frac{1}{2+q} \cdot \frac{q-1}{q} \cdot \frac{q-3}{q-2} \cdots \frac{2}{3}.$$

When p is even and q is even.

$$I_{p,\,q} = \frac{p-1}{p+q} \cdot \frac{p-3}{p+q-2} \cdot \frac{p-5}{p+q-4} \cdots \frac{1}{2+q} \cdot \frac{q-1}{q} \cdot \frac{p-3}{q-2} \cdots \frac{1}{2} \cdot \frac{\pi}{2}.$$

We have a simple rule for writing down the value of the integral in that

$$\int_0^{\pi/2} \sin^p x \cos^q x \, dx = \frac{(p-1)\,(p-3)\,\cdots\,(q-1)\,(q-3)\,\cdots}{(p+q)\,(p+q-2)\,\cdots}$$

ultimately followed by the factor π/2 only when p and q are both even; the three sets of factors, starting with (p − 1), (q − 1), (p + q), and diminishing by 2 at a time, descend to either 1 or 2 according as the first factor of the set is odd or even.

EXAMPLES

Write down the values of

(i) $\displaystyle\int_0^{\pi/2} \sin^5 x \cos^6 x \, dx,$ (ii) $\displaystyle\int_0^{\pi/2} \sin^6 x \cos^8 x \, dx.$

We have

(i) $\displaystyle\int_0^{\pi/2} \sin^5 x \cos^6 x \, dx = \frac{4 \cdot 2 \cdot 5 \cdot 3 \cdot 1}{11 \cdot 9 \cdot 7 \cdot 5 \cdot 3 \cdot 1} = \frac{8}{693}.$

(ii) $\displaystyle\int_0^{\pi/2} \sin^6 x \cos^8 x \, dx = \frac{5 \cdot 3 \cdot 1 \cdot 7 \cdot 5 \cdot 3 \cdot 1}{14 \cdot 12 \cdot 10 \cdot 8 \cdot 6 \cdot 4 \cdot 2} \cdot \frac{\pi}{2} = \frac{5\pi}{4096}.$

EXERCISES

Evaluate

(i) $\displaystyle\int_0^{\pi/2} \sin^3\theta \cos^4\theta\, d\theta$,

(ii) $\displaystyle\int_0^{\pi/2} \cos^5 x \sin^4 x\, dx$,

(iii) $\displaystyle\int_0^{\pi/2} \cos^4 x \sin 3x\, dx$,

(iv) $\displaystyle\int_0^{\pi/2} \cos^3 2x \sin^4 4x\, dx$.

ANSWERS

(i) $2/35$.　　(ii) $8/315$.　　(iii) $13/35$.　　(iv) $128/1155$.

Cor. *The value of the definite integral*

$$\int_0^{\pi/2} \sin^p x \cos^q x\, dx$$

enables us to write down the values of the following integrals :

(i) $\displaystyle\int_0^\infty \frac{x^n\, dx}{(1+x^2)^m}$,

(ii) $\displaystyle\int_0^\infty \frac{x^n\, dx}{(1+x^2)^{(m+1/2)}}$,

(iii) $\displaystyle\int_0^{2a} x^m \sqrt{2ax - x^2}\, dx$,

where n, m are positive integers.

(i) Putting $x = \tan\theta$, we see that

$$\int_0^\infty \frac{x^n}{(1+x^2)^m}\, dx = \int_0^{\pi/2} \frac{\sin^n\theta \cos^{2m}\theta}{\cos^n\theta}\cdot \sec^2\theta\, d\theta$$

$$= \int_0^{\pi/2} \sin^n\theta \cos^{2m-(n+2)}\theta\, d\theta,$$

whose value is known.

(ii) Putting $x = \tan\theta$, we see that

$$\int_0^\infty \frac{x^n}{(1+x^2)^{(m+1/2)}}\, dx = \int_0^{\pi/2} \sin^n\theta \cos^{2m-(n+1)}\theta\, d\theta,$$

whose value is known.

(iii) We write

$$\int_0^{2a} x^m \sqrt{2ax - x^2}\, dx = \int_0^{2a} x^m \sqrt{a^2 - (a-x)^2}\, dx.$$

We put $a - x = a \cos \theta$

so that $dx = a \sin \theta \; d\theta.$

Also $x = a \, (1 - \cos \theta) = 2a \sin^2 (\theta/2).$

Now, $\theta = 0$ and π when $x = 0$ and $2a$ respectively.

$\therefore$ the given integral

$$= \int_0^\pi 2^m a^m \sin^{2m} \frac{\theta}{2} \cdot a \sin \theta \cdot a \sin \theta \; d\theta$$

$$= (2a)^{m+2} \int_0^\pi \sin^{2m+2} \frac{\theta}{2} \cos^2 \frac{\theta}{2} \; d\theta.$$

We now put $(\theta/2) = \phi$ and see that the integral

$$(2a)^{m+2} \cdot 2 \int_0^{\pi/2} \sin^{2m+2} \phi \cos^2 \phi \; d\phi$$

whose value could now be put down.

EXAMPLES

1. *Evaluate :* $\displaystyle\int_0^1 x^2 \, (1 - x^2)^{3/2} \; dx.$

(*Ravishankar, 1999; Rewa, 2000; Jiwaji, 2000*)

Put $x = \sin \theta \;\Rightarrow\; dx = \cos \theta \; d\theta.$

$$\therefore \quad \int_0^1 x^2 \, (1 - x^2)^{3/2} \; dx = \int_0^{\pi/2} \sin^2 \theta \, (1 - \sin^2 \theta)^{3/2} \cos \theta \; d\theta$$

$$= \int_0^{\pi/2} \sin^2 \theta \cos^4 \theta \; d\theta$$

$$= \frac{1 \cdot 3 \cdot 1}{6 \cdot 4 \cdot 2} \cdot \frac{\pi}{2} = \frac{\pi}{32}.$$

2. *Find the value of* $\displaystyle\int_0^{\pi/2} \cos^3 x \cos 2x \; dx.$

$$I = \int_0^{\pi/2} \cos^3 x \, (\cos^2 x - \sin^2 x) \; dx$$

$$= \int_0^{\pi/2} \sin^0 x \cos^5 x \; dx - \int_0^{\pi/2} \sin^2 x \cos^3 x \; dx$$

$$= \frac{4}{5} \cdot \frac{2}{3} - \frac{1 \cdot 2}{5 \cdot 3 \cdot 1} = \frac{8}{15} - \frac{2}{15} = \frac{2}{5}.$$

3. *Evaluate* $\displaystyle\int_0^{\pi/6} \cos^6 3\theta \sin^2 6\theta \, d\theta.$ *(Bilaspur, 2000; Jiwaji, 2001)*

$$I = \int_0^{\pi/6} \cos^6 3\theta \sin^2 6\theta \, d\theta$$

$$= \int_0^{\pi/6} \cos^6 3\theta \, (2 \sin 3\theta \cos 3\theta)^2 \, d\theta$$

$$= 4 \int_0^{\pi/6} \sin^2 3\theta \cos^8 3\theta \, d\theta$$

$$= \frac{4}{3} \int_0^{\pi/2} \sin^2 t \cos^8 t \, dt, \quad [\text{Put } 3\theta = t, \, 3 \, d\theta = dt]$$

$$= \frac{4}{3} \cdot \frac{1 \cdot 7 \cdot 5 \cdot 3 \cdot 1}{10 \cdot 8 \cdot 6 \cdot 4 \cdot 2} \cdot \frac{\pi}{2} = \frac{7\pi}{384}.$$

4. *Prove that* $\displaystyle\int_0^1 x^{3/2} \, (1-x)^{3/2} \, dx = \frac{3\pi}{128}.$

(Indore, 2000; Sagar, 1998, 2001)

Put $x = \sin^2 \theta \implies dx = 2 \sin \theta \cos \theta \, d\theta.$

$$I = \int_0^{\pi/2} \sin^3 \theta \cos^3 \theta \cdot 2 \sin \theta \cos \theta \, d\theta$$

$$= 2 \int_0^{\pi/2} \sin^4 \theta \cos^4 \theta \, d\theta$$

$$= 2 \cdot \frac{3 \cdot 1 \cdot 3 \cdot 1}{8 \cdot 6 \cdot 4 \cdot 2} \cdot \frac{\pi}{2} = \frac{3\pi}{128}.$$

5. *Evaluate* : $\displaystyle\int_0^{2a} x^3 \, (2ax - x^2)^{3/2} \, dx.$ *(Bhopal, 1996; Sagar, 2000)*

$$I = \int_0^{2a} x^{9/2} \, (2a - x)^{3/2} \, dx.$$

Put $x = 2a \sin^2 \theta \implies dx = 4a \sin \theta \cos \theta \, d\theta.$

$$= \int_0^{\pi/2} (2a)^{9/2} \sin^9 \theta \, (2a)^{3/2} \cos^3 \theta \cdot 4a \sin \theta \cos \theta \, d\theta$$

$$= 256a^7 \int_0^{\pi/2} \sin^{10} \theta \cos^4 \theta \, d\theta$$

$$= 256a^7 \cdot \frac{9 \cdot 7 \cdot 5 \cdot 3 \cdot 1 \cdot 3 \cdot 1}{14 \cdot 12 \cdot 10 \cdot 8 \cdot 6 \cdot 4 \cdot 2} \cdot \frac{\pi}{2}$$

$$= \frac{9\pi a^7}{16}.$$

EXERCISES

Evaluate the following definite integrals :

1. $\displaystyle\int_0^\infty \frac{x^2}{(1+x^2)^4} \, dx.$ 2. $\displaystyle\int_0^\infty \frac{x}{(1+x^2)^3} \, dx.$

3. $\displaystyle\int_0^\infty \frac{x^2}{(1+x^2)^{7/2}} \, dx.$ 4. $\displaystyle\int_0^\infty \frac{x^3}{(1+x^2)^{9/2}} \, dx.$

5. $\displaystyle\int_0^\infty \frac{t^4 \, dt}{(1+t^2)^4}.$ 6. $\displaystyle\int_0^{2a} x^2 \sqrt{2ax - x^2} \, dx.$

7. $\displaystyle\int_0^2 x^3 \sqrt{2x - x^2} \, dx.$ 8. $\displaystyle\int_0^2 x^{5/2} \sqrt{2 - x} \, dx.$

9. $\displaystyle\int_0^{2a} x^{9/2} (2a - x)^{-1/2} \, dx.$ 10. $\displaystyle\int_0^\infty \frac{x^3 \, dx}{(4 + x^2)^2}.$

11. $\displaystyle\int_0^1 x^{3/2} (1 - x)^{3/2} \, dx.$

ANSWERS

1. $\dfrac{\pi}{32}$.   2. $\dfrac{1}{4}$.   3. $\dfrac{2}{15}$.   4. $\dfrac{2}{35}$.   5. $\dfrac{\pi}{32}$.   6. $\dfrac{5\pi}{8} a^4$.

7. $\dfrac{7\pi}{8}$.   8. $\dfrac{5\pi}{8}$.   9. $\dfrac{63\pi}{8} a^5$.   10. $\dfrac{1}{3}$.   11. $\dfrac{3\pi}{128}$.

4.4. Integration of $\tan^n x$ and $\cot^n x$ where n is a positive integer.
Evaluation of the integral of a positive integral power of $\tan x$ and $\cot x$ can be effected by means of the reduction formula which we now proceed to obtain.

4.4.1. Reduction formula for $\int \tan^n x \, dx$.

(*Rohilkhand, 2001; Jabalpur, 1997*)

We have

$$
\begin{aligned}
\bullet \int \tan^n x \, dx &= \int \tan^{n-2} x \tan^2 x \, dx \\
&= \int \tan^{n-2} x \, (\sec^2 x - 1) \, dx \\
&= \int \tan^{n-2} x \sec^2 x \, dx - \int \tan^{n-2} x \, dx \\
&= \frac{\tan^{n-1} x}{n-1} - \int \tan^{n-2} x \, dx, \qquad\qquad ...(D)
\end{aligned}
$$

which is the required reduction formula.

4.4.2. Reduction formula for $\int \cot^n x \, dx$.

We have

$$
\begin{aligned}
\int \cot^n x \, dx &= \int \cot^{n-2} x \cdot \cot^2 x \, dx \\
&= \int \cot^{n-2} x \cdot (\operatorname{cosec}^2 x - 1) \, dx \\
&= \int \cot^{n-2} x \operatorname{cosec}^2 x \, dx - \int \cot^{n-2} x \, dx \\
&= -\frac{\cot^{n-1} x}{n-1} - \int \cot^{n-2} x \, dx, \qquad\qquad ...(E)
\end{aligned}
$$

which is the required reduction formula.

EXAMPLES

1. *Evaluate* $\int \tan^6 x \, dx$. $\qquad\qquad\qquad$ (*Jabalpur, 2000*)

Putting $n = 6, 4, 2$ successively in (D), we get

$$
\int \tan^6 x \, dx = \frac{\tan^5 x}{5} - \int \tan^4 x \, dx. \qquad\qquad ...(i)
$$

$$
\int \tan^4 x \, dx = \frac{\tan^3 x}{3} - \int \tan^2 x \, dx. \qquad\qquad ...(ii)
$$

$$
\int \tan^2 x \, dx = \frac{\tan x}{1} - \int \tan^0 x \, dx = \tan x - x. \qquad\qquad ...(iii)
$$

From (*ii*) and (*iii*), we obtain

$$
\int \tan^4 x \, dx = \frac{\tan^3 x}{3} - \tan x + x \qquad\qquad ...(iv)
$$

From (*i*) and (*iv*), we obtain

$$
\int \tan^6 x \, dx = -\frac{\tan^5 x}{5} - \frac{\tan^3 x}{3} + \tan x - x.
$$

2. *If* $I_n = \displaystyle\int_0^{\pi/3} \tan^n x \, dx$ *show that* $(n - I)\,(I_n + I_{n-2}) = (\sqrt{3})^{n-1}$.

We have

$$I = \int_0^{\pi/3} \tan^n x \, dx = \int_0^{\pi/3} \tan^{n-2} x \, \tan^2 x \, dx$$

$$= \int_0^{\pi/3} \tan^{n-2} x \, (\sec^2 x - 1) \, dx$$

$$= \int_0^{\pi/3} \tan^{n-2} x \, \sec^2 x \, dx - I_{n-2}$$

or $\qquad I_n + I_{n-2} = \left[\dfrac{\tan^{n-1} x}{n-1} \right]_0^{\pi/3} = \dfrac{(\sqrt{3})^{n-1}}{n-1}$.

Hence $\qquad (n-1)(I_n + I_{n-2}) = (\sqrt{3})^{n-1}$.

3. *If* $\phi(n) = \displaystyle\int_0^{\pi/4} \tan^n x \, dx$, *show that* $\phi(n) + \phi(n-2) = \dfrac{1}{n-1}$, *and*

deduce the value of $\phi(5)$.

(Vikram, 1999; Sagar, 1995, 98; Jabalpur, 1997, 2001;
Jiwaji, 1996, 99; Rewa, 2000; Rohilkhand, 1997, 98, 2000)

$$\phi(n) = \int_0^{\pi/4} \tan^n x \, dx$$

$$= \left[\frac{\tan^{n-1} x}{n-1} \right]_0^{\pi/4} - \int_0^{\pi/4} \tan^{n-2} x \, dx$$

$$= \frac{1}{n-1} - \phi(n-2)$$

$$\Rightarrow \quad \phi(n) + \phi(n-2) = \frac{1}{n-1}.$$

Now, $\quad \phi(5) = \dfrac{1}{4} - \phi(3) = \dfrac{1}{4} - \left[\dfrac{1}{2} - \phi(1) \right]$

$$= -\frac{1}{4} + \phi(1) = -\frac{1}{4} + \int_0^{\pi/4} \tan x \, dx$$

$$= -\frac{1}{4} + \left[\log \sec x \right]_0^{\pi/4} = -\frac{1}{4} + \log \sqrt{2}$$

$$= -\frac{1}{4} + \frac{1}{2} \log 2.$$

EXERCISES

Evaluate

(i) $\displaystyle\int \tan^3 x \, dx$, $\quad\quad$ (ii) $\displaystyle\int \cot^5 x \, dx$, $\quad\quad$ (iii) $\displaystyle\int \cot^6 x \, dx$,

(iv) $\displaystyle\int_0^{\pi/4} \tan^4 x \, dx$ $\;(Ravishankar,\ 1995)$, $\quad\quad$ (v) $\displaystyle\int_{\pi/4}^{\pi/2} \cot^4 x \, dx$,

(vi) $\displaystyle\int_0^{\pi/4} \tan^5 x \, dx$ $\;(Sagar,\ 1995, 97;\ Ravishankar,\ 1995)$,

(vii) $\displaystyle\int \tan^4 x \, dx$ $\;(Ravishankar,\ 2001;\ Jiwaji,\ 2001)$.

ANSWERS

(i) $\dfrac{1}{2}\tan^2 x - \log \sec x.$ $\quad\quad$ (ii) $-\dfrac{1}{4}\cot^4 x + \dfrac{1}{2}\cot^2 x + \log \sin x.$

(iii) $-\dfrac{1}{5}\cot^5 x + \dfrac{1}{3}\cot^3 x - \cot x - x.$

(iv) $(3\pi - 8)/12.$ $\quad\quad\quad\quad\quad$ (v) $(3\pi - 8)/12.$

(vi) $\dfrac{1}{2}\log 2 - \dfrac{1}{4}.$ $\quad\quad\quad\quad$ (vii) $\dfrac{1}{3}\tan^3 x - \tan x + x.$

4.5.1. Integration of $\sec^n x$ where n is a positive integer.

$(Vikram,\ 1995;\ Ravishankar,\ 1996S;\ Indore,\ 2000)$

When n is a positive integer, the function $\sec^n x$ may be integrated with the help of a reduction formula. But if n is an even positive integer, the function can also be integrated by means of the substitution $\tan x = t$ and this method is simpler than that of reduction formula.

Let n be an even positive integer, say, $2k$ where k is a positive integer. Put $\tan x = t$ so that $\sec^2 x \, dx = dt.$

We see that

$$\int \sec^n x \, dx = \int \sec^{2k} x \, dx$$
$$= \int \sec^{2k-2} x \sec^2 x \, dx$$
$$= \int (1+t^2)^{k-1} \, dt,$$

which may be evaluated by expanding $(1 + t^2)^{k-1}$ by means of the Binomial theorem.

Reduction formula for $\int \sec^n x \, dx.$

We have

$$\int \sec^n x \, dx = \int \sec^{n-2} x \cdot \sec^2 x \, dx.$$

Integrating by parts, we obtain

$$\int \sec^n x\, dx = \tan x \cdot \sec^{n-2} x - \int \tan x \cdot (n-2)\sec^{n-2} x \cdot \tan x\, dx$$

$$= \tan x \cdot \sec^{n-2} x - (n-2)\int \sec^{n-2} x\,(\sec^2 x - 1)\, dx$$

$$= \tan x \cdot \sec^{n-2} x - (n-2)\left[\int \sec^n x\, dx - \int \sec^{n-2} x\, dx\right].$$

Transposing $(n-2)\int \sec^n x\, dx$ to the left and dividing by $1 + (n-2)$ i.e., $n-1$, we get

$$\int \sec^n x\, dx = \frac{\tan x \cdot \sec^{n-2} x}{n-1} + \frac{n-2}{n-1}\int \sec^{n-2} x\, dx \qquad \text{...(F)}$$

which is the formula connecting the integrals of $\sec^n x$ and $\sec^{n-2} x$.

4.5.2. Integration of $\operatorname{cosec}^n x$ where n is a positive integer. We can easily show that when n is even, $\operatorname{cosec}^n x$ can be integrated by the substitution $\cot x = t$, and that when n is odd we require a reduction formula which can also be obtained as in § 4.5.1.

Reduction formula for $\int \operatorname{cosec}^n x\, dx$ is

$$\int \operatorname{cosec}^n x\, dx = -\frac{\cot x \operatorname{cosec}^{n-2} x}{n-1} + \frac{n-2}{n-1}\int \operatorname{cosec}^{n-2} x\, dx \qquad \text{...(G)}$$

EXAMPLES

1. *Evaluate* $\int \operatorname{cosec}^5 x\, dx.$

We have

$$\int \operatorname{cosec}^n x\, dx = -\frac{1}{(n-1)}\operatorname{cosec}^{n-2} x \cot x + \frac{n-2}{n-1}\int \operatorname{cosec}^{n-2} x\, dx$$

$$\therefore \int \operatorname{cosec}^5 x\, dx = -\frac{1}{4}\operatorname{cosec}^3 x \cot x + \frac{3}{4}\int \operatorname{cosec}^3 x\, dx$$

$$= -\frac{1}{4}\operatorname{cosec}^3 x \cot x + \frac{3}{4}\left[-\frac{1}{2}\operatorname{cosec} x \cot x + \frac{1}{2}\int \operatorname{cosec} x\, dx\right]$$

$$= -\frac{1}{4}\operatorname{cosec}^3 x \cot x - \frac{3}{8}\operatorname{cosec} x \cot x + \frac{3}{8}\log(\operatorname{cosec} x - \cot x).$$

2. *Evaluate* $\displaystyle\int_0^a (a^2 + x^2)^{5/2}\, dx.$ *(Ravishankar, 1994)*

Let $x = a \tan \theta$, so that $dx = a \sec^2 \theta\, d\theta.$

$$\therefore \int_0^a (a^2 + x^2)^{5/2}\, dx = \int_0^{\pi/4} (a^2 + a^2 \tan^2 \theta)^{5/2}\, a \sec^2 \theta\, d\theta$$

$$= a^6 \int_0^{\pi/4} \sec^7 \theta \, d\theta.$$

Now, we have

$$\int \sec^n x \, dx = \frac{\sec^{n-2} x \tan x}{(n-1)} + \frac{n-2}{n-1} \int \sec^{n-2} x \, dx.$$

Then

$$\int_0^a (a^2 + x^2)^{5/2} \, dx = a^6 \left[\left(\frac{\sec^5 x \tan x}{6} \right)_0^{\pi/4} + \frac{5}{6} \int_0^{\pi/4} \sec^5 x \, dx \right]$$

$$= a^6 \left[\frac{(\sqrt{2})^5}{6} + \frac{5}{6} \left(\frac{\sec^3 x \tan x}{4} \right)_0^{\pi/4} + \frac{3}{4} \int_0^{\pi/4} \sec^3 x \, dx \right]$$

$$= a^6 \left[\frac{4\sqrt{2}}{6} + \frac{5}{6} \frac{(\sqrt{2})^3}{4} + \frac{5}{8} \left\{ \left(\frac{\sec x \tan x}{2} \right)_0^{\pi/4} + \frac{1}{2} \int_0^{\pi/4} \sec x \, dx \right\} \right]$$

$$= a^6 \left[\frac{4\sqrt{2}}{6} + \frac{5\sqrt{2}}{12} + \frac{5}{8} \cdot \frac{\sqrt{2}}{2} + \frac{5}{16} \left\{ \log(\sec x + \tan x) \right\}_0^{\pi/4} \right]$$

$$= a^6 \left[\frac{67\sqrt{2}}{48} + 15 \log(\sqrt{2} + 1) \right]$$

$$= \frac{a^6}{48} [67\sqrt{2} + 15 \log(\sqrt{2} + 1)].$$

EXERCISES

1. Evaluate :

(i) $\int \sec^3 x \, dx$,   (ii) $\int \sec^4 x \, dx$,

(iii) $\int \sec^5 x \, dx$,   (iv) $\int \sec^6 x \, dx$.

2. Evaluate :

(i) $\int \csc^3 x \, dx$,   (ii) $\int \csc^4 x \, dx$.

3. Evaluate $\int_0^{\pi/4} \sec^3 x \, dx$.   *(Indore, 1996)*

ANSWERS

1. (i) $\frac{1}{2} \tan x \sec x + \frac{1}{2} \log(\sec x + \tan x)$.

(ii) $\frac{1}{3} \tan x \sec^2 x + \frac{2}{3} \tan x$.

(iii) $\dfrac{1}{4} \tan x \sec^3 x + \dfrac{3}{8} \tan x \sec x + \dfrac{3}{8} \log (\sec x + \tan x).$

(iv) $\dfrac{1}{5} \tan x \sec^4 x + \dfrac{4}{15} \tan x \sec^2 x + \dfrac{8}{15} \tan x.$

2. (i) $-\dfrac{1}{2} \cot x \operatorname{cosec} x + \dfrac{1}{2} \log \tan \left(\dfrac{1}{2} x\right).$

(ii) $-\dfrac{1}{2} \cot x \operatorname{cosec}^2 x - \dfrac{2}{3} \cot x.$

3. $\dfrac{1}{\sqrt{2}} + \dfrac{1}{2} \log (\sqrt{2} + 1).$

Note. As the negative integral powers of $\sin x$, $\cos x$, $\tan x$, $\cot x$, $\sec x$, $\operatorname{cosec} x$ are the positive integral powers of $\operatorname{cosec} x$, $\sec x$, $\cot x$, $\tan x$, $\cos x$, $\sin x$, respectively, we see that, with the help of § 4.1 – 4.5, any positive or negative integral power of $\sin x$, $\cos x$, $\tan x$, $\cot x$, $\sec x$ and $\operatorname{cosec} x$ can be integrated.

The integrals of the fractional powers of these functions such as

$$\sin^{1/2} x, \quad \tan^{1/5} x$$

cannot, in general, be integrated in terms of the *elementary functions*. There is, however, a special case where $\sin^p x \cos^q x$ can be integrated. This is considered in the next article.

4.6. The integration of $\sin^p x \cos^q x$, when $p + q$ is a negative even integer.

Let $p + q = -2n$, where n is a positive integer. In this case we make the substitution

$$\tan x = t \;\Rightarrow\; \sec^2 x \, dx = dt \;\Rightarrow\; dx = dt / (1 + t^2).$$

Also $\qquad \sin x = \dfrac{t}{\sqrt{1 + t^2}}, \quad \cos x = \dfrac{1}{\sqrt{1 + t^2}}.$

$$\therefore \int \sin^p x \cos^q x \, dx = \int \frac{t^p}{(1 + t^2)^{p/2}} \cdot \frac{1}{(1 + t^2)^{q/2}} \cdot \frac{dt}{1 + t^2}$$

$$= \int t^p \cdot \frac{1}{(1 + t^2)^{(p + q + 2)/2}} \, dt$$

$$= \int t^p (1 + t^2)^{n - 1} \, dt$$

which may be evaluated on expanding $(1 + t^2)^{n-1}$ by the Binomial theorem.

EXAMPLES

1. *Evaluate :* $\displaystyle \int \sqrt{\cot x} \cdot \sec^4 x \, dx.$

We have

$$\sqrt{\cot x} \cdot \sec^4 x = \sin^{-1/2} x \cos^{-7/2} x,$$

so that $p + q = -4$, is a negative even integer.

Putting $\tan x = t \Rightarrow dx = dt / (1 + t^2)$, we obtain

$$\int \sqrt{\cot x} \cdot \sec^4 x \, dx = \int \frac{1}{\sqrt{t}} \cdot (1 + t^2)^2 \cdot \frac{dt}{1 + t^2}$$

$$= \int \frac{1 + t^2}{\sqrt{t}} \, dt$$

$$= 2\sqrt{t} + \frac{2}{5} t^{5/2}$$

$$= 2\sqrt{\tan x} + \frac{3}{5} \sqrt{\tan^5 x}.$$

2. Evaluate : $\int \sec^{2/3} x \, \mathrm{cosec}^{4/3} x \, dx.$

We have $\sec^{2/3} x \, \mathrm{cosec}^{4/3} x = \sin^{-4/3} x \cos^{-2/3} x$ so that $p + q = -\dfrac{4}{3} - \dfrac{2}{3}$
$= -2$ which is an even negative integer. Thus, we write

$$\int \sec^{2/3} x \, \mathrm{cosec}^{4/3} x \, dx = \int \frac{\sec^2 x}{\tan^{4/3} x} \, dx.$$

Putting $\tan x = t \Rightarrow dx = \dfrac{dt}{\sec^2 x}.$

$\therefore \quad \int \sec^{2/3} x \, \mathrm{cosec}^{4/3} x \, dx = \int t^{-4/3} \, dt$

$$= \frac{t^{-1/3}}{-1/3} = -3 \tan^{-1/3} x.$$

3. Evaluate : $\int \dfrac{1}{\sqrt{\cos^3 x \sin^5 x}} \, dx.$

$$\int \frac{1}{\sqrt{\cos^3 x \sin^5 x}} \, dx = \int \frac{1}{\cos^{3/2} x \sin^{5/2} x} \, dx.$$

Here $p + q = -\dfrac{3}{2} - \dfrac{5}{2} = -4$, a negative even integer.

$\therefore \quad \int \dfrac{dx}{\sqrt{\cos^3 x \sin^5 x}} = \int \dfrac{\cos^{5/2} x \cdot dx}{\cos^4 x \sin^{5/2} x}$

$$= \int \frac{\sec^2 x}{\tan^{5/2} x} \sec^2 x \, dx$$

$$= \int \frac{(1 + t^2)}{t^{5/2}} \, dt, \text{ where } t = \tan x$$

$$= \int (t^{-5/2} + t^{-1/2}) \, dt = -\frac{2}{3} t^{-3/2} + 2t^{1/2}$$

$$= -\frac{2}{3} (\tan x)^{-3/2} + 2 (\tan x)^{1/2} = 2 \sqrt{\tan x} - \frac{2}{3} (\tan x)^{-3/2}.$$

EXERCISES

1. Show that :

$$\int \frac{dx}{\sin^3 x \cos x} = -\frac{1}{2 \tan^2 x} + \log \tan x.$$

$$\int \frac{dx}{\sin^2 x \cos^4 x} = \frac{\sin x (1 + 2 \cos^2 x)}{3 \cos^3 x} - 2 \cot 2x.$$

2. Evaluate :

(i) $\displaystyle\int \frac{dx}{\sin^{3/2} x \cos^{5/2} x}$,

(ii) $\displaystyle\int \frac{\sqrt{\tan x}}{\sin x \cos x} \, dx$,

(iii) $\displaystyle\int \frac{(1 - \cos x)^{3/5}}{(1 + \cos x)^{8/5}} \, dx$,

(iv) $\displaystyle\int \sec^{4/7} x \, \text{cosec}^{10/7} x \, dx$.

3. Evaluate :

(i) $\displaystyle\int \frac{(1 - \cos x)^{2/7}}{(1 + \cos x)^{9/7}} \, dx$,

(ii) $\displaystyle\int \frac{1}{\sin \theta \cos^3 \theta} \, d\theta$,

(iii) $\displaystyle\int \sec^{8/9} x \, \text{cosec}^{10/9} x \, dx$,

(iv) $\displaystyle\int \frac{1}{\sqrt{\cos^3 x \sin^5 x}} \, dx$,

(v) $\displaystyle\int \sqrt{\tan x} \, \sec x \, \text{cosec} \, x \, dx$.

ANSWERS

2. (i) $\dfrac{2}{3} \sqrt{\tan^3 x} - 2 \sqrt{\cot x}$.

(ii) $2 \sqrt{\tan x}$.

(iii) $\dfrac{5}{15} \left(\tan \dfrac{1}{2} x \right)^{11/5}$.

(iv) $-\dfrac{7}{3} (\cot x)^{3/7}$.

3. (i) $\dfrac{7}{11} \left(\tan \dfrac{1}{2} x \right)^{11/7}$.

(ii) $\log \tan \theta + \dfrac{1}{2} \tan^2 \theta$.

(iii) $-9 (\cot x)^{1/9}$.

(iv) $2 \tan^{1/2} x - \dfrac{2}{3} \tan^{-3/2} x$.

(v) $2 \sqrt{\tan x}$.

4.6.1. Evaluation of $\int \sin^p x \cos^q x \, dx$**, where either** p, q **or both are negative integers.**

We will now obtain a system of reduction formulae for the integral $\int \sin^p x \cos^q x \, dx$.

I. As in § 4.3, we have

$$\int \sin^p x \cos^q x \, dx$$

$$= -\int \sin^{p-1} x \cdot (\sin x \cos^q x) \, dx$$

$$= -\frac{\cos^{q+1} x}{q+1} \sin^{p-1} x + \int \frac{\cos^{q+1} x}{q+1} (p-1) \sin^{p-2} x \cos x \, dx$$

$$= -\frac{\cos^{q+1} x \sin^{p-1} x}{q+1} + \frac{p-1}{q+1} \int \sin^{p-2} x \cos^{q+2} x \, dx \quad ...(A)$$

This reduction formula proves useful when q is a negative integer and p is a positive integer.

II. If we write

$$\int \sin^p x \cos^q x \, dx = \int \cos^{q-1} x \, (\cos x \sin^p x) \, dx,$$

and, as above, apply the rule of integration by parts, we will obtain the reduction formula

$$\int \sin^p x \cos^q x \, dx$$

$$= \frac{\sin^{p+1} x \cdot \cos^{q-1} x}{1+p} + \frac{q-1}{1+p} \int \sin^{p+2} x \cos^{q-2} x \, dx \quad ...(B)$$

which proves useful when p is a negative and q is a positive integer.

III. If in the formula (A) above, we change

$$\cos^{q+2} x \text{ to } \cos^q x \, (1 - \sin^2 x),$$

then, as in § 4.3, we prove that

$$\int \sin^p x \cos^q x \, dx$$

$$= -\frac{\cos^{q+1} x \sin^{p-1} x}{p+q} + \frac{p-1}{p+q} \int \sin^{p-2} x \cos^q x \, dx.$$

Changing p to $p+2$ and making some necessary changes we get

$$\int \sin^p x \cos^q x \, dx$$

$$= \frac{\cos^{q+1} x \sin^{p+1} x}{p+1} + \frac{p-2+q}{p+1} \int \sin^{p+2} x \cos^q x \, dx$$

which proves useful when q is a negative integer.

IV. We may similarly obtain a formula connecting

$$\int \sin^p x \cos^q x \, dx \text{ with } \int \sin^p x \cos^{q+2} x \, dx$$

which proves useful when q is a negative integer.

Note. From the above it appears that the integral

$$\int \sin^p x \cos^q x \, dx$$

can be connected with any one of the *six* following integrals :

$$\int \sin^{p-2} x \cos^q x \, dx; \qquad \int \sin^p x \cos^{q-2} x \, dx;$$

$$\int \sin^{p-2} x \cos^{q+2} x \, dx; \qquad \int \sin^{p+2} x \cos^{q-2} x \, dx;$$

$$\int \sin^{p+2} x \cos^q x \, dx; \qquad \int \sin^p x \cos^{q+2} x \, dx.$$

These reduction formulae can also be obtained in another way as we now show.

Another Method. Instead of obtaining the reduction formulae by applying the rule of integration by parts, as is done above, we can also proceed differently as follows :

(*i*) Put

$$P = \sin^{\lambda + 1} x \cos^{\mu + 1} x,$$

where λ and μ are the smaller of the indices of $\sin x$ and $\cos x$ respectively in the two integrands whose integrals are to be connected.

(*ii*) Find $(d\,P\,/\,dx)$ and re-arrange its value as a linear combination of the two integrands whose integrals are to be connected.

(*iii*) Finally integrate to obtain the required reduction formula.

ILLUSTRATION

Connect the integrals

$$\int \sin^p x \cos^q x \, dx \text{ and } \int \sin^{p-2} x \cos^q x \, dx.$$

Here

$$\lambda = p - 2, \ \mu = q,$$

so that we write

$$P = \sin^{p-1} x \cos^{q+1} x.$$

$$\Rightarrow \quad \frac{dP}{dx} = (p-1) \sin^{p-2} x \cos^{q+2} x - (q+1) \sin^p x \cos^q x.$$

On changing $\cos^{q+2} x$ to $\cos^q x \, (1 - \sin^2 x)$, we get

$$\frac{dP}{dx} = (p-1) \sin^{p-2} x \cos^q x \,(1 - \sin^2 x) - (q+1) \sin^p x \cos^q x$$

$$= (p-1) \sin^{p-2} x \cos^q x - (p+q) \sin^p x \cos^q x.$$

Integrating, we get

$$P = (p-1) \int \sin^{p-2} x \cos^q x \, dx - (p+q) \int \sin^p x \cos^q x \, dx.$$

$$\Rightarrow \int \sin^p x \cos^q x \, dx$$

$$= -\frac{\sin^{p-1} x \cos^{q+1} x}{p+q} + \frac{p-1}{p+q} \int \sin^{p-2} x \cos^q x \, dx.$$

We may similarly obtain the remaining reduction formulae left out.

EXERCISES

Show that

(i) $\displaystyle \int \frac{\sin^3 x}{\cos^4 x} \, dx = \frac{\sin^2 x}{3 \cos^3 x} - \frac{2}{3} \sec x.$

(ii) $\displaystyle \int \frac{\sin^4 x}{\cos^5 x} \, dx = \frac{\sin^3 x}{3 \cos^4 x} - \frac{3 \sin x}{8 \cos^2 x} + \frac{3}{8} \log \tan \left(\frac{x}{2} + \frac{\pi}{4} \right).$

(iii) $\displaystyle \int \frac{\cos^5 x}{\sin^4 x} \, dx = -\frac{\cos^4 x}{3 \sin^3 x} + \frac{4 \cos^2 x}{3 \sin x} + \frac{8 \sin x}{3}.$

4.7. Integration of R (cos x, sin x) where R (cos x, sin x) denotes an expression which is rational in the two functions sin x and cos x such as

$$\frac{1}{4 + 5 \cos x}, \quad \frac{1}{3 + 4 \cos x + 5 \sin x}, \quad \frac{2 \sin x + 3 \cos x}{4 + 5 \cos^2 x + 6 \sin x}$$

The transformation

$$t = \tan \left(\frac{x}{2} \right),$$

converts the integral of a rational function of cos x and sin x into that of a rational function of t which may then be evaluated by the methods as given in Chapter II. We have

$$dt = \frac{1}{2} \sec^2 \frac{x}{2} \, dx \quad \Rightarrow \quad dx = \frac{2t}{1+t^2}.$$

Also $\quad \sin x = \dfrac{2 \tan (x/2)}{1 + \tan^2 (x/2)} = \dfrac{2 \, dt}{1+t^2},$

$$\cos x = \frac{1 - \tan^2 (x/2)}{1 + \tan^2 (x/2)} = \frac{1-t^2}{1+t^2}.$$

$$\therefore \quad \int R (\cos x, \sin x) \, dx = \int R \left[\frac{1-t^2}{1+t^2}, \frac{2t}{1+t^2} \right] \frac{2 \, dt}{1+t^2}.$$

The integrand, now, is a rational function of t.

EXAMPLES

1. *Evaluate* $\displaystyle\int \frac{dx}{a + b \cos x}$.   *(Sagar, 1999; Jabalpur, 1999)*

Putting $t = \tan(x/2)$, we get

$$\int \frac{dx}{a + b \cos x} = \int \frac{2\, dt}{(1 + t^2)\left[a + b\, \dfrac{1 - t^2}{1 + t^2}\right]}$$

$$= \int \frac{2\, dt}{(a + b) + (a - b)\, t^2}$$

$$= \frac{2}{a - b} \int \frac{dt}{t^2 + (a + b)/(a - b)}, \text{ if } a \neq b.$$

Writing

$$\frac{a + b}{a - b} = \frac{(a + b)^2}{a^2 - b^2},$$

we see that $(a + b)/(a - b)$ is positive or negative according as

$$a^2 > \text{ or } < b^2.$$

First Case. Let

$$a^2 > b^2 \text{ so that } (a + b)/(a - b)$$

is positive.

We have

$$\int \frac{dx}{a + b \cos x} = \frac{2}{a - b} \int \frac{dt}{t^2 + \left[\sqrt{\dfrac{a + b}{a - b}}\right]^2}$$

$$= \frac{2}{a - b} \sqrt{\frac{a - b}{a + b}} \tan^{-1}\left[t \sqrt{\frac{a - b}{a + b}}\right]$$

$$= \frac{2}{\sqrt{a^2 - b^2}} \tan^{-1}\left[\sqrt{\frac{a - b}{a + b}} \tan \frac{x}{2}\right].$$

Second Case. Let

$$a^2 < b^2 \text{ so that } (a + b)/(a - b)$$

is negative.

We have

$$\int \frac{dx}{a + b \cos x} = \frac{2}{a - b} \int \frac{dt}{t^2 - (b + a)/(b - a)}$$

$$= \frac{2}{a-b} \int \frac{dt}{t^2 - \left[\sqrt{\dfrac{b+a}{b-a}}\right]^2} = \frac{2}{a-b} \int \frac{dt}{t^2 - \alpha^2},$$

where we have written α for $\sqrt{(b+a)/(b-a)}$. Now

$$\int \frac{dt}{t^2 - \alpha^2} = \frac{1}{2\alpha} \int \left(\frac{1}{t-\alpha} - \frac{1}{t+\alpha}\right) dt = \frac{1}{2\alpha} \log \frac{t-\alpha}{t+\alpha}$$

$$\therefore \quad \int \frac{dx}{a+b\cos x} = \frac{2}{a-b} \cdot \frac{1}{2\alpha} \log \frac{t-\alpha}{t+\alpha}$$

where $$\alpha = \sqrt{(b+a)/(b-a)}.$$

Third Case. Let

$$a^2 = b^2 \text{ so that } b = a \text{ or } b = -a.$$

If $b = a$, we have

$$\int \frac{dx}{a+b\cos x} = \frac{1}{a} \int \frac{dx}{1+\cos x}$$

$$= \frac{1}{2a} \int \sec^2 \frac{x}{2} \, dx = \frac{1}{a} \tan \frac{x}{2}.$$

If $b = -a$, we have

$$\int \frac{dx}{a+b\cos x} = \frac{1}{a} \int \frac{dx}{1-\cos x}$$

$$= \frac{1}{2a} \int \text{cosec}^2 \frac{x}{2} \, dx = -\frac{1}{a} \cot \frac{x}{2}.$$

2. *Evaluate* : $\displaystyle\int_0^{\pi/2} \frac{dx}{4+5\sin x}$.

(*Ravishankar, 1999, 2000; Bhopal, 1998; Jabalpur, 1998;*
Indore, 1998; Rewa, 1998; Bilaspur, 2001)

$$\int_0^{\pi/2} \frac{dx}{4+5\sin x} = \int_0^{\pi/2} \frac{dx}{4\left(\cos^2 \dfrac{x}{2} + \sin^2 \dfrac{x}{2}\right) + 5 \cdot 2 \sin \dfrac{x}{2} \cos \dfrac{x}{2}}$$

$$= \int_0^{\pi/2} \frac{\sec^2 \dfrac{x}{2} \, dx}{4 + 4\tan^2 \dfrac{x}{2} + 10 \tan \dfrac{x}{2}}$$

$$= \int_0^1 \frac{2\,dt}{4t^2 + 10t + 4} \qquad \left[\text{On putting } \tan \frac{x}{2} = t\right]$$

$$= \frac{1}{2} \int_0^1 \frac{dt}{\left(t + \frac{5}{2}\right)^2 - \frac{9}{16}}$$

$$= \frac{1}{2} \left[\frac{2}{2\left(\frac{3}{4}\right)} \log \left\{ \frac{\left(t + \frac{5}{4}\right) - \frac{3}{4}}{\left(t + \frac{5}{4}\right) + \frac{3}{4}} \right\} \right]_0^1$$

$$= \frac{1}{3} \log 2.$$

3. Prove that : $\displaystyle\int_0^\alpha \frac{d\theta}{\cos \alpha + \cos \theta} = \operatorname{cosec} \alpha \, \log \, (\sec \alpha).$

$$\int \frac{d\theta}{\cos \alpha + \cos \theta} = \int \frac{d\theta}{\cos \alpha \left(\cos^2 \frac{\theta}{2} + \sin^2 \frac{\theta}{2} \right) + \left(\cos^2 \frac{\theta}{2} - \sin^2 \frac{\theta}{2} \right)}$$

$$= \int \frac{\sec^2 \frac{\theta}{2} \, d\theta}{(1 + \cos \alpha) - (1 - \cos \alpha) \tan^2 \frac{\theta}{2}}$$

$$= \frac{2}{(1 - \cos \alpha)} \int \frac{dt}{\dfrac{(1 + \cos \alpha)}{(1 - \cos \alpha)} - t^2}, \text{ where } t = \tan \frac{\theta}{2}$$

$$= \frac{2}{\sin^2 \dfrac{\alpha}{2}} \int \frac{dt}{\cot^2 \dfrac{\alpha}{2} - t^2}$$

$$= \frac{1}{\sin^2 \dfrac{\alpha}{2}} \cdot \frac{1}{2 \cot \dfrac{\alpha}{2}} \log \left(\frac{\cot \dfrac{\alpha}{2} + t}{\cot \dfrac{\alpha}{2} - t} \right)$$

$$= \frac{1}{\sin \alpha} \log \left(\frac{\cos \dfrac{\alpha}{2} \cos \dfrac{\theta}{2} + \sin \dfrac{\theta}{2} \sin \dfrac{\alpha}{2}}{\cos \dfrac{\alpha}{2} \cos \dfrac{\theta}{2} - \sin \dfrac{\theta}{2} \sin \dfrac{\alpha}{2}} \right)$$

$$= \operatorname{cosec} \alpha \, \log \left[\frac{\cos \left(\dfrac{\alpha - \theta}{2} \right)}{\cos \left(\dfrac{\alpha + \theta}{2} \right)} \right].$$

$$\therefore \int_0^\alpha \frac{d\theta}{\cos\alpha + \cos\theta} = \operatorname{cosec}\alpha\,[\log(1/\cos\alpha) - \log(1)]$$

$$= \operatorname{cosec}\alpha \log \sec\alpha.$$

4. *Prove that* : $\displaystyle\int_0^\pi \frac{dx}{1 - 2a\cos x + a^2} = \frac{\pi}{1-a^2}$ *or* $\dfrac{\pi}{a^2-1}$, *according as*
$a <$ *or* > 1.

$$\int_0^\pi \frac{dx}{1 + a^2 - 2a\cos x} = \int_0^\pi \frac{dx}{(1 + a^2 - 2a)\cos^2\dfrac{x}{2} + (1 + a^2 + 2a)\sin^2\dfrac{x}{2}}$$

$$= \int_0^\pi \frac{\sec^2\dfrac{x}{2}\,dx}{(1-a)^2 + (1+a)^2 \tan^2\dfrac{x}{2}}$$

$$= \frac{2}{(1+a)^2} \int_0^\infty \frac{dt}{\left(\dfrac{1-a}{1+a}\right)^2 + t^2}, \text{ where } t = \tan\frac{x}{2}.$$

If $a < 1$, then the integral

$$= \frac{2}{(1+a)^2} \cdot \frac{1+a}{1-a}\left[\tan^{-1}\left(\frac{1+a}{1-a}\right)\right]_0^\infty$$

$$= \frac{2}{1-a^2}[\tan^{-1}\infty - \tan^{-1}0] = \frac{\pi}{1-a^2}.$$

If $a > 1$, then the integral

$$= \frac{2}{(1+a)^2} \cdot \frac{1+a}{1-a}\left[\tan^{-1}\left\{\left(\frac{1+a}{1-a}\right)t\right\}\right]_0^\infty$$

$$= -\frac{2}{a^2-1}[\tan^{-1}(-\infty) - \tan^{-1}0] = \frac{\pi}{a^2-1}.$$

5. *Evaluate* : $\displaystyle\int_{-\pi/2}^{\pi/2} \frac{dx}{5 + 7\cos x + \sin x}.$

Putting $\tan(x/2) = t$, we get

$$\int \frac{dx}{5 + 7\cos x + \sin x} = \int \frac{2\,dt}{(1+t^2)\left[5 + 7\dfrac{1-t^2}{1+t^2} + \dfrac{2t}{1+t^2}\right]}$$

$$= \int \frac{dt}{-t^2 + t + 6}$$

$$= \int \frac{dt}{(3-t)(t+2)}$$

$$= \frac{1}{5} \int \left(\frac{1}{3-t} + \frac{1}{2+t} \right) dt$$

$$= \frac{1}{5} \left[-\log(3-t) + \log(2+t) \right].$$

Now, $t = 1$ when $x = \pi/2$, and $t = -1$ when $x = -\pi/2$.

$$\therefore \quad \int_{-\pi/2}^{\pi/2} \frac{dx}{5 + 7\cos x + \sin x} = \frac{1}{5} \left| \log \frac{(2+t)}{(3-t)} \right|_{-1}^{1}$$

$$= \frac{1}{5} \left(\log \frac{3}{2} - \log \frac{1}{4} \right) = \frac{1}{5} \log 6.$$

EXERCISES

1. Evaluate the following :

(i) $\displaystyle\int_0^{\pi/2} \frac{dx}{5 + 4\cos x}$,   *(Rewa, 2000; Bilaspur, 1999)*

(ii) $\displaystyle\int_0^{\pi} \frac{dx}{2 + \cos x}$,   (iii) $\displaystyle\int_0^{\pi} \frac{d\theta}{5 + 3\cos\theta}$.

2. Evaluate :

(i) $\displaystyle\int \frac{dx}{a + b\sin x}$,

(ii) $\displaystyle\int_0^{\pi/2} \frac{dx}{4 + 5\cos x}$,   *(Indore, 1997; Vikram, 1997S; Sagar, 2002;*
                                     Jabalpur, 1997; Bilaspur, 2000)

(iii) $\displaystyle\int \frac{\mathrm{cosec}\, x\, dx}{2 + \mathrm{cosec}\, x}$,   (iv) $\displaystyle\int \frac{dx}{\cos\alpha + \cos x}$.

3. Show that

$$\int_0^{\pi/2} \frac{d\theta}{1 + 2\cos\theta} = \frac{1}{\sqrt{3}} \log(2 + \sqrt{3}). \quad \text{(Ravishankar, 1997S)}$$

4. Show that

(i) $\displaystyle\int_0^{\pi} \frac{dx}{3 + 2\sin x + \cos x} = \frac{\pi}{4}$,

(ii) $\displaystyle\int_0^{\pi/2} \frac{dx}{1 + 2\sin x + \cos x} = \frac{1}{2}\log 3,$

(iii) $\displaystyle\int_0^{\pi} \frac{dx}{a + b\cos x} = \frac{\pi}{\sqrt{a^2 - b^2}},$ if $a^2 > b^2.$

5. Prove that

$$\int_0^{\alpha} \frac{dx}{1 - \cos\alpha\cos x} = \frac{\pi}{2\sin\alpha}.$$

6. Prove that

$$\int_0^{\pi} \frac{dx}{3 + 2\sin x + \cos x} = \frac{\pi}{4}. \qquad (\textit{Vikram, 1998; Jiwaji, 1996})$$

7. Show that $\displaystyle\int_0^{\pi} \frac{dx}{(2 + \cos x)^2} = \frac{2\pi}{3\sqrt{3}}.$

ANSWERS

1. (i) $\dfrac{2}{3}\tan^{-1}\dfrac{1}{3}.$ (ii) $\dfrac{\pi}{\sqrt{3}}.$ (iii) $\dfrac{\pi}{4}.$

2. (i) $\dfrac{2}{\sqrt{a^2 - b^2}}\tan^{-1}\dfrac{a\tan(x/2) + b}{\sqrt{a^2 - b^2}}$ if $a^2 > b^2;$

$\dfrac{2}{\sqrt{b^2 - a^2}}\log\dfrac{a\tan(x/2) + b - \sqrt{b^2 - a^2}}{a\tan(x/2) + b + \sqrt{b^2 - a^2}}$ if $b^2 > a^2;$

$-\dfrac{1}{a}\tan\left(\dfrac{\pi}{4} - \dfrac{\pi}{2}\right)$ if $b = a$ and $\dfrac{1}{a}\cot\left(\dfrac{\pi}{4} - \dfrac{x}{2}\right)$ if $b = -a.$

(ii) $\dfrac{1}{3}\log 2.$ (iii) $\dfrac{1}{\sqrt{3}}\log\dfrac{\sin(x/2) + (2 - \sqrt{3})\cos(x/2)}{\sin(x/2) + (2 + \sqrt{3})\cos(x/2)}.$

(iv) $\dfrac{1}{\sin\alpha}\log\dfrac{\cos\dfrac{1}{2}(\alpha - x)}{\cos\dfrac{1}{2}(\alpha + x)}.$

4.7.1. Other important transformations. Theoretically, the transformation $\tan(x/2) = t$, enables us to integrate every rational function of $\sin x$ and $\cos x$. But it is not always the most convenient transformation, as the degree of the denominator of the rational function thus obtained is generally high.

Sometimes other transformations, like $\sin x = t$, $\cos x = t$, $\tan x = t$, prove more convenient. We now solve a few examples to illustrate the various possibilities of frequent occurrence.

EXAMPLES

1. *Evaluate*

$$\int_0^{\pi/2} \frac{\cos x \, dx}{(1 + \sin x)(2 + \sin x)}.$$

We put $\sin x = t$ so that $\cos x \, dx = dt$.

Also $t = 0$ when $x = 0$ and $t = 1$ when $x = \pi/2$.

$$\therefore \quad \text{the integral} = \int_0^1 \frac{dt}{(1 + t)(2 + t)}$$

$$= \int_0^1 \left(\frac{1}{t + 1} - \frac{1}{2 + t} \right) dt$$

$$= \left| \log \frac{1 + t}{2 + t} \right|_0^1 = \log \frac{2}{3} - \log \frac{1}{2} = \log \frac{4}{3}.$$

2. *Evaluate*

$$\int \frac{dx}{\sin x \, (a + b \cos x)}.$$

We put $\cos x = t$ so that $- \sin x \, dx = dt$. Thus

$$\int \frac{dx}{\sin x \, (a + b \cos x)}$$

$$= - \int \frac{dt}{\sin^2 x \, (a + b \cos x)}$$

$$= - \int \frac{dt}{(1 - t)(1 + t)(a + bt)}$$

$$= \int \left[\frac{1}{2(a + b)} \cdot \frac{1}{1 - t} + \frac{1}{2(a - b)} \cdot \frac{1}{1 + t} + \frac{b^2}{b^2 - a^2} \cdot \frac{1}{a + bt} \right] dt$$

$$= \frac{1}{2(a + b)} \log(1 - t) - \frac{1}{2(a - b)} \log(1 + t) + \frac{b}{a^2 - b^2} \log(a + bt)$$

$$= \frac{1}{2(a + b)} \log(1 - \cos x) - \frac{1}{2(a - b)} \log(1 + \cos x)$$

$$+ \frac{b}{a^2 - b^2} \log(a + b \cos x)$$

$$= \frac{1}{a+b} \log \sin \frac{x}{2} - \frac{1}{a-b} \log \cos \frac{x}{2} + \frac{b}{a^2 - b^2} \log (a + b \cos x)$$

where we have omitted the constant $- b \log 2 / (a^2 - b^2)$.

3. Evaluate

$$\int \frac{dx}{a^2 \sin^2 x + b^2 \cos^2 x}.$$

We write

$$\int \frac{dx}{a^2 \sin^2 x + b^2 \cos^2 x} = \int \frac{\sec^2 x \, dx}{b^2 + a^2 \tan^2 x}.$$

Putting $t = \tan x$, we see that the given integral

$$= \int \frac{dt}{b^2 + a^2 t^2} = \frac{1}{a^2} \int \frac{dt}{(t^2 + b^2 / a^2)}$$

$$= \frac{1}{a^2} \cdot \frac{a}{b} \tan^{-1} \left(\frac{at}{b} \right) = \frac{1}{ab} \tan^{-1} \left(\frac{a \tan x}{b} \right).$$

4. Evaluate

$$\int \frac{\sin x \cos x}{a^2 \cos^2 x + b^2 \sin^2 x} dx.$$

Dividing the numerator and denominator by $\cos^2 x$, we have

$$\int \frac{\sin x \cos x}{a^2 \cos^2 x + b^2 \sin^2 x} dx = \int \frac{\tan x \, dx}{a^2 + b^2 \tan^2 x}.$$

Putting $\tan^2 x = t$, we see that the integral

$$= \int \frac{dt}{2 (1 + t) (a^2 + b^2 t)}$$

$$= \frac{1}{2} \int \left(\frac{1}{a^2 + b^2} \cdot \frac{1}{1 + t} + \frac{b^2}{b^2 - a^2} + \frac{1}{a^2 + b^2 t} \right) dt$$

$$= \frac{1}{2} \left[\frac{1}{a^2 - b^2} \log (1 + t) + \frac{b^2}{b^2 - a^2} \cdot \frac{1}{b^2} \log (a^2 + b^2 t) \right]$$

$$= \frac{1}{2 (a^2 - b^2)} \log \frac{\sec^2 x}{a^2 + b^2 \tan^2 x}$$

$$= - \frac{1}{2 (a^2 - b^2)} \log (a^2 \cos^2 x + b^2 \sin^2 x).$$

Note. The integral may also be evaluated by putting

$$\sin^2 x = t, \text{ or } \cos^2 x = t.$$

EXERCISES

Evaluate the following integrals :

1. (*i*) $\displaystyle\int \frac{\cos x}{1 + \sin^2 x}\, dx,$ (*ii*) $\displaystyle\int_0^{\pi/2} \frac{\sin^2 \theta \cos \theta}{1 + e^2 \sin^2 \theta}\, d\theta,$

(*iii*) $\displaystyle\int \frac{dx}{\sin x + \sin 2x},$ (*Jiwaji, 1998; Vikram, 1999*)

(*iv*) $\displaystyle\int_0^{\pi/2} \frac{\sin x \cos x}{\cos^2 x + 3 \cos x + 2}\, dx.$

2. (*i*) $\displaystyle\int \frac{2 - \sin x}{\sin x\,(1 - \cos x)}\, dx,$ (*ii*) $\displaystyle\int \frac{\sec x}{1 + \csc x}\, dx,$

(*iii*) $\displaystyle\int \frac{dx}{1 + \cos^2 x},$ (*iv*) $\displaystyle\int_0^{\pi/2} \frac{dx}{2 + \sin^2 x},$

(*v*) $\displaystyle\int \frac{d\theta}{5 + 4 \cos 2\theta}.$

3. (*i*) $\displaystyle\int \frac{dx}{1 - \cos^4 x},$ (*ii*) $\displaystyle\int \frac{dx}{(2 \sin x + \cos x)^2},$

                                                      (*Jabalpur, 1995*)

(*iii*) $\displaystyle\int_0^{\pi/2} \frac{dx}{1 + 4 \sin^2 x},$ (*iv*) $\displaystyle\int_0^{\pi/2} \frac{\sin x \cos x}{a^2 \sin^2 x + b^2 \cos^2 x}\, dx,$

(*v*) $\displaystyle\int_0^{\pi/2} \frac{dx}{a^2 - b^2 \cos^2 x},\ (a^2 > b^2),$

(*vi*) $\displaystyle\int \frac{dx}{3 \sin x + \sin^3 x}.$

4. Show that

$$\int_0^{\pi/4} \frac{\sin \theta + \cos \theta}{9 + 16 \sin 2\theta} = \frac{1}{20} \log 3.$$

5. Show that $\displaystyle\int_0^{\pi/2} \frac{dx}{a^2 \cos^2 x + b^2 \sin^2 x} = \frac{\pi}{2ab}$ if a and b are positive.

                                            (*Jabalpur, 1995; Bilaspur, 1997*)

ANSWERS

1. (*i*) $\tan^{-1}(\sin x)$.   (*ii*) $(e - \tan^{-1} e)/e^3$.

(*iii*) $\frac{1}{3}\log[\sin x(1 + \cos x)/(1 + 2\cos x)^2]$.   (*iv*) $\log(9/8)$.

2. (*i*) $\log \tan \frac{1}{2}x + \cot \frac{1}{2}x - \frac{1}{2}\operatorname{cosec}^2 \frac{1}{2}x$.

(*ii*) $\frac{1}{4}\log[(1 + \sin x)/(1 - \sin x)] + \frac{1}{2}(1 + \sin x)$.

(*iii*) $\sqrt{1/2}\,\tan^{-1}(\tan x/\sqrt{2})$.   (*iv*) $\sqrt{6}\,\pi/12$.

(*v*) $\frac{1}{3}\tan^{-1}\left(\frac{1}{3}\tan\theta\right)$.

3. (*i*) $-\frac{1}{2}\cot x + \frac{1}{2}\sqrt{\frac{1}{2}}\left(\tan^{-1}\sqrt{\frac{1}{2}}\tan x\right)$.

(*ii*) $-\dfrac{\cos(x/2)}{(2\sin x + \cos x)}$.   (*iii*) $\dfrac{\pi}{2\sqrt{5}}$.

(*iv*) $\dfrac{1}{(a^2 - b^2)}\log\dfrac{a}{b}$, if $a^2 \neq b^2$ and $\dfrac{1}{2a^2}$ if $a^2 = b^2$.

(*v*) $\pi/(2a\sqrt{a^2 - b^2})$.

(*vi*) $\dfrac{1}{6}\log\dfrac{t-1}{t+1} + \dfrac{1}{12}\log\dfrac{2+t}{2-t}$ where $t = \cos x$.

4.8.1. To integrate

$$(a\cos x + b\sin x)/(c\cos x + d\sin x).$$

We note that the derivative of the denominator $c\cos x + d\sin x$ is $-c\sin x + d\cos x$ and proceed to determine two constants λ and μ such that

$$a\cos x + b\sin x \equiv \lambda(-c\sin x + d\cos x) + \mu(c\cos x + d\sin x).$$

Equating the coefficients of $\cos x$ and $\sin x$, we see that the constants λ and μ are given by the equations

$$a = d\lambda + \mu, \quad b = -c\lambda + d\mu$$

$$\Rightarrow \lambda = \frac{ad - bc}{d^2 + c^2}, \quad \mu = \frac{ac - bd}{d^2 + c^2}$$

$$\therefore \int \frac{a\cos x + b\sin x}{c\sin x + d\sin x}\,dx = \lambda \int \frac{-c\sin x + d\cos x}{c\cos x + d\sin x}\,dx + \mu$$

$$= \lambda\log(c\cos x + d\sin x) + \mu x.$$

4.8.2. To integrate $\dfrac{a \cos x + b \sin x + c}{d \cos x + e \sin x + f}$.

We determine three constants λ, μ, ν such that

$a \cos x + b \sin x + c = \lambda \, (d \cos x + e \sin x + f)$

$\qquad\qquad\qquad\qquad\qquad + \mu \, (- d \sin x + e \cos x) + \nu.$

These are given by the equations

$\qquad\qquad a = d\,\lambda + e\mu, \; b = e\lambda - d\mu, \; c = f\lambda + \nu.$

With these values of λ, μ, ν, we have

$$\int \frac{a \cos x + b \sin x + c}{d \cos x + e \sin x + f}\, dx = \int \lambda \, dx + \mu \int \frac{- d \sin x + e \cos x}{d \cos x + e \sin x + f}\, dx$$

$$+ \nu \int \frac{dx}{d \cos x + e \sin x + f}$$

$$= \lambda x + \mu \log (d \cos x + e \sin x + f)$$

$$+ \nu \int \frac{dx}{d \cos x + e \sin x + f}$$

where $\displaystyle \int \frac{dx}{d \cos x + e \sin x + f}$

is to be evaluated with the substitution $\tan (x/2) = t$.

EXAMPLES

1. *Evaluate* : $\displaystyle \int \frac{2 \sin x + 3 \cos x}{3 \sin x + 4 \cos x}\, dx.$

Let $2 \sin x + 3 \cos x = A \, (3 \sin x + 4 \cos x) + B \, (3 \cos x - 4 \sin x)$

$\Rightarrow \quad 2 = 3A - 4B$ and $3 = 4A + 3B$

$\Rightarrow \quad A = \dfrac{18}{25}, \; B = \dfrac{1}{25}$

$\therefore \quad$ given integral $= \dfrac{18}{25} \displaystyle\int dx + \dfrac{1}{25} \int \dfrac{(3 \cos x - 4 \sin x)}{(3 \sin x + 4 \cos x)}\, dx$

$$= \frac{18}{25}\, x + \frac{1}{25} \log (3 \sin x + 4 \cos x).$$

2. *Evaluate* : $\displaystyle \int \frac{d\theta}{(a \sin^2 \theta + b \cos^2 \theta)^2}.$ *(Jiwaji, 1998)*

Dividing the numerator and denominator by $\cos^4 \theta$, we get

$$I = \int \frac{\sec^4 \theta \, d\theta}{(b + a \tan^2 \theta)^2}$$

$$= \int \frac{(1 + t^2)\, dt}{(b + at^2)^2}, \text{ where } t = \tan \theta$$

$$= \frac{1}{a} \int \frac{(b + at^2) + a - b}{(b + at^2)^2} \, dt$$

$$= \frac{1}{a^2} \int \frac{dt}{c + t^2} + \frac{a - b}{a^3} \int \frac{dt}{(c + t^2)^2}, \text{ where } c = \frac{b}{a}$$

$$= \frac{1}{a^2} \int \frac{dt}{c + t^2} + \frac{a - b}{a^3} \left[\frac{1}{2c\,(c + t^2)} + \frac{1}{2c} \int \frac{dt}{(c + t^2)} \right], \text{ etc.}$$

3. *Evaluate* : $\displaystyle\int \frac{dx}{\sin(x - a)\,\sin(x - b)}$.   *(Indore, 2002)*

We have

$$\cot(x - a) - \cot(x - b) = \frac{\sin(a - b)}{\sin(x - a)\,\sin(x - b)}$$

$$\therefore \quad \text{Integral} = \int \frac{\cot(x - a) - \cot(x - b)}{\sin(a - b)} \, dx$$

$$= \operatorname{cosec}(a - b)\,[\log \sin(x - a) - \log \sin(x - b)].$$

4. *Evaluate* : $\displaystyle\int \sqrt{\sec x - 1} \, dx$.

We have

$$\int \sqrt{\sec x - 1} \, dx = \int \sqrt{\frac{1 - \cos x}{\cos x}} \, dx$$

$$= \int \frac{\sqrt{1 - \cos^2 x} \; dx}{\sqrt{\cos x\,(1 + \cos x)}}$$

$$= \int \frac{\sin x \, dx}{\sqrt{\left(\cos x + \dfrac{1}{2}\right)^2 - \dfrac{1}{4}}}$$

$$= \int \frac{- \, du}{\sqrt{u^2 - \dfrac{1}{4}}} = - \cosh^{-1}\left(\frac{u}{1/2}\right)$$

$$\left[\text{Putting } \cos x + \frac{1}{2} = u \right]$$

$$= - \cosh^{-1}(2 \cos x + 1).$$

EXERCISES

Evaluate the following :

(i) $\displaystyle\int_0^{\pi/2} \dfrac{dx}{1+\cot x},$

(ii) $\displaystyle\int \dfrac{2\sin x + 3\cos x}{3\sin x + 4\cos x}\,dx,$

(iii) $\displaystyle\int \dfrac{dx}{a + b\tan x},$

(iv) $\displaystyle\int \dfrac{3\cos x + 4\sin x}{4\cos x + 5\sin x}\,dx,$

(v) $\displaystyle\int \dfrac{\cos x + 2\sin x + 3}{4\cos x + 5\sin x + 6}\,dx,$

(vi) $\displaystyle\int \dfrac{5\cos x + 6}{2\cos x + \sin x + 3}\,dx.$

ANSWERS

(i) $\dfrac{\pi}{4}.$

(ii) $\dfrac{18}{25}x + \dfrac{1}{25}\log(3\sin x + 4\cos x).$

(iii) $[ax + b\log(a\cos x + b\sin x)]/(a^2 + b^2).$

(iv) $[3x - \log(4\cos x + 5\sin x)]/41.$

(v) $\dfrac{14}{41}x - \dfrac{3}{41}\log(4\cos x + 5\sin x + 6)$

$$+ \dfrac{39}{41}\cdot\dfrac{1}{\sqrt5}\log\dfrac{2\sin\dfrac{1}{2}x + (5-\sqrt5)\cos\dfrac{1}{2}x}{2\sin\dfrac{1}{2}x + (5+\sqrt5)\cos\dfrac{1}{2}x}.$$

(vi) $2x + \log(2\cos x + \sin x + 3).$

4.9. Reduction formula for $\int \cos^m x \cos nx\,dx.$

Applying the rule of integration by parts, we obtain

$$\int \cos^m x \cos nx\,dx = \cos^m x \cdot \dfrac{\sin nx}{n}$$

$$+ \dfrac{m}{n}\int \cos^{m-1} x \sin x \sin nx\,dx, \quad ...(i)$$

Now,

$$\cos(n-1)x = \cos nx \cos x + \sin nx \sin x.$$

Replacing $\sin nx \sin x$ by $\cos(n-1)x - \cos nx \cos x$ in the integral on the right of (i), we get

$$\int \cos^m x \cos nx\,dx = \dfrac{\cos^m x \sin nx}{n} + \dfrac{m}{n}\int \cos^{m-1} x \cos(n-1)x\,dx$$

$$- \dfrac{m}{n}\int \cos^m x \cos nx\,dx$$

$$\Rightarrow \left(1 + \frac{m}{n}\right) \int \cos^m x \cos nx \, dx$$

$$= \frac{\cos^m x \sin nx}{n} + \frac{m}{n} \int \cos^{m-1} x \cos (n-1) x \, dx$$

$$\Rightarrow \int \cos^m x \cos nx \, dx = \frac{\cos^m x \sin nx}{m+n}$$

$$+ \frac{m}{m+n} \int \cos^{m-1} x \cos (n-1) x \, dx$$

which is the required reduction formula.

Note 1. We can similarly obtain a reduction formula for the integral $\int \cos^m x \sin nx \, dx$.

Note 2. If, instead of replacing $\sin x \sin nx$ by

$$\cos (n-1) x - \cos nx \cos x$$

in the integral on the right of (i), we had integrated this integral by parts, taking $\sin nx$ as the first and $\cos^{m-1} x \sin x$ as the second factor, we would have got the reduction formula

$$\int \cos^m x \cos nx \, dx = \frac{n \sin nx \cos x - m \cos nx \sin x}{n^2 - m^2} \cos^{m-1} x$$

$$- \frac{m(m-1)}{n^2 - m^2} \int \cos^{m-2} x \cos nx \, dx.$$

4.9.1. Reduction Formula for $\int e^{ax} \sin^n bx \, dx.$

Let

$$I_n = \int e^{ax} \sin^n bx \, dx$$

$$= \frac{e^{ax} \sin^n bx}{a} - \frac{nb}{a} \left[\frac{e^{ax}}{a} \sin^{n-1} bx \cos bx \right.$$

$$\left. - \frac{1}{a} \int e^{ax} \{b(n-1) \sin^{n-2} bx \cos^2 bx - \sin^{n-1} bx (\sin bx) b\} \right] dx$$

$$= \frac{e^{ax} \sin^n bx}{a} - \frac{nb}{a^2} e^{ax} \sin^{n-1} bx \cos bx$$

$$+ \frac{nb}{b^2} \int e^{ax} [b(n-1) \sin^{n-2} bx (1 - \sin^2 bx) - b \sin^{n-1} bx \sin bx] \, dx$$

$$= \frac{e^{ax} \sin^n bx}{a} - \frac{nb}{a^2} e^{ax} \sin^{n-1} bx \cos bx$$

$$+ n(n-1) \frac{b^2}{a^2} \int e^{ax} \sin^{n-2} bx \, dx$$

$$= \frac{e^{ax} \sin^n bx}{a} - \frac{nb}{a^2} e^{ax} \sin^{n-1} bx \cos bx$$

$$+ n(n-1) \frac{b^2}{a^2} I_{n-2} - n(n-1) \frac{b^2}{a^2} I_n - \frac{nb^2}{a^2} I_n$$

$$= \frac{e^{ax} \sin^n bx}{a} - \frac{nb}{a^2} e^{ax} \sin^{n-1} bx \cos bx$$

$$+ n(n-1) \frac{b^2}{a^2} I_{n-2} - n^2 \frac{b^2}{a^2} I_n$$

$$\Rightarrow \quad I_n \left(1 + \frac{nb^2}{a^2} \right)$$

$$= \frac{e^{ax} \sin^n bx}{a} - \frac{nb}{a^2} e^{ax} \sin^{n-1} bx \cos bx + n(n-1) \frac{b^2}{a^2} I_{n-2}$$

$$\Rightarrow \quad I_n = \frac{e^{ax}}{a^2 + n^2 b^2} (a \sin^n bx - nb \sin^{n-1} bx \cos bx)$$

$$+ \frac{n(n-1) b^2}{a^2 + n^2 b^2} I_{n-2}.$$

Similarly a reduction formula for $\int e^{ax} \cos^n bx \, dx$ can be determined as :

$$\int e^{ax} \cos^n bx \, dx = \frac{e^{ax}}{a^2 + n^2 b^2} (a \cos^n bx + nb \sin bx \cos^{n-1} bx)$$

$$+ \frac{n(n-1)}{a^2 + n^2 b^2} I_{n-2}.$$

4.9.2. Reduction Formula for $\int \dfrac{\sin nx}{\sin x} \, dx$.

We have

$$\sin nx - \sin(n-2) x = 2 \cos(n-1) x \sin x$$
$$\Rightarrow \quad \sin nx = \sin(n-2) x + 2 \cos(n-1) x \sin x$$

$$\therefore \quad \int \frac{\sin nx}{\sin x} \, dx = \int \frac{2 \cos(n-1) x \sin x + \sin(n-2) x}{\sin x} \, dx$$

$$= 2 \int \cos(n-1) x \, dx + \int \frac{\sin(n-2) x}{\sin x} \, dx$$

or $\quad \displaystyle\int \frac{\sin nx}{\sin x} \, dx = \frac{2 \sin(n-1) x}{n-1} + \int \frac{\sin(n-2) x}{\sin x} \, dx.$

EXAMPLES

1. *If* $I_{m,n} = \displaystyle\int_0^{\pi/2} \cos^m x \cos nx \, dx$, *prove that*

$$I_{m,n} = \frac{m(m-1)}{m^2 - n^2} I_{m-2,n}.$$

We have

$$I_{m,n} = \left[\frac{\cos^m x \sin nx}{n} \right]_0^{\pi/2} + \frac{m}{n} \int_0^{\pi/2} \cos^{m-1} x \sin x \sin nx \, dx$$

$$= 0 + \frac{m}{n} \int_0^{\pi/2} (\cos^{m-1} x \sin x) \sin nx \, dx$$

$$= \frac{m}{n} \left[\left\{ (\cos^{m-1} x \sin x)\left(-\frac{\cos nx}{n} \right) \right\}_0^{\pi/2} \right.$$

$$\left. - \int_0^{\pi/2} \{(m-1)\cos^{m-2} x\,(-\sin^2 x) + \cos^m x\}\left(-\frac{\cos nx}{n} \right) dx \right]$$

$$= \frac{m}{n} \left[0 + \frac{1}{n} \int_0^{\pi/2} \{\cos^m x \cos nx - (m-1)\cos^{m-2} x \sin^2 x \cos nx\} \, dx \right]$$

$$= \frac{m}{n^2} \int_0^{\pi/2} \cos^m x \cos nx \, dx$$

$$- \frac{m(m-1)}{n^2} \int_0^{\pi/2} \cos^{m-2} x\,(1 - \cos^2 x) \cos nx \, dx$$

$$= \frac{m}{n^2} I_{m,n} - \frac{m(m-1)}{n^2} \int_0^{\pi/2} \cos^{m-2} x \cos nx \, dx$$

$$+ \frac{m(m-1)}{n^2} \int_0^{\pi/2} \cos^m x \cos nx \, dx$$

$$= \frac{m^2}{n^2} I_{m,n} - \frac{m(m-1)}{n^2} I_{m-2,n}$$

or $\quad \left(1 - \dfrac{m^2}{n^2} \right) I_{m,n} = -\dfrac{m(m-1)}{n^2} I_{m-2,n}$

or $\quad -\left(\dfrac{m^2 - n^2}{n^2}\right) I_{m,\,n} = -\dfrac{m\,(m-1)}{n^2} I_{m-2,\,n}$

$\therefore \quad I_{m,\,n} = \dfrac{m\,(m-1)}{m^2 - n^2} I_{m-2,\,n}.$

2. *Prove that* $\displaystyle\int_0^{\pi/2} \cos^{n-2} x \sin nx \, dx = \dfrac{1}{n-1}$ $(n > 1)$.

By reduction formula,

$$\int \cos^m x \sin nx \, dx = I_{m,\,n} = -\dfrac{\cos^m x \cos nx}{m+n} + \dfrac{m}{m+n} I_{m-1,\,n-1}.$$

Here

$$I_{n-2,\,n} = -\left[\dfrac{\cos^{n-2} x \cos nx}{2n-2}\right]_0^{\pi/2} + \dfrac{n-2}{2\,(nm-1)} I_{n-2,\,n-1}$$

$$= \dfrac{1}{2\,(n-1)} + \dfrac{n-2}{2\,(n-1)} I_{n-2,\,n-1}.$$

But $I_{n-2,\,n-1} = \dfrac{1}{2\,(n-2)} + \dfrac{n-3}{2\,(n-2)} I_{n-4,\,n-2}.$

Therefore

$$I_{n-2,\,n} = \dfrac{1}{2\,(n-1)} + \dfrac{n-2}{2\,(n-1)}\left[\dfrac{1}{2\,(n-2)} + \dfrac{n-3}{2\,(n-2)} I_{n-4,\,n-2}\right]$$

$$= \dfrac{1}{2\,(n-1)} + \dfrac{1}{2^2\,(n-1)\,2^3\,(n-1)} + \ldots + \text{to } (n-2) \text{ terms}$$

$$+ \dfrac{1}{2^{n-2}\,(n-1)} I_{0,\,1}$$

$$= \dfrac{1}{(n-1)}\left[\dfrac{1}{2} + \dfrac{1}{2^2} + \ldots + \text{to } (n-1) \text{ terms}\right]$$

$$+ \dfrac{1}{2^{n-2}\,(n-1)}\int_0^{\pi/2} (\cos x)^0 \sin 2x \, dx$$

$$= \dfrac{1}{(n-1)}\left[\dfrac{1}{2}\left\{\dfrac{\left(1 - \dfrac{1}{2^{n-1}}\right)}{\left(1 - \dfrac{1}{2}\right)}\right\}\right] + \dfrac{1}{2^{n-2}\,(n-1)}\left[-\dfrac{\cos 2x}{2}\right]_0^{\pi/2}$$

$$= \frac{1}{(n-1)} \left[1 - \frac{1}{2^{n-1}} \right] + \frac{1}{2^{n-1}(n-1)}$$

$$= \frac{1}{(n-1)} \left[1 - \frac{1}{2^{n-1}} + \frac{1}{2^{n-1}} \right] = \frac{1}{n-1}.$$

3. Prove that $\displaystyle\int_0^{\pi/2} \cos^n x \cos nx \, dx = \frac{\pi}{2^{n+1}}$, *n being a positive integer.*

(Rohilkhand, 1993, 99; Ravishankar, 1997, 2000;
Indore, 1998, 2000)

Let

$$I_{m,\,n} = \int_0^{\pi/2} \cos^n x \cos nx \, dx.$$

By the reduction formula

$$I_{m,\,n} = \frac{\cos^m x \sin nx}{m+n} + \frac{m}{m+n} I_{m-1,\,n-1},$$

we get

$$I_{n,\,n} = \left[\frac{\cos^n x \sin nx}{2n} \right]_0^{\pi/2} + \frac{1}{2} \int_0^{\pi/2} \cos^{n-1} x \cos(n-1)x \, dx$$

$$= \frac{1}{2} I_{n-1,\,n-1} = \frac{1}{2} \left[\frac{1}{2} I_{n-2,\,n-2} \right]$$

$$= \left[\frac{1}{2} \cdot \frac{1}{2} \, \ldots \ldots \text{ to } n \text{ factors} \right] I_0$$

$$= \frac{1}{2^n} \int_0^{\pi/2} \cos^0 x \cos(0 \cdot x) \, dx = \frac{1}{2^n} \int_0^{\pi/2} dx$$

$$= \frac{\pi}{2^{n+1}}.$$

4. *Integrating by parts twice, or otherwise, obtain a reduction formula for*

$$I_m = \int_0^{\infty} e^{-x} \sin^m x \, dx$$

where $m \geq 2$ in the form $(1 + m^2) I_m = m(m-1) I_{m-2}$ and hence evaluate I_4.

On integrating twice by parts taking e^{-x} as second function we have

$$I_m = \left[-\sin^m xe^{-x} \right]_0^\infty - \int_0^\infty m \sin^{m-1} x \cos x \, (-e^{-x}) \, dx$$

$$= 0 + m \int_0^\infty (\sin^{m-1} x \cos x) \, e^{-x} \, dx$$

$$= m \left[\{\sin^{m-1} x \cos x\} \, (-e^{-x}) \right]_0^\infty$$

$$+ m \int_0^\infty [(m-1) \sin^{m-2} x \cos^2 x - \sin^m x] \, e^{-x} \, dx$$

$$= 0 + m \, (m-1) \int_0^\infty \sin^{m-2} x \, (1 - \sin^2 x) \, e^{-x} \, dx$$

$$- m \int_0^\infty e^{-x} \sin^m x \, dx$$

$$= m \, (m-1) \int_0^\infty e^{-x} \sin^{m-2} x \, dx - m \, (m-1) \int_0^\infty e^{-x} \sin^m x \, dx$$

$$- m \int_0^\infty e^{-x} \sin^m x \, dx$$

$$I_m = m \, (m-1) \, I_{m-2} - m^2 \, I_m$$

or $\qquad (1 + m^2) \, I_m = m \, (m-1) \, I_{m-2}$ $\qquad\qquad\qquad$ ...(i)

To evaluate I_4, put $m = 4, 2$, successively in (i), so that

$$17 I_4 = 12 I_2 \quad \text{or} \quad I_4 = \frac{12}{17} I_2$$

and $\qquad 5 I_2 = 2 I_0, \, \textit{i.e.,} \, I_2 = \frac{2}{5} I_0.$

But $I_0 = \left[-e^{-x} \right]_0^\infty = 1$

$\therefore \quad I_4 = \frac{12}{17} \times \frac{2}{5} \times 1 = \frac{24}{85}.$

EXERCISES

1. Prove that $I_{m,n} = \int \cos^m x \sin nx \, dx$,

$\Rightarrow \qquad\qquad (m + n) \, I_{m,n} = -\cos^m x \cos nx + m I_{m-1, n-1}.$

Hence or otherwise evaluate

$$\int_0^{\pi/2} \cos^5 x \sin 3x \, dx.$$

2. Prove that

$$\int_0^{\pi/2} \cos^m x \cos nx \, dx = m \int_0^{\pi/2} \cos^{m-1} x \cos(n-1) x \, dx,$$

and then deduce the value of the integral when $m > n$.

In particular, show that

$$\int_0^{\pi/2} \cos^n x \cos nx \, dx = \frac{\pi}{2^{n+1}}.$$

3. If $f(p, q) = \displaystyle\int_0^{\pi/2} \cos^p x \cos qx \, dx$, prove that

$$f(p, q) = \frac{p(p-1)}{p^2 - q^2} f(p-2, q) = \frac{p}{p+q} f(p-1, q-1).$$

4. Show that

$$\int \sin^m x \cos nx \, dx = \frac{m \cos x \cos nx + n \sin x \sin mx}{n^2 - m^2} \sin^{m-1} x$$

$$- \frac{m(m-1)}{n^2 - m^2} \int \sin^{m-2} x \cos nx \, dx$$

5. If $u_n = \displaystyle\int_0^{\pi/2} x^n \sin mx \, dx$, prove that

$$u_n = \frac{n\pi^{n-1}}{m^2 \, 2^{n-1}} - \frac{n(n-1)}{m^2} u_{n-2},$$

if m is of the form $4r + 1$.

6. If $I_n = \displaystyle\int_0^{\pi/2} x^n \sin(2p+1) x \, dx$, prove that

$$(2p+1)^2 I_n + n(n-1) I_{n-2} = (-1)^p \cdot n \cdot (\pi/2)^{n-1},$$

n and p being positive integers.

Evaluate $\displaystyle\int_0^{\pi/2} x^4 \sin 3x \, dx.$

7. Show how to evaluate the integral

$$\int x^{m} \cos nx \, dx.$$

8. Find a reduction formula for $\int e^{ax} \cos^n x \, dx$, n being a positive integer.

ANSWERS

1. $\dfrac{1}{3}$.

2. $-\dfrac{\pi}{2^{m+1}} \cdot \dfrac{\lfloor m}{\lfloor \frac{1}{2}(m+n) \cdot \lfloor \frac{1}{2}(m-n)}$, if $(m-n)$ be even,

$2^{m-1} \lfloor m \dfrac{\lfloor \frac{1}{2}(m+n-1) \cdot \lfloor \frac{1}{2}(m-n-1)}{\lfloor m+n \cdot \lfloor m-n}$, if $(m-n)$ be odd.

6. $(16 + 24\pi - 9\pi^3) / 162$.

8. $\int e^{ax} \cos^n x \, dx = \dfrac{a \cos x + n \sin x}{a^2 + n^2} e^{ax} \cos^{n-1} x$

$$+ \dfrac{n(n-1)}{a^2 + n^2} \int e^{ax} \cos^{n-2} x \, dx.$$

EXERCISES ON CHAPTER IV

1. Show that

(i) $\displaystyle\int_0^{\pi/2} \dfrac{\sin^2 x}{a^2 \sin^2 x + b^2 \cos^2 x} \, dx = \dfrac{\pi}{2a(a+b)}$,

(ii) $\displaystyle\int_0^{\infty} \dfrac{dx}{a^2 \cosh^2 x + b^2 \sinh^2 x} = \dfrac{1}{ab} \tan^{-1} \dfrac{b}{a}$.

2. Evaluate

(i) $\displaystyle\int_0^{\pi/2} \dfrac{d\theta}{a^2 \cos^2 \theta + b^2 \sin^2 \theta}$,

(ii) $\displaystyle\int_0^{\pi/2} \dfrac{d\theta}{(a^2 \sin^2 \theta + b^2 \cos^2 \theta)^2}$,

(iii) $\displaystyle\int_0^{\pi/2} \cos^2 x \sin 4x \, dx$,   (iv) $\displaystyle\int \dfrac{\cos x}{\cos x + \sin x} \, dx$.

3. Evaluate

(i) $\displaystyle\int \frac{\cos 7\theta - \cos 8\theta}{\cos 2\theta - \cos 3\theta}\, d\theta,$ (ii) $\displaystyle\int_0^{\pi/2} \frac{x + \cos x}{1 + \cos 2x}\, dx.$

4. Show that

$$\int_0^{\pi/2} \frac{d\theta}{1 + \cos \alpha \sin 2\alpha} = \begin{cases} \alpha / \sin \alpha, & \text{if } 0 < \alpha < \pi; \\ 1, & \text{if } \alpha = 0. \end{cases}$$

5. Prove that

$$\int_0^{\pi/2} \frac{dx}{1 - \sin x \cos \lambda} = (\pi - \lambda) \operatorname{cosec} \lambda, \quad (0 < \lambda < \pi).$$

6. Show that

$$\int_0^{\pi/2} \frac{\sin \theta \cos^2 \theta\, d\theta}{\sqrt{1 + a^2 \cos^2 \theta}} = \frac{\sqrt{1 + a^2}}{2a^2} - \frac{\sinh^{-1} a}{2a^3}.$$

7. Show that, if $a^2 > b^2$,

$$\int_0^{\pi} \frac{dx}{(a + b \cos x)^2} = \frac{\pi a}{(a^2 - b^2)^{3/2}}.$$

8. Evaluate

(i) $\displaystyle\int_0^{\pi/2} \frac{1 + 2 \cos x}{(2 + \cos x)^2}\, dx,$ (ii) $\displaystyle\int_0^{\pi} \frac{a^2 \sin^2 x + b^2 \cos^2 x}{a^4 \sin^2 x + b^4 \cos^2 x}\, dx,$

(iii) $\displaystyle\int_0^{\pi/2} \frac{dx}{\cosh^2 \alpha - \cos^2 x},$ (iv) $\displaystyle\int_0^{\pi/4} \frac{\sin 2x\, dx}{\sin^4 x + \cos^4 x}.$

9. Evaluate the integrals of the following functions :

(i) $\sqrt{1 + \sin x},$ (ii) $\dfrac{\sin x}{\sqrt{1 + \sin x}},$

(iii) $\sqrt{1 + \sec x},$ (iv) $\sqrt{\sec x - 1},$

(v) $\dfrac{1}{\sin^4 x + \cos^4 x},$ (vi) $\sqrt{\tan x} + \sqrt{\cot x}.$

10. Integrate

(i) $\sec^2 x \log (1 + \sin^2 x),$ (ii) $\dfrac{\sin x \log (\sin x + \cos x)}{\cos^2 x},$

(iii) $\cos 2x \log (1 + \tan x),$ (iv) $\dfrac{\cosh x + \sinh x \sin x}{1 + \cos x}.$

11. Evaluate

$$\int_0^{\pi/4} \sqrt[3]{\tan x}\, dx.$$

12. If

$$I_n = \int_0^{\pi/4} \tan^n \theta\, d\theta,$$

prove that when n is a positive integer,

$$n\,(I_{n-1} + I_{n+1}) = 1.$$

13. If

$$U_n = \int_0^{\pi/4} \tan^n x\, dx,$$

show that $U_n + U_{n-2} = \dfrac{1}{n-1}$, and deduce the value of U_5.

14. If

$$u_n = \int_0^{\pi/2} \theta \sin^n \theta\, d\theta,$$

and $n > 1$, prove that

$$u_n = \frac{n-1}{n} u_{n-2} + \frac{1}{n^2}.$$

Deduce that $u_5 = \dfrac{149}{225}$.

15. If $u_n = \int \cos n\theta \cosec \theta\, d\theta$, prove that

$$u_n - u_{n-2} = \frac{2 \cos (n-1)\,\theta}{n-1}.$$

Hence, or otherwise, prove that

$$\int_0^{\pi/2} \frac{\sin 3\theta \sin 5\theta}{\sin \theta}\, d\theta = \frac{71}{105}.$$

16. Find the reduction formula connecting

$$I_{m,\, n} = \int \cos^m x \sin^n x\, dx \quad \text{with} \quad I_{m,\, n-2} \text{ and } I_{m-2,\, n}.$$

Deduce

$$(m + n)(m + n - 2) I_{m, n}$$
$$= \{(n - 1) \sin^2 x - (m - 1) \cos^2 x\} \cos^{m-1} x \sin^{n-1} x$$
$$+ (m - 1)(n - 1) I_{m-2, n-2}.$$

17. If $u_n = \int \dfrac{dx}{\cosh^n x}$, prove that

$$(n - 1) u_n = \frac{\tanh x}{\cosh^{n-2} x} + (n - 2) u_{n-2}.$$

Evaluate the integral when $n = 5$.

18. Prove that if

$$u_n = \int_0^\pi \frac{1 - \cos nx}{1 - \cos x} \, dx,$$

where n is a positive integer or zero, then

$$u_{n+2} + u_n = 2u_{n+1}.$$

Prove that

$$\int_0^{\pi/2} \frac{\sin^2 n\theta}{\sin^2 \theta} \, d\theta = \frac{1}{2} n\pi.$$

19. Show that if n is a positive integer, then

$$\int_0^{2\pi} \frac{\cos (n - 1) x - \cos nx}{1 - \cos x} \, dx = 2\pi$$

and deduce that

$$\int_0^{2\pi} \left(\frac{\sin \dfrac{1}{2} nx}{\sin \dfrac{1}{2} x} \right)^2 dx = 2n\pi.$$

20. Prove that

$$\int_0^\pi \frac{\sin n\theta}{\sin \theta} \, d\theta$$

is equal to 0 or π according as n is an even or odd positive integer.
By means of a reduction formula or otherwise, prove that

$$\int_0^\pi \frac{\sin^2 n\theta}{\sin \theta} \, d\theta = \pi,$$

where n is a positive integer.

21. Find a reduction formula for u_n, where

$$u_n = \int_0^\pi \frac{x \sin nx}{\sin x}\, dx,$$

by evaluating $u_n - u_{n-2}$, or by any other way. Show that if n is an odd positive integer,

$$\int_0^\pi \frac{x \sin nx}{\sin x}\, dx = \frac{1}{2}\pi^2,$$

and that if n is an even positive integer, the value of the same integral tends to $-\pi^2/2$, as n is increased indefinitely.

22. Evaluate

(i) $\displaystyle\int_0^{2\pi} \frac{d\theta}{2 + \sin 2\theta},$

(ii) $\displaystyle\int_0^{2\pi} \frac{d\theta}{a \cos^2 \theta + 2h \sin \theta \cos \theta + b \sin^2 \theta},\quad (ab - h^2) > 0,$

(iii) $\displaystyle\int_0^{2\pi} \frac{dx}{(1 + \cos \alpha \cos x)^2},\ 0 < \alpha < \pi,$

(iv) $\displaystyle\int_0^{2\pi} \frac{dx}{(1 + e \cos x)^2},$ where $e < 1,$

(v) $\displaystyle\int_0^{\pi/4} \frac{\sec^2 \alpha\, dx}{\tan x - \tan \alpha},\ \alpha > \frac{\pi}{4}.$

ANSWERS

2. (i) $\dfrac{\pi}{2ab}.$ (ii) $\dfrac{\pi(a^2+b^2)}{4a^3b^3}.$

(iii) $\dfrac{1}{3}.$ (iv) $\dfrac{1}{2}[x + \log(\sin x + \cos x)].$

3. (i) $\theta + \dfrac{2}{5}\sin 5\theta.$ (ii) $\dfrac{1}{3}[(\sqrt{2}-1) + \log(\sqrt{2}+1)].$

8. (i) $\dfrac{1}{2}.$ (ii) $\dfrac{2\pi}{a^2+b^2}.$

(iii) $\dfrac{\pi}{\sinh 2\alpha},$ if $\alpha \neq 0.$ (iv) $\dfrac{\pi}{4}.$

9. (i) $-2\sqrt{1-\sin x}$.

(ii) $-2\sqrt{1-\sin x} - \sqrt{2}\, \log \tan \left(\dfrac{1}{8}\pi + \dfrac{1}{4}x\right)$.

(iii) $2 \tan^{-1}\sqrt{\sec x - 1}$.   (iv) $-2\coth^{-1}\left[\sqrt{1+\sec x}\right]$.

(v) $\dfrac{1}{\sqrt{2}} \tan^{-1}\left(\dfrac{\tan x - \cot x}{\sqrt{2}}\right)$.

(vi) $\sqrt{2}\, \tan^{-1}\left(\dfrac{\sqrt{\tan x} - \sqrt{\cot x}}{\sqrt{2}}\right)$.

10. (i) $\tan x \log(1+\sin^2 x) - 2x - \sqrt{2}\tan^{-1}(\cot x / \sqrt{2})$.

(ii) $\sec x \log(\sin x + \cos x) + \log \dfrac{\sin \dfrac{1}{2}x + \cos \dfrac{1}{2}x}{\cos \dfrac{1}{2}x - \sin \dfrac{1}{2}x}$

$+ \sqrt{2}\log \dfrac{\sin \dfrac{1}{2}x - (\sqrt{2}+1)\cos \dfrac{1}{2}x}{\sin \dfrac{1}{2}x + (\sqrt{2}-1)\cos \dfrac{1}{2}x}$.

(iii) $\dfrac{1}{2}\sin 2x \log(1+\tan x) - \dfrac{1}{2}x + \dfrac{1}{2}\log \sin\left(x + \dfrac{1}{4}\pi\right)$.

(iv) $\cosh x \tan \dfrac{1}{2}x$.

11. $\dfrac{1}{2}\left(\dfrac{\pi}{\sqrt{3}} - \log 2\right)$.   13. $\dfrac{1}{4}\log\left(\dfrac{4}{e}\right)$.

17. $\dfrac{1}{4}\dfrac{\tanh x}{\cosh^2 x} + \dfrac{3}{8}\dfrac{\tanh x}{\cosh x} + \dfrac{3}{4}\tan^{-1}(e^x)$.

21. $u_n = \dfrac{2}{(n-1)^2}[(n-1)x \sin(n-1)x + \cos(n-1)x - 1] + u_{n-1}$.

OBJECTIVE QUESTIONS

For each of the following questions, four alternatives are given for the answer. Only one of them is correct. Choose the correct alternative.

1. $\displaystyle\int \left[\sqrt{\tan x} + \sqrt{\cot x}\right] dx =$

(a) $\sqrt{2}\tan^{-1}\{\sqrt{\tan x} - \sqrt{\cot x} / \sqrt{2}\} + c$

(b) $\sqrt{2}\tan^{-1}\{\sqrt{\tan x} + \sqrt{\cot x} / \sqrt{2}\} + c$

(c) $\dfrac{1}{\sqrt{2}} \tan^{-1} \{\sqrt{2} \, (\sqrt{\tan x} - \sqrt{\cot x})\} + c$

(d) None of these.

2. If $m \neq n$, then $\displaystyle\int_{0}^{\pi} \cos mx \cos nx \, dx$ is

(a) 0   (b) $\dfrac{\pi}{2}$ (c) π (d) 2π.

3. If $(n - m)$ is odd, and $|m| \neq |n|$, then $\displaystyle\int_{0}^{\pi} \cos mx \sin nx \, dx$ is

(a) $\dfrac{2n}{n^2 - m^2}$ (b) 0

(c) $\dfrac{2n}{m^2 - n^2}$ (d) $\dfrac{2m}{n^2 - m^2}$.

4. The value of the integral $\displaystyle\int_{0}^{\pi/4} \dfrac{\sin x + \cos x}{9 + 16 \sin 2x} \, dx$ is

(a) $\log 3$ (b) $\log 2$ (c) $\dfrac{1}{20} \log 3$ (d) $\dfrac{1}{20} \log 2$.

5. $\displaystyle\int \dfrac{x + \sin x}{1 + \cos x} \, dx$ is equal to

(a) $\tan \dfrac{x}{2} + c$ (b) $x \tan \dfrac{x}{2} + c$

(c) $\cot \dfrac{x}{2} + c$ (d) $x \cos \dfrac{x}{2} + c$.

6. $\displaystyle\int \dfrac{\cos^4 x + 1}{\cot x - \tan x} \, dx = p \cos 4x + c$ is possible for

(a) $p = -1/2$ (b) $p = -1/4$

(c) $p = -1/8$ (d) No real p.

7. $\displaystyle\int \dfrac{\cos^3 x \, dx}{\sin^2 x + \sin x} \; (x \neq n\pi, \; n \in Z) =$

(a) $\log \sin x - \sin x + c$ (b) $\log |\sin x| + \sin x + c$

(c) $\log |\sin x| - \sin x + c$ (d) None of these.

8. $\displaystyle\int \dfrac{\sin x}{\sin x - \cos x} \, dx \; \left(x \neq n\pi + \dfrac{\pi}{4} \right) =$

(a) $\dfrac{1}{2}[x + \log(\sin x - \cos x)] + c$

(b) $\dfrac{1}{2}[x - \log(\sin x - \cos x)] + c$

(c) $\dfrac{1}{2}[x + \log(\cos x - \sin x)] + c$

(d) $\dfrac{1}{2}[x + \log|\cos x - \sin x|] + c.$

9. $\displaystyle\int_{0}^{\pi/2} \dfrac{dx}{2 + \cos x} =$

(a) $\dfrac{1}{\sqrt{3}} \tan^{-1}\left(\dfrac{1}{\sqrt{3}}\right)$

(b) $\dfrac{2}{\sqrt{3}} \tan^{-1}\left(\dfrac{1}{\sqrt{3}}\right)$

(c) $\sqrt{3}\, \tan^{-1}(\sqrt{3})$

(d) $2\sqrt{3}\, \tan^{-1}(\sqrt{3}).$

10. $\displaystyle\int_{0}^{1} \dfrac{dx}{(x^2 + 1)^{3/2}}$ is equal to

(a) $\dfrac{1}{2}$

(b) $\dfrac{\sqrt{2}}{2}$

(c) 1

(d) $\sqrt{2}.$

11. $\displaystyle\int \sin^2 x \cos^{-6} x\, dx =$

(a) $\tan x + \dfrac{1}{3} \tan^3 x + \dfrac{1}{5} \tan^5 x + c$

(b) $\dfrac{1}{3} \tan^3 x + \dfrac{1}{5} \tan^5 x + c$

(c) $-\dfrac{1}{3} \tan^3 x - \dfrac{1}{5} \tan^5 x + c$

(d) None of these.

12. $\displaystyle\int \dfrac{\tan x}{\sqrt{1 - \tan^2 x}}\, dx =$

(a) $-\dfrac{1}{\sqrt{2}} \cosh^{-1}(\sqrt{2} \cos x) + c$

(b) $\dfrac{1}{\sqrt{2}} \cosh^{-1}(\sqrt{2} \cos x) + c$

(c) $-\dfrac{1}{\sqrt{2}} \sinh^{-1}(\sqrt{2} \cos x) + c$

(d) None of these.

13. $\displaystyle\int \frac{dx}{1 + 2\sin x + \cos x} =$

   (a) $\log\left[1 + 2\tan(x/2)\right] + c$ (b) $\log\left[1 - 2\tan(x/2)\right] + c$

   (c) $\dfrac{1}{2}\log\left[1 + 2\tan(x/2)\right] + c$ (d) None of these.

14. If $\displaystyle\int \frac{dx}{4 + 3\cos x} = p\tan^{-1}\left[q\tan(x/2)\right] + c$, then

   (a) $p = 1/\sqrt{7}$ (b) $p = 3/\sqrt{7}$ (c) $q = 1/\sqrt{7}$ (d) $q = 2/\sqrt{7}$.

15. $\displaystyle\int \frac{\cos^3 x + \cos^5 x}{\sin^2 x + \cos^4 x}\, dx =$

   (a) $\sin x + 2\cosec x + 6\tan^{-1}(\sin x) + c$

   (b) $\sin x - 6\tan^{-1}(\sin x) + c$

   (c) $-\left[\cosec x + \cot x \cos x + 6\tan^{-1}(\sin x)\right] + c$

   (d) $\sin x - 2\cosec x + 5\tan^{-1}(\cos x) + c$.

16. $\displaystyle\int \frac{1}{a^2\cos^2 x + b^2\sin^2 x}\, dx =$

   (a) $\dfrac{1}{ab}\tan^{-1}\left(\dfrac{b}{a}\cot x\right) + c$ (b) $\dfrac{1}{ab}\tan^{-1}\left(\dfrac{a}{b}\cot x\right) + c$

   (c) $-\dfrac{1}{ab}\cot^{-1}\left(\dfrac{a}{b}\tan x\right) + c$ (d) $\dfrac{1}{ab}\cot^{-1}\left(\dfrac{a}{b}\cot x\right) + c$.

17. $\displaystyle\int \frac{2\sin x + 3\cos x}{3\sin x + 4\cos x}\, dx = Px + Q\log|3\sin x + 4\cos x| + c$, then

   (a) $P = 18/25$ (b) $P = 1/25$ (c) $Q = 3/25$ (d) $Q = 18/25$.

18. Reduction formula for $\int \sin^n x \, dx$ is

   (a) $\displaystyle\int \sin^n x \, dx = -\frac{\sin^{n-1} x \cos x}{n} + \frac{n-1}{n}\int \sin^{n-2} x \, dx$

   (b) $\displaystyle\int \sin^n x \, dx = \frac{\sin^{n-1} x \cos x}{n} + \frac{n-1}{n}\int \sin^{n-2} x \, dx$

   (c) $\displaystyle\int \sin^n x \, dx = \frac{\sin^{n-1} x \cos x}{n} - \frac{n-1}{n}\int \sin^{n-2} x \, dx$

   (d) $\displaystyle\int \sin^n x \, dx = -\frac{\sin^{n-1} x \cos x}{n} - \frac{n-1}{n}\int \sin^{n-2} x \, dx$.

19. If n is even, then $\displaystyle\int_0^{\pi/2} \sin^n x \, dx$ is equal to

(a) $\dfrac{n+1}{n+2} \cdot \dfrac{n-1}{n} \cdot \dfrac{n-3}{n-2} \cdots \dfrac{3}{4} \cdot \dfrac{1}{2} \cdot \dfrac{\pi}{2}$

(b) $\dfrac{n-1}{n} \cdot \dfrac{n-3}{n-2} \cdots \dfrac{3}{4} \cdot \dfrac{1}{2} \sqrt{\pi}$

(c) $\dfrac{n}{n-1} \cdot \dfrac{n-2}{n-3} \cdots \dfrac{4}{3} \cdot \dfrac{2}{1} \sqrt{\pi}$

(d) $\dfrac{n-1}{n} \cdot \dfrac{n-3}{n-2} \cdots \dfrac{3}{4} \cdot \dfrac{1}{2} \cdot \dfrac{\pi}{2}$.

20. Let $I_n = \displaystyle\int_0^{\pi/4} \tan^n \theta \, d\theta$, $n \in N$, then

(a) $I_{n+1} + I_{n-1} = 1/n$ (b) $I_n + I_{n-2} = 1/(n-1)$

(c) $I_4 = (3\pi + 8)/12$ (d) $I_3 = \log 2/2$.

21. If $P = \displaystyle\int e^{ax} \cos bx \, dx$ and $Q = \displaystyle\int e^{ax} \sin bx \, dx$, then

(a) $(P^2 + Q^2) \, a^2 b^2 = e^{2ax}$

(b) $\tan^{-1}(Q/P) + \tan^{-1}(b/a) = bx$

(c) $P^2 + Q^2 = e^{2ax} \cdot a^2 b^2$

(d) $\tan^{-1}(Q/P) = ax - \tan^{-1}(b/a)$.

22. If $I_n = \displaystyle\int_0^{\pi/2} x^n \sin x \, dx$ and n is greater than 1, then

$I_n + n(n-1) \, I_{n-2} =$

(a) $n(\pi)^{n-1}$ (b) $\dfrac{n}{2}(\pi)^{n-1}$

(c) $n\left(\dfrac{1}{2}\pi\right)^{n-1}$ (d) $n\left(\dfrac{1}{4}\pi\right)^{n-1}$.

23. If $I_n = \displaystyle\int_0^{\pi/2} x \sin^n x \, dx$ and $n > 1$, then $I_n - \dfrac{(n-1)}{n} I_{n-2} =$

(a) $\dfrac{1}{n}$ (b) $\dfrac{1}{n^2}$ (c) $\dfrac{1}{n^3}$ (d) $\dfrac{2}{n^2}$.

24. $\displaystyle\int_0^{\pi/2} \cos^n x \cos nx \, dx$, n being a positive integer is

(a) $\dfrac{\pi}{2}$ (b) $\dfrac{\pi}{2^n}$ (c) $\dfrac{\pi}{2^{n-1}}$ (d) $\dfrac{\pi}{2^{n+1}}$.

25. $\displaystyle\int_0^{\pi/2} \sin^m x \cos^n x \, dx$ is equal to

(a) $\dfrac{\Gamma(m)\,\Gamma(n)}{2\Gamma(m+n)}$ (b) $\dfrac{\Gamma\left(\dfrac{m+1}{2}\right)\Gamma\left(\dfrac{n+1}{2}\right)}{2\Gamma\left(\dfrac{m+n+1}{2}\right)}$

(c) $\dfrac{\Gamma\left(\dfrac{m+1}{2}\right)\Gamma\left(\dfrac{n+1}{2}\right)}{\Gamma\left(\dfrac{m+n+2}{2}\right)}$ (d) $\dfrac{\Gamma\left(\dfrac{m+1}{2}\right)\Gamma\left(\dfrac{n+1}{2}\right)}{2\Gamma\left(\dfrac{m+n+2}{2}\right)}$.

26. $\displaystyle\int \sec^3 \theta \, d\theta =$

(a) $\dfrac{1}{2}[\tan\theta \sec\theta + \log(\tan\theta + \sec\theta)] + c$

(b) $\dfrac{1}{2}[\tan\theta \sec\theta - \log(\tan\theta + \sec\theta)] + c$

(c) $\dfrac{1}{2}\left[\tan\theta \sec\theta - \log(\sec\theta - \tan\theta)\right] + c$

(d) None of these.

27. $\displaystyle\int \dfrac{e^x(1+\sin x)}{1+\cos x} \, dx$ is equal to

(a) $\log\tan x$ (b) $e^x \tan\dfrac{1}{2}x$ (c) $\sin\log x$ (d) $e^x \cot x$.

28. $\displaystyle\int x \sin^2 x \, dx =$

(a) $\dfrac{1}{8}[2x^2 - 2x\sin 2x - \cos 2x] + c$

(b) $\dfrac{1}{8}[2x^2 + 2x\sin 2x - \cos 2x] + c$

(c) $\dfrac{1}{8}[2x^2 - 2x\sin 2x + \cos 2x] + c$

(d) None of these.

29. If $\displaystyle\int \tan^4 x \, dx = p\tan^3 x + q\tan x + f(x) + c$, then

(a) $p = \dfrac{2}{3}$ (b) $q = -1$ (c) $f(x) = x^2$ (d) None of these.

ANSWERS

1. (a)	2. (a)	3. (a)	4. (c)	5. (b)
6. (c)	7. (c)	8. (d)	9. (b)	10. (b)
11. (b)	12. (a)	13. (c)	14. (c)	15. (c)
16. (d)	17. (a)	18. (a)	19. (d)	20. (a)
21. (b)	22. (c)	23. (b)	24. (d)	25. (d)
26. (a)	27. (b)	28. (a)	29. (b)	

5

Integration of Irrational Functions

5.1. Integration of rational function of x and a linear surd,

$$(ax + b)^{1/n},$$

where n is some positive integer.

The substitution $ax + b = t^n$ transforms the given integral into the integral of a rational function of t which may, then, be evaluated by the methods given in Chapter 3.

A rational function of x and of

$$\left(\frac{ax + b}{cx + d} \right)^{1/n},$$

may also be integrated by the transformation

$$\frac{ax + b}{cx + d} = t^n.$$

The following examples will make the procedure clear.

EXAMPLES

1. *Evaluate* $\displaystyle\int \frac{x}{\sqrt[3]{a + bx}}\, dx$.

We put

$$a + bx = y^3 \;\Rightarrow\; b\, dx = 3y^2\, dy$$

$$\therefore \quad \int \frac{x\, dx}{\sqrt[3]{a + bx}} = \int \frac{(y^3 - a)}{b} \cdot \frac{1}{y} \cdot \frac{3y^2\, dy}{b}$$

$$= \frac{1}{b^2} \int (y^3 - a)\, 3y\, dy$$

$$= \frac{3}{b^2} \int (y^4 - ay)\, dy$$

$$= \frac{3}{b^2} \left[\frac{y^5}{5} - \frac{ay^2}{2} \right]$$

165

$$= \frac{3}{10b^2}(2y^5 - 5ay^2)$$

$$= \frac{3}{10b^2}y^2(2y^3 - 5a)$$

$$= \frac{3}{10b^2}(a + bx)^{2/3}(2a + 2bx - 5a)$$

$$= \frac{3}{10b^2}(a + bx)^{2/3}(2bx - 3a).$$

2. *Evaluate* $\displaystyle\int \frac{1}{\sqrt{x + 1} - \sqrt[4]{x + 1}}\,dx.$

We put

$$1 + x = y^4 \implies dx = 4y^3\,dy$$

$$\therefore \quad \int \frac{dx}{\sqrt{x + 1} - \sqrt[4]{x + 1}} = \int \frac{4y^3\,dy}{y^2 - y}$$

$$= \int \frac{4y^2\,dy}{y - 1}$$

$$= 4\int \left[(y + 1) + \frac{1}{y - 1}\right]dy$$

$$= 4\left[\frac{y^2}{2} + y + \log(y - 1)\right]$$

$$= 2y^2 + 4y + \log(y - 1),$$

where $\quad x + 1 = y^4.$

3. *Evaluate* $\displaystyle\int \sqrt{\frac{1 - x}{1 + x}}\,\frac{dx}{x}.$

We put $\quad \dfrac{1 - x}{1 + x} = y^2.$

$$\implies x = \frac{1 - y^2}{1 + y^2} \implies dx = -\frac{4y\,dy}{(1 + y^2)^2}$$

$$\therefore \quad \int \sqrt{\frac{1 - x}{1 + x}}\,\frac{dx}{x} = -4\int \frac{y^2}{(1 - y^2)(1 + y^2)}\,dy$$

$$= -2\int \left(\frac{1}{1 - y^2} - \frac{1}{1 + y^2}\right)dy$$

$$= -2 \int \left[\frac{1}{2} \left(\frac{1}{1-y} + \frac{1}{1+y} \right) - \frac{1}{1+y^2} \right] dy$$

$$= \log \frac{1-y}{1+y} + 2 \tan^{-1} y$$

$$= \log \frac{\sqrt{1+x} - \sqrt{1-x}}{\sqrt{1+x} + \sqrt{1-x}} + 2 \tan^{-1} \sqrt{\frac{1-x}{1+x}}.$$

EXERCISES

1. Find the integrals of the following functions :

(i) $x \sqrt[3]{a + bx}$,

(ii) $\dfrac{x^2}{\sqrt[3]{x+2}}$,

(iii) $\dfrac{x}{(x+2)\sqrt{x+1}}$,

(iv) $\dfrac{\sqrt{x}}{x-1}$.

2. (i) $\dfrac{1}{x + \sqrt[3]{x}}$,

(ii) $\dfrac{1 + \sqrt{x} - \sqrt[3]{x^2}}{1 + \sqrt[3]{x}}$,

(iii) $\dfrac{1}{\sqrt{1+x} + \sqrt[3]{1+x}}$,

(iv) $\dfrac{\sqrt[4]{x}}{\sqrt{x} - 1}$.

3. (i) $\dfrac{x^2}{\sqrt{2x+3}}$,

(ii) $\dfrac{x^2}{(x+3)\sqrt{3x+4}}$,

(iii) $\dfrac{1}{(x^3 + x^2)\sqrt{1+x}}$,

(iv) $\dfrac{x+1}{(x+2)(x+3)^{3/2}}$,

(v) $\left(\dfrac{x+2}{2x+3} \right)^{1/2} \cdot \dfrac{1}{x}$,

(vi) $\sqrt{\dfrac{1+x^2}{x^2 - x^4}}$.

4. Evaluate

(i) $\displaystyle\int_0^\infty \dfrac{dx}{x\sqrt{1+x}}$,

(ii) $\displaystyle\int_1^\infty \dfrac{dx}{x^2\sqrt{1+x}}$,

(iii) $\displaystyle\int_8^{15} \dfrac{dx}{(x-3)\sqrt{x+1}}$,

(iv) $\displaystyle\int_3^8 \dfrac{2-3x}{x\sqrt{1+x}}\, dx$.

ANSWERS

1. (i) $3(4b^2 x^2 + abx - 3a^2) \sqrt[3]{a+bx} / 28b^2$.

(ii) $\dfrac{3}{40} (x+2)^{2/3} (5x^2 - 12x + 36)$.

(iii) $2\sqrt{x+1} - 4\tan^{-1}\sqrt{x+1}.$

(iv) $2\sqrt{x} + \log[(\sqrt{x}-1)/(\sqrt{x}+1)].$

2. (i) $\dfrac{3}{2}\log(1+\sqrt[3]{x^2}).$

   (ii) $6\left[\tan^{-1} y - y + \dfrac{1}{3}y^3 - \dfrac{1}{5}y^5 + \dfrac{1}{6}y^6 + \dfrac{1}{7}y^7 - \dfrac{1}{8}y^8\right],$

   where $x = y^6.$

   (iii) $2\sqrt{1+x} - 3\sqrt[3]{1+x} + 6\sqrt[6]{1+x} - 6\log[1+\sqrt[6]{1+x}].$

   (iv) $2\log\dfrac{\sqrt[4]{x}-1}{\sqrt[4]{x}+1} + 4\sqrt[4]{x} + \dfrac{4}{3}\sqrt[4]{x^3}.$

3. (i) $\dfrac{1}{5}(x^2 - 2x + 6)\sqrt{2x+3}.$

   (ii) $\dfrac{2}{27}(3x - 35)\sqrt{3x+4} + \dfrac{18}{\sqrt5}\tan^{-1}\sqrt{\dfrac{3x+4}{5}}.$

   (iii) $-\left(\dfrac{3x+1}{x}\right)\cdot\dfrac{1}{\sqrt{1+x}} + \dfrac{3}{2}\log\dfrac{\sqrt{1+x}+1}{\sqrt{1+x}-1}.$

   (iv) $-\dfrac{4}{\sqrt{x+3}} + \log\dfrac{\sqrt{x+3}+1}{\sqrt{x+3}-1}.$

   (v) $\dfrac{1}{\sqrt2}\log\dfrac{1+\sqrt2\,y}{1-\sqrt2\,y} - \sqrt{\dfrac{2}{3}}\log\dfrac{\sqrt3\,y+\sqrt2}{\sqrt3\,y-\sqrt2}$, where $y = \sqrt{\dfrac{x+2}{2x-3}}.$

   (vi) $\tan^{-1}\sqrt{\dfrac{1+x^2}{1-x^2}} + \dfrac{1}{2}\log\dfrac{\sqrt{1+x^2}-\sqrt{1-x^2}}{\sqrt{1+x^2}+\sqrt{1-x^2}}.$

4. (i) $2\log(\sqrt2+1).$ (ii) $\sqrt2 - \log(\sqrt2+1).$

   (iii) $(\log 5 - \log 3)/2.$ (iv) $2\log(3/2e^3).$

5.2. To evaluate the integrals

(i) $\displaystyle\int \sqrt{ax^2+bx+c}\;dx;$ (ii) $\displaystyle\int \dfrac{1}{\sqrt{ax^2+bx+c}}\;dx.$

If a be positive, we have

$$\sqrt{ax^2+bx+c} = \sqrt{a\left(x^2 + \dfrac{b}{a}x + \dfrac{c}{a}\right)}$$

$$= \sqrt{a}\,\sqrt{\left(x + \dfrac{b}{2a}\right)^2 + \dfrac{4ac-b^2}{4a^2}}.$$

(*i*) Let a and $4ac - b^2$ be both positive. We write
$$(4ac - b^2)\,/\,4a^2 = k^2 \text{ and put } x + b\,/\,2a = y,$$
so that we have
$$\int \sqrt{ax^2 + bx + c}\; dx = \sqrt{a} \int \sqrt{y^2 + k^2}\; dy$$
$$= \sqrt{a}\left[\frac{y\sqrt{y^2 + k^2}}{2} + \frac{k^2}{2}\sinh^{-1}\frac{y}{k} \right]$$

and
$$\int \frac{1}{\sqrt{ax^2 + bx + c}}\, dx = \frac{1}{\sqrt{a}}\int \frac{dy}{\sqrt{y^2 + k^2}} = \frac{1}{\sqrt{a}}\sinh^{-1}\frac{y}{k}.$$

(*ii*) Let a be positive and $4ac - b^2$ be negative. We write
$$(4ac - b^2)\,/\,4a^2 = -t^2 \text{ and put } x + b\,/\,2a = y,$$
so that we have, in this case,
$$\int \sqrt{ax^2 + bx + c}\; dx = \sqrt{a} \int \sqrt{y^2 - t^2}\; dy$$
$$= \sqrt{a}\left[\frac{y\sqrt{y^2 - t^2}}{2} - \frac{t^2}{2}\cosh^{-1}\frac{y}{t} \right]$$

and
$$\int \frac{1}{\sqrt{ax^2 + bx + c}}\, dx = \frac{1}{\sqrt{a}}\int \frac{dy}{\sqrt{y^2 - t^2}} = \frac{1}{\sqrt{a}}\cosh^{-1}\frac{y}{t}.$$

(*iii*) *Let a be negative.* We have
$$\sqrt{ax^2 + bx + c} = \sqrt{-a}\,\sqrt{-x^2 - \frac{bx}{a} - \frac{c}{a}}$$
$$= \sqrt{-a}\,\sqrt{\frac{b^2 - 4ac}{4a^2} - \left(x + \frac{b}{2a}\right)^2}$$
$$= \sqrt{-a}\,\sqrt{\left(\frac{\sqrt{b^2 - 4ac}}{2a}\right)^2 - \left(x + \frac{b}{2a}\right)^2}.$$

We have assumed that $b^2 > 4ac$, for if $b^2 < 4ac$, the expression under radical sign will always be negative.

As before, we write $(b^2 - 4ac)\,/\,4a^2 = t^2$ and $x + b\,/\,2a = y$, so that we have, in this case,
$$\int \sqrt{ax^2 + bx + c}\; dx = \sqrt{-a} \int \sqrt{t^2 - y^2}\; dy$$
$$= \sqrt{-a}\left[\frac{y\sqrt{t^2 - y^2}}{2} + \frac{t^2}{2}\sin^{-1}\frac{y}{t} \right]$$

and
$$\int \frac{1}{\sqrt{ax^2 + bx + c}} \, dx = \frac{1}{\sqrt{-a}} \int \frac{dy}{\sqrt{t^2 - y^2}} = \frac{1}{\sqrt{-a}} \sin^{-1} \frac{y}{t}.$$

EXAMPLES

1. *Integrate* : $\dfrac{1}{\sqrt{1 - 4x - 2x^2}}.$

Here
$$1 - 4x - 2x^2 = 2\left[\frac{1}{2} - (x^2 + 2x)\right]$$

$$= 2\left[\frac{3}{2} - (x + 1)^2\right]$$

$$\therefore \quad \int \frac{dx}{\sqrt{1 - 4x - 2x^2}} = \frac{1}{\sqrt{2}} \int \frac{dx}{\sqrt{\frac{3}{2} - (x + 1)^2}}$$

$$= \frac{1}{\sqrt{2}} \sin^{-1} \frac{x + 1}{\sqrt{3/2}}$$

$$= \frac{1}{\sqrt{2}} \sin^{-1} \frac{\sqrt{2}\,(x + 1)}{\sqrt{3}}.$$

2. *Integrate* : $\dfrac{1}{\sqrt{2x^2 - x + 2}}.$

Here, we have
$$\int \frac{dx}{\sqrt{2x^2 - x + 2}} = \frac{1}{\sqrt{2}} \int \frac{dx}{\sqrt{\left(x - \frac{1}{4}\right)^2 + (\sqrt{15}/4)^2}}$$

$$= \frac{1}{\sqrt{2}} \sinh^{-1} \frac{x - \frac{1}{4}}{(\sqrt{15}/4)}$$

$$= \frac{1}{\sqrt{2}} \sinh^{-1} \frac{4x - 1}{\sqrt{15}}.$$

3. *Evaluate* : $\int \sqrt{(15 - 2x - x^2)} \, dx.$

Given integral $= \int \sqrt{[16 - (x^2 + 2x + 1)]} \, dx$

$$= \int \sqrt{[16 - (x + 1)^2]} \, dx$$

$$= \frac{1}{2}[(x+1)\sqrt{\{16-(x+1)^2\}} + 16\sin^{-1}\{(x+1)/4\}]$$

$$= \frac{1}{2}(x+1)\sqrt{(15-2x-x^2)} + 8\sin^{-1}\frac{1}{4}(x+1).$$

EXERCISES

1. Integrate

(i) $\dfrac{1}{\sqrt{2x^2+3x+4}}$, (ii) $\sqrt{2x^2+3x+4}$,

(iii) $\dfrac{4}{\sqrt{3x^2-4x+1}}$, (iv) $\sqrt{3x^2-4x+1}$.

2. (i) $\dfrac{1}{\sqrt{1+2x-3x^2}}$, (ii) $\sqrt{1+2x-3x^2}$,

(iii) $\dfrac{1}{\sqrt{5x-6-x^2}}$.

ANSWERS

1. (i) $\dfrac{1}{\sqrt{2}}\sinh^{-1}\left(\dfrac{4x+3}{\sqrt{23}}\right)$.

(ii) $\dfrac{4x+3}{8}\sqrt{2x^2+3x+4} + \dfrac{23\sqrt{2}}{32}\sinh^{-1}\left(\dfrac{4x+3}{\sqrt{23}}\right)$.

(iii) $\dfrac{4}{\sqrt{3}}\cosh^{-1}(3x-2)$.

(iv) $\dfrac{3x-2}{6}\sqrt{3x^2-4x+1} - \dfrac{\sqrt{3}}{18}\cosh^{-1}(3x-2)$.

2. (i) $\sqrt{\dfrac{1}{3}}\sin^{-1}[(3x-1)/2]$.

(ii) $\dfrac{3x-1}{6}\sqrt{1+2x-3x^2} + \dfrac{2\sqrt{3}}{9}\sin^{-1}\left(\dfrac{3x-1}{2}\right)$.

(iii) $\sin^{-1}(2x-5)$.

5.3. Integration of

(i) $\dfrac{Ax+B}{\sqrt{ax^2+bx+c}}$, (ii) $(Ax+B)\sqrt{ax^2+bx+c}$.

We determine two constants λ and μ such that

$$Ax+B = \lambda(2ax+b) + \mu,$$

where $2ax + b$ is the differential coefficient of $ax^2 + bx + c$. The constants λ, μ are given by

$$A = 2a\lambda, \quad B = b\lambda + \mu,$$

$$\Rightarrow \qquad \lambda = \frac{A}{2a}, \quad \mu = \frac{2aB - Ab}{2a}.$$

(*i*) We have

$$\int \frac{Ax + B}{\sqrt{ax^2 + bx + c}}\, dx = \int \frac{\lambda\,(2ax + b) + \mu}{\sqrt{ax^2 + bx + c}}\, dx$$

$$= \lambda \int (ax^2 + bx + c)^{-1/2}\,(2ax + b)\, dx$$

$$+ \mu \int \frac{dx}{\sqrt{ax^2 + bx + c}}$$

$$= 2\lambda\,(ax^2 + bx + c)^{1/2} + \mu \int \frac{dx}{\sqrt{ax^2 + bx + c}}$$

and the integral on the right has already been considered in § 5.2.

(*ii*) Again, we have

$$\int (Ax + B)\sqrt{ax^2 + bx + c}\; dx$$

$$= \lambda \int (2ax + b)\sqrt{ax^2 + bx + c}\; dx + \mu \int \sqrt{ax^2 + bx + c}\; dx$$

$$= \frac{2\lambda}{3}\,(ax^2 + bx + c)^{3/2} + \mu \int \sqrt{ax^2 + bx + c}\; dx,$$

and $\int \sqrt{ax^2 + bx + c}\; dx$ has already been considered in § 5.2.

EXAMPLES

1. *Evaluate* : $\displaystyle\int \frac{x + 1}{\sqrt{x^2 - x + 1}}\, dx.$

Notice that $\dfrac{d}{dx}(x^2 - x + 1) = (2x - 1)$. Therefore

$$\int \frac{(x + 1)\, dx}{\sqrt{x^2 - x + 1}} = \int \frac{\frac{1}{2}(2x - 1) + \frac{3}{2}}{\sqrt{x^2 - x + 1}}\, dx$$

$$= \frac{1}{2}\int \frac{(2x - 1)\, dx}{\sqrt{x^2 - x + 1}} + \frac{3}{2}\int \frac{dx}{\sqrt{x^2 - x + 1}} \qquad ...(i)$$

To evaluate the first integral on the right hand side, let

$$x^2 - x + 1 = t^2; \text{ so that } (2x - 1) \, dx = 2t \, dt$$

$$\therefore \quad \frac{1}{2} \int \frac{(2x - 1) \, dx}{\sqrt{x^2 - x + 1}} = \frac{1}{2} \int \frac{2t \, dt}{t}$$

$$= t = \sqrt{x^2 - x + 1} \qquad \qquad ...(ii)$$

Also, $\displaystyle \int \frac{dx}{\sqrt{(x^2 - x + 1)}} = \int \frac{dx}{\sqrt{\left(x - \dfrac{1}{2}\right)^2 + \dfrac{3}{4}}}$

$$= \sinh^{-1}\left(\frac{x - 1/2}{\sqrt{3}/2}\right) \qquad \qquad ...(iii)$$

Substituting these values in (i), we get

$$\int \frac{(x + 1) \, dx}{\sqrt{x^2 - x + 1}} = \sqrt{x^2 - x + 1} + \frac{3}{2} \sinh^{-1}\left(\frac{2x - 1}{\sqrt{3}}\right).$$

2. Evaluate : $\displaystyle \int (3x - 2) \sqrt{(x^2 + x + 1)} \, dx.$

Here $d(x^2 + x + 1) = (2x + 1) \, dx.$

Therefore, let

$$3x - 2 = A(2x + 1) + B$$

$$\Rightarrow \qquad A = \frac{3}{2}, \ B = -\frac{7}{2}$$

$$\therefore \quad \int (3x - 2) \sqrt{(x^2 + x + 1)} \, dx$$

$$= \frac{3}{2} \int (2x + 1) \sqrt{(x^2 + x + 1)} \, dx - \frac{7}{2} \int \sqrt{(x^2 + x + 1)} \, dx \quad ...(i)$$

Putting $x^2 + x + 1 = t^2 \Rightarrow (2x + 1) \, dx = 2t \, dt.$

Then

$$\int (2x + 1) \sqrt{(x^2 + x + 1)} \, dx = \int 2t^2 \, dt$$

$$= \frac{2}{3} t^3 = \frac{2}{3} (x^2 + x + 1)^{3/2}.$$

Also,

$$\int \sqrt{(x^2 + x + 1)} \, dx = \int \sqrt{\left(x + \frac{1}{2}\right)^2 + \frac{3}{4}} \, dx$$

$$= \frac{1}{2}\left[\left(x + \frac{1}{2}\right)\sqrt{\left(x + \frac{1}{2}\right)^2 + \frac{3}{4}} + \frac{3}{4} \sinh^{-1}\left(\frac{x + 1}{\sqrt{3}/2}\right)\right].$$

Substituting these values in (*i*), we get

$$\int (3x - 2) \sqrt{(x^2 + x + 1)} \, dx = (x^2 + x + 1)^{3/2}$$

$$- \frac{7}{4} \left(x + \frac{1}{2} \right) \sqrt{(x^2 + x + 1)} - \frac{21}{16} \sinh^{-1} \left(\frac{2x + 1}{\sqrt{3}} \right).$$

EXERCISES

1. Evaluate

(*i*) $\int x \sqrt{1 + x - x^2} \, dx$,

(*ii*) $\int \frac{x}{\sqrt{8 + x - x^2}} \, dx$,

(*iii*) $\int \frac{2x + 3}{\sqrt{4x^2 + 5x + 6}} \, dx$,

(*iv*) $\int \frac{x}{\sqrt{3x^2 + 2x + 1}} \, dx$.

2. Evaluate

(*i*) $\int \frac{x^2 - 2x + 3}{\sqrt{x^2 + 1}} \, dx$,

(*ii*) $\int \frac{x^3 - 3}{\sqrt{x^2 + 2}} \, dx$,

(*iii*) $\int (2x - 5) \sqrt{2 + 3x - x^2} \, dx$.

ANSWERS

1. (*i*) $\dfrac{1}{24} (8x^2 - 2x - 11) \sqrt{1 + x - x^2} + \dfrac{5}{16} \sin^{-1} \dfrac{2x - 1}{\sqrt{5}}$.

   (*ii*) $-\sqrt{8 + x - x^2} + \dfrac{1}{2} \sin^{-1} \dfrac{2x - 1}{\sqrt{33}}$.

   (*iii*) $\dfrac{\sqrt{4x^2 + 5x + 6}}{2} + \dfrac{7}{8} \sinh^{-1} \dfrac{8x + 5}{\sqrt{71}}$.

   (*iv*) $\dfrac{\sqrt{3x^2 + 2x + 1}}{3} - \dfrac{1}{3\sqrt{3}} \sinh^{-1} \dfrac{3x + 1}{\sqrt{2}}$.

2. (*i*) $\dfrac{1}{2} (x - 4) \sqrt{x^2 + 1} + \dfrac{5}{2} \sinh^{-1} x$.

   (*ii*) $\dfrac{1}{3} (x^2 - 4) \sqrt{x^2 + 2} - 3 \sinh^{-1} \left(\dfrac{x}{\sqrt{2}} \right)$.

   (*iii*) $\dfrac{1}{6} (4x^2 - 18x + 1) \sqrt{2 + 3x - x^2} - \dfrac{17}{4} \sin^{-1} \dfrac{2x - 3}{\sqrt{17}}$.

5.4. Reduction Formula for

$$\int \frac{x^n}{\sqrt{ax^2 + bx + c}}\, dx,$$

where n is a positive integer.

Let $$I_n = \int \frac{x^n}{\sqrt{ax^2 + bx + c}}\, dx.$$

We will obtain a reduction formula connecting I_n with I_{n-1} and I_{n-2}.
We note that, $2ax + b$ is the derivative of $ax^2 + bx + c$.
We write

$$x^n = \frac{2ax + b - b}{2a} \cdot x^{n-1}$$

$$\therefore \quad I_n = \frac{1}{2a} \int \frac{(2ax + b)\, x^{n-1}}{\sqrt{ax^2 + bx + c}}\, dx - \frac{b}{2a} \int \frac{x^{n-1}}{\sqrt{ax^2 + bx + c}}\, dx \quad ...(i)$$

Integrating the first integral on the right by parts, we obtain

$$\int \frac{2ax + b}{\sqrt{ax^2 + bx + c}}\, x^{n-1}\, dx$$

$$= 2\sqrt{ax^2 + bx + c}\; x^{n-1} - 2 \int (n-1)\, x^{n-2} \sqrt{ax^2 + bx + c}\; dx$$

$$= 2\sqrt{ax^2 + bx + c}\; x^{n-1} - 2(n-1) \int \frac{x^{n-2}\,(ax^2 + bx + c)}{\sqrt{ax^2 + bx + c}}\, dx$$

$$= 2\sqrt{ax^2 + bx + c}\; x^{n-1} - 2a(n-1)\, I_n$$
$$\qquad\qquad - 2b(n-1)\, I_{n-1} - 2c(n-1)\, I_{n-2} \quad ...(ii)$$

From (i) and (ii), we obtain

$$I_n = \frac{1}{a}\sqrt{ax^2 + bx + c}\; x^{n-1} - (n-1)\, I_n - \frac{b(n-1)}{a}\, I_{n-1}$$

$$\qquad\qquad\qquad - \frac{c(n-1)}{a}\, I_{n-2} - \frac{b}{2a}\, I_{n-1}.$$

Transposing $(n-1)\, I_n$ and dividing by n, we obtain

$$I_n = \frac{\sqrt{ax^2 + bx + c}\; x^{n-1}}{an} - \frac{b(2n-1)}{2an}\, I_{n-1} - \frac{c(n-1)}{an}\, I_{n-2} \quad ...(A)$$

which is the required reduction formula.

As I_1 and I_0 have already been determined, we can, by successive applications of this formula, determine

$$I_2,\, I_3,\, I_4,\, \text{etc.}$$

EXAMPLE

Evaluate

$$\int \frac{x^3}{\sqrt{x^2 - 2x + 2}}\, dx.$$

Changing a to 1, b to -2, and c to 2 in (A), we get

$$\int \frac{x^n}{\sqrt{x^2 - 2x + 2}}\, dx = \frac{\sqrt{x^2 - 2x + 2}}{n}\cdot x^{n-1} + \frac{2n-1}{n}\int \frac{x^{n-1}}{\sqrt{x^2 - 2x + 2}}\, dx$$

$$- \frac{2(n-1)}{n}\int \frac{x^{n-2}}{\sqrt{x^2 - 2x + 2}}\, dx.$$

Putting $n = 3$ and $n = 2$, we get

$$\int \frac{x^3}{\sqrt{x^2 - 2x + 2}}\, dx = \frac{\sqrt{x^2 - 2x + 2}}{3}\, x^2 + \frac{5}{3}\int \frac{x^2}{\sqrt{x^2 - 2x + 2}}\, dx$$

$$- \frac{4}{3}\int \frac{x}{\sqrt{x^2 - 2x + 2}}\, dx \qquad \dots(i)$$

$$\int \frac{x^2}{\sqrt{x^2 - 2x + 2}}\, dx = \frac{\sqrt{x^2 - 2x + 2}}{2}\, x + \frac{3}{2}\int \frac{x}{\sqrt{x^2 - 2x + 2}}\, dx$$

$$- \int \frac{dx}{\sqrt{x^2 - 2x + 2}} \qquad \dots(ii)$$

Now,

$$\int \frac{x}{\sqrt{x^2 - 2x + 2}}\, dx = \frac{1}{2}\int \left[\frac{2x - 2}{\sqrt{x^2 - 2x + 2}} + \frac{2}{\sqrt{(x-1)^2 + 1}} \right] dx$$

$$= (x^2 - 2x + 2)^{1/2} + \sinh^{-1}(x - 1) \qquad \dots(iii)$$

and $\displaystyle \int \frac{dx}{\sqrt{x^2 - 2x + 2}} = \sinh^{-1}(x - 1).$ $\dots(iv)$

From the system of equations (i), (ii), (iii) and (iv), we get

$$\int \frac{x^3}{\sqrt{x^2 - 2x + 2}}\, dx = \left(\frac{2x^2 + 5x + 15}{6} \right)\sqrt{x^2 - 2x + 2} + \frac{5}{6}\sinh^{-1}(x - 1).$$

Note. The integration of $x^n / \sqrt{ax^2 + bx + c}$ can sometimes be more conveniently effected in another manner which we shall now explain.

The method is also applicable to the more general integral

$$\int \frac{\varphi(x)}{\sqrt{ax^2 + bx + c}}\, dx,$$

where $\varphi(x)$ is a polynomial in x.

The method depends upon the following result :

If $\varphi(x)$ is a polynomial of degree n, then there exists a polynomial $f(x)$ of degree $(n - 1)$ and a constant A, such that

$$\int \frac{\varphi(x)}{\sqrt{ax^2 + bx + c}}\, dx = f(x)\sqrt{ax^2 + bx + c} + A \int \frac{dx}{\sqrt{ax^2 + bx + c}}.$$

Differentiating both sides and multiplying by $\sqrt{ax^2 + bx + c}$, we get

$$\varphi(x) = f'(x)(ax^2 + bx + c) + \frac{1}{2}(2ax + b)f(x) + A.$$

Either side of this equation is a polynomial of degree n. Equating the coefficients of like powers of x, we will get $(n + 1)$ *linear* equations which will uniquely determine the n coefficients occurring in the polynomial $f(x)$ and the constant A. Thus $f(x)$ and A have been completely determined.

We will now illustrate this method by an example.

EXAMPLE

Evaluate

$$\int \frac{x^3 + 5x^2 - 3x + 4}{\sqrt{x^2 + x + 1}}\, dx.$$

Here $\varphi(x) = x^3 + 5x^2 - 3x + 4$ is a polynomial of third degree.
We write

$$\int \frac{x^3 + 5x^2 - 3x + 4}{\sqrt{x^2 + x + 1}}\, dx = (Ax^2 + Bx + C)\sqrt{x^2 + x + 1}$$

$$+ D \int \frac{1}{\sqrt{x^2 + x + 1}}\, dx.$$

Differentiating and multiplying by $\sqrt{x^2 + x + 1}$, we get

$$x^3 + 5x^2 - 3x + 4 = (2Ax + B)(x^2 + x + 1)$$

$$+ \frac{1}{2}(Ax^2 + Bx + C)(2x + 1) + D.$$

Equating the coefficients of like powers of x, we get

$$1 = 3A,$$

$$5 = \frac{5}{2}A + 2B,$$

$$-3 = 2A + \frac{3}{2}B + C$$

$$4 = B + \frac{1}{2}C + D.$$

From these, we obtain

$$A = 1/3;\ B = 25/12;\ C = -163/24;\ D = 85/16.$$

Also,

$$\int \frac{dx}{\sqrt{x^2 + x + 1}} = \int \frac{dx}{\sqrt{\left(x + \frac{1}{2}\right)^2 + \left(\frac{\sqrt{3}}{2}\right)^2}}$$

$$= \sinh^{-1}\left(\frac{2x+1}{\sqrt{3}}\right)$$

$$\therefore \int \frac{x + 5x^2 - 3x + 4}{\sqrt{x^2 + x + 1}}\, dx = \left(\frac{x^2}{3} + \frac{25}{12}x - \frac{163}{24}\right)\sqrt{x^2 + x + 1}$$

$$+ \frac{85}{16}\sinh^{-1}\left(\frac{2x+1}{\sqrt{3}}\right).$$

EXERCISES

1. Find the integrals of the following functions :

(i) $\dfrac{x^3 + 4x^2 - 6x + 3}{\sqrt{5 + 6x - x^2}}$,

(ii) $\dfrac{x^4}{\sqrt{3 + 2x + x^2}}$,

(iii) $\dfrac{x^3}{\sqrt{ax^2 + 2bx + c}}$.

2. Evaluate $\displaystyle\int \frac{x^3\, dx}{\sqrt{x^2 + 2x + 2}}$ in two different ways.

ANSWERS

1. (i) $\dfrac{1}{6}(2x^2 + 27x + 227)\sqrt{5 + 6x - x^2} - 139 \sin^{-1}[(3 - x)/\sqrt{14}]$.

(ii) $\dfrac{1}{12}(3x^3 - 7x^2 + 4x + 30)\sqrt{3 + 2x + x^2}$

$$- \frac{7}{2}\sinh^{-1}[(x+1)/\sqrt{2}].$$

(iii) $\dfrac{1}{6a^3}\left(2a^2x^2 - 5abx + 15b^2 - 4ac\right)\sqrt{ax^2 + 2bx + c}$

$$+ \dfrac{3abc - 5b^3}{2a^3}\int \dfrac{dx}{\sqrt{ax^2 + 2bx + c}}.$$

2. $\dfrac{1}{6}\left(2x^2 - 5x + 7\right)\sqrt{x^2 + 2x + 2} + \dfrac{1}{2}\sinh^{-1}(x+1).$

5.5. To evaluate

$$\int \dfrac{dx}{(Ax + B)\sqrt{ax^2 + bx + c}}.$$

The substitution $Ax + B = 1/t$ will enable us to reduce it to an integral of the form considered in § 5.2.

We have $dx = -\dfrac{1}{At^2}\,dt,$

and $x = \left(\dfrac{1}{t} - B\right)\dfrac{1}{A} = \dfrac{1 - Bt}{At}.$

Thus we have

$$\int \dfrac{dx}{(Ax + B)\sqrt{ax^2 + bx + c}}$$

$$= -\int \dfrac{dt}{\sqrt{(aB^2 - bAB + cA^2)\,t^2 + (bA - 2aB)\,t + a}}$$

which has been considered in § 5.2.

EXAMPLE

Evaluate $\displaystyle\int \dfrac{dx}{(x + 1)\sqrt{2x^2 + 3x + 4}}.$

Putting $x + 1 = 1/y$, we get

$$\int \dfrac{dx}{(x+1)\sqrt{2x^2 + 3x + 4}} = -\int \dfrac{dy}{\sqrt{3y^2 - y + 2}}$$

$$= -\dfrac{1}{\sqrt{3}}\int \dfrac{dy}{\sqrt{(y - 1/6)^2 + (\sqrt{23}/6)^2}}$$

$$= -\dfrac{1}{\sqrt{3}}\sinh^{-1}\left(\dfrac{6y - 1}{\sqrt{23}}\right)$$

$$= -\dfrac{1}{\sqrt{3}}\sinh^{-1}\left[\dfrac{5 - x}{\sqrt{23}\,(x + 1)}\right].$$

Note. The integral

$$\int \frac{dx}{(Ax + B)^r \sqrt{ax^2 + bx + c}}$$

where r is a positive integer, may also be evaluated by the substitution $Ax + B = 1/t$.

EXERCISES

Evaluate the following integrals :

1. (i) $\displaystyle\int \frac{dx}{(2 - x) \sqrt{1 - 2x + 3x^2}}$,   (ii) $\displaystyle\int \frac{dx}{(3 + 2x) \sqrt{x^2 + x + 1}}$,

   (iii) $\displaystyle\int \frac{dx}{(x + 1) \sqrt{x^2 - 1}}$,   (iv) $\displaystyle\int \frac{(x + 1)\, dx}{(2 + x) \sqrt{2x^2 - 3x + 1}}$.

2. (i) $\displaystyle\int \frac{1 + 2x}{(1 + 3x) \sqrt{x^2 + 2x + 5}}\, dx$,   (ii) $\displaystyle\int \frac{\sqrt{x^2 + 1}}{x}\, dx$,

   (iii) $\displaystyle\int \frac{x^2 + 2x - 1}{(x + 2) \sqrt{2x^2 + 3x - 4}}\, dx$,   (iv) $\displaystyle\int \frac{\sqrt{1 + x + x^2}}{1 + x}\, dx$,

3. (i) $\displaystyle\int \frac{dx}{(x - a) \sqrt{(x - a)(b - x)}}$,   (ii) $\displaystyle\int \frac{(x^2 + 1)\, dx}{x \sqrt{4x^2 + 1}}$,

   (iii) $\displaystyle\int \frac{x^3}{(x - 1) \sqrt{x^2 - x + 1}}\, dx$,   (iv) $\displaystyle\int \frac{dx}{(x + 2)^2 \sqrt{3x + 4x - 5}}$.

ANSWERS

1. (i) $\dfrac{1}{3} \sinh^{-1}\left[\dfrac{5x - 1}{\sqrt{2}\,(2 - x)}\right]$.

   (ii) $-\dfrac{1}{\sqrt{7}} \sinh^{-1}\left[\dfrac{1 - 4x}{\sqrt{3}\,(3 + 2x)}\right]$.   (iii) $\sqrt{\dfrac{x - 1}{x + 1}}$.

   (iv) $\dfrac{1}{\sqrt{2}} \cosh^{-1}(4x - 3) + \dfrac{1}{\sqrt{15}} \cosh^{-1}\left(\dfrac{8 - 11x}{2 + x}\right)$.

2. (i) $\dfrac{2}{3} \sinh^{-1}\left(\dfrac{x + 1}{2}\right) - \dfrac{1}{3\sqrt{40}} \sinh^{-1}\left(\dfrac{7 + x}{1 + 3x}\right)$.

   (ii) $\sqrt{x^2 + 1} - \operatorname{cosech}^{-1} x$.

(iii) $\dfrac{1}{2} \sqrt{2x^2 + 3x - 4} - \dfrac{3}{4\sqrt{2}} \cosh^{-1} \dfrac{4x + 3}{\sqrt{41}}$

$$+ \dfrac{1}{\sqrt{2}} \sin^{-1} \dfrac{5x + 14}{\sqrt{41}\,(x + 2)}.$$

(iv) $\sqrt{x^2 + x + 1} - \dfrac{1}{2} \sinh^{-1} \dfrac{2x + 1}{\sqrt{3}} - \sinh^{-1} \left[\dfrac{1 - x}{\sqrt{3}\,(1 + x)} \right].$

3. (i) $\dfrac{2}{a - b} \sqrt{\dfrac{b - x}{x - a}}.$ (ii) $\dfrac{1}{4} \cdot \sqrt{4x^2 + 1} - \sinh^{-1} \left(\dfrac{1}{2x} \right).$

(iii) $\dfrac{1}{4} (2x + 7) \sqrt{x^2 - x + 1} + \dfrac{11}{8} \sinh^{-1} \dfrac{2x - 1}{\sqrt{3}}$

$$- \sinh^{-1} \left[\dfrac{x + 1}{\sqrt{3}\,(x - 1)} \right].$$

(iv) $\dfrac{\sqrt{3x^2 + 4x - 5}}{x + 2} + 4 \sin^{-1} \dfrac{4x + 9}{\sqrt{19}\,(x + 2)}.$

5.6. To evaluate $\displaystyle \int \dfrac{dx}{(ax^2 + bx + c)\sqrt{Ax^2 + Bx + C}}.$

The proper substitution for this case is

$$\dfrac{Ax^2 + Bx + C}{ax^2 + bx + c} = y^2.$$

An example will illustrate the process.

EXAMPLE

Evaluate

$$\int \dfrac{dx}{(1 + x^2)\sqrt{1 - x^2}}.$$

We put $\dfrac{1 - x^2}{1 + x^2} = y^2 \Rightarrow x^2 = \dfrac{1 - y^2}{1 + y^2}$

$\Rightarrow \qquad 2x\,dx = -\dfrac{4y\,dy}{(1 + y^2)^2}.$

Also $1 + x^2 = \dfrac{2}{1 + y^2}$ and $1 - x^2 = \dfrac{2y^2}{1 + y^2}.$

$\therefore \quad \displaystyle \int \dfrac{dx}{(1 + x^2)\sqrt{1 - x^2}} = -\dfrac{1}{\sqrt{2}} \int \dfrac{dy}{\sqrt{1 - y^2}}$

$$\frac{1}{\sqrt{2}} \sin^{-1} y$$

$$= \frac{1}{\sqrt{2}} \sin^{-1} \sqrt{\frac{1-x^2}{1+x^2}}$$

EXERCISES

Evaluate the following integrals :

1. (i) $\displaystyle\int \frac{dx}{(x^2 - 1)\sqrt{x^2 + 1}}$,

(ii) $\displaystyle\int \frac{dx}{(2x^2 + 3)\sqrt{3x^2 - 4}}$,

(iii) $\displaystyle\int \frac{dx}{x^2 \sqrt{x^2 + 1}}$,

(iv) $\displaystyle\int \frac{(x+1)\,dx}{(x^2 + 4)\sqrt{x^2 + 9}}$.

2. (i) $\displaystyle\int \frac{(x^2 + 2x + 3)\,dx}{(x^2 + 1)\sqrt{x^2 - 2}}$,

(ii) $\displaystyle\int \frac{(x^3 + x^2 + x + 1)\,dx}{(x^2 + 2)\sqrt{x^2 - 3}}$,

(iii) $\displaystyle\int_0^\infty \frac{dx}{(x^2 + a^2)\sqrt{x^2 + b^2}}, (a^2 < b^2)$

(iv) $\displaystyle\int_0^{1/\sqrt{3}} \frac{dx}{(1 + x^2)\sqrt{1 - x^2}}$.

ANSWERS

1. (i) $-\dfrac{1}{\sqrt{2}} \sinh^{-1} \sqrt{\dfrac{x^2 + 1}{x^2 - 1}}$.

(ii) $\dfrac{1}{\sqrt{51}} \sinh^{-1} \sqrt{\dfrac{9x^2 - 12}{8x^2 + 12}}$.

(iii) $-\dfrac{\sqrt{1 + x^2}}{x}$.

(iv) $\dfrac{\sqrt{5}}{10} \log \dfrac{\sqrt{x^2 + 9} - \sqrt{5}}{\sqrt{x^2 + 9} + \sqrt{5}} + \dfrac{\sqrt{5}}{10} \tan^{-1} \dfrac{\sqrt{5}x}{2\sqrt{x^2 + 9}}$.

2. (i) $\cosh^{-1} \dfrac{x}{\sqrt{2}} + \dfrac{2}{\sqrt{3}} \tan^{-1} \sqrt{\dfrac{x^2 - 2}{3}} + \dfrac{2}{\sqrt{3}} \sinh^{-1} \sqrt{\dfrac{x^2 - 2}{2x^2 + 2}}$.

(ii) $\sqrt{x^2 - 3} - \dfrac{1}{\sqrt{5}} \tan^{-1} \sqrt{\dfrac{x^2 - 3}{5}} + \cosh^{-1} \dfrac{x}{\sqrt{3}}$

$$- \dfrac{1}{\sqrt{10}} \sinh^{-1} \sqrt{\dfrac{2x^2 - 6}{3x^2 + 6}}.$$

(iii) $\dfrac{1}{a\sqrt{b^2 - a^2}} \cos^{-1}\left(\dfrac{a}{b}\right)$.

(iv) $\dfrac{\pi}{4\sqrt{2}}$.

5.7. General Case. Certain irrational functions which are not already in one or other of the standard forms considered previously can be changed into an integrable form by rationalising the numerator or denominator. Some expressions can be broken up into two or more, each of which is integrable or can easily be reduced to an integrable form. A few illustrations are given below.

EXAMPLES

1. *Evaluate* : $\int \dfrac{dx}{\sqrt{1+x} + \sqrt{x}}$.

Rationalising the denominator, we have

Given integral $= \int \dfrac{\sqrt{1+x} - \sqrt{x}}{\left(\sqrt{1+x}\right)^2 - \left(\sqrt{x}\right)^2}\, dx$

$= \int \left[\sqrt{1+x} - \sqrt{x}\right] dx$

$= \dfrac{2}{3}(1+x)^{3/2} - \dfrac{2}{3}x^{3/2}$.

2. *Integrate* $\dfrac{\sqrt{x+1}}{(x+2)\sqrt{x+3}}$.

Rationalising the numerator, we have

$\int \dfrac{\sqrt{x+1}}{(x+2)\sqrt{x+3}}\, dx = \int \dfrac{x+1}{x+2} \cdot \dfrac{1}{\sqrt{(x+1)(x+3)}}\, dx$

$= \int \left(1 - \dfrac{1}{x+2}\right) \dfrac{1}{\sqrt{x^2+4x+3}}$

$= \int \dfrac{dx}{\sqrt{x^2+4x+3}} - \int \dfrac{dx}{(x+2)\sqrt{x^2+4x+3}}$

$= I_1 - I_2$ (say).

$I_1 = \int \dfrac{dx}{\sqrt{x^2+4x+3}} = \int \dfrac{dx}{\sqrt{\{(x+2)^2 - 1\}}}$

$= \cosh^{-1}(x+2)$.

Also, putting $x+2 = 1/t$ and $dx = -(1/t^2)\, dt$, we have

$I_2 = \int \dfrac{dx}{(x+2)\sqrt{(x+2)^2-1}} = \int \dfrac{-(1/t^2)\, dt}{(1/t)\sqrt{(1/t)^2 - 1}}$

$= -\int \dfrac{dt}{\sqrt{1-t^2}} = -\sin^{-1} t = -\sin^{-1}\dfrac{1}{x+2}$.

$\therefore$ The given integral

$$= \cosh^{-1}(x+2) + \sin^{-1}\frac{1}{x+2}.$$

3. *Integrate* : $x\sqrt{\dfrac{1+x}{1-x}}.$

Given integral $= \displaystyle\int \frac{x(1+x)\,dx}{\sqrt{1-x^2}}$

$$= \int \frac{x\,dx}{\sqrt{1-x^2}} + \int \frac{x^2\,dx}{\sqrt{1-x^2}}$$

$$= \frac{1}{2}\int \frac{2x\,dx}{\sqrt{1-x^2}} - \int \sqrt{1-x^2}\,dx + \int \frac{dx}{\sqrt{1-x^2}}$$

$$= -\frac{1}{2}\sqrt{1-x^2} - \frac{1}{2}x\sqrt{1-x^2} + \frac{1}{2}\sin^{-1}x.$$

4. *Integrate* : $\dfrac{1}{\{\sqrt{x+a}+\sqrt{x+b}\}}.$

$$\int \frac{dx}{\{\sqrt{x+a}+\sqrt{x+b}\}} = \int \frac{\sqrt{x+a}-\sqrt{x+b}}{(x+a)-(x+b)}\,dx$$

$$= \frac{1}{(a-b)}\int [\sqrt{x+a}-\sqrt{x+b}]\,dx$$

$$= \frac{2}{3(a-b)}[(x+a)^{3/2}-(x+b)^{3/2}].$$

EXERCISES

Integrate with respect to x :

1. $\sqrt{\dfrac{1+x}{1-x}};$ **2.** $\sqrt{\dfrac{x+1}{x-1}};$

3. $x\sqrt{\dfrac{1-x}{1+x}};$ **4.** $\dfrac{1}{x+\sqrt{x^2+1}};$

5. $\dfrac{\sqrt{1+x^2}}{1-x^2};$ **6.** $\dfrac{x+1}{(x^2+4)\sqrt{x^2+9}}.$

ANSWERS

1. $\sin^{-1}x - \sqrt{1-x^2}.$ **2.** $\sqrt{x^2-1}+\cosh^{-1}x.$

3. $\left(\dfrac{1}{2}x - 1\right)\sqrt{1 - x^2} - \dfrac{1}{2}\sin^{-1}x.$

4. $\dfrac{1}{2}[x^2 - x\sqrt{x^2 - 1} + \cosh^{-1}x].$

5. $-\log[x + \sqrt{1 + x^2}] - \dfrac{1}{\sqrt{2}}\log\left[\dfrac{\sqrt{1 + x^2} - x\sqrt{2}}{\sqrt{1 + x^2} + x\sqrt{2}}\right].$

6. $\dfrac{1}{2\sqrt{5}}\log\dfrac{\sqrt{x^2 + 9} - \sqrt{5}}{\sqrt{x^2 + 9} + \sqrt{5}} - \dfrac{1}{2\sqrt{5}}\tan^{-1}\dfrac{2\sqrt{x^2 + 9}}{2\sqrt{5}}.$

5.8. Integration of irrational algebraic functions by trigonometric transformations. In some cases, a suitable trigonometric transformation greatly simplifies the process of integration of irrational algebraic functions. Examples of this type have already appeared in § 2.4.

For, integrating functions which involve

$$\sqrt{a^2 - x^2}, \ \sqrt{a^2 + x^2} \text{ or } \sqrt{x^2 - a^2}$$

we apply the transformations

$$x = a\sin\theta, \ x = a\tan\theta, \ x = a\sec\theta$$

respectively.

The transformations $x = a\sinh\theta$, $x = a\cosh\theta$ also prove useful for functions involving $\sqrt{a^2 + x^2}$ and $\sqrt{x^2 - a^2}$ respectively.

Moreover, functions involving

$$\sqrt{(a^2 - b^2x^2)} \text{ or } \sqrt{(a^2 + b^2x^2)} \text{ or } \sqrt{(b^2x^2 - a^2)}$$

and no other irrational factor may be integrated by the trigonometric substitutions

$$bx = a\sin\theta, \text{ or } bx = a\tan\theta, \text{ or } bx = a\sec\theta$$

respectively.

Since $\sqrt{(ax^2 + bx + c)}$ can easily be reduced to one of the above forms, trigonometrical substitutions are also applicable in the case of functions involving $\sqrt{(ax^2 + bx + c)}$.

If some power of x, say x^{n-1} is a factor of the integrand and the remaining part is a function of x^n alone, the substitution $x^n = t$ often simplifies the integration.

EXAMPLES

1. *Evaluate* $\displaystyle\int\dfrac{1}{x^2\sqrt{1 - x^2}}\,dx.$

Putting $x = \sin\theta$, we see that the given integral

$$= \int \operatorname{cosec}^2\theta\, d\theta = -\cot\theta = -\frac{\sqrt{1-x^2}}{x}.$$

2. Evaluate $\displaystyle\int_0^1 x\sqrt{\frac{1-x^2}{1+x^2}}\, dx.$

We put $x^2 = \cos\theta \implies 2x\, dx = -\sin\theta\, d\theta.$

Now, $\theta = \pi/2$ when $x = 0$ and $\theta = 0$ when $x = 1$. Therefore the given integral

$$= -\int_{\pi/2}^0 \sqrt{\frac{1-\cos\theta}{1+\cos\theta}}\,\frac{\sin\theta}{2}\, d\theta$$

$$= -\int_0^{\pi/2} \frac{\sin(\theta/2)}{\cos(\theta/2)}\sin(\theta/2)\cos(\theta/2)\, d\theta$$

$$= -\int_0^{\pi/2} \sin^2(\theta/2)\, d\theta = \frac{1}{2}\int_0^{\pi/2}(1-\cos\theta)\, d\theta = \frac{\pi-2}{4}.$$

3. Integrate $\dfrac{x^5}{\sqrt{1+x^3+x^6}}.$

Putting $x^3 = t$ and $3x^2\, dx = dt$, we have

$$\int \frac{x^5\, dx}{\sqrt{1+x^3+x^6}} = \frac{1}{3}\int \frac{t\, dt}{\sqrt{1+t+t^2}}$$

$$= \frac{1}{6}\int \frac{(2t+1)\, dt}{\sqrt{t^2+t+1}} - \frac{1}{6}\int \frac{dt}{\sqrt{t^2+t+1}}$$

$$= \frac{2}{6}\sqrt{t^2+t+1} - \frac{1}{6}\int \frac{dt}{\sqrt{\left(t+\dfrac{1}{2}\right)^2+\dfrac{3}{4}}}$$

$$= \frac{1}{3}\sqrt{t^2+t+1} - \frac{1}{6}\log\left[\left(t+\frac{1}{2}\right)+\sqrt{\left(t+\frac{1}{2}\right)^2+\frac{3}{4}}\right]$$

$$= \frac{1}{3}\sqrt{1+x^3+x^6} - \frac{1}{6}\log\left[x^3+\frac{1}{2}+\sqrt{1+x^3+x^6}\right].$$

4. Evaluate : $\displaystyle\int_\alpha^\beta \sqrt{(x-\alpha)(\beta-x)}\, dx,\ \beta > \alpha.$

For this type of integrals, the best substitution is

$$x = \alpha \cos^2 \theta + \beta \sin^2 \theta$$

$$\Rightarrow \quad dx = 2 (\beta - \alpha) \sin \theta \cos \theta \, d\theta$$

$$\Rightarrow \quad x - \alpha = (\alpha \cos^2 \theta + \beta \sin^2 \theta) - \alpha = (\beta - \alpha) \sin^2 \theta$$

and $\quad \beta - x = (\beta - \alpha) \cos^2 \theta$.

When $x = \alpha$, we have $\sin^2 \theta = 0$, *i.e.*, $\theta = 0$.

When $x = \beta$, we have $\cos^2 \theta = 0$, *i.e.*, $\theta = \pi / 2$.

$$\therefore \quad \text{Given integral} = \int_{\alpha}^{\beta} \sqrt{(x - \alpha)(\beta - x)} \, dx$$

$$= (\beta - \alpha)^2 \int_{0}^{\pi/2} 2 \sin^2 \theta \cos^2 \theta \, d\theta$$

$$= \frac{1}{4} (\beta - \alpha)^2 \int_{0}^{\pi/2} (1 - \cos 4\theta) \, d\theta$$

$$= \frac{(\beta - \alpha)^2}{4} \left[\theta - \frac{\sin 4\theta}{4} \right]_{0}^{\pi/2} = \frac{\pi (\beta - \alpha)^2}{8}.$$

5. *Integrate* : $(1 + x^{1/4}) / (1 + x^{1/2})$.

Putting $x = t^4$, we have

$$\int \frac{(1 + x^{1/4}) \, dx}{(1 + x^{1/2})} = \int \frac{(1 + t) \, 4t^3 \, dt}{(1 + t^2)}$$

$$= 4 \int \frac{t^4 + t^3}{t^2 + 1} \, dt$$

$$= 4 \int \left[t^2 + t - 1 - \frac{t - 1}{t^2 + 1} \right] dt$$

$$= 4 \left[\int (t^2 - t - 1) \, dt - \frac{1}{2} \int \frac{2t \, dt}{t^2 + 1} + \int \frac{dt}{t^2 + 1} \right]$$

$$= \frac{4}{3} t^3 + 2t^2 - 4t - 2 \log (t^2 + 1) + 4 \tan^{-1} t$$

$$= \frac{4}{3} x^{3/4} + 2 \sqrt{x} - 4 x^{1/4} - 2 \log (\sqrt{x} + 1) + 4 \tan^{-1} x^{1/4}.$$

6. *Evaluate* $\int \dfrac{dx}{(1 + x^2)^{3/2}}$.

Putting $x = \tan \theta$, we see that the given integral

$$= \int \cos \theta \, d\theta = \sin \theta = \frac{x}{\sqrt{1 + x^2}}.$$

EXERCISES

1. Evaluate

(i) $\int \dfrac{1}{x^2 \sqrt{1+x^2}}\, dx$,　　　　(ii) $\int \dfrac{dx}{(4+x^2)^{3/2}}$,

(iii) $\int \dfrac{1}{(2ax+x^2)^{3/2}}\, dx$,　　　(iv) $\int \dfrac{dx}{(x^2+2x+10)^{3/2}}$.

2. (i) $\int x \sqrt{\dfrac{1-x}{1+x}}\, dx$,　　　　(ii) $\int \dfrac{\sqrt{x^2-a^2}}{x}\, dx$,

(iii) $\displaystyle\int_{\alpha}^{\beta} \dfrac{dx}{\sqrt{(x-\alpha)(\beta-x)}}$, $(\beta > \alpha)$,

(iv) $\int \dfrac{dx}{(x^2-a^2)^{3/2}}$,　　　(v) $\int \dfrac{(1+x\cos\alpha)\, dx}{(1+2x\cos\alpha+x^2)^{3/2}}$.

3. Show that

$$\int_{0}^{1/2} \dfrac{dx}{(1-2x^2)\sqrt{1-x}} = \dfrac{1}{2}\log(2+\sqrt{3}).$$

ANSWERS

1. (i) $-\dfrac{\sqrt{1+x^2}}{x}$.　　　　　　(ii) $\dfrac{1}{4}\dfrac{x}{\sqrt{4+x^2}}$.

(iii) $-\dfrac{1}{a^2}\cdot\dfrac{a+x}{\sqrt{2ax+x^2}}$.　　　(iv) $\dfrac{1}{9}\cdot\dfrac{x+1}{\sqrt{x^2+2x+10}}$.

2. (i) $\dfrac{1}{2}\cos^{-1}x + \dfrac{1}{2}(x-2)\sqrt{1-x^2}$.

(ii) $a\sqrt{x^2-a^2} - a\cos^{-1}(a/x)$.　　　(iii) π.

(iv) $-\dfrac{x}{a^2\sqrt{x^2-a^2}}$.　　　　(v) $\dfrac{x}{\sqrt{x^2+2x\cos\alpha+1}}$.

5.9. Integration of $x^m (a+bx^n)^p$.

Case 1. When p is a positive integer.

In this case, expand $(a+bx^n)^p$ by Binomial theorem into a finite series. This transforms the integrand into a sum of a finite number of terms each of which is easily integrable.

EXAMPLES

1. *Evaluate* : $\int x^{1/4} (2 + 3x^{1/3})^2 \, dx.$

Here $\qquad x^{1/4} (2 + 3x^{1/3})^2 = x^{1/4} (4 + 12x^{1/3} + 9x^{2/3})$

$$= 4x^{1/4} + 12x^{7/12} + 9x^{11/12}.$$

Therefore

$$\int x^{1/4} (2 + 3x^{1/3})^2 \, dx = \int (4x^{1/4} + 12x^{7/12} + 9x^{11/12}) \, dx$$

$$= 4 \cdot \frac{4}{5} x^{5/4} + 12 \cdot \frac{12}{19} x^{19/12} + 9 \cdot \frac{12}{23} x^{23/12}$$

$$= \frac{16}{5} x^{5/4} + \frac{144}{19} x^{19/12} + \frac{108}{23} x^{23/12}$$

Case 2. When $\dfrac{m + 1}{n}$ is an integer.

In this case, if p is not an integer, then it must be of the form $p = r/s$ and the integration can be effected by the substitution

$$a + bx^n = t^s.$$

Case 3. When $p + \dfrac{m + 1}{n}$ is an integer, p is not an integer.

In this case, we put $x = 1/t$. Thus

$$\int x^m (a + bx^n)^p \, dx = -\int \frac{1}{t^{m+2}} \left(a + \frac{b}{t^n} \right)^p dt$$

$$= -t^{-(m+np+2)} (b + at^n)^p \, dt.$$

This integral comes under Case 2, since

$$\frac{-(m + np + 2) + 1}{n}, \; i.e., \; -\left(p + \frac{m + 1}{n} \right) \text{ is an integer.}$$

Hence to evaluate the transformed integral, put

$$b + at^n = u^s, \text{ where } p = r/s.$$

2. *Evaluate* : $\int x^{-2/3} (1 + x^{1/2})^{-5/3} \, dx.$

Here $p + \dfrac{m + 1}{n} = -\dfrac{5}{3} + \dfrac{-\dfrac{2}{3} + 1}{\dfrac{1}{2}} = -1$ which is an integer. Hence

putting $x = 1/t$, we obtain

$$\int x^{-2/3} (1 + x^{1/2})^{-5/3} \, dx = -\int t^{2/3 + 5/6 - 2} (t^{1/2} + 1)^{-5/3} \, dt$$

$$= -\int t^{-1/2} (1 + t^{1/2})^{-5/3} \, dt.$$

Again, putting $1 + t^{1/2} = u^3$ and $\dfrac{1}{2} t^{-1/2} \, dt = 3u^2 \, du$, we have

$$\int x^{-2/3} (1 + x^{1/2})^{-5/3} \, dx = -6 \int u^{-5} \cdot u^2 \, du = 3u^{-2}$$

$$= 3(1 + t^{1/2})^{-2/3} = 3(1 + x^{-1/2})^{-2/3}.$$

EXERCISES

Integrate with respect to x :

1. $x^{2/3} (1 + x^{6/5})^2$.

2. $x^{1/3} (1 + x^{3/4})^3$.

3. $x (1 + x^3)^{1/3}$.

4. $x^3 (1 + x^2)^{1/3}$.

5. $x^2 (1 + 2x^4)^{-3/4}$.

6. $x^{2n-1} (a + bx^n)^p$.

7. $x^5 (a^3 + x^3)^{1/2}$.

8. $x^{1/2} (a^3 + x^3)^{1/2}$.

ANSWERS

1. $\dfrac{3}{5} x^{5/3} + \dfrac{30}{43} x^{43/15} + \dfrac{15}{61} x^{61/15}$.

2. $\dfrac{3}{4} x^{4/3} + \dfrac{36}{25} x^{25/12} + \dfrac{18}{17} x^{17/6} + \dfrac{12}{43} x^{43/12}$.

3. $\dfrac{u}{3(u^3 - 1)} + \dfrac{1}{9} \log \dfrac{\sqrt{u^2 + u + 1}}{u - 1} + \dfrac{1}{3\sqrt{3}} \tan^{-1} \dfrac{2u + 1}{\sqrt{3}}$,

where $u = x^{-1} (1 + x^3)^{1/3}$.

4. $\dfrac{3}{56} (1 + x^2)^{4/3} (4x^2 - 3)$.

5. $\dfrac{1}{2^{7/4}} \tan^{-1} \dfrac{u}{2^{1/4}} + \dfrac{1}{2^{11/4}} \log \dfrac{u + 2^{1/4}}{u - 2^{1/4}}$, where $u^4 = 2 + x^{-4}$.

6. $\dfrac{(a + bx^n)^{p+1} \{(p + 1) bx^n - a\}}{nb^2 (p + 1)(p + 2)}$.

7. $\dfrac{4}{25} (a^3 + x^3)^{3/2} (3x^3 - 2a^3)$.

8. $\dfrac{a^3}{6} \left(\dfrac{2u}{u^2 - 1} - \log \dfrac{u - 1}{u + 1} \right)$, where $u^2 = 1 + a^3 x^{-3}$.

5.10. Reduction Formula for $\displaystyle\int \dfrac{dx}{(x^2 + a^2)^n}$**,** n **being a positive integer.**

(Jabalpur, 1995; Rewa, 1998)

Let $I_n = \displaystyle\int \dfrac{dx}{(x^2 + a^2)^n}$, then

$$I_{n-1} = \int \frac{dx}{(x^2 + a^2)^{n-1}}.$$

Taking $I_{n-1} = \int 1 \cdot \frac{1}{(x^2 + a^2)^{n-1}} \, dx$

and integrating by parts taking 1 as second function, we get

$$I_{n-1} = \frac{x}{(x^2 + a^2)^{n-1}} - \int -(n-1) \frac{2x}{(x^2 + a^2)^n} \, x \, dx$$

$$= \frac{x}{(x^2 + a^2)^{n-1}} + 2(n-1) \int \frac{x^2}{(x^2 + a^2)^n} \, dx$$

$$= \frac{x}{(x^2 + a^2)^{n-1}} + 2(n-1) \int \frac{x^2 + a^2 - a^2}{(x^2 + a^2)^n} \, dx$$

$$= \frac{x}{(x^2 + a^2)^{n-1}} + 2(n-1) \int \frac{dx}{(x^2 + a^2)^{n-1}}$$

$$- 2(n-1) a^2 \int \frac{dx}{(x^2 + a^2)^n}$$

or $$I_{n-1}(1 - 2n + 2) = \frac{2x}{(x^2 + a^2)^{n-1}} - 2(n-1) a^2 I_n$$

or $$2(n-1) a^2 I_n = \frac{x}{(x^2 + a^2)^{n-1}} + (2n-3) I_{n-1}$$

or $$I_n = \frac{x}{a^2 (2n-2)(x^2 + a^2)^{n-1}} + \frac{(2n-3)}{2(n-1) a^2} I_{n-1}.$$

This is the required reduction formula.

5.11. Reduction Formula for $\int x^m (a + bx^n)^p \, dx$ **where** m, n, p **are positive or negative integers or fractions.**

Let $$I_m = \int x^m (a + bx^n)^p \, dx = \int x^{m-n+1} x^{n-1} (a + bx^n)^p \, dx$$

as $$d(a + bx^n) = nbx^{n-1} \, dx.$$

So $$I_n = \frac{1}{nb} \int x^{m-n+1} (nbx^{n-1})(a + bx^n)^p \, dx$$

$$= \frac{1}{nb} \left[x^{m-n+1} \frac{(a + bx)^{p+1}}{p+1} \right.$$

$$\left. - \frac{(m-n+1)}{p+1} \int x^{m-n} (a + bx)^{p+1} \, dx \right]$$

[by using integration by parts method taking $(nbx^{n-1})(a + bx^n)^p$ as second function and x^{m-n+1} as first function].

$$= \frac{1}{nb} \cdot \frac{x^{m-n+1} (a+bx^n)^{p+1}}{(p+1)} \int x^{m-n} (a+bx^n)^p (a+bx^n) \, dx$$

$$= \frac{1}{nb} \cdot \frac{x^{m-n+1}}{(p+1)} (a+bx^n)^{p+1} - \frac{(m-n+1)\,a}{(p+1)\,nb} \int x^{m-n} (a+bx^n)^p \, dx$$

$$- \frac{(m-n+1)\,b}{(p+1)\,nb} \int x^m (a+bx^n)^p \, dx.$$

Therefore,

$$I_m = \frac{1}{nb} \cdot \frac{x^{m-n+1}}{(p+1)} (a+bx^n)^{p+1} - \frac{(m-n+1)\,a}{(p+1)\,nb} \int x^{m-n} (a+bx^n)^p \, dx$$

$$- \frac{(m-n+1)}{(p+1)\,nb} I_m$$

or $$I_m \left\{ 1 + \frac{m-n+1}{(p+1)^n} \right\} = \frac{x^{m-n+1} (a+bx^n)^{p+1}}{nb\,(p+1)} - \frac{(m-n+1)\,a}{(p+1)\,nb} I_{m-n}.$$

Hence $$\int x^m (a+bx^n)^p \, dx = \frac{x^{m-n+1} (a+bx^n)^{p+1}}{b\,(nb+m+2)}$$

$$- \frac{a\,(m-n+1)}{b\,(np+m+1)} \int x^{m-n} (a+bx^n)^p \, dx.$$

Note. $\int x^m (a+bx^n)^p \, dx$ can be connected with six possible relations as given below.

1. $$\int x^n (a+bx^n)^p \, dx = \frac{x^{m-n+1} (a+bx^n)^{p+1}}{b\,(np+m-1)}$$

$$- \frac{a\,(m-n+1)}{b\,(np+m+1)} \int x^{m-n} (a+bx^n)^p \, dx$$

2. $$\int x^m (a+bx^n)^p \, dx = \frac{x^{m+1} (a+bx^n)^p}{np+m+1}$$

$$- \frac{(npa)}{np+m+1} \int x^m (a+bx^n)^{p-1} \, dx$$

3. $$\int x^m (a+bx^n)^p \, dx = - \frac{x^{m+1} (a+bx^n)^{p+1}}{(p+1)\,na}$$

$$+ \frac{(m+np+n+1)}{(p+1)\,na} \int x^m (a+bx^n)^{p+1} \, dx$$

4. $\int x^m (a+bx^n)^p \, dx = -\dfrac{x^{m+1}(a+bx^n)^{p+1}}{(m+1)\,a}$

$$- \dfrac{b\,(m+np+n+a)}{(m+1)\,a} \int x^{m+n}(a+bx^n)^p \, dx$$

5. $\int x^m (a+bx^n)^p \, dx = \dfrac{x^{m-n+1}(a+bx^n)^{p+1}}{np\,(p+1)}$

$$- \dfrac{(m-n+1)}{nb\,(p+1)} \int x^{m-n}(a+bx^n)^{p+1} \, dx$$

6. $\int x^m (a+bx^n)^p \, dx = -\dfrac{x^{m+1}(a+bx^n)^p}{(m+1)}$

$$- \dfrac{bnp}{(m+1)} \int x^{m+n}(a+bx^n)^{p+1} \, dx$$

5.12. Reduction Formula for $\int (a^2+x^2)^{n/2} \, dx.$ (*Sagar, 1993*)

Let

$$I = \int (a^2+x^2)^{n/2} \, dx$$

$$= \int (a^2+x^2)^{n/2} \cdot 1 \, dx$$

$$= x\,(a^2+x^2)^{n/2} - \frac{n}{2} \cdot 2 \int (a^2+x^2)^{n/2-1} \cdot 1 \, dx$$

$$= x\,(a^2+x^2)^{n/2} - n \cdot \int (a^2+x^2)^{n/2-1} \, x^2 \, dx$$

$$= x\,(a^2+x^2)^{n/2} - n \int (a^2+x^2)^{n/2-1}\,(a^2+x^2-a^2) \, dx$$

$$= x\,(a^2+x^2)^{n/2} - n \int (a^2+x^2)^{n-2} \, dx + na^2 \int (a^2+x^2)^{n/2-1} \, dx$$

Therefore

$$I\,(n+1) = x\,(a^2+x^2)^{n/2} + na^2 \int (a^2+x^2)^{n/2-1} \, dx$$

$$\therefore \quad I = \frac{x\,(a^2+x^2)^{n/2}}{1+n} + \frac{na^2}{1+n} \int (a^2+x^2)^{n/2-1} \, dx.$$

EXAMPLE

If m be a positive integer, find a reduction formula for

$$\int x^m \sqrt{2ax-x^2} \, dx.$$

Hence obtain the value of

$$\int_0^{2a} x^3 \sqrt{2ax - x^2}\, dx.$$

We have $\quad x^m (2ax - x^2)^{1/2} = x^{m + 1/2} (2a - x)^{1/2}.$

We shall connect

$$\int x^{m + 1/2} (2a - x)^{1/2}\, dx \text{ with } \int x^{m + 1/2 - 1} (2a - x)\, dx$$

i.e., $\quad \int x^{m - 1/2} (2a - x)^{1/2}\, dx.$

We take

$$P = x^{m - 1/2 + 1} (2a - x)^{1/2 + 1} = x^{m + 1/2} (2a - x)^{3/2}$$

$$\Rightarrow \quad \frac{dP}{dx} = \left(m + \frac{1}{2}\right) x^{m - 1/2} (2a - x)^{3/2} - \frac{3}{2} x^{m + 1/2} (2a - x)^{1/2}$$

$$= \left(m + \frac{1}{2}\right) x^{m - 1/2} (2a - x)^{1/2} (2a - x) - \frac{3}{2} x^{m + 1/2} (2a - x)^{1/2}$$

$$= (2m + 1)\, ax^{m - 1/2} (2a - x)^{1/2} - \left(m + \frac{1}{2}\right) x^{m + 1/2} (2a - x)^{1/2}$$

$$- \frac{3}{2} x^{m + 1/2} (2a - x)^{1/2}$$

$$= (2m + 1)\, ax^{m - 1/2} (2a - x)^{1/2} - (m + 2) x^{m + 1/2} (2a - x)^{1/2}.$$

Integrating, we get

$$P = (2m + 1)\, a \int x^{m - 1/2} (2a - x)^{1/2}\, dx$$

$$- (m + 2) \int x^{m + 1/2} (2a - x)^{1/2}\, dx.$$

This gives on transposition, etc.

$$\int x^m \sqrt{2ax - x^2}\, dx = - \frac{x^{m + 1/2} (2a - x)^{2/3}}{m + 2}$$

$$+ \frac{(2m + 1)\, a}{m + 2} \int x^{m - 1} \sqrt{2ax - x^2}\, dx.$$

Taking limits from 0 to $2a$, we get

$$I_m = \int_0^{2a} x^m \sqrt{2ax - x^2}\, dx$$

$$= \frac{(2m + 1)\, a}{m + 2} \int_0^{2a} x^{m - 1} \sqrt{2ax - x^2}\, dx \cdot$$

$$= \frac{(2m+1)\,a}{m+2}\,I_{m-1}. \qquad (Bhopal,\ 2001)$$

$$I_3 = \frac{7a}{5}\,I_2,$$

$$I_2 = \frac{5a}{4}\,I_1,$$

$$I_1 = \frac{3a}{3}\,I_0.$$

Also

$$I_0 = \int_0^{2a} \sqrt{2ax - x^2}\ dx$$

$$= \int_0^{2a} \sqrt{a^2 - (x-a)^2}\ dx$$

$$= \left| \frac{(x-a)\sqrt{a^2-(x-a)^2}}{2} + \frac{a^2}{2}\sin^{-1}\frac{x-a}{a} \right|_0^{2a}$$

$$= \pi a^2 / 2$$

$$\therefore \quad I_3 = \frac{7}{8}\,\pi a^5. \qquad (Indore,\ 1999;\ Sagar,\ 1994;$$
$$Bhopal,\ 1996)$$

EXERCISES

1. If n be a positive integer, find a reduction formula for

$$\int (a^2 + x^2)^{n/2}\ dx,$$

and apply it to evaluate

$$\int (a^2 + x^2)^{5/2}\ dx.$$

2. If $u_n = \int x^n \sqrt{a^2 - x^2}\ dx$, prove that

$$u_n = -\frac{x^{n-1}(a^2-x^2)^{3/2}}{n+2} + \frac{n-1}{n+2}\,a^2\,u_{n-2}.$$

Evaluate $\quad \displaystyle\int_0^a x^4 \sqrt{a^2 - x^2}\ dx.$

3. Obtain suitable reduction formulae for the integrals of

$$\frac{x^n}{\sqrt{2ax - x^2}} \quad \text{and} \quad \frac{1}{x^n \sqrt{x^2 - 1}}$$

and integrate each of them when $n = 3$.

4. If $I_n = \int x^n \sqrt{a - x}\; dx,$ prove that

$$(2n + 3)\; I_n = 2an I_{n-1} - 2x^n (a - x)^{3/2}. \qquad (Jiwaji,\ 1997)$$

Evaluate $\displaystyle\int_0^a x^2 \sqrt{ax - x^2}\; dx.$

ANSWERS

1. $\displaystyle\int (a^2 + x^2)^{n/2}\, dx = \frac{x(a^2 + x^2)^{n/2}}{n+1} + \frac{na^2}{n+1} \int (a^2 + x^2)^{(n-1)/2}\, dx.$

$\displaystyle\int (a^2 + x^2)^{5/2}\, dx = \frac{1}{48}\, x\, (8x^4 + 26a^2 x^2 + 33a^4)\, \sqrt{a^2 + x^2}$

$$+ \frac{5}{16}\, a^6 \sinh^{-1}(x/a).$$

2. $\pi a^6 / 32.$

3. $nI_n = -\dfrac{x^n (2a - x)}{\sqrt{2ax - x^2}} + (2n - \mathrm{I})\, aI_{n-1};$

$$I_3 = \frac{2x^4 + ax^3 + 5a^2 x^2 - 30a^3 x}{6\sqrt{2ax - x^2}} + \frac{5a^3}{2} \sin^{-1} \frac{x - a}{a}.$$

$(n - 1)\, I_n = \sqrt{x^2 - 1}\,/\,x^{n-1} + (n - 2)\, I_{n-2};$

$$I_3 = \sqrt{x^2 - 1}\,/\,2x^2 + \frac{1}{2} \sec^{-1} x.$$

4. $5\pi a^4 / 128.$

EXERCISES ON CHAPTER 5

1. Evaluate

(i) $\displaystyle\int \frac{x\, dx}{\sqrt{x + 1}},$ (ii) $\displaystyle\int \frac{2x^2 + 3}{\sqrt{3 - 2x - x^2}}\, dx,$

(iii) $\displaystyle\int \frac{dx}{(x - 1)\sqrt{x^2 + 2x + 3}},$ (iv) $\displaystyle\int \frac{dx}{(1 + x)^2 \sqrt{x}},$

(v) $\displaystyle\int \sqrt{(x - 3)(4 - x)}\; dx,$ (vi) $\displaystyle\int \frac{\sqrt{1 + x + x^2}}{x + 1}\, dx.$

2. Evaluate

(i) $\displaystyle\int x^3 \sqrt{a + bx^2}\; dx,$ (ii) $\displaystyle\int \frac{dx}{x\sqrt{x(x - a)}},$

(iii) $\displaystyle\int \frac{2a+x}{a+x} \sqrt{\frac{a-x}{a+x}}\, dx,$ (iv) $\displaystyle\int x^3 \sqrt{\frac{1+x^2}{1-x^2}}\, dx,$

(v) $\displaystyle\int_1^\infty \frac{dx}{(x-\cos\alpha)\sqrt{x^2-1}},$ when $\pi > \alpha > 0.$

3. Show that

$$\int_1^2 \frac{dx}{(x+1)\sqrt{x^2-1}} = \frac{1}{\sqrt{3}}.$$

4. Evaluate

(i) $\displaystyle\int \frac{x\, dx}{(a-x)^2 \sqrt{2ax-x^2}},$ (ii) $\displaystyle\int \frac{1-\sqrt{1-x^2}}{x\sqrt{1-x^2}}\, dx.$

5. Prove that

$$\int_a^\infty \frac{dx}{x^4 \sqrt{a^2+x^2}} = \frac{2-\sqrt{2}}{3a^4}, \text{ when } a > 0.$$

6. With the help of the substitution $x = 1/\sqrt{t^2+1}$, or otherwise, prove that

$$\int_0^\infty \frac{dx}{(9+25x^2)\sqrt{1+x^2}} = \frac{1}{12} \tan^{-1} \frac{4}{3}.$$

7. Show that

$$\int \frac{dx}{(x^2+6x+5)^{3/2}} = -\frac{x+3}{4\sqrt{x^2+6x+5}}.$$

8. Prove that the value of $\displaystyle\int_0^4 x^3 \sqrt{4x-x^2}\, dx$ is nearly 88.

9. Prove that

(i) $\displaystyle\int_0^a \frac{dx}{x+\sqrt{a^2-x^2}} = \frac{1}{4}\pi,$

(ii) $\displaystyle\int_0^a \frac{a\, dx}{[x+\sqrt{a^2-x^2}]^2} = \frac{1}{\sqrt{2}} \log(1+\sqrt{2}).$

10. Evaluate

$$\int [x + \sqrt{1 + x^2}]^n \, dx.$$

11. Evaluate

    (i) $\displaystyle\int \sqrt{\frac{e^x + a}{e^x - a}} \, dx,$ (ii) $\displaystyle\int \sqrt{\frac{x + a}{x + b}} \frac{dx}{x + c}.$

12. Integrate

    (i) $\displaystyle\frac{1 - x^2}{(1 + x^2)\sqrt{1 + x^4}},$ (ii) $\displaystyle\frac{x^4 - 1}{x^2\sqrt{x^4 + x^2 + 1}}.$

ANSWERS

1.   (i) $\dfrac{2}{3}(x - 2)\sqrt{1 + x}.$

     (ii) $9 \sin^{-1}[(x + 1)/2] + (3 - x)\sqrt{3 - 2x - x^2}.$

     (iii) $-\sqrt{\dfrac{1}{6}} \sinh^{-1}[(x + 2)\sqrt{2}/(x - 1)].$

     (iv) $\tan^{-1}\sqrt{x} + \sqrt{x}/(1 + x).$

     (v) $\dfrac{1}{4}(2x - 7)\sqrt{(x - 3)(4 - x)} + \dfrac{1}{8}\sin^{-1}(2x - 7).$

     (vi) $\sqrt{x^2 + x + 1} - \sinh^{-1}[(1 - x)/\sqrt{3}(1 + x)]$

$$- \frac{1}{2}\sinh^{-1}[(2x + 1)/\sqrt{3}].$$

2.   (i) $(3bx^2 - 2a)(a + bx^2)^{3/2}/15b^2.$ (ii) $2\sqrt{x - a}/a\sqrt{x}.$

     (iii) $\sqrt{a^2 - x^2} - 2a\sqrt{(a - x)/(a + x)}.$

     (iv) $\dfrac{1}{2}\tan^{-1}y - y(1 + 3y^2)/2(1 + y^2)^2,$

     where $\sqrt{1 + x^2} = y\sqrt{1 - x^2}.$ (v) $(\pi - \alpha)/\sin \alpha.$

4.   (i) $\dfrac{1}{a}\left[\dfrac{\sqrt{2ax - x^2}}{a - x} - \log\dfrac{\sqrt{2a - x} + \sqrt{x}}{\sqrt{2a - x} - \sqrt{x}}\right].$

     (ii) $\sqrt{\log x + \operatorname{sech}^{-1} x}.$

10. $\dfrac{[x + \sqrt{1 + x^2}]^{n+1}}{2(n + 1)} + \dfrac{[x + \sqrt{1 + x^2}]^{n-1}}{2(n - 1)}.$

11.   (i) $\cosh^{-1}(e^x/a) + \sec^{-1}(e^x/a)$.

     (ii) $\cosh^{-1}\dfrac{2x+a+b}{a-b}$

$$+ \sqrt{\frac{c-a}{c-b}}\cosh^{-1}\frac{2(c-b)(c-a)+(a+b-2c)(x+c)}{(a-b)(c+x)}.$$

12.   (i) $\dfrac{1}{\sqrt{2}}\sin^{-1}\left(\dfrac{\sqrt{2}\,x}{1+x^2}\right)$.   (ii) $\dfrac{\sqrt{x^4+x^2+1}}{x}$.

MISCELLANEOUS EXERCISES I

1. Evaluate :

   (i) $\displaystyle\int_1^2 \frac{dx}{x(1+x^4)}$,   (ii) $\displaystyle\int \frac{x^2\,dx}{x^4-x^2-12}$,

   (iii) $\displaystyle\int \frac{x^5\,dx}{(1+x^2)^3}$,   (iv) $\displaystyle\int \frac{x^5\,dx}{(a^2-x^2)^2}$,

   (v) $\displaystyle\int \frac{x^2}{(1-x^2)^3}\,dx$,   (vi) $\displaystyle\int \frac{(x^3+x^2+2)\,dx}{x(x-1)^2(x^2+1)}$.

2. Integrate the following :

   (i) $e^{mx}\sin^3 x$,   (ii) $\dfrac{1}{1-\sin x\cos x}$,

   (iii) $\dfrac{\cos 2x}{3+\cos x+\sin x}$,   (iv) $\dfrac{1}{\cos 2\alpha-\cos x}$.

3. Evaluate

$$\int_0^{\pi/2} \frac{dx}{2\cos x+\sin x+a},$$

for the two cases when $a=1$ and $a=3$.

4.   (i) Show that if $0 < \alpha < \pi$,

$$\int_0^\infty \frac{dx}{x^2+2x\cos\alpha+1} = \frac{\alpha}{\sin\alpha}.$$

   (ii) Evaluate

$$\int_0^\infty \frac{(x^2+1)\,dx}{x^4+2x^2\cos\alpha+1} \quad\text{and}\quad \int_0^\infty \frac{dx}{x^4+2x^2\cos\alpha+1},$$

for the same range of α.

5. Show that

$$\int_0^1 \frac{dx}{\sqrt{x} + \sqrt{2-x}} = \sqrt{2} - \log(\sqrt{2} + 1).$$

6. Find the value of

$$\int_0^4 x^2 (4x - x^2)^{1/2} \, dx.$$

7. Prove that

$$\int \frac{x^2 \, dx}{(x \sin x + \cos x)^2} = \frac{\sin x - x \cos x}{\cos x + x \sin x}.$$

[Write $\dfrac{x^2 \, dx}{(x \sin x + \cos x)^2} = \dfrac{x \cos x}{(x \sin x + \cos x)^2} \cdot x \sec x$, and integrate by parts, remembering that $x \cos x$, is the derivative of $x \sin x + \cos x$].

8. Prove that $\displaystyle\int \frac{\sin x - \cos x}{\sqrt{\sin 2x}} \, dx = -\cosh^{-1}(\cos x + \sin x).$

9. Evaluate $\int (\tan x + \sec x)^4 \sec^2 x \, dx.$

10. Show that $\displaystyle\int_0^{\pi/2} \frac{a \, d\theta}{a^2 + \sin^2 \theta} = \frac{\pi}{2\sqrt{a^2 + 1}}.$

11. If $a > b > 0$, show that

$$\int_0^{\pi} \frac{dx}{a^2 + b^2 - 2ab \cos x} = \frac{\pi}{a^2 - b^2}.$$

What is the value of the integral if $b > a > 0$?

12. Show that, if $c > a > 0$,

$$\int_0^a \frac{\sqrt{a^2 - x^2}}{(c^2 - x^2)} \, dx = \frac{\pi [c - \sqrt{c^2 - a^2}]}{2c}.$$

13. Prove that

$$\int_0^1 \frac{dx}{(1 + x)(2 + x)\sqrt{x(1 - x)}} = \pi \left(\frac{1}{\sqrt{2}} - \frac{1}{\sqrt{6}} \right).$$

[Put $x = \sin^2 t$].

14. Prove that, if $a > b > 0$,

$$\int_0^{\pi} \frac{\sin^2 x \, dx}{a^2 - 2ab \cos x + b^2} = \frac{\pi}{2a^2}.$$

What is the value of the integral if $b > a > 0$?

15. Evaluate :

(i) $\displaystyle\int \frac{x^4\,dx}{(1+x^2)^2},$ (ii) $\displaystyle\int \frac{x\,dx}{(x^3-1)^2},$

(iii) $\displaystyle\int \frac{dx}{(x^3-a^3)^2},$ (iv) $\displaystyle\int_0^\infty \frac{dx}{(x^2+a^2)^2\,(x^2+b^2)}.$

16. Evaluate $\displaystyle\int_{-1}^{+1} (1-x^2)^m\,(1-x)^n\,dx.$

17. Evaluate $\displaystyle\int \frac{\sin x}{\sin 4x}\,dx.$

18. Evaluate $\displaystyle\int_0^{\pi/2} \frac{\sin 4\theta}{\sin \theta}\,d\theta.$

19. By means of the substitution

$$\sqrt{1+x^4} = (1+x^2)\cos\theta,$$

or otherwise, prove that

$$\int_0^1 \frac{1-x^2}{1+x^2}\,\frac{dx}{\sqrt{1+x^4}} = \frac{\pi}{4\sqrt{2}}.$$

20. Prove that $\displaystyle\int_0^{\pi/2} \log \sin x\,dx = \frac{\pi}{2}\log\frac{1}{2}$ and deduce that

$$-\int_0^1 \frac{x^2\log x}{\sqrt{1-x^2}}\,dx = \frac{\pi}{4}\left(\frac{1}{2}+\log\frac{1}{2}\right).$$

21. Evaluate $\displaystyle\int_0^{\pi/4} (\pi x - 4x^2)\log(1+\tan x)\,dx.$

22. Evaluate $\displaystyle\int_0^\pi \theta \sin\theta \cosh(\cos\theta)\,d\theta.$

23. Evaluate $\displaystyle\int \frac{\sin 2\theta}{a-b\tan\theta}\,d\theta.$

24. Show that

$$\int_0^\pi \theta^3 \log\sin\theta\,d\theta = \frac{3\pi}{2}\int_0^\pi \theta^2 \log(\sqrt{2}\,\sin\theta)\,d\theta. \quad \text{(Use § 4.9.2)}$$

25. Show that

$$\int_0^1 x^{\alpha-1} (\log x)^n \, dx = \frac{(-1)^n \, n!}{\alpha^{n+1}},$$

where n is a positive integer and α is a positive number.

26. Evaluate $\displaystyle\int_0^{\pi/2} \left(\sqrt{\sin x} + \sqrt{\cos x}\right)^{-4} dx.$

27. If $\quad y^2 = ax^2 + 2bx + c,$

and $\quad u_n = \displaystyle\int \frac{x^n}{y} \, dx,$

prove that

$$(n+1) \, au_{n+1} + (2n+1) \, bu_n + ncu_{n-1} = x^n y,$$

and deduce that

$$au_1 = y - bu_0; \quad 2a^2u_2 = y \, (ax - 3b) - (ac - 3b^2) \, u_0.$$

28. Show that

$$\int_0^1 \cot^{-1} (1 - x + x^2) \, dx = \frac{\pi}{2} - \log 2.$$

29. Show that

(i) $\displaystyle\int_0^{\pi/2} \sin \theta \log \sin \theta \, d\theta = \log \frac{2}{e},$

(ii) $\displaystyle\int_0^{\pi} \cos 2x \log \sin x \, dx = -\frac{1}{2} \, \pi.$

30. By means of the substitution

$$v^2 = x + 1 + 1/x,$$

evaluate

$$\int \frac{x-1}{x+1} \frac{dx}{\sqrt{x \, (x^2 + x + 1)}}.$$

31. Evaluate $\displaystyle\int_{-\pi/2}^{\pi/2} \frac{\sin 2\theta}{\sqrt{1 + \sin \theta \sin 2\beta}} \, d\theta,$ when $0 \le \beta \le \frac{1}{2} \pi.$

32. If $\quad u_n = \int (\sin x + \cos x)^n \, dx,$ then prove that

$$nu_n = (\sin x + \cos x)^{n-1} (\sin x - \cos x) + 2 \, (n-1) \, u_{n-2}.$$

33. If $\quad I_{(m, n)} = \displaystyle\int_{0}^{\pi/2} \sin^m x \cos nx \, dx,$

and $\quad J_{(m, n)} = \displaystyle\int_{0}^{\pi/2} \sin^m x \sin nx \, dx, \ m > 1,$

prove that

$$(m + n) \, I_{(m, n)} = \sin\left(\frac{1}{2} n\pi\right) - m \, J_{(m-1, \, n-1)}$$

and express $I_{(m, n)}$ in terms of $I_{(m-2, \, n-2)}$.

34. Show how, by the differentiation of

$$\sin x / (a + b \cos x)^{n-1},$$

to obtain a reduction formula for

$$\int \frac{dx}{(a + b \cos x)^n}.$$

35. If m and n are positive integers, and

$$I_{(m, n)} = \int_{0}^{1} x^m (1 - x)^n \, dx,$$

then

$$(m + n + 1) \, I_{(m, n)} = n \, I_{(m, \, n-1)}.$$

Deduce that

$$I_{(m, n)} = \frac{m! \, n!}{(m + n + 1)!}.$$

36. If m and n are positive integers, then, with the help of the substitution

$$x = a + (b - a) y,$$

prove that

$$\int_{a}^{b} (x - a)^m (b - x)^n \, dx = \frac{m! \, n! \, (b - a)^{m+n+1}}{(m + n + 1)!}.$$

37. If $I_{(m, n)} = \displaystyle\int \frac{x^m \, dx}{(x^3 + 1)^n}$, prove that

$$(2n - 2) \, I_{(m, n)} = - x^{m-1} (x^2 + 1)^{-n+1}$$
$$+ (m - 1) \, I_{(m-2, \, n-1)}.$$

ANSWERS

1. (i) $\dfrac{1}{4} \log \dfrac{32}{17}$. 　　　　　(ii) $\dfrac{1}{7}\left[\log \dfrac{x-2}{x+2} + \sqrt{3} \tan^{-1} \dfrac{x}{\sqrt{3}}\right].$

(iii) $\dfrac{1}{2}\log(1+x^2) + (1+x^2)^{-1} - \dfrac{1}{4}(1+x^2)^{-2}$.

(iv) $a^2 \log(a^2 - x^2) + x^2(2a^2 - x^2)/2(a^2 - x^2)$.

(v) $\dfrac{1}{16}\left[\dfrac{4x}{(1-x^2)^2} - \dfrac{2x}{1-x^2} + \log\dfrac{1-x}{1+x}\right]$.

(vi) $2\log x - \dfrac{3}{2}\log(x-1) - \dfrac{1}{4}\log(1+x^2)$

$$- 2(x-1)^{-1} + \dfrac{1}{2}\tan^{-1} x.$$

2.   (i) $\dfrac{e^{mx}}{4}\left[\dfrac{3}{\sqrt{m^2+1}}\sin(x - \cot^{-1} m)\right.$

$$\left. - \dfrac{1}{\sqrt{m^2+9}}\sin\left(3x - \tan^{-1}\dfrac{3}{m}\right)\right].$$

(ii) $\dfrac{2}{\sqrt{3}}\tan^{-1}\left[\dfrac{2\tan x - 1}{\sqrt{3}}\right]$.

(iii) $(\sin x + \cos x) - 3\log(3 + \sin x + \cos x)$.

(iv) $\dfrac{1}{\sin 2\alpha}\log\dfrac{\sin\left(\dfrac{1}{2}x - \alpha\right)}{\sin\left(\dfrac{1}{2}x + \alpha\right)}$.

3. $\dfrac{1}{2}\log 3$; $\tan^{-1}\dfrac{1}{3}$.

4.   (ii) $\dfrac{1}{2}\pi\sec\left(\dfrac{1}{2}\alpha\right)$, $\dfrac{1}{4}\pi\sec\left(\dfrac{1}{2}\alpha\right)$.

6. 10π.   9. $\dfrac{1}{10}(\tan x + \sec x)^5 + \dfrac{1}{6}(\tan x + \sec x)^3$.

11. $\pi/(b^2 - a^2)$.   14. $\pi/2b^2$.

15.   (i) $x + \dfrac{1}{2}x(1+x^2)^{-1} - \dfrac{3}{2}\tan^{-1} x$.

(ii) $\dfrac{1}{18}\log\dfrac{x^2+x+1}{(x-1)^2} - \dfrac{1}{9}\cdot\dfrac{1}{x-1} - \dfrac{1}{9}\cdot\dfrac{2x+1}{x^2+x+1}$

$$- \dfrac{1}{3\sqrt{3}}\tan^{-1}\dfrac{2x+1}{\sqrt{3}}.$$

$$(iii)\ \frac{1}{9a^5}\left[\log\frac{a^2+ax+x^2}{(x-a)^2}-\frac{x}{x-a}+\frac{2ax+x^2}{a^2+ax+x^2}\right.$$

$$\left.+\frac{6}{\sqrt{3}}\tan^{-1}\frac{2x+a}{\sqrt{3}\,a}\right].$$

$(iv)\ \pi\,(2a+b)\,/\,4a^2b\,(a+b)^2.$

16. $2^{2m+n+1}\,(m+n)\,!\cdot(m\,!)\,/\,(2m+n+1)\,!.$

17. $\dfrac{1}{4}\log\tan\left(\dfrac{1}{4}\pi-\dfrac{1}{2}x\right)+\dfrac{1}{4\sqrt{2}}\log\left[\dfrac{(1+\sqrt{2}\,\sin x)}{(1-\sqrt{2}\,\sin x)}\right].$

18. $4\,/\,3.$ **21.** $\pi^3\log 2\,/\,192.$ **22.** $\dfrac{1}{2}\pi\,(e-e^{-1}).$

23. $-\dfrac{2ab^2}{(a^2-b^2)^2}\log\,(a\cos\theta-b\sin\theta)+\dfrac{b\,(a^2-b^2)}{(a^2+b^2)^2}\,\theta$

$$-\frac{(a\cos\theta+b\sin\theta)\cos\theta}{a^2+b^2}.$$

26. $1\,/\,3.$ **30.** $-\,2\,\operatorname{cosec}^{-1}\,(x^{1/2}+x^{-1/2}).$

31. $-\dfrac{4}{3}\tan\beta\sec\beta,$ if $0<\beta\le\dfrac{1}{4}\pi;$

$-\dfrac{4}{3}\cot\beta\operatorname{cosec}\beta,$ if $\dfrac{1}{4}\pi\le\beta<\dfrac{1}{2}\pi;$

$0,$ if $\beta=0$ or $\dfrac{1}{2}\pi.$

33. $I_{(m,n)}=\dfrac{1}{m+n}\sin\dfrac{n\pi}{2}+\dfrac{m}{(m+n)\,(m+n-2)}\cos\dfrac{(n-1)\,\pi}{2}$

$$-\frac{m\,(m-1)}{(m+n)\,(m+n-2)}\,I_{(m-2,\,n-2)}.$$

34. If $u_n=\int dx\,/\,(a+b\cos x)^n,$ then

$$(n-1)\,(a^2-b^2)\,u_n=-\,b\sin x\,/\,(a+b\cos x)^{n-1}$$
$$+\,(2n-3)\,au_{n-1}-(n-2)\,u_{n-2}.$$

MISCELLANEOUS EXERCISES II

1. Show that

$$(i)\ \int_0^{\pi}x\,\varphi\,(\sin x)\,dx=\frac{\pi}{2}\int_0^{\pi}\varphi\,(\sin x)\,dx,$$

$$(ii)\ \int_a^{\pi-a}x\,f\,(\sin x)\,dx=\frac{\pi}{2}\int_a^{\pi-a}f\,(\sin x)\,dx.$$

2. Show that

$$(i) \quad \int_{-a}^{a} f(x)^2 \, dx = 2 \int_{0}^{a} f(x)^2 \, dx, \qquad (ii) \quad \int_{-a}^{a} x f(x)^2 \, dx = 0.$$

3. If $f(x + mp) = f(x)$ for all integral values of m, prove that

$$\int_{0}^{np} f(x) \, dx = n \int_{0}^{\pi} f(x) \, dx,$$

where n is a positive or a negative integer.

4. Show that

$$\int_{0}^{n\pi} f(\cos^2 x) \, dx = n \int_{0}^{\pi} f(\cos^2 x) \, dx,$$

n being a positive integer.

5. Show that

$$(i) \quad \int_{0}^{b-c} f(x + c) \, dx = \int_{c}^{b} f(x) \, dx,$$

$$(ii) \quad \int_{a}^{b} f(a + b - x) \, dx = \int_{a}^{b} f(x) \, dx.$$

6. If $f(x) = \dfrac{1}{2} a_0 + \sum_{m=1}^{n} (a_m \cos mx + b_m \sin mx)$, and $m \le n$, then

$$\pi a_0 = \int_{0}^{2\pi} f(x) \, dx; \quad \pi a_m = \int_{0}^{2\pi} f(x) \cos mx \, dx;$$

$$\pi b_m = \int_{0}^{2\pi} f(x) \sin mx \, dx.$$

7. If m, n are positive integers and $m > n$, prove that

$$\int_{0}^{\pi} \cos mx \, (\cos x)^n \, dx = 0.$$

8. Show that

$$\int_{0}^{\pi} \frac{\sin\left(n + \dfrac{1}{2}\right) x}{\sin \dfrac{1}{2} x} \, dx = \pi; \; n \text{ being a positive integer.}$$

$$\left[\textbf{Hint.} \; \frac{1}{2} \sin\left(n + \frac{1}{2}\right) x \operatorname{cosec} \frac{1}{2} x = \frac{1}{2} + \cos x + \ldots + \cos nx \right].$$

9. If p, q are positive integers,

$$\int_0^\pi \cos px \sin qx \, dx = \begin{cases} 2q/(q^2 - p^2), \text{ if } (q - p) \text{ is odd,} \\ 0, \text{ if } (q - p) \text{ is even.} \end{cases}$$

10. Prove that if

$$u_n = \int_0^1 x^n \tan^{-1} x \, dx$$

when

$$(n + 1) u_n + (n - 1) u_{n-2} = -1/n.$$

Evaluate u_{4m} and prove that $4mu_{4m} \to \dfrac{1}{2} \log 2$ as $m \to \infty$.

11. If

$$I_n = \int_{-1}^{+1} (1 - x^2)^n \cos mx \, dx,$$

prove that when n is not less than or equal to 2,

$$m^2 I_n = 2n (2n - 1) I_{n-1} - 4n (n - 1) I_{n-2}.$$

12. Prove that

$$\int f^n (x) g (x) \, dx = f^{n-1} (x) g (x) - f^{n-2} (x) g' (x) + \ldots\ldots$$

$$+ (-1)^n \int f (x) g^n (x) \, dx.$$

13. If

$$I_n = \int_0^\pi (\pi x - x^2)^n \cos mx \, dx,$$

prove that, if $n > 1$ and is an integer, then

$$m^2 I_n - 2n (2n - 1) I_{n-1} + n (n - 1) \pi^2 I_{n-2} = 0.$$

Prove that

$$\int_0^\pi (\pi x - x^2)^3 \cos 2x \, dx = \frac{3}{4} \pi (\pi^2 - 15).$$

14. Show that

$$\int \sin n\theta \sec \theta \, d\theta = -2 \cos (n - 1) \theta / (n - 1)$$

$$- \int \sin (n - 2) \theta \sec \theta \, d\theta.$$

15. Prove that

$$(i) \quad \int_{-a}^{+a} f(x)\, f(-x)\, dx = 2 \int_{0}^{\infty} f(x)\, f(-x)\, dx,$$

$$(ii) \quad \int_{0}^{\infty} \frac{dx}{(1+4x^2)\sqrt{1+3x^2}} = \frac{\pi}{6},$$

$$(iii) \quad \int_{0}^{\infty} \frac{dx}{(1+x)\sqrt{1+x+x^2}} = \log 3.$$

16. Find the reduction formula for $I_{m,\,n}$ where

$$I_{m,\,n} = \int_{0}^{\pi/2} \cos^m x \sin nx \, dx.$$

Deduce that

$$I_{m,\,n} = \frac{1}{2^{m+1}} \left[2 + \frac{2^2}{2} + \frac{2^3}{3} + \dots + \frac{2^m}{m} \right].$$

17. Evaluate the following :

$$(i) \quad \int_{0}^{1} \frac{\sin^{-1} x}{x}\, dx,$$

$$(ii) \quad \int \frac{1+\cos x}{\sin x \cos x}\, dx,$$

$$(iii) \quad \int \frac{x}{1+\sin x}\, dx,$$

$$(iv) \quad \int \frac{x+\sin x}{1+\cos x}\, dx,$$

$$(v) \quad \int \left(\frac{\tan x^{-1}}{x} \right)^2 dx,$$

$$(vi) \quad \int \frac{dx}{x \sqrt{x^n - 1}},$$

$$(vii) \quad \int \frac{dx}{(2\sin x + \cos x)^2},$$

$$(viii) \quad \int \log[\sqrt{x-a} + \sqrt{x-b}]\, dx,$$

$$(ix) \quad \int_{0}^{\pi/2} \frac{\sin^2 \theta \, d\theta}{\sin^2 \theta + 4\cos^2 \theta},$$

$$(x) \quad \int_{0}^{\pi/2} \cos^3 x \sin 5x \, dx.$$

18. Prove that

$$\int_{0}^{1} \frac{\sqrt{1-x^2}}{1-x^2 \sin^2 \alpha}\, dx = \frac{\pi}{4\cos^2 \frac{1}{2}\alpha}.$$

19. Show that

(i) $\int \text{sech}^3 x \, dx = \frac{1}{2} \sec^{-1} x \cosh x + \frac{1}{2} \text{sech} \, x \tanh x,$

(ii) $\int \frac{1}{(e^x - 1)^2} dx = x - \log(e^x - 1) - \frac{1}{e^x - 1}.$

20. Prove that

$$\int_0^{\pi/2} \cos^{n-2} x \sin nx \, dx = \frac{1}{n-1}, \quad (n > 1 \text{ and integral}).$$

ANSWERS

17. (i) $\frac{1}{2} \pi \log 2.$ (ii) $\log\left(\tan x \tan \frac{1}{2} x\right).$

(iii) $x\left(\tan \frac{1}{2} x - 1\right) \Big/ \left(\tan \frac{1}{2} x + 1\right) + 2 \log\left(\cos \frac{1}{2} x + \sin \frac{1}{2} x\right).$

(iv) $x \tan \frac{1}{2} x.$ (v) $x^{-1} - \tan(x^{-1}).$

(vi) $(2/n) \tan^{-1} \sqrt{x^n - 1}.$ (vii) $-\cos(x/2)(2\sin x + \cos x).$

(viii) $x \log[\sqrt{x-a} + \sqrt{x-b}] - \frac{1}{2}\sqrt{(x-a)(x-b)}$

$$- \frac{1}{4}(a+b) \cosh^{-1}\left[\frac{2x-(a+b)}{(a-b)}\right].$$

(ix) $\pi/6.$ (x) $1/4.$

OBJECTIVE QUESTIONS

For each of the following questions, four alternatives are given for the answer. Only one of them is correct. Choose the correct alternative.

1. Given that

$$\int_0^\infty \frac{x^2 \, dx}{(x^2+a^2)(x^2+b^2)(x^2+c^2)} = \frac{\pi}{2(a+b)(b+c)(c+a)},$$

then the value of $\displaystyle\int_0^\infty \frac{dx}{(x^2+4)(x^2+9)}$ is

(a) $\pi/60$ (b) $\pi/20$ (c) $\pi/40$ (d) $\pi/80.$

2. $\displaystyle\int \frac{(x-1) \, dx}{(x-2)(x-3)}$ is equal to

(a) $\log\{(x-3)^2/(x-2)\}$ (b) $\log\{(x-3)/(x-2)^2\}$

(c) $\log\{(x-2)(x-3)\}$ (d) None of these.

3. $\int \dfrac{dx}{x\,(x^5 + 1)}$, $(x > 0)$ is equal to

    (a) $\log x^5\,(x^5 + 1)$

    (b) $\log x - \dfrac{1}{5}\log\,(x^5 + 1)$

    (c) $\dfrac{1}{5}\log\,\{x^5 / (x^5 + 1)\}$

    (d) None of these.

4. $\displaystyle\int_{0}^{\infty} \dfrac{dx}{(x^2 + a^2)\,(x^2 + b^2)}$ is

    (a) $\pi ab / (a + b)$

    (b) $\pi / 2\,(a + b)$

    (c) $\pi / [2ab\,(a + b)]$

    (d) $\pi\,(a + b) / ab$.

5. $\displaystyle\int_{0}^{16} \dfrac{x^{1/4}\,dx}{1 + \sqrt{x}}$ is equal to

    (a) $4/3 + \tan^{-1} 2$

    (b) $8/3 + 4\tan^{-1} 2$

    (c) $2/3 + \tan^{-1} 2$

    (d) None of these.

6. If $\displaystyle\int \dfrac{dx}{x\sqrt{1 - x^3}} = a \log \left| \dfrac{\sqrt{(1 + x^3)} - 1}{\sqrt{(1 - x^3)} + 1} \right| + b$, then $a =$

    (a) $1/3$
    (b) $2/3$
    (c) $-1/3$
    (d) $-2/3$

7. $\displaystyle\int \dfrac{dx}{x\sqrt{(1 + x)}} =$

    (a) $\log \left| \dfrac{\sqrt{(1 + x)} - 1}{\sqrt{(1 + x)} + 1} \right|$

    (b) $\log \left| \dfrac{\sqrt{(1 + x)} + 1}{\sqrt{(1 + x)} - 1} \right|$

    (c) $\dfrac{1}{2}\log \left| \dfrac{\sqrt{(1 + x)} - 1}{\sqrt{(1 + x)} + 1} \right|$

    (d) None of these.

8. $\displaystyle\int \dfrac{dx}{x^2 + x + 1}$ is equal to

    (a) $\dfrac{1}{2}\log \left| \dfrac{x - 1}{x + 1} \right|$

    (b) $\dfrac{1}{\sqrt{2}}\log \left| \dfrac{x - \sqrt{2}}{x + \sqrt{2}} \right|$

    (c) $\dfrac{2}{\sqrt{3}}\tan^{-1} \left(\dfrac{2x + 1}{3} \right)$

    (d) None of these.

9. $\int \dfrac{x^3 - 7x + 6}{x^2 + 3x}\, dx =$

　(a) $\dfrac{1}{2} x^2 - 3x + 2 \log x$　　　　　　(b) $\dfrac{1}{2} x^2 + 3x + 2 \log x$

　(c) $\dfrac{1}{2} x^2 - 3x - 2 \log x$　　　　　　(d) None of these.

10. $\int \dfrac{x^4 + x^2 + 1}{x^2 - x + 1}\, dx =$

　(a) $\dfrac{1}{3} x^3 + \dfrac{1}{2} x^2 + x$　　　　　　(b) $\dfrac{1}{3} x^3 - \dfrac{1}{2} x^2 + x$

　(c) $\dfrac{1}{3} x^3 + \dfrac{1}{2} x^2 - x$　　　　　　(d) None of these.

11. $\int \dfrac{\cos x\, dx}{(1 + \sin x)(2 + \sin x)} =$

　(a) $\log \left(\dfrac{1 + \sin x}{2 + \sin x} \right)$　　　　　　(b) $\log \left(\dfrac{2 + \sin x}{1 + \sin x} \right)$

　(c) $\dfrac{\log (1 + \sin x)}{\log (2 + \sin x)}$　　　　　　(d) None of these.

12. $\int \dfrac{dx}{\sqrt{(x^2 + x + 1)}} =$

　(a) $\sinh^{-1} \left(\dfrac{2x + 1}{\sqrt{3}} \right)$

　(b) $\log \left[\left(x + \dfrac{1}{2} \right) - \sqrt{(x^2 + x + 1)} \right]$

　(c) $\log \left[(2x + 1) + 2\sqrt{(x^2 + x + 1)} \right]$

　(d) None of these.

13. $\int \dfrac{dx}{\sqrt{(3 - 5x - x^2)}} =$

　(a) $\sin^{-1} [(2x + 5) / \sqrt{37}] + c$　　(b) $\cos^{-1} [(2x + 5) / \sqrt{37}] + c$

　(c) $-\sin^{-1} [(2x + 5) / \sqrt{37}] + c$　(d) $\cos^{-1} [(2x - 5) / \sqrt{37}] + c.$

14. If $\int \dfrac{3x+4}{x^3-2x-4}\,dx = \log|x-2|+p\log f(x)+c$, then

   (a) $p = 1/4$ (b) $f(x) = x^2 - x - 2$

   (c) $f(x) = x^2 + 2x + 2$ (d) $p = 1/2$.

15. Neglecting the constant of integration, $\int \dfrac{dx}{\sqrt{(x-2)(x-3)}} =$

   (a) $2\log[\sqrt{(x-2)}-\sqrt{(x-3)}]$ (b) $\sinh^{-1}(2x-5)$

   (c) $\log[(x-5/2)+\sqrt{(x^2-5x+6)}]$ (d) None of these.

ANSWERS

1. (a)	2. (a)	3. (c)	4. (b)	5. (a)
6. (a)	7. (a)	8. (c)	9. (a)	10. (a)
11. (a)	12. (c)	13. (a)	14. (c)	15. (c)

6

Definite Integrals

6.1. We have so far regarded integration as inverse of differentiation. The definite integral

$$\int_{a}^{b} f(x)\,dx$$

has been defined to be equal to

$$F(b) - F(a)$$

where $F(x)$ is a function such that

$$F'(x) = f(x).$$

The application of the process of integration to determining areas, lengths of arcs, volumes and surfaces of solids of revolution has also been based on this anti-derivative aspect of the notion of definite integral.

It will now be shown that a definite integral can also be represented as the limit of the sum of certain number of terms, when the number of terms tends to infinity and each term tends to zero. This aspect of a definite integral is more fundamental and of far more reaching character that of its anti-derivative character and it is this aspect of integration which really lies at the basis of all its applications. On the theoretical side also, it has led to very extensive and refined developments of the subject. But it is not within the scope of this elementary book to go into these developments. Here the purpose is just to introduce the reader to this aspect. But the beginner should not minimise the importance of this *summation aspect of the integral*, as he may feel inclined to do in view of the comparatively short space devoted to it in this book.

6.2. Properties of Definite Integrals

1. Prove that $\displaystyle\int_{a}^{b} \phi(x)\,dx = \int_{a}^{b} \phi(t)\,dt.$

Let $\displaystyle\int \phi(x)\,dx = F(x) + c_1,$ thereby

$$\int \phi(t)\,dt = F(t) + c_2.$$

213

Therefore $\displaystyle\int_a^b \phi(x)\,dx = \Big[F(x)+c_1\Big]_a^b$

$$= F(b) - F(a).$$

Similarly, $\displaystyle\int_a^b \phi(t)\,dt = \Big[F(t)+c_2\Big]_a^b$

$$= F(b) - F(a).$$

$$\therefore \quad \int_a^b \phi(x)\,dx = \int_a^b \phi(t)\,dt.$$

2. Prove that $\displaystyle\int_a^b \phi(x)\,dx = \int_a^c \phi(x)\,dx + \int_c^b \phi(x)\,dx.$

We have $\displaystyle\int_a^c \phi(x)\,dx + \int_c^b \phi(x)\,dx$

$$= \Big[F(x)+c\Big]_a^c + \Big[F(x)+c\Big]_c^b$$

$$= F(c) - F(a) + F(b) - F(c)$$

$$= F(b) - F(a) = \int_a^b \phi(x)\,dx.$$

$\Rightarrow$ R.H.S. = L.H.S.

3. Prove that $\displaystyle\int_a^b \phi(x)\,dx = -\int_b^a \phi(x)\,dx.$

R.H.S. $= -\displaystyle\int_b^a \phi(x)\,dx = -\Big[F(x)+c\Big]_b^a$

$$= -\big[\{F(a)+c\} - \{F(b)+c\}\big]$$

$$= -F(a) + F(b)$$

$$= \int_a^b \phi(x)\,dx.$$

$\Rightarrow$ R.H.S. = L.H.S.

4. Prove that $\displaystyle\int_0^a \phi(x)\,dx = \int_0^a \phi(a-x)\,dx.$ *(Kanpur, 2002)*

R.H.S. $= \displaystyle\int_0^a \phi\,(a-x)\,dx.$

Put $a - x = t,\ - dx = dt.$

Upper limit for $x = 0,\ t = 0.$

Lower limit for $x = 0,\ t = a.$

$\therefore$ R.H.S. $= -\displaystyle\int_a^0 \phi\,(t)\,dt$

$\qquad\qquad = \displaystyle\int_0^a \phi\,(t)\,dt$ [by Prop. 3]

$\qquad\qquad = \displaystyle\int_0^a \phi\,(x)\,dx$ [by Prop. 1]

$\qquad\qquad = $ L.H.S.

5. Prove that

$$\int_0^{2a} \phi\,(x)\,dx = 2 \int_0^a \phi\,(x)\,dx,\ \text{if}\ \phi\,(2a-x) = \phi\,(x)$$

$$= 0,\ \text{if}\ \phi\,(2a-x) = -\phi\,(x).$$

We have

L.H.S. $= \displaystyle\int_0^{2a} \phi\,(x)\,dx = \int_0^a \phi\,(x)\,dx + \int_a^{2a} \phi\,(x)\,dx$ ...(i)

Now consider $\displaystyle\int_a^{2a} \phi\,(x)\,dx.$

Put $2a - x = t$ or $2a - t = x,\ - dx = dt.$

Upper limit for $x = 2a,\ t = 0$ and lower limit for $x = a,\ t = a.$

$\therefore\quad \displaystyle\int_a^{2a} \phi\,(x)\,dx = -\int_a^0 \phi\,(2a-t)\,dt$

$\qquad\qquad\qquad = \displaystyle\int_0^a \phi\,(2a-t)\,dt$

$\qquad\qquad\qquad = \displaystyle\int_0^a \phi\,(2a-x)\,dx$

Then $\quad$ L.H.S. $= \displaystyle\int_0^a \phi(2a-x)\,dx + \int_0^a \phi(x)\,dx$ $\qquad$ ...(ii)

Now, if $\phi(2a-x) = \phi(x)$.

Then $\quad \displaystyle\int_0^{2a} \phi(x)\,dx = \int_0^a \phi(x)\,dx + \int_0^a \phi(x)\,dx$

$$= 2\int_0^a \phi(x)\,dx.$$

Again, if $\phi(2a-x) = -\phi(x)$.

Then $\quad \displaystyle\int_0^{2a} \phi(x)\,dx = \int_0^a \phi(x)\,dx - \int_0^a \phi(x)\,dx$

$$= 0.$$

6. Prove that $\displaystyle\int_{-a}^a \phi(x)\,dx = 0$, if $\phi(-x) = -\phi(x)$

$$= 2\int_0^a \phi(x)\,dx, \text{ if } \phi(-x) = \phi(x).$$

We have

$$\int_{-a}^a \phi(x)\,dx = \int_{-a}^0 \phi(x)\,dx + \int_0^a \phi(x)\,dx.$$

In $\displaystyle\int_{-a}^0 \phi(x)\,dx.$

Put $x = -t$, $dx = -dt$.

Upper limit for $x = 0$, $t = 0$, lower limit for $x = -a$, $t = a$.

$$\therefore \int_{-a}^0 \phi(x)\,dx = -\int_a^0 \phi(-t)\,dt = \int_0^a \phi(-t)\,dt$$

$$= \int_0^a \phi(-x)\,dx$$

$$\therefore \int_{-a}^a \phi(x)\,dx = \int_0^a \phi(-x)\,dx + \int_0^a \phi(x)\,dx.$$

If $\phi(-x) = -\phi(x)$, then

$$\int_{-a}^{a} \phi(x)\, dx = -\int_{0}^{a} \phi(x)\, dx + \int_{0}^{a} \phi(x)\, dx$$

$$= 0$$

and if $\phi(-x) = \phi(x)$, then

$$\int_{a}^{a} \phi(x)\, dx = \int_{0}^{a} \phi(x)\, dx + \int_{0}^{a} \phi(x)\, dx$$

$$= 2\int_{0}^{a} \phi(x)\, dx.$$

Note. The following results should be committed to memory.

(i) $\displaystyle\int_{0}^{\pi/2} f(\sin x)\, dx = \int_{0}^{\pi/2} f\left[\sin\left(\frac{\pi}{2} - x\right)\right] dx$

$$= \int_{0}^{\pi/2} f(\cos x)\, dx.$$

(ii) $\displaystyle\int_{0}^{\pi/2} f(\sin 2x) \cos x\, dx$

$$= \int_{0}^{\pi/2} f\left[\sin 2\left(\frac{\pi}{2} - x\right)\right]\cos\left(\frac{\pi}{2} - x\right) dx$$

$$= \int_{0}^{\pi/2} f(\sin 2x)\sin x\, dx.$$

(iii) $\displaystyle\int_{0}^{\pi/2} \sin^{n} x\, dx = \int_{0}^{\pi/2} \sin^{n}\left(\frac{\pi}{2} - x\right) dx$

$$= \int_{0}^{\pi/2} \cos^{n} x\, dx.$$

EXAMPLES

1. *Evaluate* $\displaystyle\int_{0}^{\pi} x \sin^{6} x \cos^{4} x\, dx.$

We have

$$I = \int_0^\pi x \sin^6 x \cos^4 x \, dx$$

$$= \int_0^\pi (\pi - x) \sin^6 (\pi - x) \cos^4 (\pi - x) \, dx$$

$$= \pi \int_0^\pi \sin^6 x \cos^4 x \, dx - \int_0^\pi x \sin^6 x \cos^4 x \, dx$$

$$= 2\pi \int_0^{\pi/2} \sin^6 x \cos^4 x \, dx - I$$

$$\therefore \quad 2I = \pi \cdot \frac{\dfrac{5}{2} \cdot \dfrac{3}{2} \cdot \dfrac{1}{2} \sqrt{\pi} \cdot \dfrac{3}{2} \cdot \dfrac{1}{2} \sqrt{\pi}}{5 \cdot 4 \cdot 3 \cdot 2 \cdot 1}$$

$$= \frac{3\pi^2}{256}$$

$$\therefore \quad I = \frac{3\pi^2}{512}.$$

2. *Evaluate* : $\displaystyle \int_0^{\pi/2} \frac{\sqrt{\sin x}}{\sqrt{\sin x} + \sqrt{\cos x}} \, dx.$

(Rohilkhand, 1994; Bundelkhand, 1995;
Kanpur, 1996; Avadh, 2001)

Let

$$I = \int_0^{\pi/2} \frac{\sqrt{\sin x}}{\sqrt{\sin x} + \sqrt{\cos x}} \, dx$$

$$= \int_0^{\pi/2} \frac{\sqrt{\sin (\pi/2 - x)}}{\sqrt{\sin (\pi/2 - x)} + \sqrt{\cos (\pi/2 - x)}} \, dx$$

$$= \int_0^{\pi/2} \frac{\sqrt{\cos x}}{\sqrt{\cos x} + \sqrt{\sin x}} \, dx.$$

Thus,

$$2I = \int_0^{\pi/2} \frac{\sqrt{\cos x} + \sqrt{\sin x}}{\sqrt{\cos x} + \sqrt{\sin x}} \, dx$$

$$= \int_0^{\pi/2} dx = \frac{\pi}{2}.$$

$$\therefore \quad I = \frac{\pi}{4}.$$

3. *Evaluate* $\int_0^{\pi} \frac{x \sin x}{1 + \cos^2 x} dx.$ *(Agra, 2000; Kumaon, 1994; Sagar, 1996; Rohilkhand, 1998)*

Let

$$I = \int_0^{\pi} \frac{x \sin x}{1 + \cos^2 x} dx$$

$$= \int_0^{\pi} \frac{(\pi - x) \sin (\pi - x)}{1 + \cos^2 (\pi - x)} dx$$

$$= \int_0^{\pi} \frac{(\pi - x) \sin x}{1 + \cos^2 x} dx$$

$$= \pi \int_0^{\pi} \frac{\sin x}{1 + \cos^2 x} dx - I$$

$$\therefore \quad 2I = 2\pi \int_0^{\pi} \frac{\sin x}{1 + \cos^2 x} dx$$

$$\therefore \quad I = -\pi \left[\tan^{-1} (\cos x) \right]_0^{\pi/2} = \frac{\pi^2}{4}.$$

4. *Evaluate* $\int_0^{\pi/2} \frac{\sin^2 x}{\sin x + \cos x} dx.$

(Rohilkhand, 1999; Kumaon, 1996, 97, 99, 2001, 03; Agra, 1996; Kanpur, 1994; Bundelkhand, 1994)

$$I = \int_0^{\pi/2} \frac{\sin^2 x}{\sin x + \cos x} dx$$

$$I = \int_0^{\pi/2} \frac{\sin^2 (\pi/2 - x)}{\sin (\pi/2 - x) + \cos (\pi/2 - x)} dx$$

$$= \int_0^{\pi/2} \frac{\cos^2 x}{\sin x + \cos x} dx$$

$$\therefore \quad 2I = \int_0^{\pi/2} \frac{\sin^2 x + \cos^2 x}{\sin x + \cos x}\,dx$$

$$= \int_0^{\pi/2} \frac{dx}{\sin x + \cos x}$$

$$= \frac{1}{\sqrt{2}} \int_0^{\pi/2} \frac{dx}{\frac{1}{\sqrt{2}}\sin x + \frac{1}{\sqrt{2}}\cos x}$$

$$= \frac{1}{\sqrt{2}} \int_0^{\pi/2} \frac{dx}{\sin\left(x + \frac{\pi}{4}\right)}$$

$$= \frac{1}{\sqrt{2}} \int_0^{\pi} \operatorname{cosec}\left(x + \frac{\pi}{4}\right) dx$$

$$= \frac{1}{\sqrt{2}} \left[\log \tan\left(\frac{1}{2}x + \frac{1}{8}\pi\right) \right]_0^{\pi/2}$$

$$= \frac{1}{\sqrt{2}} \left[\log \tan \frac{3}{8}\pi - \log \tan \frac{1}{8}\pi \right]$$

$$= \frac{1}{\sqrt{2}} \left[\log \frac{\tan \frac{3}{8}\pi}{\tan \frac{1}{8}\pi} \right]$$

$$= \frac{1}{\sqrt{2}} \left[\log \frac{\tan\left(\frac{\pi}{2} - \frac{1}{8}\pi\right)}{\tan \frac{1}{8}\pi} \right]$$

$$= \frac{1}{\sqrt{2}} \log \frac{\cot \frac{\pi}{8}}{\tan \frac{\pi}{8}} = \frac{1}{2} \log \frac{\cos^2 \frac{1}{8}\pi}{\sin^2 \frac{1}{8}\pi}$$

$$= \frac{1}{\sqrt{2}} \log \frac{1 + \cos \frac{\pi}{4}}{1 - \cos \frac{\pi}{4}} = \frac{1}{\sqrt{2}} \log \left(\frac{\sqrt{2} + 1}{\sqrt{2} - 1} \right)$$

$$= \sqrt{2} \log (\sqrt{2} + 1).$$

$$\therefore \quad I = \frac{1}{\sqrt{2}} \log (\sqrt{2} + 1).$$

5. *Evaluate* $I = \int\limits_0^{\pi/2} \log \sin x \, dx.$

(Rohilkhand, 1995, 96; Bilaspur, 1995; Kumaon, 1998, 2001; Agra, 1996; Bundelkhand, 1995; Kanpur, 1995, 2001; Avadh, 2002)

We have

$$I = \int\limits_0^{\pi/2} \log \sin x \, dx \qquad \qquad \qquad ...(i)$$

$$= \int\limits_0^{\pi/2} \log \sin\left(\frac{\pi}{2} - x\right) dx$$

$$\therefore \quad I = \int\limits_0^{\pi/2} \log \cos x \, dx \qquad \qquad \qquad ...(ii)$$

Adding (i) and (ii), we get

$$I + I = \int\limits_0^{\pi/2} \log \sin x \, dx + \int\limits_0^{\pi/2} \log \cos x \, dx$$

or $\quad 2I = \int\limits_0^{\pi/2} \log \sin x \cos x \, dx$

$$= \int\limits_0^{\pi/2} \log\left(\frac{\sin 2x}{2}\right) dx$$

$$= \int\limits_0^{\pi/2} \log \sin 2x \, dx - \int\limits_0^{\pi/2} \log 2 \, dx$$

$$= \int\limits_0^{\pi/2} \log \sin 2x \, dx - \log 2 \left[x\right]_0^{\pi/2}$$

$$= \int\limits_0^{\pi/2} \log \sin 2x \, dx - \frac{\pi}{2} \log 2.$$

Put $2x = u$ $\therefore$ $2 \, dx = du.$

For $x = \dfrac{\pi}{2}$, $u = \pi$ (upper limit).

For $x = 0$, $u = 0$ (lower limit).

Then (from Example 5) $2I = \dfrac{1}{2} \displaystyle\int_0^\pi \log \sin u \, du - \dfrac{\pi}{2} \log 2$

$$= \dfrac{2}{2} \int_0^{\pi/2} \log \sin u \, du - \dfrac{\pi}{2} \log 2$$

$$= \int_0^{\pi/2} \log \sin x \, dx - \dfrac{\pi}{2} \log 2$$

$$= I - \dfrac{\pi}{2} \log 2$$

$\therefore \qquad I = -\dfrac{\pi}{2} \log 2$

$\therefore \qquad \displaystyle\int_0^{\pi/2} \log \sin x \, dx = -\dfrac{\pi}{2} \log 2 = \dfrac{\pi}{2} \log \dfrac{1}{2}.$

Similarly, $\qquad \displaystyle\int_0^{\pi/2} \log \cos x \, dx = -\dfrac{\pi}{2} \log 2$

$$= \dfrac{\pi}{2} \log \dfrac{1}{2}.$$

6. *Evaluate* $I = \displaystyle\int_0^\pi \log (1 + \cos x) \, dx.$

(*Kumaon, 1997*; *Rohilkhand, 1997*)

We have

$$I = \int_0^\pi \log \left(2 \cos^2 \dfrac{x}{2} \right) dx$$

$$= \int_0^\pi \log 2 \, dx + 2 \int_0^\pi \log \cos \dfrac{x}{2} \, dx$$

$$= \log 2 \left[x \right]_0^\pi + 2 \int_0^\pi \log \cos \dfrac{x}{2} \, dx.$$

Put $\dfrac{x}{2} = u, \ \dfrac{dx}{2} = du.$

$$= \pi \log 2 + 4 \int_0^{\pi/2} \log \cos u \, du$$

$$= \pi \log 2 + 4 \left(-\frac{\pi}{2} \log 2 \right) \qquad \text{(from Example 5)}$$

$$= \pi \log 2 - 2\pi \log 2$$

$$= -\pi \log 2 = \pi \log \frac{1}{2}.$$

7. Evaluate $\displaystyle\int_0^1 \frac{\log x}{\sqrt{1-x^2}}\, dx.$

We have

$$I = \int_0^1 \frac{\log x}{\sqrt{1-x^2}}\, dx.$$

Put $x = \sin\theta$, $dx = \cos\theta\, d\theta.$
Lower limit $0 = \sin\theta$, $\theta = 0.$

$$\therefore \quad I = \int_0^{\pi/2} \frac{(\log \sin\theta)\cos\theta\, d\theta}{\cos\theta}$$

$$= \int_0^{\pi/2} \log \sin\theta\, d\theta$$

$$= -\frac{\pi}{2} \log 2. \qquad \text{(from Example 5)}$$

8. Evaluate $\displaystyle\int_0^{\pi/2} x \cot x\, dx.$

We have

$$I = \int_0^{\pi/2} x \cot x\, dx$$

$$= \left[x \log \sin x \right]_0^{\pi/2} - \int_0^{\pi/2} \log \sin x\, dx \qquad \text{(Integrating by parts)}$$

$$= \left[\frac{\pi}{2} \log \sin \frac{\pi}{2} - \lim_{x\to 0} x \log \sin x \right] + \frac{\pi}{2} \log 2 \qquad \text{(from Example 5)}$$

$$= 0 - \lim_{x\to 0} \frac{\csc^2 x}{1/x} + \frac{\pi}{2} \log 2$$

$$= -\lim_{x\to 0} \frac{\cot x}{-1/x^2} + \frac{\pi}{2} \log 2$$

$$= -\lim_{x \to 0} \frac{\text{cosec}^2 \, x}{2/x^3} + \frac{\pi}{2} \log 2$$

$$= -\lim_{x \to 0} \frac{x}{2} \frac{x^2}{\sin^2 x} + \frac{\pi}{2} \log 2$$

$$= 0 + \frac{\pi}{2} \log 2$$

$$= \frac{\pi}{2} \log 2.$$

9. Evaluate $\displaystyle \int_0^\infty log\left(x + \frac{1}{x}\right) \frac{dx}{1 + x^2}.$ *(Kumaon, 1995, 99)*

We have

$$I = \int_0^\infty \log\left(x + \frac{1}{x}\right) \frac{dx}{1 + x^2}.$$

Put $x = \tan \theta,\, dx = \sec^2 \theta \, d\theta.$

Upper limit, $\infty = \tan \theta,\ \theta = \pi / 2.$

Lower limit, $0 = \tan \theta,\ \theta = 0.$

$$\therefore \quad I = \int_0^{\pi/2} \log\left(\tan \theta + \frac{1}{\tan \theta}\right) \frac{\sec^2 \theta \, d\theta}{1 + \tan^2 \theta}$$

$$= \int_0^{\pi/2} \log\left(\frac{\tan^2 \theta + 1}{\tan \theta}\right) d\theta$$

$$= \int_0^{\pi/2} \log \frac{1}{\sin \theta \cos \theta} \, d\theta$$

$$= -\int_0^{\pi/2} \log \sin \theta \, d\theta - \int_0^{\pi/2} \log \cos \theta \, d\theta$$

$$= \frac{\pi}{2} \log 2 + \frac{\pi}{2} \log 2$$

$$= \pi \log 2. \qquad \text{(from Example 5)}$$

10. Show that $\displaystyle \int_0^{\pi/4} log\, (1 + tan\, \theta) \, d\theta = \frac{\pi}{8} log\, 2.$

(Agra, 2001; Bundelkhand, 1996;
Kanpur, 1995, 2002; Kumaon, 1999; Avadh, 2003)

Let

$$I = \int_0^{\pi/4} \log (1 + \tan \theta)\, d\theta$$

$$= \int_0^{\pi/4} \log \left\{ 1 + \tan \left(\frac{\pi}{4} - \theta \right) \right\} d\theta$$

$$= \int_0^{\pi/4} \log \left\{ 1 + \left(\frac{1 - \tan \theta}{1 + \tan \theta} \right) \right\} d\theta$$

$$= \int_0^{\pi/4} \log \left(\frac{2}{1 + \tan \theta} \right) d\theta$$

$$= \log 2 \int_0^{\pi/4} d\theta - \int_0^{\pi/4} \log (1 + \tan \theta)\, d\theta$$

$$= \frac{\pi}{4} \log 2 - I.$$

$$\therefore \quad 2I = \frac{1}{4} \pi \log 2$$

$$\Rightarrow \quad I = \frac{1}{8} \pi \log 2.$$

EXERCISES

Evaluate :

1. $\int_0^{\pi} \cos^6 x \, dx.$

2. $\int_0^{\pi} \sin^4 x \, dx.$

3. $\int_0^{\pi} \theta \sin^3 \theta \, d\theta.$

4. $\int_0^{\pi} \theta \sin \theta \cos^2 \theta \, d\theta.$

Show that :

5. $\int_0^{\pi} \cos^{2n+1} x \, dx = 0.$

6. $\int_0^{2\pi} \dfrac{dx}{a + b \cos x + c \sin x} = \dfrac{2\pi}{\sqrt{a^2 - b^2 - c^2}}.$

Evaluate the following :

7. $\displaystyle\int_{0}^{\pi} \frac{x\,dx}{1+\sin x}.$ \hfill (*Garhwal, 1998; Kanpur, 2000*)

8. $\displaystyle\int_{0}^{\pi} \frac{x}{1+\cos^2 x}\,dx.$ **9.** $\displaystyle\int_{0}^{\pi} \frac{x\,dx}{a^2-\cos^2 x},\ a>1.$

10. $\displaystyle\int_{0}^{\pi} \frac{x\,dx}{(a^2\cos^2 x + b^2\sin^2 x)}.$

\hfill (*Kumaon, 1992, 95, 97; Meerut, 1996P; Avadh, 1993*)

11. $\displaystyle\int_{0}^{\pi} \frac{\sin x}{\sin x + \cos x}\,dx.$ **12.** $\displaystyle\int_{0}^{\pi} \frac{dx}{1+\cot x}.$ (*Rohilkhand, 2001*)

13. $\displaystyle\int_{0}^{\pi} x\,\log(\sin x)\,dx.$

14. $\displaystyle\int_{0}^{\pi/2} \log\tan x\,dx.$

\hfill (*Garhwal, 1999, 2000; Kumaon, 2000, 02; Bhopal, 2002*)

15. $\displaystyle\int_{0}^{1} \frac{\sin^{-1}x}{x}\,dx.$ \hfill (*Kumaon, 1994*)

16. $\displaystyle\int_{0}^{\pi/2} x^2\,\mathrm{cosec}^2 x\,dx.$ **17.** $\displaystyle\int_{0}^{\pi/2} \left(\frac{\theta}{\sin\theta}\right)^2 d\theta.$ (*Garhwal, 2001*)

18. $\displaystyle\int_{0}^{\infty} \frac{\log(1+x^2)}{1+x^2}\,dx.$ \hfill (*Agra, 2000; Garhwal, 1996, 2001*)

19. $\displaystyle\int_{0}^{\pi/2} \log\cot x\,dx.$

20. Prove that $\displaystyle\int_{0}^{\pi/4} \log(1+\tan\theta)\,d\theta = \frac{\pi}{8}\log_e 2.$ (*Kumaon, 1999*)

21. Show that $\displaystyle\int_{0}^{\pi} \frac{x\tan x\,dx}{\sec x + \tan x} = \pi\left(\frac{\pi}{2}-1\right).$

\hfill (*Garhwal, 1994, 2002;*
\hfill *Kumaon, 1995, 98; Kanpur, 1997, 2003; Meerut, 1995*)

22. Prove that $\int_0^\pi \dfrac{x \tan x}{\sec x + \cos x}\, dx = \dfrac{\pi^2}{4}.$

23. Prove that $\int_0^\pi \dfrac{x\, dx}{1 + \cos \alpha \sin x} = \dfrac{\pi \alpha}{\sin \alpha}.$ *(Garhwal, 2000)*

24. Prove that $\int_0^\pi \dfrac{x \sin x}{1 + \sin x}\, dx = \pi\left(\dfrac{\pi}{2} - 1\right).$

ANSWERS

1. $\dfrac{5\pi}{16}.$ **2.** $\dfrac{3\pi}{8}.$ **3.** $\dfrac{2\pi}{3}.$ **4.** $-\dfrac{\pi}{3}.$

7. $\pi.$ **8.** $\dfrac{1}{4}\pi^2\sqrt{2}.$ **9.** $\pi^2 / \sqrt{(a^2 - 1)}\ 2a.$

10. $\dfrac{\pi^2}{2ab}.$ **11.** $\dfrac{1}{4}\pi.$ **12.** $\dfrac{1}{4}\pi.$

13. $-\dfrac{1}{2}\pi^2 \log 2.$ **14.** $0.$ **15.** $\dfrac{1}{2}\pi \log 2.$

16. $\pi \log 2.$ **17.** $\pi \log 2.$ **18.** $\pi \log 2.$ **19.** $0.$

6.3. Fundamental Theorem of Integral Calculus. Definite integral as the limit of a sum. *Let the interval* $[a, b]$, *be divided into n equal parts and let the length of each part be, h, so that nh = b − a; then*

$$\int_a^b f(x)\, dx = \lim h\,[\,f(a + h) + f(a + 2h) + \ldots\ldots + f(a + nh)\,],$$

when $n \to \infty$, $h \to 0$ **and** $nh = b - a.$

Here

$$a,\ a + h,\ a + 2h,\ \ldots\ldots,\ a + (r - 1)\, h,\ \ldots\ldots,\ a + (n - 1)\, h,\ a + nh$$

are the points of division obtained when the interval $[a, b]$ is divided into n equal parts; h being the length of each part.

We suppose that the function $f(x)$ monotonically increases from a to b.

Let G, H be points on the curve $y = f(x)$ with abscissae a, b respectively.

Draw GA, HB $\perp$ X-axis.

Let M, N be the points of division of the rth strip MN corresponding to

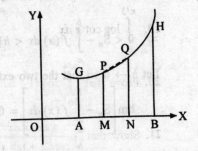

the division of the interval $[a, b]$ into n equal parts so that $OM = a + (r-1)\,h$, $ON = a + rh$; we have

$$MP = f\,[a + (r-1)\,h], \quad NQ = f\,(a + rh).$$

We write

$$S_n = h\,[f(a+h) + f(a+2h) + \ldots + f(a+nh)].$$

Complete the rectangles MQ, NP.

The sum of the areas of the rectangles of the type NP which are *inscribed* in the area GABH

$$= h \sum_{r=1}^{r=n} f\,[a + (r-1)\,h]$$
$$= h\,[f(a) + f(a+h) + \ldots + f\{a + (n-1)\,h\}]$$
$$= S_n - h\,[f(a+nh) - f(a)]$$
$$= S_n - h\,[f(b) - f(a)], \text{ for } nh = b - a. \qquad \ldots(i)$$

The sum of the areas of the rectangles of the type MQ which are *circumscribed* to the area GABH

$$= \sum_{r=1}^{r=n} h\,f(a+rh)$$
$$= h\,[f(a+h) + f(a+2h) + \ldots + f(a+nh)]$$
$$= S_n. \qquad \ldots(ii)$$

The area of the region GABH $= \displaystyle\int_a^b f(x)\,dx. \qquad \ldots(iii)$

From the figure, we see that the area of the region GABH lies between the sums of the areas of the two sets of rectangles (i) and (ii).

Thus we have

$$S_n - h\,[f(b) - f(a)] < \int_a^b f(x)\,dx < S_n$$

$$\Rightarrow \quad 0 < S_n - \int_a^b f(x)\,dx < h\,[f(b) - f(a)].$$

Let $h \to 0$ so that the two extremes tend to 0. Therefore

$$\lim\left[S_n - \int_a^b f(x)\,dx\right] = 0$$

$$\Rightarrow \quad \lim S_n = \int_a^b f(x)\,dx.$$

Thus we have proved the result for the case when $f(x)$ *increases* as x increases from a 'to b. It may similarly be shown that the result remains true in the case when $f(x)$ monotonically *decreases* as x increases from a to b. In this case, the directions of the inequalities in (iv) and (v) will be reversed.

Note 1. The above proof is *geometrical* in nature, the *rigorous analytical* proof being beyond the scope of this book.

Note 2. The result of the theorem can be concisely stated as follows :

$$\int_a^b f(x)\, dx = \lim \sum_{r=1}^{r=n} h f(a+rh),$$

when $h \to 0$, $n \to \infty$; $nh = b - a$.

Note 3. It should be noted that, since each term in $\Sigma\, h f(a + rh)$ tends to 0, the addition or omission of a certain finite number of terms of the similar type will not alter the limit.

EXAMPLES

1. *Evaluate* $\displaystyle\int_a^b x^2\, dx$ *as the limit of a sum.*

Here $f(x) = x^2$.

$$\therefore \int_a^b x^2\, dx$$

$$= \lim h\,[f(a+h) + f(a+2h) + \ldots\ldots + f(a+nh)]$$

$$\text{when } h \to 0,\ n \to \infty \text{ and } nh = b - a,$$

$$= \lim h\,[(a+h)^2 + (a+2h)^2 + \ldots\ldots + (a+nh)^2]$$

$$= \lim h\,[na^2 + 2ah(1 + 2 + \ldots\ldots + n) + h^2(1^2 + 2^2 + \ldots\ldots + n^2)]$$

$$= \lim h\left[na^2 + n(n+1)\,ah + \frac{1}{6}n(n+1)(2n+1)\,h^2\right]$$

$$= \lim \left[nha^2 + nh(nh+h)\,a + \frac{1}{6}nh(nh+h)(2nh+h)\right]$$

$$= \lim \Bigg[(b-a)\,a^2 + (b-a)(b-a+h)\,a$$

$$+ \frac{1}{6}(b-a)(b-a+h)\,\{2(b-a+h)\}\Bigg]$$

$$= (b-a)\,a^2 + (b-a)^2\,a + \frac{1}{3}(b-a)^3$$

$$= \frac{1}{3}(b^3 - a^3).$$

2. *Evaluate* $\int\limits_a^b e^x \, dx$ *as the limit of a sum.*

Here $f(x) = e^x$.

$\therefore \quad \int\limits_a^b e^x \, dx$

$$= \lim h [e^{a+h} + e^{a+2h} + \ldots + e^{a+nh}],$$

$$\text{when } h \to 0, \, n \to \infty \text{ and } nh = b - a,$$

$$= \lim \frac{h e^{a+h} (1 - e^{nh})}{1 - e^h}$$

$$= \lim \left[e^a \cdot (1 - e^{b-a}) \, e^h \cdot \frac{h}{1 - e^h} \right]$$

$$= (e^a - e^b) \cdot \lim e^h \cdot \lim \frac{h}{1 - e^h}$$

$$= (e^a - e^b)(-1) = e^b - e^a,$$

for, $\lim \{ h / (1 - e^h) \} = -1$, as $h \to 0$.

3. *Evaluate* $\int\limits_a^b \cos x \, dx$ *as the limit of a sum.* (*Gorakhpur, 2002*)

Here $f(x) = \cos x$. Therefore

$$\int\limits_a^b \cos x \, dx = \lim h [\cos(a+h) + \cos(a+2h) + \ldots + \cos(a+nh)].$$

Let

$$S = \cos(a+h) + \cos(a+2h) + \ldots + \cos(a+nh).$$

Multiplying both sides by $2 \sin \dfrac{1}{2} h$, we get

$$2 \sin \frac{1}{2} h \cdot S = 2 \sin \frac{1}{2} h \cos(a+h) + 2 \sin \frac{1}{2} h \cos(a+2h)$$

$$+ \ldots + 2 \sin \frac{1}{2} h \cos(a+nh)$$

$$= \sin\left(a + \frac{3}{2} h\right) - \sin\left(a + \frac{1}{2} h\right) + \sin\left(a + \frac{5}{2} h\right)$$

$$- \sin\left(a + \frac{3}{2} h\right) + \ldots + \sin\left[a + \frac{1}{2}(2n+1) h\right] - \sin\left[a + \frac{1}{2}(2n-1) h\right]$$

$$= \sin\left[a + \frac{1}{2}(2n+1)h\right] - \sin\left[a + \frac{1}{2}h\right]$$

$$= \sin\left[b + \frac{1}{2}h\right] - \sin\left[a + \frac{1}{2}h\right], \text{ for } nh = b - a.$$

Thus

$$\int_a^b \cos x \, dx = \lim \frac{h\left[\sin\left(b + \frac{1}{2}h\right) - \sin\left(a + \frac{1}{2}h\right)\right]}{2\sin\frac{1}{2}h}$$

$$= \lim \frac{\frac{1}{2}h}{\sin\frac{1}{2}h}\left[\sin\left(b + \frac{1}{2}h\right) - \sin\left(a + \frac{1}{2}h\right)\right]$$

$$= 1 \cdot (\sin b - \sin a) = \sin b - \sin a.$$

EXERCISES

Evaluate the following definite integrals as limits of sums :

1. (i) $\displaystyle\int_a^b x \, dx,$ (ii) $\displaystyle\int_2^3 x^3 \, dx.$

2. (i) $\displaystyle\int_a^b \sin x \, dx,$ (ii) $\displaystyle\int_a^b \sin^2 x \, dx.$

3. (i) $\displaystyle\int_a^b \frac{1}{\sqrt{x}} \, dx,$ (ii) $\displaystyle\int_a^b \frac{1}{x^2} \, dx.$

4. (i) $\displaystyle\int_a^b \sinh x \, dx,$ (ii) $\displaystyle\int_a^b \cosh 2x \, dx.$

ANSWERS

1. (i) $\dfrac{1}{2}(b^2 - a^2).$ (ii) $65/4.$

2. (i) $\cos a - \cos b.$ (ii) $\dfrac{1}{2}(b - a) + (\sin a \cos a - \sin b \cos b).$

3. (i) $2(\sqrt{b} - \sqrt{a}).$ (ii) $(b - a)/ab.$

4. (i) $\cosh b - \cosh a.$ (ii) $\sinh b \cosh b - \sinh a \cosh a.$

6.4. Summation of Series. It is possible to express the limits of sums of certain types of series as definite integrals, and thus to evaluate them. We shall now consider the characteristics of the series the limit of whose sum can be so expressed and also learn how to obtain the corresponding definite integrals. It will also be shown that *it is always possible to so transform such a series that the lower and upper limits of the corresponding definite integral are 0 and 1 respectively.*

We have seen that when $h \to 0$, $n \to \infty$ and $nh = b - a$

$$\int_a^b f(x)\, dx = \lim h\, [f(a + h) + f(a + 2h) + \ldots$$

$$+ f(a + rh) + \ldots + f(a + nh)].$$

Changing h to $(b - a) / n$, we see that when $n \to \infty$, we have

$$\int_a^b f(x)\, dx$$

$$= (b - a) \lim \frac{1}{n} \left[f\left\{ a + (b - a)\frac{1}{n} \right\} + f\left\{ a + (b - a)\frac{2}{n} \right\} + \ldots \right.$$

$$\left. + f\left\{ a + (b - a)\frac{r}{n} \right\} + \ldots + f\left\{ a + (b - a)\frac{n}{n} \right\} \right]$$

$$= (b - a) \lim \frac{1}{n} \sum_{r=1}^{r=n} f\left[a + (b - a)\frac{r}{n} \right].$$

From § 9.2, we easily see that when $n \to \infty$,

$$\lim \frac{1}{n} \sum_{r=1}^{r=n} f\left[a + (b - a)\frac{r}{n} \right] = \int_0^1 f\left[a + (b - a)\, x \right] dx.$$

$$\therefore \quad \int_a^b f(x)\, dx = (b - a) \int_0^1 f\left[a + (b - a)\, x \right] dx.$$

We now notice the following :

The general term $(1 / n)\, f\left[a + (b - a)(r / n) \right]$ of the sum

$$(1 / n)\, \Sigma\, f\left[a + (b - a)(r / n) \right]$$

is a function of (r / n) such that the various terms in the series are obtained by giving values 1, 2, 3, ..., n to r and also the new integrand $f\left[a + (b - a)\, x \right]$ is obtained by changing (r / n) to x.

Also $(1 / n)$ is a factor of each term.

From above we deduce that in the case of a series the limit of whose sum can be expressed as a definite integral, *the general term is the product of $1 / n$ and a function $\varphi (r / n)$ of r / n, so that the various terms of the series can be obtained from it by changing r to 1, 2, 3, ..., n, successively.*

The equivalent definite integral, then, is obtained by *changing* (r/n), in the general term, to x and taking $0, 1$ as the two limits.

Rule. Thus it is important to remember that

$$\lim_{n \to \infty} \left[\sum_{r=1}^{r=n} \frac{1}{n} \, \varphi\left(\frac{r}{n}\right) \right] = \int_0^1 \varphi(x)\, dx.$$

Note. Here the number of terms is n but, since each term tends to 0, the addition or omission of a *finite* number of terms will not affect the required limit.

EXAMPLES

1. *Find the limit when n tends to infinity of the series*

$$\frac{n^2}{(n^2+1)^{3/2}} + \frac{n^2}{(n^2+2^2)^{3/2}} + \frac{n^2}{(n^2+3^2)^{3/2}} + \dots + \frac{n^2}{[n^2+(n-1)^2]^{3/2}}.$$

Here the general rth term

$$= \frac{n^2}{(n^2+r^2)^{3/2}} = \frac{1}{n} \left\{ \frac{1}{\left[1 + \left(\dfrac{r}{n}\right)^2 \right]^{3/2}} \right\}$$

which is the product of $1/n$ and the function

$$1 / \left[1 + \left(\frac{r}{n}\right)^2 \right]^{3/2}$$

of r/n.

Thus, by the above rule, the required limit is equal to

$$\int_0^1 \frac{1}{(1+x^2)^{3/2}}\, dx.$$

Putting $x = \tan\theta$, it can be seen that this integral is equal to $1/\sqrt{2}$.

2. *Find the limit, when n tends to infinity, of the series*

$$\frac{\sqrt{n}}{\sqrt{n^3}} + \frac{\sqrt{n}}{\sqrt{(n+4)^3}} + \frac{\sqrt{n}}{\sqrt{(n+8)^3}} + \frac{\sqrt{n}}{\sqrt{(n+12)^3}} + \dots + \frac{\sqrt{n}}{\sqrt{[n+4(n-1)]^3}}.$$

Here, the rth term

$$= \frac{\sqrt{n}}{\sqrt{[n+4(r-1)]^3}} = \frac{1}{n} \frac{1}{\sqrt{\left[1 + \dfrac{4(r-1)}{n} \right]^3}}.$$

As the rth term contains $(r - 1)$, we consider the $(r + 1)$th term. The $(r + 1)$th term

$$= \frac{1}{n} \frac{1}{\sqrt{\left(1 + \frac{4r}{n}\right)^3}}.$$

Changing (r / n) in $1 / \sqrt{\left(1 + \frac{4r}{n}\right)^3}$ to x, we see that the required limit

$$= \int_0^1 \frac{dx}{\sqrt{(1 + 4x)^3}} = \int_0^1 (1 + 4x)^{-3/2} \, dx = \frac{1}{10} (5 - \sqrt{5}).$$

3. *Find the value of*

$$\lim_{n \to \infty} \frac{[(n + 1)(n + 2) \dots (n + n)]^{1/n}}{n}.$$

(*Sagar, 1996; Bhopal, 1998; Kumaon, 1994;*
Kanpur, 2003; Gorakhpur, 2003)

Let $y = \dfrac{[(n + 1)(n + 2) \dots (2n)]^{1/n}}{n}.$

We have

$$\log y = \frac{1}{n} \{\log (n + 1) + \log (n + 2) + \dots + \log 2n\} - \log n$$

$$= \frac{1}{n} \{[\log (n + 1) - \log n] + [\log (n + 2) - \log n] + \dots$$

$$+ [\log 2n - \log n]\}$$

$$= \frac{1}{n} \left\{ \log \left(1 + \frac{1}{n}\right) + \log \left(1 + \frac{2}{n}\right) + \dots + \log \left(1 + \frac{n}{n}\right) \right\}.$$

The rth term $= \dfrac{1}{n} \log \left(1 + \dfrac{r}{n}\right).$

Therefore, when n tends to infinity, we have

$$\lim \log y = \int_0^1 \log (1 + x) \, dx$$

$$= \left| x \log (1 + x) \right|_0^1 - \int_0^1 \frac{x}{1 + x} \, dx$$

$$= \log 2 - \left| x - \log (1 + x) \right|_0^1$$

$$= \log 2 - (1 - \log 2)$$

$$= 2\log 2 - 1 = \log 4 - \log e = \log(4/e),$$

$$\therefore \quad \lim y = 4/e.$$

4. *Find the limit when* $n \to \infty$ *of the series*

$$\frac{1}{n} + \frac{n^2}{(n+1)^3} + \ldots + \frac{1}{8n}.$$

(Kumaon, 1999, 2002; Garhwal, 1993; Kanpur, 2002)

The given series is

$$\frac{n^2}{n^3} + \frac{n^2}{(n+1)^3} + \frac{n^2}{(n+2)^3} + \ldots + \frac{n^2}{(n+n)^3}.$$

General term, *i.e.*, *r*th term is

$$\frac{n^2}{(n+r)^3}.$$

$$\lim_{n \to \infty} \sum_{r=0}^{n-1} \frac{n^2}{(n+r)^3} = \lim_{n \to \infty} \sum_{r=0}^{n-1} \frac{1}{n} \cdot \frac{n^3}{(n+r)^3}$$

$$= \lim_{n \to \infty} \sum_{r=0}^{n-1} \frac{1}{n} \cdot \frac{1}{\left(1 + \dfrac{r}{n}\right)^3}$$

$$= \int_0^1 \frac{dx}{(1+x)^3}$$

$$= -\frac{1}{2} \left[\frac{1}{(1+x)^3} \right]_0^1 = \frac{3}{8}.$$

5. *Evaluate* $\displaystyle \lim_{n \to \infty} \sum_{r=1}^{n} \frac{\sqrt{n}}{\sqrt{r}\,(3\sqrt{r} + 4\sqrt{n})^2}.$ *(Rohilkhand, 1992)*

We have

$$\lim_{n \to \infty} \sum_{r=1}^{n} \frac{\sqrt{n}}{\sqrt{r}\,(3\sqrt{r} + 4\sqrt{n})^2}$$

$$= \lim_{n \to \infty} \sum_{r=1}^{n} \frac{\sqrt{n}}{\sqrt{r} \cdot n \left\{ 3\left(\dfrac{\sqrt{r}}{\sqrt{n}}\right) + 4 \right\}^2}$$

$$= \lim_{n \to \infty} \sum_{r=1}^{n} \frac{1}{n} \frac{1}{\left\{ \sqrt{\dfrac{r}{n}} \left(\sqrt{\dfrac{r}{n}} + 4 \right) \right\}^2}$$

$$= \int_0^1 \frac{1}{\sqrt{x}\left\{3\sqrt{x}+4\right\}^2}\,dx.$$

Put $3\sqrt{x}+4 = t$, $\dfrac{3}{2\sqrt{x}}\,dx = dt$

$$= \frac{2}{3}\int_4^7 \frac{1}{t^2}\,dt = \frac{2}{3}\left[-\frac{1}{t}\right]_4^7$$

$$= \frac{2}{3}\left[-\frac{1}{7}+\frac{1}{4}\right] = \frac{1}{14}.$$

6. Evaluate

$$\lim_{n \to \infty}\left[\frac{1}{n^2}\sec^2\frac{1}{n^2} + \frac{2}{n^2}\sec^2\frac{4}{n^2} + \frac{3}{n^2}\sec^2\frac{9}{n^2} + \ldots + \frac{1}{n}\sec^2 1\right].$$

(*Garhwal, 1993, 94; Kumaon, 1997, 2003*)

The given limit $= \displaystyle\lim_{n \to \infty}\sum_{r=1}^n \frac{r}{n^2}\sec^2\left(\frac{r^2}{n^2}\right)$

$$= \lim_{n \to \infty}\sum_{r=1}^n \frac{1}{n}\cdot\left(\frac{r}{n}\right)\sec^2\left(\frac{r}{n}\right)^2$$

$$= \int_0^1 x \sec^2 x^2\,dx$$

$$= \frac{1}{2}\int_0^1 2x \sec^2 x^2\,dx = \frac{1}{2}\left[\tan x^2\right]_0^1 = \frac{1}{2}\tan 1.$$

7. Prove that

$$\lim_{n \to \infty}\left\{\left(1+\frac{1}{n^2}\right)\left(1+\frac{2^2}{n^2}\right)\left(1+\frac{3^2}{n^2}\right)\ldots\left(1+\frac{n^2}{n^2}\right)\right\}^{1/n}$$

is equal to $2e^{(\pi - 4)/2}$.   (*Kumaon, 1996; Rohilkhand, 2000, 01; Jabalpur, 1999; Gorakhpur, 1995, 2001; Avadh, 2000*)

Let the given product be A.

Then $\log A = \displaystyle\lim_{n \to \infty}\sum_{r=1}^n \frac{1}{n}\log\left(1+\frac{r^2}{n^2}\right)$

$$= \int_0^1 \log(1+x^2)\,dx$$

$$= \left[x \log (1 + x^2)\right]_0^1 - \int \frac{2x^2}{1 + x^2} dx$$

$$= \log 2 - 2 \int_0^1 \frac{x^2 + 1 - 1}{1 + x^2} dx$$

$$= \log 2 - 2 \left[x - \tan^{-1} x\right]_0^1$$

$$= \log 2 - 2 + \frac{\pi}{2} = \log 2 + \log e^{(\pi - 4)/2}$$

$\therefore \quad \log A = \log 2e^{(\pi - 4)/2}$.

Hence $\quad A = 2e^{(\pi - 4)/2}$.

8. *Apply the definition of a definite integral as the limit of a sum to evaluate*

$$\lim_{n \to \infty} \left(\frac{n!}{n^n}\right)^{1/n}.$$

(*Rohilkhand, 1995, 98, 2000; Bhopal, 1999; Agra, 1996, 2001; Bundelkhand, 1996; Kanpur, 1997*)

Let $\quad A = \lim_{n \to \infty} \left(\frac{n!}{n^n}\right)^{1/n}$

$$= \lim_{n \to \infty} \left\{\frac{1 \cdot 2 \cdot 3 \cdot 4 \cdot 5 \dots n}{n^n}\right\}^{1/n}$$

$$= \lim_{n \to \infty} \left\{\left(\frac{1}{n}\right)\left(\frac{2}{n}\right)\left(\frac{3}{n}\right) \dots \left(\frac{n}{n}\right)\right\}^{1/n}$$

$\therefore \quad \log A = \lim_{n \to \infty} \frac{1}{n}\left[\log\left(\frac{1}{n}\right) + \log\left(\frac{2}{n}\right) + \log\left(\frac{3}{n}\right) + \dots + \log\left(\frac{n}{n}\right)\right]$

$$= \lim_{n \to \infty} \sum_{r=1}^n \frac{1}{n} \log\left(\frac{r}{n}\right) = \int_0^1 \log x \, dx$$

$$= \left[(\log x) \cdot x\right]_0^1 - \int_0^1 \frac{1}{x} \cdot x \, dx.$$

Integrating by parts

$$= 0 - \int_0^1 dx = -\left[x\right]_0^1 = -1$$

$\therefore \quad A = e^{-1} = \frac{1}{e}$.

9. *Evaluate*

$$\lim_{n \to \infty} \left[\tan \frac{\pi}{2n} \tan \frac{2\pi}{2n} \tan \frac{3\pi}{2n} \ldots \tan \frac{n\pi}{2n} \right]^{1/n}$$

Let

$$A = \lim_{n \to \infty} \left[\tan \frac{\pi}{2n} \tan \frac{2\pi}{2n} \ldots \tan \frac{n\pi}{2n} \right]^{1/n}$$

$$\log A = \lim_{n \to \infty} \frac{1}{n} \left[\log \left(\tan \frac{\pi}{2n} \right) + \log \left(\tan \frac{2\pi}{2n} \right) + \ldots + \log \left(\tan \frac{n\pi}{2n} \right) \right]$$

$$= \lim_{n \to \infty} \sum_{r=1}^{n} \frac{1}{n} \cdot \log \tan \left(\frac{r\pi}{2n} \right)$$

$$= \int_{0}^{1} \log \left(\tan \frac{\pi}{2} x \right) dx$$

$$= \frac{2}{\pi} \int_{0}^{\pi/2} \log \tan \theta \, d\theta, \text{ putting } \frac{\pi}{2} x = \theta$$

$$= \frac{2}{\pi} \left[\int_{0}^{\pi/2} \log \sin \theta \, d\theta - \int_{0}^{\pi/2} \log \cos \theta \, d\theta \right]$$

$$= \frac{2}{\pi} (0) = 0.$$

$$\therefore \quad A = e^0 = 1.$$

10. *Show that the limit of the sum*

$$\frac{1}{n} + \frac{1}{n+1} + \frac{1}{n+2} + \ldots + \frac{1}{3n},$$

when n is indefinitely increased is log 3.

(Rohilkhand, 1994; Kumaon, 1998, 2000;
Avadh, 1995; Kanpur, 1994, 97; Meerut, 1996)

In the given series, we have $(3n - n) + 1 = (2n + 1)$ terms.

Now, rth term $= \dfrac{1}{n+r} = \dfrac{1}{n} \left\{ \dfrac{1}{1 + (r/n)} \right\}$

$\therefore$ The required limit $= \lim_{n \to \infty} \sum_{r=0}^{2n} \dfrac{1}{n} \left\{ \dfrac{1}{1 + (r/n)} \right\}.$

Here for the corresponding definite integral the lower limit $= \lim_{n \to \infty} \left(\dfrac{r}{n} \right)$

for the first term $= \lim_{n \to \infty} \left(\dfrac{0}{n} \right) = 0$ $(\because \ r = 0$ for the last term$)$

Upper limit $= \lim_{n \to \infty} \left(\dfrac{r}{n}\right)$ for the last term

$$= \lim_{n \to \infty} \left(\dfrac{2n}{n}\right) \qquad (\because r = 2n \text{ for the last term})$$

$$= 2.$$

$\therefore$ The required limit $= \displaystyle\int_0^2 \dfrac{dx}{(1+x)}$

$$= \Big[\log(1+x)\Big]_0^2 = \log 3.$$

EXERCISES

Find the limit, when n tends to infinity, of the series

1. $\dfrac{1}{n+1} + \dfrac{1}{n+2} + \dfrac{1}{n+3} + \dots + \dfrac{1}{n+n}$.

(*Rohilkhand, 1996; Garhwal, 1992; Kanpur, 2001*)

2. $\dfrac{1}{\sqrt{n^2}} + \dfrac{1}{\sqrt{n^2 - 1}} + \dfrac{1}{\sqrt{n^2 - 2^2}} + \dots + \dfrac{1}{\sqrt{[n^2 - (n-1)^2]}}$.

3. $\dfrac{n+1}{n^2 + 1^2} + \dfrac{n+2}{n^2 + 2^2} + \dfrac{n+3}{n^2 + 3^2} + \dots + \dfrac{1}{n}$.

4. $\dfrac{1}{\sqrt{2n - 1^2}} + \dfrac{1}{\sqrt{4n - 2^2}} + \dfrac{1}{\sqrt{6n - 3^2}} + \dots + \dfrac{1}{n}$. (*Gorakhpur, 2000*)

5. $\dfrac{1}{n} + \dfrac{1}{n+1} + \dfrac{1}{n+2} + \dots + \dfrac{1}{4n}$.

6. Show that

$$\lim_{n \to \infty} \left[\dfrac{n}{n^2 + 1^2} + \dfrac{n}{n^2 + 2^2} + \dfrac{n}{n^2 + 3^2} + \dots + \dfrac{1}{2n} \right] = \dfrac{\pi}{4}.$$

(*Garhwal, 1996; Kumaon, 1995*)

Find the limit, when n tends to infinity, of the following sums :

7. $\displaystyle\sum_{r=1}^{n-1} \dfrac{1}{\sqrt{n - r^2}}$.

8. $\displaystyle\sum_{r=1}^{n} \dfrac{\sqrt{n}}{(9n + 40r)^{3/2}}$.

9. $\displaystyle\sum_{r=1}^{n} \dfrac{r^3}{r^4 + n^4}$.

10. $\displaystyle\sum_{r=1}^{n} \dfrac{n^3}{(n^2 + r^2)(n^2 + 2r^2)}$.

11. $\displaystyle\sum_{r=1}^{n-1} \dfrac{1}{n} \sqrt{\dfrac{n+r}{n-r}}$.

12. $\displaystyle\sum_{r=1}^{n} \dfrac{n}{(n+r)\sqrt{r(2n+r)}}$.

13. $\dfrac{1}{n} \displaystyle\sum_{r=1}^{n} \sin^{2k} \dfrac{r\pi}{2n}.$ 14. $\displaystyle\sum_{r=1}^{3n} \dfrac{n^3}{(3n+r)^3}.$

15. Find the limiting value of

$$\left[\frac{(n^3+1^3)\,(n^3+2^3)\,(n^3+3^3)\,.....\,(n^3+n^3)}{n^{3n}} \right]^{1/n},$$

when n tends to infinity.

16. Prove that the limit, when n tends to infinity, of

$$\left[1+\left(\frac{1}{n}\right)^4\right]\left[1+\left(\frac{2}{n}\right)^4\right]^{1/2}\left[1+\left(\frac{3}{n}\right)^4\right]^{1/3}\ .....[2]^{1/n}$$

is

$$e^{\pi^2/48}.$$

17. Show that the limit, when n tends to infinity, of

$$\left[\phi(a)\cdot\phi\left(a+\frac{h}{n}\right)\cdot\phi\left(a+\frac{2h}{n}\right).....\phi\left(a+\frac{nh}{n}\right)\right]^{1/n}$$

is e^t where t is

$$\frac{1}{h}\int_{a}^{a+h} \log \phi(x)\,dx.$$

Deduce the limit of

$$\left[\left(1+\frac{1}{n^2}\right)\left(1+\frac{2^2}{n^2}\right).....\left(1+\frac{n^2}{n^2}\right)\right]^{1/n}.$$

18. If $na = 1$ always and n tends to infinity, find the limiting value of

$$\prod_{r=1}^{n} [1+(ra)^2]^{1/r}.$$

ANSWERS

1. $\log 2$.   2. $\pi/2$.   3. $\dfrac{1}{4}\pi + \dfrac{1}{2}\log 2$.   4. $\dfrac{1}{2}\pi$.

5. $\log 4$.   7. $\pi/2$.   8. $1/105$.   9. $\dfrac{1}{4}\log 2$.

10. $\sqrt{2}\,\tan^{-1}\sqrt{2} - \dfrac{1}{4}\pi$.   11. $\dfrac{1}{2}\pi + 1$.   12. $\dfrac{1}{3}\pi$.

13. $(2k)\,!\,/\,(2^{2k})\,(k\,!)^2$.   14. $1/24$.   15. $4e^{\pi/\sqrt{3}}\,e^{-3}$.

17. $2e^{1/\{2\,(\pi-4)\}}$.   18. $e^{\pi^2/24}$.

OBJECTIVE QUESTIONS

For each of the following questions, four alternatives are given for the answer. Only one of them is correct. Choose the correct alternative.

1. If $a < c < b$, then $\int_a^b f(x)\, dx$ is equal to :

(a) $\int_a^b f(x)\, dx + \int_b^c f(x)\, dx$ (b) $\int_a^c f(x)\, dx + \int_c^b f(x)\, dx$

(c) $\int_a^c f(x)\, dx - \int_c^b f(x)\, dx$ (d) None of these.

2. The value of $\int_0^{\pi/2} \log \sin x\, dx$ is equal to :

(a) $\dfrac{1}{4}\pi \log 2$ (b) $-\dfrac{1}{2}\pi \log 2$

(c) $\dfrac{1}{2}\pi \log 2$ (d) $\pi \log 2$.

(Rohilkhand, 2002; Avadh, 2001)

3. $\int_0^{2a} f(x)\, dx = 2\int_0^a f(x)\, dx$ holds when :

(a) $f(x)$ is even   (b) $f(2a) = f(x)$

(c) $f(2a - x) = f(x)$ (d) $f(a - x) = f(x)$.

(Avadh, 2001)

4. If $f(x)$ is continuous in $[3, 7]$, then $\int_3^7 f(x)\, dx$ is equal to :

(a) $f(7) - f(3)$ (b) $f(3) - f(7)$

(c) $\phi(7) - \phi(3)$, where $f(x) = \phi'(x)$

(d) $\phi(3) - \phi(7)$, where $f(x) = \phi'(x)$.

5. $\int_0^{\pi/2} \dfrac{\sin x}{\sin x + \cos x}\, dx$ is equal to :

(a) π (b) $\pi/2$ (c) $\pi/3$ (d) $\pi/4$.

(Avadh, 2002)

6. The value of $\int_{0}^{\pi} \cos^{2n+1} x \, dx$ is :

(a) π (b) $\pi/2$ (c) 0 (d) $2n+1$.

7. The value of $\lim\limits_{n \to \infty} \left[\dfrac{n}{n^2+1^2} + \dfrac{n}{n^2+2^2} + \dots + \dfrac{1}{2n} \right]$ is :

(a) $\pi/4$ (b) $\pi/2$ (c) π (d) e.

8. The value of $\lim\limits_{n \to \infty} \left[\dfrac{1}{n} + \dfrac{1}{n+1} + \dfrac{1}{n+2} + \dots + \dfrac{1}{3n} \right]$ is :

(a) $\log 1$ (b) $\log 2$ (c) $\log 3$ (d) $\log 5$.

9. $\int_{0}^{a} f(x) \, dx =$

(a) $\int_{0}^{a} f(-x) \, dx$ (b) $\int_{0}^{a} f(a+x) \, dx$

(c) $\int_{0}^{a} f(a-x) \, dx$ (d) $\int_{0}^{a} f(2a-x) \, dx$.

(Avadh, 2003)

10. $\int_{-a}^{a} f(x) \, dx = 0$ if :

(a) $\phi(-x) = -\phi(x)$ (b) $\phi(-x) = \phi(x)$

(c) $\phi(-x) = \pm \phi(x)$ (d) None of these.

11. $\int_{0}^{\pi/2} \sin^n x \, dx =$

(a) $-\int_{0}^{\pi/2} \sin^n x \, dx$ (b) $\int_{0}^{\pi/2} \cos^n x \, dx$

(c) $-\int_{0}^{\pi/2} \cos^n x \, dx$ (d) None of these.

12. Value of $\int_{0}^{\pi/2} \dfrac{\sqrt{\sin x}}{\sqrt{\sin x} + \sqrt{\cos x}} \, dx$ is :

(a) $\pi/2$ (b) π (c) $\pi/4$ (d) 0.

(Rohilkhand, 2003)

13. Value of $\int\limits_{0}^{\pi/2} \log \tan x \, dx$ is :

    (a) $\pi/2$ (b) π (c) $\pi/4$ (d) 0.

                                                (Rohilkhand, 2001)

14. Value of $\lim\limits_{n \to \infty} \sum\limits_{r=1}^{n-1} \dfrac{1}{\sqrt{n^2 - r^2}}$ is :

    (a) $\pi/2$ (b) π (c) $\pi/4$ (d) 0.

15. The integral $\int\limits_{0}^{\pi} f(\sin x) \, dx$ is equivalent to :

    (a) $2 \int\limits_{0}^{\pi/2} f(\sin x) \, dx$ (b) $\int\limits_{0}^{\pi/2} f(\sin x) \, dx$

    (c) $2 \int\limits_{0}^{\pi/2} f(\cos x) \, dx$ (d) $\int\limits_{0}^{\pi/2} f(\cos x) \, dx$.

                                                (Garhwal, 2001)

16. Value of $\int\limits_{0}^{\pi/2} x \sin^6 x \cos^4 x \, dx$ is :

    (a) $\dfrac{\pi^2}{4}$ (b) $\dfrac{3\pi^2}{4}$ (c) $\dfrac{3\pi^2}{512}$ (d) None of these.

17. Value of integral $\int\limits_{0}^{1} \dfrac{\log x}{\sqrt{1-x^2}}$ is :

    (a) $\dfrac{\pi}{2} \log 2$ (b) $-\dfrac{\pi}{2} \log 2$ (c) $\pi \log 2$ (d) $-\pi \log 2$.

18. The value of the integral $\int\limits_{0}^{\pi/2} \sin^4 x \cos^2 x \, dx$ is :

    (a) $\pi/4$ (b) $\pi/8$ (c) $\pi/16$ (d) $\pi/32$.

                                                (Garhwal, 2001)

19. Value of $\int\limits_{0}^{\pi} \cos^6 x \, dx$ is :

    (a) $\dfrac{5\pi}{16}$ (b) $\dfrac{5\pi}{8}$ (c) $\dfrac{5\pi}{4}$ (d) $\dfrac{5\pi}{2}$.

20. Value of the integral $\int\limits_0^\pi \theta \sin^2 \theta \cos \theta \, d\theta$ is :

(a) $\dfrac{2}{9}$ (b) $-\dfrac{2}{9}$ (c) $\dfrac{4}{9}$ (d) $-\dfrac{4}{9}$.

ANSWERS

1. (b)	**2.** (b)	**3.** (c)	**4.** (d)
5. (d)	**6.** (c)	**7.** (a)	**8.** (c)
9. (c)	**10.** (a)	**11.** (b)	**12.** (c)
13. (d)	**14.** (a)	**15.** (a)	**16.** (c)
17. (b)	**18.** (d)	**19.** (a)	**20.** (d)

7

Beta and Gamma Functions

7.1. Definitions. The first and second Eulerian Integrals which are also called Beta and Gamma functions respectively are defined as follows :

$$B(m, n) = \int_0^1 x^{m-1} (1-x)^{n-1} \, dx$$

and

$$\Gamma n = \int_0^\infty e^{-x} x^{n-1} \, dx.$$

$B(m, n)$ is read as **Beta m, n** and Γn is read as **Gamma n**.

Here the quantities m and n are positive numbers which may or may not be integrals.

7.2. Properties of Beta and Gamma Functions.

(a) **The function $B(m, n)$ is symmetrical w.r.t. m, n, i.e.,**

$$B(m, n) = B(n, m). \qquad (\textit{Jabalpur, 1997; Indore, 2001})$$

We have $B(m, n) = \int_0^1 x^{m-1} (1-x)^{n-1} \, dx.$

Now, by property of definite integrals, we have

$$\int_0^a f(x) \, dx = \int_0^a f(a-x) \, dx$$

$$\therefore \quad B(m, n) = \int_0^1 (1-x)^{m-1} \{1 - (1-x)\}^{n-1} \, dx$$

$$= \int_0^1 x^{n-1} (1-x)^{m-1} \, dx$$

$$= B(n, m).$$

$$\therefore \quad B(m, n) = B(n, m).$$

(b) **Evaluation of Beta Function $B(m, n)$.**

We have,

$$B(m, n) = \int_0^1 x^{m-1} (1-x)^{n-1} \, dx.$$

Let us suppose that n is a positive integer; then integrating by parts keeping $(1 - x)^{n-1}$ as first function, we have

$$B(m, n) = \left[\frac{x^m}{m}(1-x)^{n-1}\right]_0^1 + \frac{(n-1)}{m}\int_0^{1} x^m(1-x)^{n-2}\, dx$$

or

$$B(m, n) = \frac{(n-1)}{m}\int_0^1 x^m(1-x)^{n-2}\, dx.$$

Again integrating by parts as above, we get

$$B(m, n) = \frac{(n-1)}{m}\cdot\frac{(n-2)}{m+1}\int_0^1 x^{m+1}(1-x)^{n-3}\, dx.$$

Continuing the above process of integrating by parts

$$B(m, n) = \frac{(n-1)(n-2)\,.....\,2\cdot1}{m(m+1)\,.....\,(m+n-2)}\int_0^1 x^{m+n-2}\, dx$$

or

$$\mathbf{B}(m, n) = \frac{(n-1)!}{m(m+1)\,.....\,(m+n-2)(m+n-1)},$$

n being a positive integer.

In case m alone is a positive integer, then since $B(m, n) = B(n, m)$, we can say that

$$\mathbf{B}(m, n) = \frac{(m-1)!}{n(n+1)\,.....\,(n+m-1)},$$

m being a positive integer.

In case both m and n are positive integers, then multiplying above and below by $1\cdot2\cdot3\,.....\,(m-1)$ or $1\cdot2\cdot3\,.....\,(n-1)$, we can say that

$$\mathbf{B}(m, n) = \frac{(m-1)!\,(n-1)!}{(m+n-1)!},$$

both m and n are positive integers.

(c) Evaluation of Gamma Function, $n > 1$. To prove that

$$\Gamma n = (n-1)\,\Gamma(n-1).$$

We have, $\quad \Gamma n = \displaystyle\int_0^\infty x^{n-1}e^{-x}\, dx.$

Integrating by parts keeping x^{n-1} as first function,

$$\Gamma n = \left[-e^{-x}x^{n-1}\right]_0^\infty + (n-1)\int_0^\infty x^{n-2}e^{-x}\, dx.$$

Now $\qquad \lim\limits_{x \to 0} \dfrac{x^{n-1}}{e^x} = 0$

as $\qquad \lim\limits_{x \to \infty} \dfrac{x^{n-1}}{e^x} = \lim\limits_{x \to \infty} \dfrac{x^{n-1}}{1 + x + \dfrac{x^2}{2!} + \dots + \dfrac{x^n}{n!} + \dots}$

$\qquad = \lim\limits_{x \to \infty} \dfrac{1}{\dfrac{1}{x^{n-1}} + \dfrac{1}{x^{n-2} \cdot 1!} + \dfrac{1}{x^{n-3} \cdot 2!} + \dots + \dfrac{x}{n!} + \dots}$

$\qquad = \dfrac{1}{\infty} = 0.$

$\therefore \quad \Gamma n = (n-1) \displaystyle\int_0^\infty x^{n-2} e^{-x}\, dx = (n-1)\, \Gamma(n-1).$

Hence we conclude that $\Gamma n = (n - 1)\, \Gamma(n - 1).$

Arguing as above, we can say that

$\qquad \Gamma(n - 1) = (n - 2)\, \Gamma(n - 2).$

Hence in case n be a positive integer, then proceeding as above, we get

$\qquad \Gamma n = (n - 1)(n - 2)(n - 3) \dots 3 \cdot 2 \cdot 1 \cdot \Gamma 1$

where $\quad \Gamma 1 = \displaystyle\int_0^\infty x^{1-1} e^{-x}\, dx = \left[-e^{-x}\right]_0^\infty = 1$ $\qquad$ (*Jabalpur, 1997*)

$\therefore \quad \Gamma n = (n - 1)(n - 2)(n - 3) \dots 3 \cdot 2 \cdot 1 = (n - 1)\,!.$

Hence we can say that

$\qquad \Gamma n = (n - 1)\, \Gamma (n - 1),$ **for all values of** $n.$

$\qquad \Gamma n = (n - 1)\,!,$ **when** n **is a positive integer and** $\Gamma 1 = 1.$

Also, it can be verified that $\Gamma 0$ and $\Gamma(- n) = \infty$, where n is a positive integer.

7.3. Transformations of Gamma Function.

We have $\qquad \Gamma n = \displaystyle\int_0^\infty e^{-x} x^{n-1}\, dx$ $\qquad\qquad$ ...(*i*)

(1) Put $x = \lambda y$ or $dx = \lambda\, dy.$

Then from (*i*), we get

$$\Gamma n = \int_0^\infty e^{-\lambda y} (\lambda y)^{n-1} \lambda\, dy = \lambda^n \int_0^\infty e^{-\lambda y} y^{n-1}\, dy$$

or $\qquad \displaystyle\int_0^\infty y^{n-1} e^{-\lambda y}\, dy = \dfrac{\Gamma n}{\lambda^n}.$

$\qquad\qquad\qquad\qquad\qquad$ (*Garhwal, 1999; Jabalpur, 1999; Avadh, 2003*)

(2) Put $x^n = z$ in (i), then $nx^{n-1} dx = dz$ and $x = z^{1/n}$.

∴ From (i), we get

$$\Gamma n = \int_0^\infty e^{-z^{1/n}} \left(\frac{1}{n}\right) dz$$

or $$\int_0^\infty e^{-z^{1/n}} dz = n\,\Gamma n = \Gamma(n+1).$$

(3) Put $e^{-x} = t$ in (i).

Then $-e^{-x} dx = dt$ and $e^x = \frac{1}{t}$.

∴ From (i), we get

$$\Gamma n = \int_1^0 (-\log t)^{n-1}(-dt) = \int_0^1 \left[\log\left(\frac{1}{t}\right)\right]^{n-1} dt$$

∴ $$\int_0^\infty \left[\log\left(\frac{1}{t}\right)\right]^{n-1} dt = \Gamma n \qquad \qquad ...(iv)$$

(4) Value of $\left(\frac{1}{2}\right)$.

Substituting $\frac{1}{2}$ for n in (iii), we get

$$\frac{1}{2}\Gamma\frac{1}{2} = \int_0^\infty e^{-z^2} dz = \frac{1}{2}\sqrt{\pi}$$

or $$\Gamma\left(\frac{1}{2}\right) = \sqrt{\pi}. \qquad\qquad \textit{(Agra, 2000)}$$

7.3.1. Transformations of Beta Function.

We know that

$$B(m, n) = \int_0^1 x^{m-1}(1-x)^{n-1} dx \qquad\qquad ...(i)$$

(1) Put $x = \frac{1}{1+y}$ or $dx = -\frac{1}{(1+y)^2} dx$.

Also, $(1-x) = 1 - \frac{1}{1+y} = \frac{y}{1+y}$.

Also, when $x = 0$, $y = \infty$ and when $x = 1$, $y = 0$.

$\therefore$ From (i), we get

$$B(m, n) = \int\limits_{\infty}^{0} \left(\frac{1}{1+y}\right)^{m-1} \cdot \left(\frac{y}{1+y}\right)^{n-1} \left\{\frac{-1}{(1+y)^2}\right\} dy$$

$$= \int\limits_{0}^{\infty} \frac{y^{n-1} \, dy}{(1+y)^{m-1+n-1+2}}$$

or $$B(m, n) = \int\limits_{0}^{\infty} \frac{y^{n-1} \, dy}{(1+y)^{m+n}}.$$ ...(ii)

(Bhopal, 1999; Indore, 2002)

(2) Also as $B(m, n) = B(n, m)$, therefore, interchanging m and n in (ii), we have

$$B(n, m) = \int\limits_{0}^{\infty} \frac{y^{m-1} \, dy}{(1+y)^{m+n}}.$$ (Garhwal, 1998; Bhopal, 1998, 99; Jiwaji, 2003; Ravishankar, 2003)

7.3.2. Relation between Beta and Gamma Functions

(Rohilkhand, 2001, 02, 03; Agra, 2001; Garhwal, 1999;
Ravishankar, 2002; Jiwaji, 1997, 99, 2002; Sagar, 2000;
Jabalpur, 1998, 99; Bhopal, 1999; Bilaspur, 1997, 99; Rewa, 1998)

We know that

$$\int\limits_{0}^{\infty} y^{n-1} e^{-xy} \, dy = \frac{n}{x^n}$$ [§ 7.3, eqn. (ii)]

or $$\Gamma n = \int\limits_{0}^{\infty} x^n y^{n-1} e^{-xy} \, dy$$ ...(i)

Also, $$\Gamma m = \int\limits_{0}^{\infty} x^{m-1} e^{-x} \, dx.$$ ...(ii)

Multiplying both sides of (i) by $x^{m-1} e^{-x}$, we get

$$\Gamma n \cdot x^{m-1} e^{-x} = \int\limits_{0}^{\infty} x^{n+m-1} y^{n-1} e^{-(y+1)x} \, dy.$$

Integrating both sides with respect to x within limits $x = 0$ to $x = \infty$, we have

$$\Gamma n \int\limits_{0}^{\infty} x^{m-1} e^{-x} \, dx = \int\limits_{0}^{\infty} \left[\int\limits_{0}^{\infty} x^{n+m-1} e^{-(y+1)x} \, dx \, y^{n-1} \right.$$

But $\displaystyle\int_0^\infty x^{(n+m)-1} e^{-(y+1)x} dx$ ...(ii)

$$= \frac{\Gamma(n+m)}{(1+y)^{m+n}},$$

[by putting $\lambda = 1 + y$ and 'n' $= m + n$ in § 7.3 (ii)]

Hence with the help of this result and (ii), we get

$$\Gamma n\, \Gamma m = \int_0^\infty \Gamma(n+m) \cdot \frac{y^{n-1}}{(1+y)^{m+n}}\, dy$$

$$= \Gamma(m+n) \int_0^\infty \frac{y^{n-1}\, dy}{(1+y)^{m+n}} = \Gamma(m+n) \cdot B(m, n)$$

$$\therefore\quad B(m, n) = \frac{\Gamma m \cdot \Gamma n}{(m+n)}.$$

7.4. Some Important Deductions.

(1) To prove that $\Gamma n\, \Gamma(1-n) = \dfrac{\pi}{\sin n\pi}.$

(Garhwal, 1993; Rohilkhand, 1995, 2000;
Bhopal, 1996; Jiwaji, 1998)

We know that

$$B(m, n) = \frac{\Gamma m \cdot \Gamma n}{\Gamma(m+n)}.$$

Putting $m + n = 1$ or $m = (1-n)$, we get

$$\frac{\Gamma n \cdot \Gamma(1-n)}{\Gamma(1)} = B(n, 1-n) \qquad \text{...(i)}$$

We have

$$B(m, n) = \int_0^\infty \frac{y^{n-1}\, dy}{(1+y)^{m+n}}$$

$$\therefore\quad B(n, 1-n) = \int_0^\infty \frac{y^{n-1}\, dy}{(1+y)} = \frac{\pi}{\sin n\pi}, \ n < 1.$$

$\therefore$ From (i), we have

$$\Gamma n\, \Gamma(1-n) = \frac{\pi}{\sin n\pi}.$$

(2) To prove that $\Gamma(1+n)\,\Gamma(1-n) = \dfrac{n\pi}{\sin\, n\pi}.$

We have proved in (1) that

$$\Gamma n\cdot\Gamma(1-n) = \frac{\pi}{\sin n\pi}.$$

Multiplying both sides by n, we get

$$(n\,\Gamma n)\,\Gamma(1-n) = \frac{n\pi}{\sin n\pi}$$

or $\qquad \Gamma(1+n)\,\Gamma(1-n) = \dfrac{n\pi}{\sin n\pi}.$

(3) To prove that $\Gamma\left(\dfrac{1}{2}\right) = \sqrt{\pi}.$ $\qquad\qquad$ (*Kumaon, 1994*)

We have $\Gamma n\cdot\Gamma(1-n) = \dfrac{\pi}{\sin n\pi}.$

Putting $n = \dfrac{1}{2}$, we get

$$\Gamma\left(\frac{1}{2}\right)\cdot\Gamma\left(1-\frac{1}{2}\right) = \frac{\pi}{\sin\left(\dfrac{1}{2}\pi\right)}$$

or $\qquad \left\{\Gamma\left(\dfrac{1}{2}\right)\right\}^2 = \pi \qquad \Gamma\left(\dfrac{1}{2}\right) = \sqrt{\pi}.$

7.41. To prove that $\displaystyle\int_0^{\pi/2} \sin^m\theta\,\cos^n\theta\,d\theta = \dfrac{\Gamma\left(\dfrac{m+1}{2}\right)\Gamma\left(\dfrac{n+1}{2}\right)}{2\Gamma\left(\dfrac{m+n+2}{2}\right)}.$

(*Gorakhpur, 2001; Avadh, 2002*)

We know that

$$B(p, q) = \int_0^1 x^{p-1}(1-x)^{q-1}\,dx$$

$$= \frac{\Gamma p\cdot\Gamma q}{\Gamma(p+q)}.$$

Putting $x = \sin^2\theta$ and $dx = 2\sin\theta\cos\theta\,d\theta$, we get

$$\int_0^1 x^{p-1}(1-x)^{q-1}\,dx$$

$$= \int_0^{\pi/2} (\sin^2 \theta)^{p-1} (1 - \sin^2 \theta)^{q-1} \cdot 2 \sin \theta \cos \theta \, d\theta$$

$$= 2 \int_0^{\pi/2} \sin^{2p-1} \theta \cos^{2q-1} \theta \, d\theta$$

$$\therefore \quad \int_0^{\pi/2} \sin^{2p-1} \theta \cos^{2q-1} \theta \, d\theta = \frac{1}{2} B(p, q)$$

$$= \frac{\Gamma p \cdot \Gamma q}{2\Gamma (p + q)}.$$

Putting $2p - 1 = m$ and $2q - 1 = n$,

or $\quad p = \left(\dfrac{m+1}{2}\right)$ and $q = \left(\dfrac{n+1}{2}\right)$,

we get

$$\int_0^{\pi/2} \sin^m \theta \cos^n \theta \, d\theta = \frac{\Gamma\left(\dfrac{m+1}{2}\right) \Gamma\left(\dfrac{n+1}{2}\right)}{2\Gamma\left(\dfrac{m+n+2}{2}\right)}.$$

7.5. Duplication Formula

To prove that $\Gamma m \, \Gamma\left(m + \dfrac{1}{2}\right) = \dfrac{\sqrt{\pi}}{2^{2m-1}} \cdot \Gamma(2m)$.

(*Agra, 2001; Rohilkhand, 1997, 99; Vikram, 1997, 99;*
Bilaspur, 2000, 02; Sagar, 1997, 99; Indore, 1998;
Ravishankar, 1997, 2000; Jabalpur, 2002)

We have from § 7.41

$$\int_0^{\pi/2} \sin^{2m-1} \theta \cos^{2n-1} \theta \, d\theta = \frac{\Gamma(m) \, \Gamma(n)}{2\Gamma(m + n)} \qquad \ldots(i)$$

Putting $n = 0$ in (i)

$$\int_0^{\pi/2} \sin^{2m-1} \theta \, d\theta = \frac{\Gamma(m) \, \Gamma\left(\dfrac{1}{2}\right)}{2\Gamma\left(m + \dfrac{1}{2}\right)}$$

$$= \frac{\Gamma(m) \sqrt{\pi}}{2\Gamma\left(m + \dfrac{1}{2}\right)} \qquad \ldots(ii)$$

$$\left[\because \ \Gamma\left(\frac{1}{2}\right) = \sqrt{\pi} \right]$$

Again putting $n = m$ in (i), we get

$$\int_0^{\pi/2} \sin^{2m-1}\theta \cos^{2m-1}\theta \, d\theta = \frac{\{\Gamma(m)\}^2}{2\Gamma(2m)}$$

i.e.,

$$\frac{1}{2^{2m}} \int_0^{\pi/2} (\sin 2\theta)^{2m-1} 2 \, d\theta = \frac{\{\Gamma(m)\}^2}{2\Gamma(2m)}.$$

Putting $2\theta = \phi$ and $2\,d\theta = d\phi$, we get

$$\frac{1}{2^{2m}} \int_0^{\pi} \sin^{2m-1}\phi \, d\phi = \frac{\{\Gamma(m)\}^2}{2\Gamma(2m)}$$

or

$$\frac{2}{2^{2m}} \int_0^{\pi/2} \sin^{2m-1}\phi \, d\phi = \frac{\{\Gamma(m)\}^2}{2\Gamma(2m)}$$

or

$$\int_0^{\pi/2} \sin^{2m-1}\phi \, d\phi = \frac{2^{2n-1}\{\Gamma(m)\}^2}{2\Gamma(2m)} \qquad \qquad ...(iii)$$

Equating the two values of $\int_0^{\pi/2} \sin^{2m-1}\theta \, d\theta$ from (ii) and (iii), we get

$$\frac{2^{2m-1}\{\Gamma(m)\}^2}{2\Gamma(2m)} = \frac{\Gamma(m)\cdot\sqrt{\pi}}{2\Gamma\left(m+\frac{1}{2}\right)}.$$

Hence

$$\Gamma(m)\,\Gamma\left(m+\frac{1}{2}\right) = \frac{\sqrt{\pi}}{2^{2m-1}}\,\Gamma(2m).$$

EXAMPLES

1. *Compute* : $\Gamma\left(-\dfrac{1}{2}\right), \Gamma\left(-\dfrac{3}{2}\right), \Gamma\left(-\dfrac{5}{2}\right).$

We have

$$\Gamma(n)\,\Gamma(1-n) = \frac{\pi}{\sin n\pi} \qquad\qquad ...(i)$$

(i) Putting $n = -\dfrac{1}{2}$ in (i), we get

$$\Gamma\left(-\frac{1}{2}\right)\cdot\Gamma\left(\frac{3}{2}\right) = \frac{\pi}{\sin\left(-\frac{1}{2}\pi\right)} = -\pi$$

or

$$\Gamma\left(-\frac{1}{2}\right) = -\frac{\pi}{\Gamma\left(\frac{3}{2}\right)} = -\frac{\pi}{\frac{1}{2}\Gamma\left(\frac{1}{2}\right)} = -2\sqrt{\pi} \qquad\qquad ...(ii)$$

(ii) Putting $n = -\dfrac{3}{2}$ in (i), we get

$$\Gamma\left(-\frac{3}{2}\right)\Gamma\left(\frac{5}{2}\right) = \frac{\pi}{\sin\left(-\dfrac{3}{2}\pi\right)} = -\frac{\pi}{\sin\left(\dfrac{3}{2}\pi\right)} = \pi$$

or $$\Gamma\left(-\frac{3}{2}\right) = \frac{\pi}{\Gamma\left(\dfrac{5}{2}\right)} = \frac{\pi}{\dfrac{3}{2}\cdot\dfrac{1}{2}\cdot\sqrt{\pi}} = \frac{4\sqrt{\pi}}{3} \qquad\qquad ...(iii)$$

(iii) Putting $n = -\dfrac{5}{2}$ in (i), we get

$$\Gamma\left(-\frac{5}{2}\right)\Gamma\left(\frac{7}{2}\right) = \frac{\pi}{\sin\left(-\dfrac{5}{2}\pi\right)} = -\frac{\pi}{\left(\sin\dfrac{5}{2}\pi\right)} = -\pi$$

or $$\Gamma\left(-\frac{5}{2}\right) = \frac{\pi}{\Gamma\left(\dfrac{7}{2}\right)} = -\frac{\pi}{\dfrac{5}{2}\cdot\dfrac{3}{2}\cdot\dfrac{1}{2}\cdot\sqrt{\pi}} = -\frac{8\sqrt{\pi}}{15} \qquad ...(iv)$$

2. *Evaluate* : $\displaystyle\int_0^\infty \frac{dx}{1+x^4}$.   (*Vikram, 1998*)

Putting $x^4 = y$ or $dx = \dfrac{dy}{4x^3}$, we have

$$\int_0^\infty \frac{dx}{1+x^4} = \int_0^\infty \frac{\dfrac{1}{4}y^{-3/4}\,dy}{(1+y)} = \frac{1}{4}\int_0^\infty \frac{y^{(1/4-1)}}{1+y}\,dy.$$

Also, we have

$$\int_0^\infty \frac{x^{n-1}}{1+x}\,dx = \frac{\pi}{\sin n\pi},$$

we get

$$\int_0^\infty \frac{dx}{1+x^4} = \frac{1}{4}\cdot\frac{\pi}{\sin(\pi/4)} = \frac{\pi\sqrt{2}}{4}.$$

3. *Prove that* $\displaystyle\int_0^1 \frac{x^2\,dx}{\sqrt{1-x^4}}\cdot\int_0^1 \frac{dx}{\sqrt{1-x^4}} = \frac{\pi}{4\sqrt{2}}$.

Let $I_1 = \displaystyle\int_0^1 \frac{x^2\,dx}{\sqrt{1-x^4}}$, and $\qquad I_2 = \int\limits_0^1 \dfrac{x^2\, dx}{\sqrt{1 + x^4}}.$

Then $\qquad I_1 = \int\limits_0^{\pi/2} \dfrac{\sin\theta}{\cos\theta} \cdot \dfrac{\cos\theta\, d\theta}{2\sqrt{\sin\theta}},$

$\qquad\qquad\qquad\qquad$ (Putting $x^2 = \sin\theta$, $2x\, dx = \cos\theta\, d\theta$)

or $\qquad dx = \dfrac{\cos\theta\, d\theta}{2x} = \dfrac{\cos\theta\, d\theta}{2\sqrt{\sin\theta}}.$

Then, $\qquad I_1 = \dfrac{1}{2} \int\limits_0^{\pi/2} \sqrt{\sin\theta}\, d\theta = \dfrac{1}{2} \int\limits_0^{\pi/2} \sin^{1/2}\theta \cos^0\theta\, d\theta$

$$= \dfrac{1}{2} \dfrac{\Gamma\left\{\dfrac{1}{2}\left(\dfrac{1}{2} + 1\right)\right\} \cdot \Gamma\left\{\dfrac{1}{2}(0 + 1)\right\}}{2\Gamma\left\{\dfrac{1}{2}\left(\dfrac{1}{2} + 0 + 2\right)\right\}}$$

$$= \dfrac{\Gamma\left(\dfrac{3}{4}\right) \cdot \Gamma\left(\dfrac{1}{2}\right)}{4 \cdot \Gamma\left(\dfrac{5}{4}\right)} = \dfrac{\Gamma\left(\dfrac{3}{4}\right) \cdot \Gamma\left(\dfrac{1}{2}\right)}{4 \cdot \dfrac{1}{4}\Gamma\left(\dfrac{1}{4}\right)}$$

$$= \dfrac{\Gamma\left(\dfrac{3}{4}\right) \cdot \Gamma\left(\dfrac{1}{2}\right)}{\Gamma\left(\dfrac{1}{4}\right)} \qquad\qquad\qquad ...(i)$$

Also, $\qquad I_2 = \int\limits_0^{\pi/4} \dfrac{1}{\sec\theta} \cdot \dfrac{\sec^2\theta\, d\theta}{2\sqrt{\tan\theta}},$

$\qquad\qquad\qquad\qquad$ (Putting $x^2 = \tan\theta$, $2x\, dx = \sec^2\theta\, d\theta$)

or $\qquad dx = \dfrac{\sec^2\theta\, d\theta}{2x} = \dfrac{\sec^2\theta\, d\theta}{2\sqrt{\tan\theta}}$

$$= \dfrac{1}{2} \int\limits_0^{\pi/4} \dfrac{\sec\theta}{\sqrt{\tan\theta}}\, d\theta = \dfrac{1}{\sqrt{2}} \int\limits_0^{\pi/4} \dfrac{d\theta}{\sqrt{2\sin\theta\cos\theta}}$$

$$= \dfrac{1}{\sqrt{2}} \int\limits_0^{\pi/4} \dfrac{d\theta}{\sqrt{\sin 2\theta}} = \dfrac{1}{2\sqrt{2}} \int\limits_0^{\pi/4} \dfrac{dz}{\sqrt{\sin z}}, \text{ putting } 2\theta = z$$

$$= \dfrac{1}{2\sqrt{2}} \cdot \int\limits_0^{\pi/2} (\sin z)^{-1/2} \cos^0 z\, dz$$

$$= \frac{1}{2\sqrt{2}} \cdot \frac{\Gamma\left\{\frac{1}{2}\left(-\frac{1}{2}+1\right)\right\}\Gamma\left\{\frac{1}{2}(0+1)\right\}}{2\Gamma\left\{\frac{1}{2}\left(-\frac{1}{2}+0+2\right)\right\}}$$

$$= \frac{1}{4\sqrt{2}} \cdot \frac{\Gamma\left(\frac{1}{4}\right)\cdot\Gamma\left(\frac{1}{2}\right)}{\Gamma\left(\frac{3}{4}\right)}. \qquad \qquad ...(ii)$$

Multiplying (i) and (ii), we get

$$\int_0^1 \frac{x^2\, dx}{\sqrt{1-x^4}} \cdot \int_0^1 \frac{dx}{\sqrt{1+x^4}} = \frac{\Gamma\left(\frac{3}{4}\right)\cdot\Gamma\left(\frac{1}{2}\right)}{\Gamma\left(\frac{1}{4}\right)} \cdot \frac{\Gamma\left(\frac{1}{4}\right)\cdot\Gamma\left(\frac{1}{2}\right)}{4\sqrt{2}\,\Gamma\left(\frac{3}{4}\right)}$$

$$= \frac{\left\{\Gamma\left(\frac{1}{2}\right)\right\}^2}{4\sqrt{2}} = \frac{(\sqrt{\pi})^2}{4\sqrt{2}} = \frac{\sqrt{\pi}}{4\sqrt{2}}.$$

4. *Evaluate* $\displaystyle\int_0^{\pi/2} (\sin x)^{8/3}\,(\sec x)^{1/2}\, dx.$

The given integral may be written as,

$$\int_0^{\pi/2} (\sin x)^{8/3}\,(\cos x)^{-1/2}\, dx = \frac{\Gamma\left\{\frac{1}{2}\left(\frac{8}{3}+1\right)\right\}\Gamma\left\{\frac{1}{2}\left(-\frac{1}{2}+1\right)\right\}}{2\Gamma\left\{\frac{1}{2}\left(\frac{8}{3}-\frac{1}{2}+2\right)\right\}}$$

$$= \frac{\Gamma\left(\frac{11}{6}\right)\Gamma\left(\frac{1}{4}\right)}{2\Gamma\left(\frac{25}{12}\right)}.$$

5. *Evaluate* $\displaystyle\int_0^a \frac{dx}{(a^n-x^n)^{1/n}}.$

Put $x^n = a^n \sin^2\theta \Rightarrow dx = \dfrac{2a}{n}\sin^{(2/n-1)}\theta\cos\theta\,d\theta.$

$$\therefore \int_0^a \frac{dx}{(a^n-x^n)^{1/n}} = \frac{2a}{n}\int_0^{\pi/2} \frac{\sin^{(2/n-1)}\theta\cos\theta\,d\theta}{a\cos^{2/n}\theta}$$

$$= \frac{2}{n} \int_0^{\pi/2} \sin^{(2/n-1)} \theta \, \cos^{(1-2/n)} \theta \, d\theta$$

$$= \frac{2}{n} \cdot \frac{\Gamma\left(\dfrac{1}{n}\right) \cdot \Gamma\left(1 - \dfrac{1}{n}\right)}{2\Gamma 1} = \frac{1}{n} \cdot \frac{\pi}{\sin (\pi / n)}.$$

6. Show that $\displaystyle \int_0^{\pi/2} \tan^n \theta \, d\theta = \frac{1}{2} \pi \sec\left(\frac{1}{2} n\pi\right).$

(Rewa, 1999; Jiwaji, 2000)

We have

$$\int_0^{\pi/2} \tan^n \theta \, d\theta = \int_0^{\pi/2} \sin^n \theta \, (\cos\theta)^{-n} \, d\theta$$

$$= \frac{\Gamma\left\{\dfrac{1}{2}(n+1)\right\} \cdot \Gamma\left\{\dfrac{1}{2}(-n+1)\right\}}{2\Gamma\left\{\dfrac{1}{2}(n-n+2)\right\}}$$

$$= \frac{\Gamma\dfrac{(n+1)}{2} \cdot \Gamma\left(1 - \dfrac{n+1}{2}\right)}{2\Gamma 1}$$

$$= \frac{1}{2} \cdot \frac{\pi}{\sin \dfrac{1}{2}(n+1)\pi}, \quad \left[\because \ \Gamma n \, \Gamma(1-n) = \frac{\pi}{\sin n\pi}\right]$$

$$= \frac{1}{2} \pi \operatorname{cosec}\left\{\frac{1}{2}(n+1)\pi\right\}$$

$$= \frac{1}{2} \pi \operatorname{cosec}\left(\frac{\pi}{2} + \frac{n\pi}{2}\right) = \frac{1}{2} \pi \sec\left(\frac{n\pi}{2}\right).$$

7. Show that $\displaystyle \int_0^1 \frac{dx}{\sqrt{1 - x^n}} = \frac{\sqrt{\pi} \ \Gamma\left(\dfrac{1}{n}\right)}{n \, \Gamma\left(\dfrac{1}{n} + \dfrac{1}{2}\right)}.$

Put $x^n = \sin^2 \theta$ or $x = \sin^{2/n} \theta$

$$\therefore \quad dx = \frac{2}{n} \sin^{(2/n-1)} \theta \, \cos\theta \, d\theta$$

$$\therefore \int \frac{dx}{\sqrt{1-x^n}} = \int_{0}^{\pi/2} \frac{\left(\dfrac{2}{n}\right) \sin^{(2/n-1)} \theta \cos \theta \, d\theta}{\sqrt{1-\sin^2 \theta}}$$

$$= \frac{2}{n} \int_{0}^{\pi/2} \sin^{(2/n-1)} \theta \cos^0 \theta \, d\theta$$

$$= \frac{2}{n} \cdot \frac{\Gamma\left\{\dfrac{1}{2}\left(\dfrac{2}{n}-1+1\right)\right\} \Gamma\left\{\dfrac{1}{2}(0+1)\right\}}{2\Gamma\left\{\dfrac{1}{2}\left(\dfrac{2}{n}-1+0+2\right)\right\}}$$

$$= \frac{1}{n} \cdot \frac{\Gamma\left(\dfrac{1}{n}\right) \cdot \Gamma\left(\dfrac{1}{2}\right)}{\Gamma\left\{\dfrac{1}{2}\left(\dfrac{2}{n}+1\right)\right\}} = \frac{\Gamma\left(\dfrac{1}{n}\right) \cdot \sqrt{\pi}}{n \, \Gamma\left(\dfrac{1}{n}+\dfrac{1}{2}\right)}.$$

8. *Evaluate* $\displaystyle\int_{0}^{1} \frac{x^{m-1}+x^{n-1}}{(1+x)^{m+n}} dx$.   *(Kumaon, 2002; Garhwal, 1997; Bhopal, 1997, 2002; Jiwaji, 1996, 98)*

The given integral

$$I = \int_{0}^{1} \frac{x^{m-1}}{(1+x)^{m+n}} dx + \int_{0}^{1} \frac{x^{n-1}}{(1+x)^{m+n}} dx$$

or $I = I_1 + I_2$ (say)   ...(i)

Putting $x = \dfrac{1}{z}$ in I_2, we have

$$I_2 = \int_{\infty}^{1} \frac{\left(\dfrac{1}{z}\right)^{n-1}\left(-\dfrac{1}{z^2}\right) dz}{\left[1+\left(\dfrac{1}{z}\right)\right]^{m+n}}$$

$$= \int_{1}^{\infty} \frac{z^{m+1} \, dz}{(1+z)^{m+n}}$$

$$= \int_{1}^{\infty} \frac{x^{m-1} \, dx}{(1+x)^{m+n}}.$$

$\therefore$ From equation (i)

$$I = \int_{0}^{1} \frac{x^{m-1} \, dx}{(1+x)^{m+n}} + \int_{1}^{\infty} \frac{x^{m-1} \, dx}{(1+x)^{m+n}}$$

$$= \int_0^\infty \frac{x^{m-1}\, dx}{(1+x)^{m+n}} = B(m, n)$$

$$= \frac{\Gamma(m) \cdot \Gamma(n)}{\Gamma(m+n)}.$$

9. *Show that* $\displaystyle\int_0^{\pi/2} \sqrt{\tan\theta}\, d\theta = \frac{1}{2}\Gamma\left(\frac{3}{4}\right)\Gamma\left(\frac{1}{4}\right) = 2\int_0^\infty \frac{x^2\, dx}{1+x^4}.$

(*Kumaon, 2001*)

We have

$$\int_0^{\pi/2} \sqrt{\tan\theta}\, d\theta = \int_0^{\pi/2} (\sin\theta)^{1/2}\, (\cos\theta)^{-(1/2)}\, d\theta$$

$$= \frac{\Gamma\left\{\frac{1}{2}\left(\frac{1}{2}+1\right)\right\} \Gamma\left\{\frac{1}{2}\left(-\frac{1}{2}+1\right)\right\}}{2\Gamma\left\{\frac{1}{2}\left(\frac{1}{2}-\frac{1}{2}+2\right)\right\}}$$

$$= \frac{\Gamma\left(\frac{3}{4}\right)\Gamma\left(\frac{1}{4}\right)}{2\Gamma(1)}$$

$$= \frac{1}{2}\Gamma\left(\frac{3}{4}\right)\Gamma\left(\frac{1}{4}\right)$$

$$= \frac{1}{2}B\left(\frac{3}{4}, \frac{1}{4}\right) \qquad \left[\because\ B(m, n) = \frac{\Gamma m \cdot \Gamma n}{\Gamma(m+n)}\right]$$

$$= \frac{1}{2}\int_0^\infty \frac{y^{(3/4-1)}}{(1+y)}\, dy$$

$$\because\ B(m, n) = \int_0^\infty \frac{y^{m-1}\, dy}{(1+y)^{m+n}}$$

$$= \frac{1}{2}\int_0^\infty \frac{x^{-1} \cdot 4x^3\, dx}{(1+x^4)}, \qquad [\text{Putting } y = x^4,\ dy = 4x^3\, dx]$$

$$= 2\int_0^\infty \frac{x^2\, dx}{1+x^4}.$$

10. *Express* $\int_0^1 x^m (1-x^n)^p \, dx$ *in terms of the beta function, and hence evaluate* $\int_0^1 x^5 (1-x^3)^{10} \, dx$.

(Ravishankar, 1996; Jabalpur, 1996; Bhopal, 2001; Gorakhpur, 2003)

Also show that $\int_0^1 x^{m-1} \cdot (1-x^2)^{n-1} \, dx = \dfrac{1}{2} B\left(\dfrac{m}{2}, n\right)$.

The given integral

$$I = \int_0^1 x^m (1-x^n)^p \, dx$$

$$= \int_0^1 z^{m/n} (1-z) \cdot \frac{1}{n} z^{(1/n - 1)} \, dz.$$

Putting $x^n = z$ or $x = z^{1/n}$

and $\quad dx = \dfrac{1}{n} z^{(1/n - 1)} \, dz$

$$I = \frac{1}{n} \int_0^1 z^{\{(m + 1/n) - 1\}} (1-z)^{(p+1) - 1} \, dz$$

$$= \frac{1}{n} B\left(\frac{m+1}{n}, p+1\right) \qquad \qquad \qquad ...(i)$$

Putting $m = 5$, $n = 3$, $p = 10$ in (i), we get

$$\int_0^1 x^5 (1-x^3)^{10} \, dx = \frac{1}{3} B\left\{\frac{1}{3}(5+1), 10+1\right\}$$

$$= \frac{1}{3} B(2, 11)$$

$$= \frac{1}{3} \cdot \frac{\Gamma(2) \cdot \Gamma(11)}{\Gamma(2+11)}$$

$$= \frac{1}{3} \cdot \frac{(1)! \, (10)!}{(12)!} = \frac{1}{396}.$$

Again put $m = (m-1)$, $n = 2$ and $p = (n-1)$ in (i), we get

$$\int_0^1 x^{m-1} (1-x^2)^{n-1} \, dx$$

$$= \frac{1}{2} B\left(\frac{m-1+1}{2}, \; n-1+1\right)$$

$$= \frac{1}{2} B\left(\frac{m}{2}, n\right).$$

11. *Prove that* $\Gamma\left(\frac{3}{2} - x\right) \cdot \Gamma\left(\frac{3}{2} + x\right) = \left(\frac{1}{4} - x^2\right) \pi \sec \pi x.$

(Ravishankar, 2001; Gorakhpur, 2000)

L.H.S. $= \left(\frac{1}{2} - x\right) \Gamma\left(\frac{1}{2} - x\right) \cdot \Gamma\left(\frac{1}{2} + x\right) \Gamma\left(\frac{1}{2} + x\right)$

$$[\because \;\; \Gamma(n+1) = n \, \Gamma n]$$

$$= \left(\frac{1}{4} - x^2\right) \Gamma\left(\frac{1}{2} - x\right) \cdot \Gamma\left(\frac{1}{2} + x\right)$$

$$= \left(\frac{1}{4} - x^2\right) \cdot \frac{x}{\sin\left(\frac{1}{2} - x\right)\pi} \qquad \left[\because \;\; \Gamma n \, \Gamma(1-n) = \frac{\pi}{\sin n\pi}\right]$$

$$= \left(\frac{1}{4} - x^2\right) \cdot \frac{\pi}{\sin\left(\frac{\pi}{2} - \pi x\right)}$$

$$= \left(\frac{1}{4} - x^2\right) \pi \sec \pi x.$$

12. *Show that* $B\,(m, n) = B\,(m + 1, n) + B\,(m, n + 1).$

(Kumaon, 1997; Garhwal, 1996; Bhopal, 1998; Indore, 1996)

We have

$$\text{R.H.S.} = \frac{\Gamma(m+1) \cdot \Gamma n}{\Gamma(m+1+n)} + \frac{\Gamma m \cdot \Gamma(n+1)}{\Gamma(m+n+1)}$$

$$= \frac{m \, \Gamma m \cdot \Gamma n}{(m+n)\,\Gamma(m+n)} + \frac{\Gamma m \cdot n \, \Gamma n}{(m+n)\,\Gamma(m+n)}$$

$$= \frac{\Gamma m \cdot \Gamma n}{\Gamma(m+n)} \left[\frac{m}{m+n} + \frac{n}{m+n}\right]$$

$$= \frac{\Gamma m \cdot \Gamma n}{\Gamma(m+n)} = B\,(m, n).$$

13. *With certain restrictions on the values of a, b, m and n, prove that*

$$\int_{0}^{\infty} \int_{0}^{\infty} e^{-(ax^2 + by^2)} \, x^{2m-1} \, y^{2n-1} \, dx \, dy = \frac{\Gamma(m)\,\Gamma(n)}{4a^m b^n}.$$

Let $I = \int\limits_0^\infty e^{-ax^2} x^{2m-1} dx \times \int\limits_0^\infty e^{-by^2} y^{2n-1} dy.$

In the first integral, let $ax^2 = z \Rightarrow 2ax\, dx = dz$, we have

$$\int\limits_0^\infty e^{-ax^2} x^{2m-1} dx = \frac{1}{2} \int\limits_0^\infty \left(\frac{z}{a}\right)^{m-1} e^{-z} \frac{dz}{a}$$

$$= \frac{1}{2a^m} \int\limits_0^\infty z^{m-1} e^{-y} dy = \frac{1}{2a^m} \Gamma(m).$$

Similarly, $\int\limits_0^\infty e^{-by^2} y^{2n-1} dy = \dfrac{\Gamma(n)}{2b^n}$

$\therefore \quad I = \dfrac{\Gamma(m)\,\Gamma(n)}{4a^m\,b^n}.$

EXERCISES

1. Show that

(a) $\dfrac{\Gamma\left(\frac{1}{3}\right) \cdot \Gamma\left(\frac{5}{6}\right)}{\Gamma\left(\frac{2}{3}\right)} = \sqrt{\pi}\, 2^{1/3};$ (b) $\dfrac{\left[\Gamma\left(\frac{1}{3}\right)\right]^2}{\Gamma\left(\frac{1}{6}\right)} = \dfrac{\sqrt{\pi} \cdot 2^{1/3}}{3^{1/2}};$

(c) $2^p\, \Gamma\left(\dfrac{p+1}{2}\right) \Gamma\left(\dfrac{p+2}{2}\right) = \sqrt{\pi}\, \Gamma(p+1).$

2. Show that

(a) $\dfrac{B(m, n+1)}{n} = \dfrac{B(m+1, n)}{m} = \dfrac{B(m, n)}{m+n}.$

(Jiwaji, 1999; Indore, 2000)

(b) $2^{2n-1} B(n, n) = \dfrac{\sqrt{\pi}\, \Gamma(n)}{\Gamma\left(n+\frac{1}{2}\right)},\quad n > 0.$

3. Prove that

(a) $\int\limits_0^\infty x^4 e^{-x} dx = 24;$ (b) $\int\limits_0^\infty e^{-4x} x^{3/2} dx = \dfrac{3}{128}\sqrt{\pi};$

(c) $\int\limits_0^\infty x^3 e^{-x} dx = 6;$ (d) $\int\limits_0^\infty \sqrt{x}\, e^{-x^3} dx = \dfrac{1}{3}\sqrt{\pi};$

(e) $\displaystyle\int_0^\infty x^2 e^{-x^2} dx = \frac{\sqrt{\pi}}{4}$;   (f) $\displaystyle\int_0^\infty 4x^4 e^{-x^4} dx = \Gamma\left(\frac{5}{4}\right)$.

(Ravishankar, 2001)

4. Prove that

(a) $\displaystyle\int_0^1 x^4 (1-x)^3 \, dx = \frac{1}{280}$;   (b) $\displaystyle\int_0^2 \frac{x^2}{\sqrt{2-x}} \, dx = \frac{64\sqrt{2}}{15}$;

(c) $\displaystyle\int_0^2 x (8-x^3)^{1/3} \, dx = \frac{16\pi}{9\sqrt{3}}$;   (Agra, 2000)

(d) $\displaystyle\int_0^a x^4 \sqrt{a^2 - x^2} \, dx = \frac{\pi a^6}{32}$.

5. Show that $\displaystyle\int_0^\infty \frac{e^{-st}}{\sqrt{t}} \, dt = \frac{\sqrt{\pi}}{s}$, $s > 0$.   (Ravishankar, 1999)

6. Show that

(a) $\displaystyle\int_0^1 \left(\log \frac{1}{x}\right)^{n-1} dx = \Gamma(n)$, $n > 0$;

(Garhwal, 2000; Kumaon, 2000; Rewa, 1998; Rohilkhand, 2001)

(b) $\displaystyle\int_0^1 x^{n-1}\left(\log \frac{1}{x}\right)^{m-1} dx = \frac{\Gamma(m)}{n^m}$, $(m, n > 0)$.

(Ravishankar, 1998; Rewa, 2002)

7. Prove that

(a) $\displaystyle\int_0^1 (1-x^n)^{1/n} \, dx = \frac{1}{n} \frac{[\Gamma(1/n)]^2}{2\,\Gamma(2/n)}$;

(b) $\displaystyle\int_0^\infty \frac{x^c}{c^x} \, dx = \frac{\Gamma(c+1)}{(\log c)^{c+1}}$.   (Rohilkhand, 2000; Garhwal, 1994; Kumaon, 1996; Vikram, 1998, 2002)

8. Show that :

(a) $\displaystyle\int_0^1 x^2 (1-x)^3 = 60$;   (b) $\displaystyle\int_0^2 (4-x^2)^{3/2} \, dx = 3\pi$;

(c) $\displaystyle\int_0^3 \frac{dx}{\sqrt{3x-x^2}} = \pi$;   (d) $\displaystyle\int_0^1 \frac{dx}{\sqrt{1-x^3}} = \frac{\sqrt{\pi}\,\Gamma(1/3)}{3\,\Gamma(5/6)}$.

9. Prove that

(a) $\displaystyle\int_0^1 \frac{x^2\,dx}{\sqrt{1-x^3}} = \frac{2}{3}$;   (b) $\displaystyle\int_0^\infty \frac{x\,dx}{1+x^6} = \frac{\pi}{3\sqrt{3}}$;

(c) $\displaystyle\int_0^\infty \frac{x^2\,dx}{(1+x^4)} = \frac{\pi}{2\sqrt{2}}$.

10. Define gamma function, and show that

$$\left[\Gamma\left(\frac{1}{2}\right)\right]^2 = 4 \int_0^\infty \int_0^\infty e^{-(x^2+y^2)}\,dy\,dx.$$

11. (a) Show that

$$\int_0^{\pi/2} \sqrt{\tan\theta}\,d\theta = \int_0^{\pi/2} \sqrt{\cot\theta}\,d\theta = \frac{\pi}{\sqrt{2}}.$$

(b) Prove that

$$\int_0^{\pi/2} \frac{d\theta}{\sqrt{\sin\theta}} \times \int_0^{\pi/2} \sqrt{\sin\theta}\,d\theta = \pi.$$

(*Garhwal, 1999*; *Sagar, 1996*; *Indore, 1999*)

12. Prove that

$$\int_0^{\pi/2} \frac{d\theta}{(a\cos^4\theta + b\sin^4\theta)} = \frac{[\Gamma(1/4)]^2}{4\,(ab)^{1/4}\,\sqrt{\pi}}.$$

13. (i) $\displaystyle\int_0^\infty \cos x^2\,dx = \frac{1}{2}\frac{\sqrt{\pi}}{2}$;

(ii) $\displaystyle\int_0^\infty \cos\left(\frac{\pi x^2}{2}\right)dx = 1.$

14. Show that $\displaystyle\int_0^{\pi/2} \frac{x^{m-1}\,(1-x)^{n-1}}{(x+a)^{m+n}}\,dx = \frac{B\,(m,\,n)}{a^n\,(1+a)^m}.$

$$\left[\textbf{Hint.}\ \text{In } B\,(m,\,n) = \int_0^1 y^{m-1}\,(1-y)^{n-1}\,dy,\ \text{put } \frac{y}{1+a} = \frac{x}{x+a}.\right]$$

15. Show that, if $n > -1$,

$$\int_0^\infty x^n\,e^{-k^2x^2}\,dx = \frac{1}{2k^{n+1}}\,\Gamma\left(\frac{n+1}{2}\right).$$

7.6. To find the value of

$$\Gamma\left(\frac{1}{n}\right)\Gamma\left(\frac{2}{n}\right)\Gamma\left(\frac{3}{n}\right)\ldots\Gamma\left(\frac{n-1}{n}\right),$$

where n is a positive integer.

Let $P = \Gamma\left(\frac{1}{n}\right)\Gamma\left(\frac{2}{n}\right)\ldots\Gamma\left(\frac{n-2}{n}\right)\Gamma\left(\frac{n-1}{n}\right)$ ...(i)

or $P = \Gamma\left(\frac{1}{n}\right)\Gamma\left(\frac{2}{n}\right)\ldots\Gamma\left(1-\frac{2}{n}\right)\Gamma\left(1-\frac{1}{n}\right).$

Writing in the reverse order,

$$P = \Gamma\left(1-\frac{1}{n}\right)\Gamma\left(1-\frac{2}{n}\right)\ldots\Gamma\left(\frac{2}{n}\right)\Gamma\left(\frac{1}{n}\right) \quad ...(ii)$$

Multiplying (i) and (ii), we get

$$P^2 = \left[\Gamma\left(\frac{1}{n}\right)\Gamma\left(1-\frac{1}{n}\right)\right]\left[\Gamma\left(\frac{2}{n}\right)\Gamma\left(1-\frac{2}{n}\right)\right]$$

$$\ldots\left[\Gamma\left(\frac{n-2}{n}\right)\Gamma\left(1-\frac{n-2}{n}\right)\right]\left[\Gamma\left(\frac{n-1}{n}\right)\Gamma\left(1-\frac{n-1}{n}\right)\right].$$

Now, we know that $\Gamma(n)\,\Gamma(1-n) = \dfrac{\pi}{\sin n\pi}$

or $\Gamma\left(\frac{1}{n}\right)\cdot\Gamma\left(1-\frac{1}{n}\right) = \dfrac{\pi}{\sin\dfrac{\pi}{n}}$ ...(iii)

$\therefore\quad P^2 = \dfrac{\pi}{\sin\dfrac{\pi}{n}}\cdot\dfrac{\pi}{\sin\dfrac{2\pi}{n}}\ldots\dfrac{\pi}{\sin\dfrac{n-2}{n}\pi}\cdot\dfrac{\pi}{\sin\dfrac{n-1}{n}\pi}$ ...(iv)

From Trigonometry, we know that

$$\frac{\sin n\theta}{\sin\theta} = 2^{n-1}\sin\left(\theta+\frac{\pi}{n}\right)\sin\left(\theta+\frac{2\pi}{n}\right)$$

$$\ldots\sin\left(\theta+\frac{n-2}{n}\pi\right)\sin\left(\theta+\frac{n-1}{n}\pi\right).$$

Putting $\theta = 0$,

$$\lim_{\theta\to 0}\frac{\sin n\theta}{\sin\theta} = \lim_{\theta\to 0}\frac{n\cos n\theta}{\cos\theta} = n$$

$\therefore\quad n = 2^{n-1}\sin\dfrac{\pi}{n}\sin\dfrac{2\pi}{n}\ldots\sin\dfrac{n-2}{n}\pi\cdot\sin\dfrac{n-1}{n}\pi$

$\therefore\quad P^2 = \pi^{n-1}\cdot\dfrac{2^{n-1}}{n}$

$$\therefore \quad P = \frac{(2\pi)^{n-1/2}}{\sqrt{n}}.$$

Hence

$$\Gamma\left(\frac{1}{n}\right)\Gamma\left(\frac{2}{n}\right)\dots\Gamma\left(\frac{n-1}{n}\right) = \frac{(2\pi)^{(n-1/2)}}{\sqrt{n}}.$$

7.7. Evaluate the integrals

$$\int_0^\infty e^{-ax}\cos bx \cdot x^{m-1}\, dx \quad \text{and} \quad \int_0^\infty e^{-ax}\sin bx \cdot x^{m-1}\, dx.$$

Both the above integrals are respectively the real and imaginary parts of

$$\int_0^\infty e^{-ax}\, e^{ibx} \cdot x^{m-1}\, dx$$

or

$$\int_0^\infty e^{-(a-ib)x} \cdot x^{m-1}\, dx.$$

Now, we have

$$\int_0^\infty e^{-kx}\, x^{n-1}\, dx = \frac{\Gamma n}{k^n}$$

$$\therefore \quad \int_0^\infty e^{-(a-ib)x}\, x^{m-1}\, dx = \frac{\Gamma m}{(a-ib)^m}$$

$$= \Gamma m \cdot \frac{(a+ib)^m}{(a^2+b^2)^m}.$$

Let us put $a = r\cos\theta$, $b = r\sin\theta$ in R.H.S.

$$\therefore \quad \int_0^\infty e^{-ax}(\cos bx + i\sin bx)\, x^{m-1}\, dx$$

$$= \Gamma \frac{r^m(\cos\theta + i\sin\theta)^m}{r^{2m}}$$

or

$$\int_0^\infty [e^{-ax}\cos bx \cdot x^{m-1} + ie^{-ax}\sin bx \cdot x^{m-1}\, dx]$$

$$= \frac{m}{r^m}(\cos m\theta + i\sin m\theta).$$

Equating real and imaginary parts, we get

$$\int_0^\infty e^{-ax} \cos bx \cdot x^{m-1} \, dx = \frac{\Gamma m}{r^m} \cos m\theta$$

and

$$\int_0^\infty e^{-ax} \sin bx \cdot x^{m-1} \, dx = \frac{\Gamma m}{r^m} \sin m\theta$$

where $r = \sqrt{a^2 + b^2}$ and $\theta = \tan^{-1} \dfrac{b}{a}$.

EXAMPLES

1. *Evaluate* $\Gamma\left(\dfrac{1}{9}\right)\Gamma\left(\dfrac{2}{9}\right)\Gamma\left(\dfrac{3}{9}\right)\ldots\Gamma\left(\dfrac{8}{9}\right)$.

$$\Gamma\left(\frac{1}{9}\right)\Gamma\left(\frac{2}{9}\right)\ldots\Gamma\left(\frac{9-1}{9}\right)$$

$$= \frac{(2\pi)^{(9-1)/2}}{(9)^{1/2}} = \frac{(2\pi)^4}{3}$$

$$= \frac{16}{3}\pi^4.$$

2. *Prove that* $\displaystyle\int_0^\infty xe^{-ax} \cos bx \cdot dx = \frac{a^2 - b^2}{(a^2 + b^2)^2}$, *where* $a > 0$.

Put $m - 1 = 1$, *i.e.*, $m = 2$

$$\int_0^\infty xe^{-ax} \cos bx \, dx = \frac{\Gamma 2}{r^2} \cos 2\theta$$

$$= \frac{1}{(a^2 + b^2)} \cdot \frac{1 - \tan^2 \theta}{1 + \tan^2 \theta} = \frac{1}{(a^2 + b^2)} \cdot \frac{\left(1 - \dfrac{b^2}{a^2}\right)}{\left(1 + \dfrac{b^2}{a^2}\right)}$$

$$= \frac{a^2 - b^2}{(a^2 + b^2)^2}.$$

3. *Prove that* $\displaystyle\int_0^\infty \cos(bz^{1/n}) \, dz = \frac{\Gamma(n+1) \cos \dfrac{n\pi}{2}}{b^n}$.

Put $z^{1/n} = x$, $z = x^n$ or $dz = nx^{n-1}\,dx$, then

$$I = n \int_0^\infty x^{n-1} \cos bx \, dx \qquad \qquad \text{...}(i)$$

We know that

$$\int_0^\infty e^{-ax} \cos bx \cdot x^{m-1} \, dx = \frac{\Gamma m}{r^m} \cos m\theta$$

where $r = \sqrt{a^2 + b^2}$ and $\theta = \tan^{-1} \dfrac{b}{a}$.

Now, put $m = n$ and $a = 0$, we get

$$\int_0^\infty x^{n-1} \cos bx \, dx = \frac{\Gamma n}{r^n} \cos n\theta.$$

Now $r = b$ and $\theta = \tan^{-1} \dfrac{b}{0} = \dfrac{\pi}{2}$

$$\therefore \int_0^\infty x^{n-1} \cos bx \, dx = \frac{\Gamma n}{b^n} \cos \frac{n\pi}{2}.$$

By putting the value in (i), we get

$$I = \frac{n\,\Gamma n}{b^n} \cos \frac{n\pi}{2} = \frac{\Gamma(n+1) \cos \dfrac{n\pi}{2}}{b^n}.$$

EXERCISES

1. Prove that

$$\Gamma(.1)\,\Gamma(.2)\,\Gamma(.3) \,.....\, \Gamma(.9) = \frac{(2\pi)^{9/2}}{\sqrt{10}}.$$

2. Prove that

$$(i) \int_0^\infty \cos x^2 \, dx = \frac{1}{2}\sqrt{\pi/2};$$

$$(ii) \int_{-\infty}^\infty \frac{\cos \pi x^2}{2} \, dx = 1.$$

3. Evaluate $\displaystyle\int_0^\infty x^{m-1} \cos bx \, dx$ and $\displaystyle\int_0^\infty x^{m-1} \sin bx \, dx$.

4. Prove that $\displaystyle\int_0^\infty x^{m-1} e^{-ax^2} \, dx = \frac{\Gamma n}{2a^n}$.

5. Evaluate $\int\limits_0^\infty \dfrac{\cos bz}{z^n}\,dz$ and $\int\limits_0^\infty \dfrac{\sin bz}{z^n}\,dz$.

ANSWERS

3. $\dfrac{\Gamma m}{b^m}\cos\dfrac{m\pi}{2}$; $\dfrac{\Gamma m}{b^m}\sin\dfrac{m\pi}{2}$.

5. $\dfrac{b^{n-1}}{\Gamma n}\cdot\dfrac{\pi}{2}\sec\dfrac{n\pi}{2}$; $\dfrac{b^{n-1}}{\Gamma n}\cdot\dfrac{\pi}{2}\operatorname{cosec}\dfrac{n\pi}{2}$.

OBJECTIVE QUESTIONS

For each of the following questions, four alternatives are given for the answer. Only one of them is correct. Choose the correct alternative.

1. If $m, n > 0$, then the beta function B (m, n) is defined to be the integral :

    (a) $\int\limits_{-1}^{1} x^{m-1}(1-x)^{n-1}\,dx$ (b) $\int\limits_{0}^{\pi/2} x^{m-1}(1-x)^{n-1}\,dx$

    (c) $\int\limits_{0}^{1} x^{m-1}(1-x)^{n-1}\,dx$ (d) $\int\limits_{0}^{1} (1-x)^{m-1}(1-x)^{n-1}\,dx$.

(Avadh, 2003)

2. Another form of B (m, n) is :

    (a) $\int\limits_{0}^{\infty} \dfrac{x^{m-1}}{(1+x)^n}\,dx$ (b) $\int\limits_{0}^{\infty} \dfrac{x^{n-1}}{(1+x)^n}\,dx$

    (c) $\int\limits_{0}^{\infty} \dfrac{x^{m+n-1}}{1+x}\,dx$ (d) $\int\limits_{0}^{\infty} \dfrac{x^{m-1}}{(1+x)^{m+n}}\,dx$.

3. If $n > 0$, then the gamma function is defined as :

    (a) $\int\limits_{0}^{1} e^{-x} x^{n-1}\,dx$ (b) $\int\limits_{0}^{1} e^{-nx} x^{n-1}\,dx$

    (c) $\int\limits_{0}^{\infty} e^{-x} x^{n+1}\,dx$ (d) $\int\limits_{0}^{\infty} e^{-x} x^{n-1}\,dx$.

(Avadh, 2002)

4. $\int\limits_{0}^{\infty} e^{-cx} x^{n-1}\,dx$ is equal to :

    (a) $c^n\,\Gamma(n)$ (b) $c^{n-1}\,\Gamma(n)$ (c) $\Gamma(n)/c^n$ (d) $\Gamma(n)/c^{n-1}$.

5. The value of $\int\limits_0^\infty \dfrac{x^c}{c^x}\,dx$ is :

(a) $\dfrac{\Gamma(c+1)}{(\log c)^{c+1}}$

(b) $\dfrac{\Gamma(c+1)}{(\log c)^{c-1}}$

(c) $\dfrac{\Gamma(c-1)}{(\log c)^{c+1}}$

(d) $\dfrac{\Gamma(c-1)}{(\log c)^{c-1}}$.

6. The value of $\int\limits_0^\infty \dfrac{x^{p-1}}{1+x}\,dx$, where $0 < p < 1$, is :

(a) $\dfrac{\pi}{\sin \frac{1}{2} p\pi}$

(b) $\dfrac{\pi}{\sin p\pi}$

(c) $\dfrac{\pi}{\cos p\pi}$

(d) $\dfrac{\pi}{\cos \frac{1}{2} p\pi}$.

7. The integral $\int\limits_0^\infty x^{n-1} e^{-x}\,dx$ is defined as :

(a) Beta function

(b) Gamma function

(c) Beta and gamma function

(d) None of these.

(*Garhwal, 2001*)

8. In terms of gamma function, B (m, n) is :

(a) $\dfrac{\Gamma\left(\dfrac{m+1}{2}\right)\Gamma\left(\dfrac{n+1}{2}\right)}{2\Gamma\left(\dfrac{m+n+2}{2}\right)}$

(b) $\dfrac{\Gamma(m)\,\Gamma(n)}{2\Gamma(m+n)}$

(c) $\dfrac{\Gamma(m)\,\Gamma(n)}{\Gamma(m+n)}$

(d) None of these.

9. If $0 < n < 1$, then $\Gamma(n)\,\Gamma(1-n)$ is equal to :

(a) 1   (b) $\dfrac{1}{2}\pi$ (c) $\pi / \sin n\pi$ (d) $\sin n\pi$.

10. Legendre's duplication formula is :

(a) $\Gamma(n)\,\Gamma\left(n+\dfrac{1}{2}\right) = \dfrac{\sqrt{\pi}}{2^{n-1}}\,\Gamma(2n)$

(b) $\Gamma(n)\,\Gamma\left(n+\dfrac{1}{2}\right) = \dfrac{\pi}{2^{n-1}}\,\Gamma(2n)$

(c) $\Gamma(n)\,\Gamma\left(n+\dfrac{1}{2}\right) = \dfrac{\pi}{2^{2n-1}}\,\Gamma(2n)$

(d) $\Gamma(n)\,\Gamma\left(n+\dfrac{1}{2}\right) = \dfrac{\sqrt{\pi}}{2^{2n-1}}\,\Gamma(2n).$

11. The value of $\displaystyle\int_0^1 x^4\,(1-x)^3\,dx$ is :

(a) $\dfrac{1}{280}$ (b) $\dfrac{1}{180}$ (c) $\dfrac{1}{380}$ (d) $\dfrac{1}{80}.$

12. Value of $\displaystyle\int_0^\infty \left[\log\left(\dfrac{1}{t}\right)\right]^{n-1} dt$ is :

(a) $2\Gamma n$ (b) Γn (c) $\Gamma(n+1)$ (d) $\Gamma\left(n+\dfrac{1}{2}\right).$

13. Value of $\Gamma\left(-\dfrac{3}{2}\right)$ is :

(a) $-2\sqrt{\pi}$ (b) $\dfrac{4\sqrt{\pi}}{3}$ (c) $-\dfrac{8\sqrt{\pi}}{15}$ (d) None of these.

14. Value of $\displaystyle\int_0^{\pi/2} \tan^n \theta\, d\theta$ is :

(a) $\pi \sec\left(\dfrac{1}{3}n\pi\right)$ (b) $2\pi \sec\left(\dfrac{1}{3}n\pi\right)$

(c) $\dfrac{1}{2}\pi \sec\left(\dfrac{1}{3}n\pi\right)$ (d) None of these.

15. Value of $\displaystyle\int_0^\infty x^4 e^{-x}\,dx$ is :

(a) 24 (b) 12 (c) 48 (d) 6.

16. Value of $\displaystyle\int_0^\infty 4x^4\, e^{-x^4}\,dx$ is :

(a) $\Gamma\left(\dfrac{5}{4}\right)$ (b) $\Gamma\left(\dfrac{3}{4}\right)$ (c) $\Gamma\left(\dfrac{1}{4}\right)$ (d) $2\,\Gamma\left(\dfrac{5}{4}\right).$

17. Value of $\displaystyle\int_0^2 \frac{x^2}{\sqrt{2-x}}\, dx$ is :

    (a) $\dfrac{64\sqrt{2}}{15}$ (b) $\dfrac{32\sqrt{2}}{15}$ (c) $\dfrac{32\sqrt{5}}{5}$ (d) $\dfrac{64\sqrt{2}}{5}$.

18. Value of $\displaystyle\int_0^2 (4-x^2)^{3/2}\, dx$ is :

    (a) π (b) 2π (c) 3π (d) $\pi/2$.

19. Value of $\displaystyle\int_0^\infty \frac{x\, dx}{1+x^6}$ is :

    (a) $\dfrac{\pi}{3}$ (b) $\dfrac{\pi}{3\sqrt{3}}$ (c) $\dfrac{2\pi}{3\sqrt{3}}$ (d) $\dfrac{4\pi}{3\sqrt{3}}$.

20. Value of $\displaystyle\int_0^\infty xe^{-ax}\cos bx\, dx$, where $a > 0$ is :

    (a) $\dfrac{a^2-b^2}{(a^2+b^2)^2}$ (b) $\dfrac{a^2+b^2}{(a^2-b^2)^2}$

    (c) $\dfrac{a^2-b^2}{a^2+b^2}$ (d) $\dfrac{a^2+b^2}{a^2-b^2}$.

ANSWERS

1. (c)	2. (d)	3. (d)	4. (c)	5. (a)
6. (b)	7. (b)	8. (c)	9. (c)	10. (d)
11. (a)	12. (b)	13. (b)	14. (c)	15. (a)
16. (a)	17. (a)	18. (c)	19. (b)	20. (a)

APPLICATIONS

8

Areas of Plane Regions

QUADRATURE

8.1. It has been shown in § 1.8, that the *area bounded by a curve* $y = f(x)$, *the axis of x and two ordinates*, $x = a$ *and* $x = b$, *is given by the definite integral*

$$\int_a^b f(x)\, dx.$$

It can similarly be shown that the *area bounded by a curve* $x = f(y)$, *the axis of y and the two abscissae*, $y = c$ *and* $y = d$, *is given by the definite integral*

$$\int_c^d f(y)\, dy.$$

The area which are not situated in any of these two ways can sometimes be expressed as combination of areas which are thus situated.

The process of determining the area of a plane region is known as *Quadrature*.

We shall now consider some examples.

Note. It is always necessary to trace the curve with reference to which the region whose area is to be determined is given. The trace of the curve will enable the area to be expressed as a definite integral or a suitable combination of such integrals.

In connection with this and the following chapters on the determination of lengths of arcs and volumes and surfaces of solids of revolution, the student is strongly advised to familiarise himself with elementary aspects of the subject of curve tracing and specially with* the following curves which will occur very frequently in the following.

---

* Reference may be made to the chapter '*Some Important Curves*' and the chapter '*Curve Tracing*' in the Author's *Differential Calculus*.

Cartesian Equations :

$$Ellipse \ : \ \frac{x^2}{a^2} + \frac{y^2}{b^2} = 1. \qquad Hyperbola \ : \ \frac{x^2}{a^2} - \frac{y^2}{b^2} = 1.$$

$$Parabola \ : \ y^2 = 4ax. \qquad \qquad Catenary \ : \ y = c \cosh (x / c).$$

$$Cissoid \ : \ y^2 (a - x) = x^3. \qquad Strophoid \ : \ (x^2 + y^2) x = a^2 (x^2 - y^2).$$

$$Folium \ : \ x^3 + y^3 = 3axy. \qquad Lemniscate \ : \ (x^2 + y^2)^2 = a^2 (x^2 - y^2).$$

$$Astroid \ : \ x^{2/3} + y^{2/3} = a^{2/3} \ \Leftrightarrow \ x = a \cos^3 \theta, \ y = a \sin^3 \theta.$$

$$Cycloid \ : \ x = a \ (\theta - \sin \theta), \ y = a \ (1 - \cos \theta).$$

The equations of a cycloid are also often given in the forms

(I) $x = a \ (\theta + \sin \theta), \ y = a \ (1 + \cos \theta),$

(II) $x = a \ (\theta + \sin \theta), \ y = a \ (1 - \cos \theta).$

These cycloids with different equations are differently situated with respect to the coordinate axes.

$$Tractrix \ : \ x = a \left(\cos t + \frac{1}{2} \log \tan^2 \frac{1}{2} t \right), \ y = a \sin t.$$

Polar Equations :

$$Cardioide \ : \quad r = a \ (1 \pm \cos \theta).$$

$$Lemniscate \ : \quad r^2 = a^2 \cos 2\theta.$$

$$Equiangular \ Spiral \ : \quad r = ae^{b\theta}.$$

$$Conic \ : \quad l / r = 1 + e \cos \theta.$$

$$Three\text{-}leaved \ Rose \ : \quad r = a \sin 3\theta.$$

$$Four\text{-}leaved \ Rose \ : \quad r = a \sin 2\theta.$$

8.11. Area Enclosed by Two Curves

Let the two curves $y = \phi_1 (x)$ and $y = \phi_2 (x)$ intersect in the two points (a, c), (b, d) and let between these points, the first curve lies above the second curve as in fig. (a).

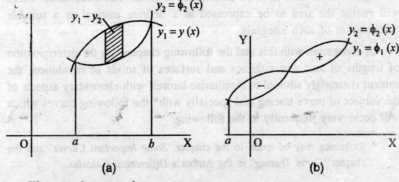

(a)   (b)

The area between the curves

= area under first curve − area under second curve

$$= \int_a^b \phi_1(x)\,dx - \int_a^b \phi_2(x)\,dx$$

$$= \int_a^b [\phi_1(x) - \phi_2(x)]\,dx$$

$$= \int_a^b (y_1 - y_2)\,dx.$$

Note. The curves intersect between (a, c) and (b, d) as in fig. (b) the definite integral $\int_a^b [\phi_1(x) - \phi_2(x)]\,dx$ gives the algebraic sum of areas in which each part is assigned positive or negative sign according as the curve $y = \phi_1(x)$ is above or below the curve $y = \phi_2(x)$.

EXAMPLES

1. *Find the area bounded by the ellipse*

$$\frac{x^2}{a^2} + \frac{y^2}{b^2} = 1.$$ *(Jiwaji, 1997; Indore, 1998; Rohilkhand, 2003; Avadh, 2002; Agra, 2000)*

The ellipse is symmetrical about both the coordinate axes, so that the

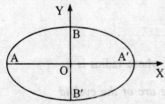

two axes divide it into four portions whose areas are equal. We will determine the area of one of the portion OAB lying in the first quadrant and multiply the same by four to get the area of the ellipse.

Solving the equation of the ellipse for y in terms of x, we see that for any point (x, y) on the arc AB, we have

$$y = \frac{b}{a}\sqrt{a^2 - x^2}.$$

$$\therefore \quad \text{area OAB} = \int_0^a y\,dx = \frac{b}{a}\int_0^a \sqrt{a^2 - x^2}\,dx$$

$$= \frac{b}{a}\left| \frac{x\sqrt{a^2 - x^2}}{2} + \frac{a^2}{2}\sin^{-1}\frac{x}{a} \right|_0^a$$

$$= \frac{b}{a}\left[\frac{a^2}{2}\cdot\frac{\pi}{2} \right] = \frac{\pi}{4}ab$$

$\therefore$ area of the ellipse $= \pi ab$.

2. *Prove that the area of the region bounded by the curve*

$$a^4 y^2 = x^5 (2a - x),$$

is to that of the circle whose radius is, a, is 5 to 4. (*Jabalpur, 1998*)

The curve consists of a loop lying between the line $x = 0$ and $x = 2a$ and is symmetrical about the x-axis.

The required area

$$= \frac{2}{a^2} \int_0^{2a} x^{5/2} \sqrt{2a - x} \, dx.$$

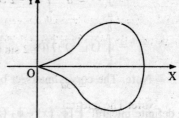

To evaluate this integral, we put $x = 2a \sin^2 \theta$.

When $x = 0$, $\theta = 0$ and when $x = 2a$, $\theta = \frac{1}{2} \pi$.

∴ The required area

$$= \frac{2}{a^2} \int_0^{\pi/2} (2a)^{5/2} \sin^5 \theta \cdot \sqrt{2a} \cdot \cos \theta \cdot 4a \sin \theta \cos \theta \, d\theta$$

$$= 64a^2 \int_0^{\pi/2} \sin^6 \theta \cos^2 \theta \, d\theta$$

$$= 64a^2 \cdot \frac{5 \cdot 3 \cdot 1 \cdot 1}{8 \cdot 6 \cdot 4 \cdot 2} \cdot \frac{\pi}{2}$$

$$= \frac{5a^2 \pi}{4} = \frac{5}{4} \times \text{area of the circle whose radius is } a.$$

3. *Find the area enclosed between one arc of the cycloid*

$$x = a (\theta - \sin \theta), \quad y = a (1 - \cos \theta),$$

and its base. (*Kumaon, 2001*)

To describe the first arc OPA of the cycloid, θ varies from 0 to 2π. The coordinates of A are $(2a\pi, 0)$.

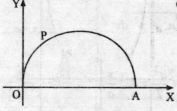

The required area $= \int_0^{2\pi a} y \, dx.$

We have

$$dx = a (1 - \cos \theta) \, d\theta.$$

∴ The required area $= \int_0^{2\pi} a (1 - \cos \theta) \cdot a (1 - \cos \theta) \, d\theta$

$$= a^2 \int_0^{2\pi} (1 - 2\cos\theta + \cos^2\theta)\, d\theta$$

$$= a^2 \int_0^{2\pi} \left(1 - 2\cos\theta + \frac{1 + \cos 2\theta}{2}\right) d\theta$$

$$= a^2 \left| \theta - 2\sin\theta + \frac{\theta}{2} + \frac{\sin 2\theta}{4} \right|_0^{2\pi}$$

$$= 3a^2\pi.$$

Note. The integral

$$\int_0^{2\pi} a^2 (1 - \cos\theta)^2\, d\theta$$

could also be evaluated differently as follows. We have

$$\int_0^{2\pi} a^2 (1 - \cos\theta)^2\, d\theta = 2a^2 \int_0^{\pi} (1 - \cos\theta)^2\, d\theta$$

$$= 8a^2 \int_0^{\pi} \sin^4 \frac{\theta}{2}\, d\theta$$

$$= 16a^2 \int_0^{\pi/2} \sin^4 \phi\, d\phi, \text{ where } \frac{\theta}{2} = \phi,$$

$$= 16a^2 \cdot \frac{3}{4} \cdot \frac{1}{2} \cdot \frac{\pi}{2} = 3a^2\pi.$$

4. *Find the whole area included between the curve* $x^2 y^2 = a^2 (y^2 - x^2)$ *and its asymptotes.*

The curve is $x^2 y^2 = a^2 (y^2 - x^2)$.

(*i*) Symmetry about both the axes as even powers of x and y occur.

(*ii*) The asymptotes are $x = \pm a$.

Therefore the required area

$$= 4 \int_0^a y\, dx$$

$$= 4 \int_0^a \frac{ax}{\sqrt{a^2 - x^2}}\, dx.$$

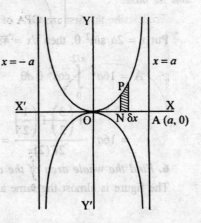

Put $x = a \sin \theta$, $dx = a \cos \theta \, d\theta$.

$$\therefore \quad A = 4a^2 \int_0^{\pi/2} \sin \theta \, d\theta$$

$$= 4a^2 \left[-\cos \theta \right]_0^{\pi/2}$$

$$= 4a^2.$$

5. *Find the area bounded by the curve $xy^2 = 4a^2 (2a - x)$ and its asymptote.* (Ravishankar, 1999, 2001; Kanpur, 2002)

The equation of the curve is $xy^2 = 4a^2 (2a - x)$.

(i) The curve is symmetrical about the x-axis as it contains even powers of y.

(ii) It passes through $(2a, 0)$.

(iii) The asymptote is $x = 0$, *i.e.*, y-axis.

The required area

$$= 2 \int_0^{2a} y \, dx = 2 \int_0^{2a} \sqrt{2a - \frac{x}{x}} \, dx.$$

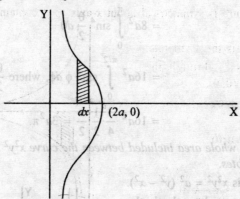

Put $x = 2a \sin^2 \theta$, then $dx = 4a \sin \theta \cos \theta \, d\theta$.

$$\therefore \quad A = 16a^2 \int_0^{\pi/2} \cos^2 \theta \, d\theta$$

$$= 16a^2 \cdot \frac{\Gamma\left(\frac{3}{2}\right) \cdot \Gamma\left(\frac{1}{2}\right)}{2\Gamma(2)} = 4\pi a^2.$$

6. *Find the whole area of the curve $xy^2 = a^2 (a - x)$ and the y-axis.*

The figure is almost the same as in solved example 5.

The required area $= 2 \int\limits_{0}^{\infty} x \, dy$

$$= 2 \int\limits_{0}^{\infty} \frac{a^3}{y^2 + a^2} \, dy$$

$$= 2 \cdot a^3 \cdot \frac{1}{a} \left[\tan^{-1} \frac{y}{a} \right]_{0}^{\infty}$$

$$= 2a^2 [\tan^{-1} \infty - \tan^{-1} 0] = 2a^2 \cdot \frac{\pi}{2}$$

$$= \pi a^2.$$

7. *Show that the area bounded by the cissoid* $x = a \sin^2 t$, $y = a \dfrac{\sin^3 t}{\cos t}$

and its asymptote is $\dfrac{3\pi^2}{4}$.   *(Bilaspur, 1996)*

Eliminating t from the given equations, the equation of the curve becomes $y^2 (a - x) = x^3$.

    (*i*) The cure is symmetrical about x-axis as it contains even powers of y.

    (*ii*) $x = a$ is the asymptote.

    (*iii*) It passes through the origin $(0, 0)$.

Hence the area

$$= 2 \int\limits_{0}^{a} y \, dx$$

$$= 2 \int\limits_{0}^{a} \frac{x^{3/2}}{\sqrt{a - x}} \, dx.$$

Put $x = a \sin^2 \theta$,

$dx = 2a \sin \theta \cos \theta \, d\theta.$

$$\therefore \quad A = 2 \int\limits_{0}^{\pi/2} \frac{a^{3/2} \sin^3 \theta \cdot 2a \sin \theta \cdot \cos \theta \, d\theta}{\sqrt{a - a \sin^2 \theta}}$$

$$= 4a^2 \int\limits_{0}^{\pi/2} \sin^4 \theta \, d\theta$$

$$= 4a^2 \frac{\Gamma\left(\frac{5}{2}\right) \cdot \Gamma\left(\frac{1}{2}\right)}{2\Gamma(3)}$$

$$= a^2 \cdot \frac{3}{2} \cdot \frac{1}{2} \sqrt{\pi} = \frac{3\pi a^2}{4}.$$

8. *Find the area of the region lying above x-axis, and included between the circle* $x^2 + y^2 = 2ax$ *and the parabola* $y^2 = ax$.

Solving the two equations simultaneously, we see that the two curves intersect at $(0, 0)$, (a, a) and $(a, -a)$.

We have to find the area of the region OABP, where P is the point of intersection (a, a). It is the difference of the areas of the regions OBPCO and OAPCO.

Area of the region OBPCO

$$= \int_0^a \sqrt{2ax - x^2} \, dx$$

Area of the region OAPCO

$$= \int_0^a \sqrt{ax} \, dx$$

$\therefore$ The required area $= \displaystyle\int_0^a \sqrt{2ax - x^2} \, dx - \int_0^a \sqrt{ax} \, dx.$

Now $\displaystyle\int_0^a \sqrt{2ax - x^2} \, dx = \int_0^a \sqrt{a^2 - (a - x)^2} \, dx.$

To evaluate this integral, we put

$$a - x = a \sin \theta$$

and obtain

$$\int_0^a \sqrt{2ax - x^2} \, dx = \int_{\pi/2}^0 (a \cos \theta)(-a \cos \theta) \, d\theta$$

$$= \int_0^{\pi/2} a^2 \cos^2 \theta \, d\theta = a^2 \cdot \frac{1}{2} \cdot \frac{\pi}{2} = \frac{\pi a^2}{4}.$$

Also $\displaystyle\int_0^a \sqrt{ax} \, dx = \left| \sqrt{a} \cdot \frac{2}{3} x^{3/2} \right|_0^a = \frac{2a^2}{3}.$

$\therefore$ The required area $= a^2\left(\dfrac{\pi}{4} - \dfrac{2}{3}\right)$.

9. *Show that the area common to the ellipses* $a^2x^2 + b^2y^2 = 1$, b^2x^2
$+ a^2y^2 = 1$, *when* $0 < a < b$ *is* $\dfrac{4}{ab}\tan^{-1}\dfrac{a}{b}$.

Solving the equations of the ellipses $a^2x^2 + b^2y^2 = 1$, and $b^2x^2 + a^2y^2$
$= 1$, we get one point of intersection as

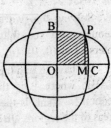

$$\left(\frac{1}{\sqrt{a^2 + b^2}}, \frac{1}{\sqrt{a^2 + b^2}}\right)$$

Here in the ellipse $a^2x^2 + b^2y^2 = 1$, x-axis is the

major axis because $\dfrac{1}{a} > \dfrac{1}{b}$ and for the second

ellipse, y-axis is the major axis.

Now, required area

$$= 4 \times \text{area OCPB} = 4 \,(\text{area OBPM} + \text{area PMC})$$

$$= 4\left[\int_0^k y_1 \, dx + \int_k^{1/b} y_2 \, dx\right], \text{ where } y = \phi_1(x).$$

For area PMC, limits are in the given equation $a^2x^2 + b^2y^2 = 1$ from OM
to OC. Now,

$$\text{OM} = \frac{1}{\sqrt{a^2 + b^2}} = k, \ y_1 = \frac{(1 - a^2x^2)^{1/2}}{b}$$

$$\text{OC} = \frac{1}{2} \text{ minor axis of the second ellipse} = \frac{1}{b^2}.$$

Similarly in the second equation $y_2 = \dfrac{\sqrt{1 - b^2x^2}}{a}$ and $k = \dfrac{1}{\sqrt{a^2 + b^2}}$.

Now $\displaystyle\int_0^k y_1 \, dx = \frac{1}{b}\int_0^k \sqrt{1 - a^2x^2} \, dx$

$$= \frac{a}{b}\int_0^k \sqrt{\left(\frac{1}{a}\right)^2 - x^2} \, dx$$

$$= \frac{a}{b}\left[\frac{1}{2}x\sqrt{\left(\frac{1}{a}\right)^2 - x^2} + \frac{1}{2a}\sin^{-1}(ax)\right]_0^k$$

$$= \frac{a}{b}\left[\frac{1}{2}k\sqrt{\left(\frac{1}{a}\right)^2 - k^2}\right] + \left[\frac{1}{2a^2}\sin^{-1}(ak)\right]$$

$$= \frac{a}{b}\left[\frac{1}{2}k\sqrt{\left(\frac{1}{a^2}\right) - k^2}\right] + \left[\frac{1}{2a^2}\sin^{-1}(ak)\right]$$

$$= \frac{a}{2b}\frac{1}{\sqrt{a^2 + b^2}}\sqrt{\frac{1}{a^2} - \frac{1}{a^2 + b^2}} + \frac{1}{2a^2}\sin^{-1}\left(\frac{a}{\sqrt{a^2 + b^2}}\right)$$

$$= \frac{1}{2(a^2 + b^2)} + \frac{1}{2ab}\tan^{-1}\left(\frac{a}{b}\right),$$

as

$$\sin^{-1}\frac{a}{\sqrt{a^2 + b^2}} = \tan^{-1}\frac{a}{b}.$$

Again, area PMC

$$= \int_k^{1/b} y_2\, dx = \frac{1}{a}\int_k^{1/b}\sqrt{1 - b^2 x^2}\, dx$$

$$= \frac{b}{a}\int_k^{1/b}\sqrt{\left(\frac{1}{b}\right)^2 - x^2}\, dx$$

$$= \frac{b}{a}\left[\frac{1}{2}x\sqrt{\left(\frac{1}{b}\right)^2 - x^2} + \frac{1}{2}\left(\frac{1}{b}\right)^2\sin^{-1}bx\right]_k^{1/b}$$

$$= -\frac{b}{2a}\left[k\sqrt{\left(\frac{1}{b}\right)^2 - k^2} + \frac{1}{2ab}(\sin^{-1}1 - \sin^{-1}bx)\right]$$

$$= -\frac{b}{2a}\sqrt{1 - b^2 - k^2}\cdot\frac{k}{b} + \frac{1}{2ab}\left(\frac{\pi}{2} - \sin^{-1}\frac{b}{\sqrt{a^2 + b^2}}\right)$$

$$= -\frac{1}{2(a^2 + b^2)} + \frac{\pi}{4}ab - \frac{1}{2}ab\tan^{-1}\left(\frac{a}{b}\right).$$

Hence the required area

$$= 4\left[\left\{\frac{1}{2(a^2 + b^2)} + \frac{1}{2ab}\tan^{-1}\left(\frac{a}{b}\right)\right\}\right.$$

$$\left. + \left\{-\frac{1}{2(a^2 + b^2)} + \frac{1}{2ab}\left(\frac{\pi}{2} - \tan^{-1}\frac{a}{b}\right)\right\}\right]$$

$$= 4\left[\frac{1}{2}ab\tan^{-1}\frac{a}{b} + \frac{1}{2}ab\tan^{-1}\frac{a}{b}\right] = \frac{2}{ab}\tan^{-1}\left(\frac{a}{b}\right).$$

10. *Find the area of the segment cut off from the parabola $y^2 = 2x$ by the straight line $y = 4x - 1$.*

In the figure, AB is the straight line $y = 4x - 1$, which cuts the parabola at A and B, and the x-axis at C.

Solving the equation of the parabola and equation of the line, we get

$$(4x - 1)^2 = 2x$$

or $\qquad 16x^2 - 10x + 1 = 0$

or $\qquad x = \dfrac{1}{2}, \dfrac{1}{8}$, whence $y = 1, -\dfrac{1}{2}$.

Therefore the coordinates of A and B are

$\left(\dfrac{1}{2}, 1\right)$ and $\left(\dfrac{1}{8}, -\dfrac{1}{2}\right)$ respectively. Also, the

coordinates of C are $\left(\dfrac{1}{4}, 0\right)$. AN and BK are

perpendiculars from A and B on the x-axis.

$$\therefore \qquad AN = 1, \; BK = \frac{1}{2}.$$

Required area = area OCA + area OCB $\hspace{2cm}$ ...(i)

Now area OCA = area OAN − area of $\triangle$ ACN

$$= \int_0^{1/2} \sqrt{2x} - \frac{1}{2} \times CN \times AN$$

$$= \sqrt{2}\left[\frac{2}{3}x^{3/2}\right]_0^{1/2} - \frac{1}{2} \times (ON - OC) \times AN$$

$$= \frac{2\sqrt{2}}{3}\left(\frac{1}{2\sqrt{2}}\right) - \frac{1}{2} \times \left(\frac{1}{2} - \frac{1}{4}\right) \times 1$$

$$= \frac{1}{3} - \frac{1}{8} = \frac{5}{24}.$$

Again, area OCB = area OBK + area of $\triangle$ BKC

$$= \int_0^{1/8} \sqrt{2x}\, dx + \frac{1}{2} \times KC \times BK$$

$$= \sqrt{2}\left[\frac{2}{3}x^{3/2}\right]_0^{1/8} + \frac{1}{2} \times (OC - OK) \times BK$$

$$= \frac{2\sqrt{2}}{3}\left(\frac{1}{8\sqrt{2}}\right) + \frac{1}{2} \times \left(\frac{1}{4} - \frac{1}{8}\right) \times \frac{1}{2}$$

$$= \frac{1}{24} + \frac{1}{32} = \frac{7}{96}.$$

$\therefore$ From (i), the required area

$$= \frac{5}{24} + \frac{7}{96} = \frac{9}{32}.$$

11. *Find the area between the curve*

$$x\,(x^2 + y^2) = a\,(x^2 - y^2),$$

and its asymptote. Also find the area of its loop.

(*Garhwal, 1996, 2002; Kumaon, 1994; Vikram, 1998, 2000*)

The curve is symmetrical about x-axis. The loop is situated between the lines $x = 0$ and $x = a$.

The line $x = -a$ is the asymptote of the curve.

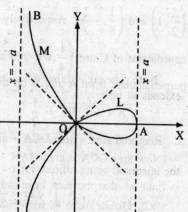

We have

$$y = \pm x\,\sqrt{\frac{a - x}{a + x}}.$$

For any point on the arc OLA,

$$y = x\,\sqrt{\frac{a - x}{a + x}},$$

and for any point on the arc OMB,

$$y = -x\,\sqrt{\frac{a - x}{a + x}}.$$

The area of the loop

$$= 2\int_0^a y\,dx = 2\int_0^a x\,\sqrt{\frac{a - x}{a + x}}\,dx \qquad\qquad\qquad ...(1)$$

The area between the curve and its asymptote

$$= 2\int_{-a}^0 y\,dx = 2\int_{-a}^0 -x\,\sqrt{\frac{a - x}{a + x}}\,dx \qquad\qquad\qquad ...(2)$$

To evaluate the integral (1), we put $x = a \sin\theta$, so that we have

$$2\int_0^a x\,\sqrt{\frac{a - x}{a + x}}\,dx = 2\int_0^a \frac{x\,(a - x)}{\sqrt{a^2 - x^2}}\,dx$$

$$= 2 \int_0^{\pi/2} a^2 (\sin\theta - \sin^2\theta)\, d\theta$$

$$= 2a^2 \left(1 - \frac{1}{2}\cdot\frac{\pi}{2}\right) = \frac{4-\pi}{2}\, a^2.$$

To evaluate the integral (2), we put $x = -a\sin\theta$, so that we obtain

$$2 \int_{-a}^{0} -x \sqrt{\frac{a-x}{a+x}}\, dx = -2 \int_{-a}^{0} \frac{x(a-x)}{\sqrt{a^2-x^2}}\, dx$$

$$= -2 \int_{\pi/2}^{0} a^2(\sin\theta + \sin^2\theta)\, d\theta$$

$$= 2 \int_{0}^{\pi/2} a^2(\sin\theta + \sin^2\theta)\, d\theta$$

$$= \frac{4+\pi}{2}\, a^2.$$

Note. The area of the region between the curve and its asymptote which extends to infinity is given by the improper integral

$$-2 \int_{-a}^{0} x \sqrt{(a-x)/(a+x)}\, dx;$$

the integrand being infinite for $x = -a$. We have seen here that this integral is finite so that the area in question is also finite.

8.2. Quadrature of hyperbola. *If A is the vertex, O the centre and P (x, y) a point on the hyperbola*

$$\frac{x^2}{a^2} - \frac{y^2}{b^2} = 1,$$

prove that

$$x = a\cosh\frac{2S}{ab}, \quad y = b\sinh\frac{2S}{ab},$$

where S is the sectorial area OPA. (Sagar, 1995)

If PM be ordinate of P (x, y), we have

$$S = \text{area OAP}$$

$$= \text{area OMP} - \text{area AMP}$$

$$= \frac{1}{2} xy - \text{AMP}$$

For a point P (x, y) on the arc AP of the hyperbola, we have

$$y = \frac{b}{a} \sqrt{x^2 - a^2}.$$

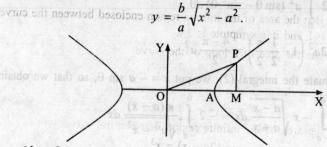

Also, OA = a,

$$\therefore \text{ area AMP} = \int_a^x y \, dx$$

$$= \frac{b}{a} \int_a^x \sqrt{x^2 - a^2} \, dx$$

$$= \frac{b}{a} \left| \frac{x \sqrt{x^2 - a^2}}{2} - \frac{a^2}{2} \cosh^{-1} \frac{x}{a} \right|_0^x$$

$$= \frac{b}{a} \left[\frac{x \sqrt{x^2 - a^2}}{2} - \frac{a^2}{2} \cosh^{-1} \frac{x}{a} \right]$$

$$\therefore \ S = \frac{1}{2} x \cdot \frac{b}{a} \sqrt{x^2 - a^2} - \frac{b}{a} \left(\frac{x \sqrt{x^2 - a^2}}{2} - \frac{a^2}{2} \cosh^{-1} \frac{x}{a} \right)$$

$$= \frac{ab}{2} \cosh^{-1} \frac{x}{a} \ \Rightarrow \ x = a \cosh \frac{2S}{ab}.$$

Hence $y = \dfrac{b}{a} \sqrt{x^2 - a^2} = b \sinh \dfrac{2S}{ab}.$

EXERCISES

1. Show that the area of a loop of the curve
$$x^4 = a^2 (x^2 - y^2) \text{ is } 2a^2 / 3.$$

2. Show that the area of the loop of the curve
$$3ay^2 = x (x - a)^2 \text{ is } 8a^2 / 15\sqrt{3}.$$

3. Find the area enclosed by the curve $xy^2 = 4 (2 - x)$ and Y-axis.

4. Show that the area enclosed between the parabolas
$$y^2 = 4a (x + a), \ y^2 = - 4a (x - a) \text{ is } 16a^2 / 3.$$

5. Find the area common to the circle $x^2 + y^2 = 4$ and the ellipse $x^2 + 4y^2 = 9$.   *(Garhwal, 2002)*

6. Show that the area of the infinite region enclosed between the curve $x^2 (1 - y) y = 1$ and its asymptote is 2π.

7. Calculate the area of a loop of the curve
$$a^4 y^2 = x^4 (a^2 - x^2).$$

8. Show that the area of a loop of the curve
$$y^2 = x^2 (4 - x^2) \text{ is } 16/3.$$

9. Find the area of the infinite region between the curve
$$y^2 (2a - x) = x^3$$
and its asymptote.   *(Rohilkhand, 2001; Ravishankar, 1996; Bhopal, 1995, 99; Indore, 1995; Bilaspur, 2000)*

10. Find the area enclosed by the curves
$$x^2 = 4ay \text{ and } x^2 + 4a^2 = 8a^3/y.$$

11. Find the area of the curvilinear triangle, with one vertex at the origin lying in the first quadrant and bounded by the curves
$$y^2 = 4ax, x^2 = 4ay, x^2 + y^2 = 5a^2.$$

12. Find the area bounded by the parabola $y^2 = 4ax$ and $x^2 = 4ay$.
(Garhwal, 1994; Bhopal, 1998; Ravishankar, 1999; Indore, 1997; Jiwaji, 1998)

13. Show that the area enclosed by the curves
$$xy^2 = a^2 (a - x) \text{ and } (a - x) y^2 = a^2 x \text{ is } (\pi - 2) a^2.$$

14. In the case of the cycloid
$$x = a (\theta + \sin \theta), y = a (1 - \cos \theta),$$
find the area included between the curve and its base.

15. Show that the whole area of the curve $a^2 x^2 = y^3 (2a - y)$ is πa^2.
(Garhwal, 1998; Bilaspur, 1997; Jabalpur, 1999)

16. Find the area enclosed by the curve given by the equations
$$x = a \cos^3 \theta, y = b \sin^3 \theta.$$

17. Find the area of the smaller portion enclosed by the curves
$$x^2 + y^2 = 9, y^2 = 8x.$$

18. Find the area between the curve
$$y^2 (a + x) = (a - x)^3$$
and its asymptote.

19. Find the area of the loop of the curve
$$y^2 x + (x + a)^2 (x + 2a) = 0.$$

20. Find the whole area of the curve
$$x^2 (x^2 + y^2) = a^2 (x^2 - y^2).$$

21. Trace the curve

$$y^2 = x (x - 2)^2 / (4 - x).$$

Find the area of the loop of the curve and also the area between the curve and its asymptote.

22. Show that the area of the curve

$$a^6 y^2 = x^6 (a^2 - x^2) \text{ is } 8a^2 / 15.$$

23. Show that the area of the loop of the curve

$$ay^2 = (x - a) (x - 5a)^2 \text{ is } 256a^2 / 15.$$

24. Show that the area of the loop of the curve

$$a^2 y^2 = x^2 (2a - x) (x - a) \text{ is } 3a^2 \pi / 8.$$

25. Show that the area of the loop of the curve

$$y^2 (a + x) = x^2 (3a - x)$$

is equal to the area between the curve and its asymptote.

26. Show that the total area included between the two branches of the curve

$$y^2 = x^2 / (4 - x) (x - 2)$$

and the two asymptotes is 6π.

27. Show that the area of the loop of the curve

$$c^2 y^2 = (x - a) (x - b)^2 \text{ is } 8 (b - a)^{5/2} / 15c.$$

Trace the curve $y = \tanh x$ and show that the area of the region in the first quadrant enclosed between the curve and its asymptote $y = 1$ is log 2.

28. Show that the ordinate $x = a$ divides the area between $y^2 (2a - x) = x^3$ and its asymptote into two parts in the ratio $3\pi - 8 : 3\pi + 8$.

(Bilaspur, 1998)

ANSWERS

3. 4π.   **5.** $9 \sin^{-1} \dfrac{\sqrt{7}}{3\sqrt{3}} + 4\pi - 8 \sin^{-1} \dfrac{\sqrt{7}}{2\sqrt{3}}$.   **7.** $\pi a^2 / 8$.

9. $3a^2 \pi$.   **10.** $\dfrac{2}{3} (3\pi - 2) a^2$.

11. $\dfrac{1}{6} \left(4 + 15 \sin^{-1} \dfrac{3}{5} \right) a^2$.   **12.** $\dfrac{16a^2}{3}$.

14. $3a^2 \pi$.   **16.** $\dfrac{3}{8} \pi ab$.

17. $2 \left(\dfrac{\sqrt{2}}{3} + \dfrac{9\pi}{4} - \dfrac{9}{2} \sin^{-1} \dfrac{1}{3} \right)$.   **18.** $3a^2 \pi$.

19. $\dfrac{1}{2} a^2 (4 - \pi)$.   **20.** $a^2 (\pi - 2)$.

21. $2 (4 - \pi), 2 (\pi + 4)$.

8.3. Sectorial Area. *If* $r = f(\theta)$ *be the equation of a curve in polar coordinates, then the area of the sector enclosed by the curve and the two radii vectors* $\theta = \alpha$ *and* $\theta = \beta$ *is*

$$\frac{1}{2} \int_{\alpha}^{\beta} r^2 \, d\theta.$$

Let $\angle XOA = \alpha$, $\angle XOB = \beta$. Let $P(r, \theta)$ be *any* point on the curve. We denote the area of the sector AOP by A so that 'A' is a function of θ.

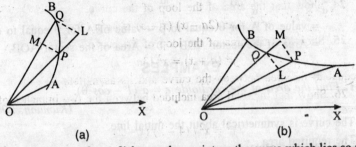

|(a)|(b)|

Let $Q(r + \Delta r, \theta + \Delta \theta)$ be another point on the curve which lies so near P that, as a point on the curve moves from P to Q, the radius vector either constantly increases as in Fig. (*a*), or constantly decreases as in Fig. (*b*). Area POQ is the increment in A consequent to the increment $\Delta \theta$ in θ. We denote it by ΔA.

With O as centre and OP, OQ as radii, draw arcs of circles cutting OQ and OP at M and L respectively. Clearly ΔA lies between the areas of the circular sectors OPM and OQL.

Area of the circular sector OPM $= \frac{1}{2} r^2 \Delta \theta$, and the area of the circular sector OQL $= \frac{1}{2}(r + \Delta r)^2 \Delta \theta$.

For Fig. (*a*), we have

$$\frac{1}{2} r^2 \Delta \theta < \Delta A < \frac{1}{2}(r + \Delta r)^2 \Delta \theta$$

$$\Rightarrow \quad \frac{1}{2} r^2 < \frac{\Delta A}{\Delta \theta} < \frac{1}{2}(r + \Delta r)^2.$$

Let $Q \to P$ so that $\Delta \theta$ and Δr both tend to zero.

In the limit, we obtain

$$\frac{dA}{d\theta} = \frac{1}{2} r^2.$$

For Fig. (*b*), we have

$$\frac{1}{2}(r + \Delta r)^2 \Delta \theta < \Delta A < \frac{1}{2} r^2 \Delta \theta$$

$$\Rightarrow \quad \frac{1}{2}(r + \Delta r)^2 < \frac{\Delta A}{\Delta \theta} < \frac{1}{2}r^2.$$

In this case also, we have

$$\frac{dA}{d\theta} = \frac{1}{2}r^2.$$

Now,

$$\int_\alpha^\beta \frac{1}{2}r^2 \, d\theta = \int_\alpha^\beta \frac{dA}{d\theta} \cdot d\theta = \left| A \right|_\alpha^\beta$$

= value of A for θ equal to β – value of A for θ equal to α

= Area of the sector AOB – 0 = Area of the sector AOB.

EXAMPLES

1. *Find the area of the cardioide* $r = a \, (1 - \cos \theta)$.

(Kumaon, 2002)

The curve is symmetrical about the initial line.

The required area

$$= 2 \int_0^\pi \frac{1}{2}r^2 \, d\theta$$

$$= a^2 \int_0^\pi (1 - \cos \theta)^2 \, d\theta$$

$$= 4a^2 \int_0^\pi \sin^4 \frac{\theta}{2} \, d\theta$$

$$= 8a^2 \int_0^{\pi/2} \sin^4 \varphi \, d\varphi, \text{ where } \frac{\theta}{2} = \varphi$$

$$= 8a^2 \frac{3}{4} \cdot \frac{1}{2} \cdot \frac{\pi}{2} = \frac{3a^2\pi}{2}.$$

2. *Find the area of a loop of the curve* $r^2 = a^2 \cos 2\theta$.

(Rohilkhand, 1997, 98, 2002)

The curve is $r^2 = a^2 \cos 2\theta$.

The values of θ, $\theta = \dfrac{-\pi}{4}$ and $\theta = \dfrac{\pi}{4}$ make $r = 0$.

Also the curve is symmetrical about the initial line.

The required area of one loop

$$= 2 \cdot \frac{1}{2} \int_0^{\pi/4} r^2 \, d\theta$$

$$= a^2 \int_0^{\pi/4} \cos 2\theta \, d\theta = \frac{a^2}{2} \left[\sin 2\theta\right]_0^{\pi/4}$$

$$= \frac{a^2}{2}.$$

3. *Find the area of one loop of the curve* $r = \sqrt{3} \cos 3\theta + \sin 3\theta$.

The equation of the curve is $r = \sqrt{3} \cos 3\theta + \sin 3\theta$

$$= 2 \left[\left(\frac{\sqrt{3}}{2}\right) \cos 3\theta + \frac{1}{2} \sin 3\theta \right]$$

$$= 2 \left[\cos \frac{\pi}{6} \cos 3\theta + \sin \frac{\pi}{6} \sin 3\theta \right]$$

$$= 2 \cos \left(3\theta - \frac{\pi}{6} \right) = 2 \cos 3 \left(\theta - \frac{\pi}{18} \right).$$

Turn the initial line through an angle $\frac{1}{18} \pi$ and putting θ as $\theta + \frac{1}{18} \pi$, the above equation reduces to $r = 2 \cos 3\theta$ and the tracing of this curve is as in figure.

Also for $r = 2 \cos 3\theta$, when $r = 0$,

we get $\cos 3\theta = 0$ or $3\theta = \pm \frac{\pi}{2}$ or

$\theta = \pm \frac{\pi}{6}$ and there is also symmetry about the initial line.

$\theta = \pi/18$

∴ Required area

$$= 2 \times \frac{1}{2} \int_0^{\pi/6} r^2 \, d\theta = 4 \int_0^{\pi/6} \cos^2 3\theta \, d\theta, \text{ as } r = 2 \cos 3\theta$$

$$= \frac{4}{3} \int_0^{\pi/6} \cos^2 \phi \, d\phi, \qquad\qquad \text{putting } 3\theta = \phi$$

$$= \frac{4}{3} \frac{\Gamma\left(\frac{3}{2}\right) \cdot \Gamma\left(\frac{1}{2}\right)}{2\Gamma 2} = \frac{1}{3} \pi.$$

4. *Prove that the sum of the areas of two loops of the limacon* $r = a + b \cos \theta$, $b < a$, *is equal to* $\frac{1}{2} \pi (2a^2 + b^2)$.

Let $\theta = \alpha$, when $r = 0$.

$$\therefore \quad \alpha = \cos^{-1}\left(-\frac{a}{b}\right)$$

which can be determined by putting $r = 0$ in $r = a + b \cos \theta$.

$\therefore$ The required area

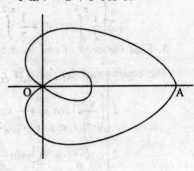

$$= 2\left[\frac{1}{2}\int_0^\alpha r^2 \, d\theta + \frac{1}{2}\int_\alpha^\pi r^2 \, d\theta\right]$$

$$= \int_0^\alpha (a + b \cos \theta)^2 \, d\theta$$

$$\qquad + \int_\alpha^\pi (a + b \cos \theta)^2 \, d\theta$$

$$= \int_0^\pi (a + b \cos \theta)^2 \, d\theta$$

$$= \int_0^\pi (a^2 + b^2 \cos^2 \theta + 2ab \cos \theta) \, d\theta$$

$$= 2a^2 \int_0^\pi d\theta + 2b^2 \int_0^\pi \cos^2 \theta \, d\theta$$

$$= \pi a^2 + 2b^2 \cdot \frac{\Gamma\left(\frac{3}{2}\right) \cdot \Gamma\left(\frac{1}{2}\right)}{2\Gamma 2} = \pi a^2 + 2b^2 \frac{\pi}{4}$$

$$= \frac{\pi}{2}(2a^2 + b^2).$$

5. *Find the area common to the circles* $r = a\sqrt{2}$ *and* $r = 2a \cos \theta$.

         (*Garhwal, 1999; Vikram, 1999; Rewa, 1999; Rohilkhand, 1999*)

The given curves are

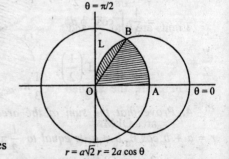

$$r = a\sqrt{2} \qquad ...(i)$$
$$r = 2a \cos \theta \qquad ...(ii)$$

From (i) and (ii)

$$a\sqrt{2} = 2a \cos \theta$$

$$\cos \theta = \frac{1}{\sqrt{2}}, \text{ or } \theta = \frac{\pi}{4}.$$

The point of intersection gives

$$\theta = \frac{\pi}{4}.$$

∴ The required area

$$= 2ABLO$$

$$= 2 \ (\text{area } ABO + \text{area } OBL)$$

$$= 2 \left[\frac{1}{2} \int\limits_{0}^{\pi/4} r_1^2 \, d\theta + \frac{1}{2} \int\limits_{\pi/4}^{\pi/2} r_2^2 \, d\theta \right]$$

$$= \int\limits_{0}^{\pi/4} 2a^2 \, d\theta + \int\limits_{\pi/4}^{\pi/2} 4a^2 \cos^2 \theta \, d\theta$$

$$= 2a^2 \int\limits_{0}^{\pi/4} d\theta + \int\limits_{\pi/4}^{\pi/2} 2 \cos^2 \theta \, d\theta$$

$$= 2a^2 \frac{\pi}{4} + 2a^2 \int\limits_{\pi/4}^{\pi/2} d\theta + 2a^2 \int\limits_{\pi/4}^{\pi/2} \cos \theta \, d\theta$$

$$= \frac{\pi a^2}{2} + 2a^2 \left[\theta \right]_{\pi/4}^{\pi/2} + 2a^2 \left[\frac{\sin 2\theta}{2} \right]_{\pi/4}^{\pi/2}$$

$$= \frac{\pi a^2}{2} + 2a^2 \left(\frac{\pi}{2} - \frac{\pi}{4} \right) + \frac{2a^2}{2} \left(\sin \pi - \sin \frac{\pi}{2} \right)$$

$$= \frac{\pi a^2}{2} + \frac{\pi a^2}{2} - a^2 = a^2 \ (\pi - 1).$$

6. *Find the ratio of the two parts into which the parabola $2a = r \ (1 + \cos \theta)$ divides the area of the cardioid $r = 2a \ (1 + \cos \theta)$.*

Solving the given equations $2a = r \ (1 + \cos \theta)$ and $r = 2a \ (1 + \cos \theta)$, we have

$$(1 + \cos \theta)^2 = 1$$

∴

$$\cos \theta = 0$$

or

$$\theta = \frac{\pi}{2}.$$

Limits are 0 to $\frac{\pi}{2}$ and $\frac{\pi}{2}$ to π.

Therefore the shaded area

$$= \text{area } OLMN$$

$$= 2 \times \text{area } OMNO$$

$$= 2 \ (\text{area } OMN + \text{area } ONO)$$

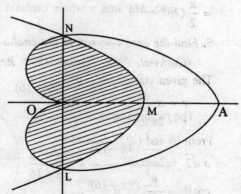

$$= 2\left[\frac{1}{2}\int_0^{\pi/2}\frac{2a}{(1+\cos\theta)^2}\,d\theta + \frac{1}{2}\int_{\pi/2}^{\pi}(1+\cos\theta)^2\,d\theta\right]$$

$$= a^2\int_0^{\pi/2}\sec\frac{4\theta}{2}\,d\theta + 4a^2\int_{\pi/2}^{\pi}(1+\cos^2\theta + 2\cos\theta)\,d\theta$$

$$= a^2\int_0^{\pi/2}\sec^3\frac{\theta}{2}\,d\theta + 4a^2\int_0^{\pi/2}(1-2\cos t + \cos^2 t)\,dt$$

By putting $\theta = \dfrac{\pi}{2}+t$ in the second integral.

$$= 2a^2\int_0^{\pi/4}\sec^4 u\,du + 4a^2\int_0^{\pi/2}(1-2\cos t + \cos^2 t)\,dt$$

By putting $\dfrac{\theta}{2}=u$ in the first integral.

$$= 2a^2 + 2a^2\left[\frac{\tan^3 u}{3}\right]_0^{\pi/4} + 4a^2\cdot\frac{\pi}{2} - 8a^2 + 4a^2\cdot\frac{\Gamma\left(\dfrac{3}{2}\right)\cdot\Gamma\left(\dfrac{1}{2}\right)}{2\cdot\Gamma 2}$$

$$= \frac{8a^2}{3} + 2\pi a^2 - 8a^2 + \pi a^2$$

$$= 3\pi a^2 - \frac{16a^2}{3}.$$

And,

unshaded area = whole cardioid − shaded area

$$= 6\pi a^2 - \left(3\pi a^2 - \frac{16a^2}{3}\right)$$

$$= \frac{a^2}{3}(9\pi + 16).$$

∴ The required ratio

$$= \frac{\dfrac{a^2}{3}(9\pi - 16)}{\dfrac{a^2}{3}(9\pi + 16)} = \frac{9\pi - 16}{9\pi + 16}.$$

7. *Find the area of the loop of the curve*
$$x^5 + y^5 = 5ax^2y^2.$$

The area of the loop is that of a sectorial area bounded by the curve
and the radii vectors $\theta = 0$, $\theta = \pi / 2$.
In fact the area of the loop is swept
out as the radius vector moves from

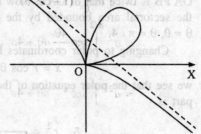

$$\theta = 0 \text{ to } \theta = \pi / 2.$$

The polar equation of the curve
is

$$r = \frac{5a \cos^2 \theta \sin^2 \theta}{\cos^5 \theta + \sin^5 \theta}.$$

Thus the area of the loop

$$= \frac{1}{2} \int_0^{\pi/2} \frac{25a^2 \cos^4 \theta \sin^4 \theta}{(\cos^5 \theta + \sin^5 \theta)^2} \, d\theta$$

(Dividing the numerator and denominator by $\cos^{10} \theta$)

$$= \frac{25a^2}{2} \int_0^{\pi/2} \frac{\tan^4 \theta \sec^2 \theta \, d\theta}{(1 + \tan^5 \theta)^2}$$

$$= \frac{25a^2}{2} \int_1^\infty \frac{1}{5} \cdot \frac{dt}{t^2}, \text{ where } 1 + \tan^5 \theta = t,$$

$$= \frac{5a^2}{2} \left| -\frac{1}{t} \right|_1^\infty = \frac{5a^2}{2}.$$

8. *Find the area between the ellipses*

$$x^2 + 2y^2 = a^2, \ 2x^2 + y^2 = a^2.$$

Rewriting the given equations as

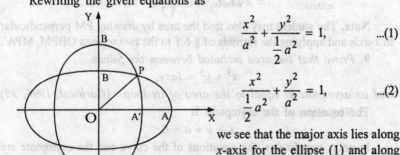

$$\frac{x^2}{a^2} + \frac{y^2}{\frac{1}{2}a^2} = 1, \qquad \ldots(1)$$

$$\frac{x^2}{\frac{1}{2}a^2} + \frac{y^2}{a^2} = 1, \qquad \ldots(2)$$

we see that the major axis lies along
x-axis for the ellipse (1) and along
y-axis for the ellipse (2).

Also the required area is four times the area OA'PB where P is a point
of intersection. Solving the two equations (1) and (2), we see that P is the
point $(a/\sqrt{3}, a/\sqrt{3})$.

Thus $\angle$ XOP $= \pi / 4$ and the equation of the line OP is $y = x$.

If we interchange x and y, we see that the equation of one ellipse is transformed into that of the other and accordingly the area of the region OA′PB is twice that of OA′P. Now the area of OA′P can be thought of as the sectorial area bounded by the curve A′P and the two radii vectors $\theta = 0, \theta = \pi / 4$.

Changing to polar coordinates by writing
$$x = r \cos \theta, \quad y = r \sin \theta,$$
we see that the polar equation of the ellipse (2) of which the arc A′P is a part is
$$r^2 = \frac{a^2}{2 \cos^2 \theta + \sin^2 \theta},$$

$\therefore$ area OA′P $= \dfrac{1}{2} \displaystyle\int_0^{\pi/4} \dfrac{a^2}{2 \cos^2 \theta + \sin^2 \theta} \, d\theta$

$= \dfrac{1}{2} \displaystyle\int_0^{\pi/4} \dfrac{a^2 \sec^2 \theta}{2 + \tan^2 \theta} \, d\theta$

$= \dfrac{1}{2} \displaystyle\int_0^1 \dfrac{a^2 \, dt}{2 + t^2}$, where $t = \tan \theta$

$= \dfrac{a^2}{2} \cdot \dfrac{1}{\sqrt{2}} \left| \tan^{-1} \dfrac{t}{\sqrt{2}} \right|_0^1 = \dfrac{a^2}{2\sqrt{2}} \tan^{-1} \dfrac{1}{\sqrt{2}}$.

$\therefore$ Required area $= 8 \times \dfrac{a^2}{2\sqrt{2}} \tan^{-1} \dfrac{1}{\sqrt{2}}$

$= 2\sqrt{2} \, a^2 \sin^{-1} \sqrt{\dfrac{1}{3}}$.

Note. The student may also find the area by drawing PM perpendicular to x-axis and applying the formula of § 6.1 to the two regions OBPM, MPA′.

9. *Prove that the area included between the folium*
$$x^3 + y^3 = 3axy,$$
and its asymptote is equal to the area of its loop. (*Garhwal, 1996, 98*)

The equation of the asymptote is
$$x + y + a = 0.$$

In polar coordinates, the equations of the curve and the asymptote are
$$r = \frac{3a \sin \theta \cos \theta}{\sin^3 \theta + \cos^3 \theta},$$
and
$$r = \frac{a}{\sin \theta + \cos \theta},$$
respectively.

The area of the loop

$$= \frac{1}{2} \int_0^{\pi/2} \frac{9a^2 \sin^2 \theta \cos^2 \theta}{(\sin^3 \theta + \cos^3 \theta)^2} d\theta$$

(Dividing numerator and
denominator by $\cos^6 \theta$.)

$$= \frac{9}{2} a^2 \int_0^{\pi/2} \frac{\tan^2 \theta \sec^2 \theta}{(1 + \tan^3 \theta)^2} d\theta$$

$$= \frac{3a^2}{2} \int_0^{\infty} \frac{dt}{t^2}, \text{ where } 1 + \tan^3 \theta = t$$

$$= \frac{3a^2}{2} - \frac{1}{t} \Big|_1^{\infty} = \frac{3a^2}{2}.$$

We shall now find the area between the curve and its asymptote.

The line (shown dotted), drawn parallel to the asymptote makes an angle $3\pi / 4$ with OX.

We draw a line through O whose vectorial angle θ lies between $3\pi / 4$ and π. Let it cut the curve and the asymptote in P and Q respectively.

We shall first find the area between the curve and its asymptote lying in the second quadrant.

This area is the limit of the area of the curvilinear region OBPQAO as the line OP starting from OA moves towards the dotted line.

The area of the $\triangle OAQ = \frac{1}{2} \int_0^{\pi} r^2 d\theta$

$$= \frac{1}{2} \int_0^{\pi} \frac{a^2}{(\sin \theta + \cos \theta)^2} d\theta.$$

The area of the region bounded by the curve and the line OP

$$= \frac{1}{2} \int_0^{\pi} \frac{9a^2 \sin^2 \theta \cos^2 \theta}{(\sin^3 \theta + \cos^3 \theta)^2} d\theta.$$

Thus the curvilinear area OBQPAO

$$= \frac{1}{2} \int_0^{\pi} \left[\frac{a^2}{(\sin \theta + \cos \theta)^2} - \frac{9a^2 \sin^2 \theta \cos^2 \theta}{(\sin^3 \theta + \cos^3 \theta)^2} \right] d\theta.$$

Now, $\int \frac{\sin^2 \theta \cos^2 \theta}{(\sin^3 \theta + \cos^3 \theta)^2} d\theta = \int \frac{\tan^2 \theta \sec^2 \theta}{(1 + \tan^3 \theta)^2} d\theta$

$$= \int \frac{dt}{3t^2}, \text{ where } t = 1 + \tan^3 \theta$$

$$= -\frac{1}{3t} = -\frac{1}{3(1 + \tan^3 \theta)}.$$

Also, $\displaystyle\int \frac{1}{(\sin \theta + \cos \theta)^2} d\theta = \int \frac{\sec^2 \theta}{(1 + \tan \theta)^2} d\theta$

$$= \int \frac{dt}{t^2}, \text{ where } t = 1 + \tan \theta$$

$$= -\frac{1}{t} = -\frac{1}{1 + \tan \theta}.$$

The curvilinear area OBQPAO

$$= \frac{a^2}{2} \left| -\frac{1}{1 + \tan \theta} + \frac{3}{1 + \tan^3 \theta} \right|_0^\pi$$

$$= \frac{a^2}{2} \left[2 - \left(-\frac{1}{1 + \tan \theta} + \frac{3}{1 + \tan^3 \theta} \right) \right].$$

We have to find its limit as $\theta \to 3\pi / 4$.

Now, $\dfrac{1}{1 + \tan \theta} - \dfrac{3}{1 + \tan^3 \theta} = \dfrac{\tan^2 \theta - \tan \theta - 2}{1 + \tan^3 \theta}$

$$= \frac{(\tan \theta + 1)(\tan \theta - 2)}{(\tan \theta + 1)(\tan^2 \theta - \tan \theta + 1)}$$

$$= \frac{\tan \theta - 2}{\tan^2 \theta - \tan \theta + 1},$$

which $\to -1$ as $\theta \to 3\pi / 4 \Rightarrow \tan \theta \to -1$.

Hence the area $= (a^2 / 2)(2 - 1) = a^2 / 2$.

Because of symmetry about the line $y = x$, $a^2 / 2$ is also the area between the curve and the asymptote lying in the fourth quadrant. Also the area in the third quadrant, being that of a triangle, is $a^2 / 2$.

Thus the area between the curve and its asymptote

$$= \frac{1}{2} a^2 + \frac{1}{2} a^2 + \frac{1}{2} a^2 = \frac{3}{2} a^2.$$

Hence the result.

10. *Find the area of loop of the curve*

$$x^4 + 3x^2 y^2 + 2y^4 = a^2 x.$$

The curve is symmetrical in opposite quadrants and the two axes $x = 0$, $y = 0$ are the two tangents at the origin. The curve has no asymptote.

Transforming to polar coordinates, we get

$$r^2 = \frac{a^2 \cos\theta \sin\theta}{\cos^4\theta + 3\cos^2\theta \sin^2\theta + 2\sin^4\theta}.$$

As θ varies from 0 to $\pi/2$, the point (r, θ) on the curve describes the loop OAPBO.

Thus the area of the loop

$$= \frac{1}{2}\int_0^{\pi/2} r^2\, d\theta$$

$$= \frac{a^2}{2}\int_0^{\pi/2} \frac{\sin\theta \cos\theta}{\cos^4\theta + 3\cos^2\theta \sin^2\theta + 2\sin^4\theta}\, d\theta$$

(Dividing the numerator and denominator of the integrand by $\cos^4\theta$)

$$= \frac{a^2}{2}\int_0^{\pi/2} \frac{\tan\theta \sec^2\theta\, d\theta}{1 + 3\tan^2\theta + 2\tan^4\theta}.$$

Putting $\tan^2\theta = t$, we see that the required area

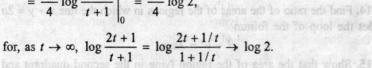

$$= \frac{a^2}{4}\int_0^\infty \frac{dt}{1 + 3t + 2t^2}$$

$$= \frac{a^2}{4}\int_0^\infty \frac{dt}{(2t+1)(t+1)}$$

$$= \frac{a^2}{4}\int_0^\infty \left(-\frac{1}{t+1} + \frac{2}{2t+1}\right) dt$$

$$= \frac{a^2}{4}\log \frac{2t+1}{t+1}\Big|_0^\infty = \frac{a^2}{4}\log 2,$$

for, as $t \to \infty$, $\log\dfrac{2t+1}{t+1} = \log\dfrac{2t+1/t}{1+1/t} \to \log 2$.

EXERCISES

1. Find the area of a loop of the curve $r = a \sin 2\theta$.

2. Find the area of a loop of the curve $r = a \sin 3\theta$. *(Indore, 1996)*

3. Find the area of the cardioid $r = a (1 + \cos\theta)$.

(Sagar, 1994; Agra, 2001)

4. Prove that the area of the loop of the folium
$$x^3 + y^3 = 3axy$$
is three times the area of one of the loops of the lemniscate
$$r^2 = a^2 \cos 2\theta.$$

5. Show that the area of the loop of the curve
$$r = a\theta \cos \theta$$
lying in the first quadrant is $a^2\pi (\pi^2 - 6) / 96$.   (*Kumaon, 2003*)

6. Show that the area of the region included between the cardioides
$$r = a (1 + \cos \theta), \; r = a (1 - \cos \theta)$$
is $a^2 (3\pi - 8) / 2$.

7. Show that the area of a loop of the curve
$$r \cos \theta = a \cos 2\theta$$
is $a^2 (4 - \pi) / 2$.

8. Find the area outside the circle $r = 2a \cos \theta$ and inside the cardioid $r = a (1 + \cos \theta)$.   (*Indore, 1997*)

9. Find the area of a loop of the curve
$$x^4 + y^4 = 2a^2xy.$$

10. Find the area bounded by the curve
$$(x^2 + y^2)^2 = a^2x^2 + b^2y^2.$$

11. Prove that the area of a loop of the curve
$$x^6 + y^6 = a^2x^2y^2 \text{ is } \pi a^2 / 12.$$

12. Show that the area of a loop of the curve
$$(x^2 + y^2)^2 - 4axy^2 = 0$$
in the positive quadrant is $\pi a^2 / 4$.

13. Show that the area of the loop of the curve
$$(x + y) (x^2 + y^2) = 2axy$$
is $a^2 (1 - \pi / 4)$; also show that the area of the portion of the curve between the curve and its asymptote is $a^2 (1 + \pi / 4)$.

14. Find the ratio of the areas of the regions in which the line $x + y = 2a$ divides the loop of the folium
$$x^3 + y^3 = 3axy.$$

15. Show that the area of the region lying in the second quadrant and bounded by the curve
$$x^5 + y^5 = 5ax^2y^2,$$
its asymptote and y-axis is a^2.

16. Show that the area common to the circle $r = a$ and the cardioid $r = a (1 + \cos \theta)$ is $\left(\dfrac{5}{4}\pi - 2\right)a^2$.   (*Garhwal, 1998*)

17. Show that the ratio of the area of the larger loop to the area of the smaller loop of the curve

$$r = \frac{1}{2} + \cos 2\theta$$

is $(4\pi + 3\sqrt{3})/(2\pi - 3\sqrt{3})$.

18. Show that the area of the region enclosed between the two loops of the curve

$$r = a (1 + 2 \cos \theta)$$

is $a^2 (\pi + 3\sqrt{3})$.

19. Find the area of the ellipse $l/r = 1 + e \cos \theta$.

20. Show that the area of the loop of the curve

$$r^2 \cos \theta = a^2 \sin 3\theta,$$

lying in the first quadrant is

$$\frac{1}{4} a^2 \log (e^3/4).$$

21. Trace the curve

$$r = a\theta/(\theta + 1),$$

as θ increases from 0 to 2π and show that the area of the region included between the curve and the initial line is

$$\frac{1}{2} a^2 [2\pi - (2\pi + 1)^{-1} - 2 \log (2\pi + 1) + 1].$$

22. Find the area lying between the cardioide

$$r = a (1 - \cos \theta),$$

and its double tangent $x = a/4$.

ANSWERS

1. $\pi a^2/8$.   **2.** $\pi a^2/12$.   **3.** $3\pi a^2/2$.

8. $\pi a^2/2$.   **9.** $\pi a^2/4$.   **10.** $\pi (a^2 + b^2)/2$.

14. $2:1$.   **19.** $\pi l^2/(1 - e^2)^{3/2}$.   **22.** $a^2 \left[\dfrac{15}{16}\sqrt{3} - \dfrac{\pi}{2} \right]$.

8.4. Area bounded by a closed curve. We know that the definite integral

$$\int_a^b y \, dx$$

gives the area of the region which is bounded by the curve $y = f(x)$, the axis of x, and the two ordinates $x = a$, $x = b$. A region, which is not so bounded, has to be first expressed as a combination of regions each of which is bounded in this manner and the area of the given region is then, equal to the sum of the areas of the component regions. Similar limitations hold for the integrals

$$\int_c^d x \, dy, \quad \frac{1}{2} \int_\alpha^\beta r^2 \, d\theta.$$

We now consider a formula which gives the area enclosed by any closed curve whatsoever, provided only, that it does not intersect itself; there being no restriction as to the manner in which the curve is situated relative to the coordinate axes.

Consider a closed curve represented by the parametric equations

$$x = f(t), \, y = \varphi(t)$$

't' being the parameter. We suppose that the curve does not intersect itself.

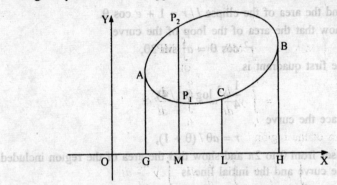

Also suppose that as the parameter 't' increases from a value t_1 to the value t_2, the point P (x, y) describes the curve completely in the counter-clockwise sense. The curve being closed, the point on it corresponding to the value t_2, of the parameter is the same as the point corresponding to the value t_1 of the parameter. Let this point be C.

It will now be shown that the area of the region bounded by such a curve is

$$\frac{1}{2} \int_{t_1}^{t_2} \left(x \frac{dy}{dt} - y \frac{dx}{dt} \right) dt.$$

Let the points on the curve with greatest and least abscissae be A, B.

We suppose that the curve is such that every line parallel to y-axis and lying between the ordinates $x = a$, $x = b$ of the points A, B, meets it in two and only two points P_1 and P_2; P_1 lying on the arc ACB and P_2 on the arc BP_2A.

The area of the region = Area AGHBP$_2$AG – Area AGHBCAG

$$= \int_a^b MP_2 \, dx - \int_a^b MP_1 \, dx$$

$$= -\int_b^a MP_2 \, dx - \int_a^b MP_1 \, dx.$$

We now express these integrals in terms of the variable t.

Let t_a, t_b denote the values of the parameter t for the points A, B.

As P (x, y) moves along the arc BP_2A from B to A, the parameter t increases from t_b to t_a.

As P (x, y) moves along the arc AC from A to C, the parameter t increases from t_a to t_2.

As P (x, y) moves along the arc CB from C to B, the parameter t increases from t_1 to t_b.

$$\therefore \quad \int_b^a MP_2 \, dx = \int_{t_b}^{t_a} y \frac{dx}{dt} \, dt,$$

and

$$\int_a^b MP_1 \, dx = \int_a^{OL} MP_1 \, dx + \int_{OL}^b MP_1 \, dx$$

$$= \int_{t_a}^{t_2} y \frac{dx}{dt} \, dt + \int_{t_1}^{t_b} y \frac{dx}{dt} \, dt.$$

$\therefore$ area of the region

$$= -\int_{t_b}^{t_a} y \frac{dx}{dt} \, dt - \int_{t_a}^{t_2} y \frac{dx}{dt} \, dt - \int_{t_1}^{t_b} y \frac{dx}{dt} \, dt$$

$$= -\int_{t_1}^{t_b} y \frac{dx}{dt} \, dt - \int_{t_b}^{t_a} y \frac{dx}{dt} \, dt - \int_{t_a}^{t_2} y \frac{dx}{dt} \, dt$$

$$= -\int_{t_1}^{t_2} y \frac{dx}{dt} \, dt. \qquad \qquad ...(i)$$

It can similarly be shown that the area of the same region is also equal to

$$\int_{t_1}^{t_2} x \frac{dy}{dt} \, dt. \qquad \qquad ...(ii)$$

Adding the two expressions, we see that the area of the region is equal to

$$\frac{1}{2} \int_{t_1}^{t_2} \left(x \frac{dy}{dt} - y \frac{dx}{dt} \right) dt. \qquad \qquad ...(iii)$$

The result also holds for the curve which is met by the lines parallel to either axis in more than two points but the details of this extension will not be given here.

Note 1. Because of symmetry, the expression (*iii*) proves convenient in practice than the expressions (*i*) and (*ii*).

Note 2. Suppose that the curve intersects itself once as shown in the figure alongside.

Let *t* vary from t_1 to t_1' as P (*x, y*) moves along the curve OAB from O back to O. Also, let *t* vary from t_1' to t_2 as P (*x, y*) moves along the curve OCD from O back to O.

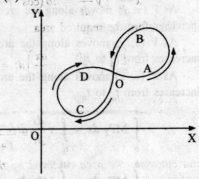

The arc OABO is described in the counter-clockwise but the arc OCD in the clockwise sense.

$$\text{The area of the loop OABO} = \frac{1}{2} \int\limits_{t_1}^{t_1'} \left(x \frac{dy}{dt} - y \frac{dx}{dt} \right) dt.$$

$$\text{The area of the loop OCDO} = -\frac{1}{2} \int\limits_{t_1'}^{t_2} \left(x \frac{dy}{dt} - y \frac{dx}{dt} \right) dt.$$

$$\text{Area OABO} - \text{Area OCDO} = \frac{1}{2} \int\limits_{t_1}^{t_2} \left(x \frac{dy}{dt} - y \frac{dx}{dt} \right) dt,$$

so that the formula gives the difference of the areas of the two loops and not their sum.

In order to find the whole area, we have to find each area separately and then to obtain their sum.

Note 3. The definite integral

$$\frac{1}{2} \int \left(x \frac{dy}{dt} - y \frac{dx}{dt} \right) dt$$

is sometimes briefly written as

$$\frac{1}{2} \int (x \, dy - y \, dx).$$

EXAMPLES

1. *Find the area of the ellipse*

$$x = a \cos t, \, y = b \sin t.$$

The ellipse is a closed curve and is completely described while *t* varies from 0 to 2π.

We have

$$x\frac{dy}{dt} - y\frac{dx}{dt} = ab(\cos^2 t + \sin^2 t) = ab.$$

Therefore the required area

$$= \frac{1}{2}\int_0^{2\pi}\left(x\frac{dy}{dt} - y\frac{dx}{dt}\right)dt = \frac{1}{2}\int_0^{2\pi} ab\,dt = \pi ab.$$

2. *Sketch the curve*

$$x = \frac{1-t^2}{1+t^2},\ y = \frac{t-t^3}{1+t^2}\ (-1 \le t \le 1)$$

and calculate the area enclosed by the loop of the curve.

The curve can be traced on eliminating t. We shall, however, *directly trace the part of the curve which is described when t varies from -1 to $+1$.

We have

$$\frac{dx}{dt} = -\frac{4t}{(1-t^2)^2},\ \frac{dy}{dt} = -\frac{t^4 + 4t^2 - 1}{(t^2+1)^2}.$$

t is negative $\Rightarrow$ dx/dt is positive;

t is positive $\Rightarrow$ dx/dt is negative.

Thus we see that

t increases from -1 to 0 $\Rightarrow$ x increases;

t increases from 0 to 1 $\Rightarrow$ x decreases.

To examine the change of sign in dy/dt, we consider the equation

$$t^4 + 4t^2 - 1 = 0$$

which gives

$$t^2 = \sqrt{5} - 2,\ -\sqrt{5} - 2.$$

Thus $(t^4 + 4t^2 - 1) = [t^2 - (\sqrt{5} - 2)][t^2 - (-\sqrt{5} - 2)]$

$$= [t^2 - (\sqrt{5} - 2)][t^2 + (\sqrt{5} + 2)].$$

Also $t^2 = \sqrt{5} - 2$ gives

$$t = \pm\sqrt{\sqrt{5} - 2} = \pm.4\ .....$$

We, therefore, have

$$\frac{dy}{dt} = -\frac{(t^2 + \sqrt{5} + 2)(t + .4\ .....)(t - .4\ .....)}{(t^2+1)^2}$$

---

* This method proves useful for drawing curves whose parametric equations are given. In particular, Cycloid and Astroid may be easily traced in this manner.

Thus

t varies from -1 to $-.4$ ... $\Rightarrow$ dy/dt is negative;

t varies from $-.4$ ... to $.4$ ... $\Rightarrow$ dy/dt is positive;

t varies from $.4$ ... to 1 $\Rightarrow$ dy/dt is negative.

Hence

t increases from -1 to $-.4$ ... $\Rightarrow$ $dy/dt < 0$ $\Rightarrow$ y decreases;

t increases from $-.4$ ... to $.4$ ... $\Rightarrow$ $dy/dt > 0$ $\Rightarrow$ y increases;

t increases from $.4$ ... to 1 $\Rightarrow$ $dy/dt < 0$ $\Rightarrow$ y decreases.

Also

$$t = -1 \quad \Rightarrow \quad x = 0, y = 0, dy/dx = -1;$$
$$t = +1 \quad \Rightarrow \quad x = 0, y = 0, dy/dx = 1.$$

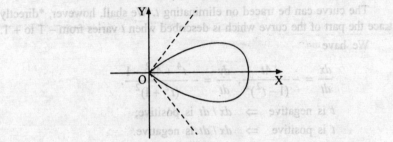

Hence we have the loop as traced.

$$x\frac{dy}{dt} - y\frac{dx}{dt} = \frac{1 - t^2 - t^4 + t^6}{(1+t^2)^3} = \frac{(1+t^2)(1-t^2)^2}{(1+t^2)^3} = \frac{(1-t^2)^2}{(1+t^2)^2}.$$

The required area

$$= \frac{1}{2} \int_{-1}^{1} \left(x\frac{dy}{dt} - y\frac{dx}{dt} \right) dt$$

$$= \frac{1}{2} \int_{-1}^{1} \frac{(1-t^2)^2}{(1+t^2)^2}\, dt.$$

Now, $\dfrac{(1-t^2)^2}{(1+t^2)^2} = 1 - \dfrac{4t^2}{(1+t^2)^2}$

$$= 1 - \frac{4(t^2+1-1)}{(t^2+1)^2} = 1 - \frac{4}{t^2+1} + \frac{4}{(t^2+1)^2}.$$

The required area

$$= \frac{1}{2} \int_{-1}^{1} 1 \cdot dt - 2 \int_{-1}^{1} \frac{dt}{t^2+1} + 2 \int_{-1}^{1} \frac{dt}{(t^2+1)^2}$$

$$= 1 - \pi + 2 \int\limits_{-1}^{1} \frac{dt}{(t^2 + 1)^2}.$$

To evaluate the integral on the right, we put

$$t = \tan \theta.$$

$$\therefore \quad \int\limits_{-1}^{1} \frac{dt}{(1 + t^2)^2} = \int\limits_{-\pi/4}^{\pi/4} \cos 2\theta \, d\theta$$

$$= \frac{1}{2} \int\limits_{-\pi/4}^{\pi/4} (1 + \cos 2\theta) \, d\theta$$

$$= \frac{1}{2} \left| \theta + \sin \theta \cos \theta \right|_{-\pi/4}^{\pi/4} = \frac{1}{2} \left(\frac{1}{2} \pi + 1 \right).$$

$$\therefore \quad \text{area} = 1 - \pi + \left(\frac{1}{2} \pi + 1 \right) = 2 - \frac{1}{2} \pi.$$

Note. On eliminating t from the given parametric equations, we obtain $x (x^2 + y^2) = x^2 - y^2$ as the implicit cartesian equation of the given curve. The curve may also be easily traced with the help of this form of the equation. (Refer Figure of Example 5, page 301.)

EXERCISES

1. Sketch the curve

$$x = a (1 - t^2), \ y = at (1 - t^2), \ -1 \le t \le 1,$$

and show that the area of the loop obtained is $8a^2 / 15$.

2. Trace the curve

$$x = t - t^3, \ y = 1 - t^4$$

for all values of t and prove that it forms a loop of area $16 / 35$.

3. Show that the curve

$$x = (t - 1) \, e^{-t}, \ y = tx$$

has a loop and find its area.

4. Find the area enclosed by the curve

$$x = a \cos^3 t, \ y = b \sin^3 t.$$

5. Sketch the curve

$$x = a \sin 2t, \ y = a \sin t$$

and find the area of one of its loops.

6. Find the area enclosed by the curve

$$x = a \cos t + b \sin t + c,$$
$$y = a' \cos t + b' \sin t + c'.$$

7. Trace the curve
$$x = a\,(3\cos\theta - \cos^3\theta),\ y = a\,(3\sin\theta - \sin^3\theta)$$
and find the area enclosed by it.

8. Find the area of the curve
$$x = a\,(3\sin\theta - \sin^3\theta),\ y = a\cos^3\theta.$$

9. Show that the area enclosed by the curve
$$x = a\sin 2\theta\,(1 + \cos 2\theta),$$
$$y = a\cos 2\theta\,(1 - \cos 2\theta),$$

is $\dfrac{1}{2}a^2\pi$.

10. Trace the curve
$$x = a\left(\sin\theta + \frac{1}{3}\sin 3\theta\right),$$
$$y = a\left(\cos\theta - \frac{1}{3}\cos 3\theta\right),$$

and show that its area is $\dfrac{2}{3}a^2\pi$.

ANSWERS

3. $1/e$.   **4.** $3\pi ab/8$.   **5.** $4a^2/3$.

6. $\pi\,(ab' - a'b)$.   **7.** $39a^2\pi/8$.   **8.** $15a^2\pi/8$.

8.5. Simpson's rule for approximate evaluation of definite integrals and areas. The method given above of finding an area requires

(*i*) that we know the equation $y = f(x)$ of the curve; and

(*ii*) that it is possible to determine a function whose derivative is the given function $f(x)$, *i.e.*, it is possible to find the indefinite integral of the given function.

In mechanical work, a curve is often plotted from a finite number of isolated observations so that we do not know its equation. Moreover, even if the equation of a curve be known, it is not always possible to find the indefinite integral required.

For example, let the value of $\displaystyle\int_0^{\pi/2}\sqrt{\sin x}\ dx$ be required.

As we cannot find the indefinite integral of $\sqrt{\sin x}$ in terms of elementary functions we, therefore, cannot find the exact value of the definite integral. But by Simpson's and other similar rules, it is possible to calculate approximately its value.

Simpson's rule only will be considered here.

Lemma. Consider the parabola

$$y = l + mx + nx^2,$$

and three points P_1, P_2, P_3 on it such that the ordinates P_1A_1 and P_3A_3 of P_1 and P_3 are equidistant from the ordinate P_2A_2 of P_2.

Let $A_1A_2 = A_2A_3 = h$.

Also, let $OA_2 = a$ so that $OA_1 = a - h$, $OA_3 = a + h$.

Area of the region $P_1A_1A_3P_3P_1$

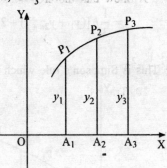

$$= \int_{a-h}^{a+h} (l + mx + nx^2)\, dx$$

$$= \left| lx + \frac{m}{2}x^2 + \frac{n}{3}x^3 \right|_{a-h}^{a+h}$$

$$= 2h\left(l + ma + na^2 + \frac{1}{3}nh^2\right) \quad ...(i)$$

We express this area in terms of the ordinates y_1, y_2, y_3 of the points P_1, P_2, P_3.

We have

$$y_1 = P_1A_1 = l + m(a - h) + n(a - h)^2, \qquad ...(ii)$$
$$y_2 = P_2A_2 = l + ma + na^2, \qquad ...(iii)$$
$$y_3 = P_3A_3 = l + m(a + h) + n(a + h)^2. \qquad ...(iv)$$

$$\therefore \quad y_1 + y_3 = 2(l + ma + na^2 + nh^2) = 2(y_2 + nh^2),$$

$$\Rightarrow \quad \frac{y_1 + y_3 - 2y_2}{2} = nh^2 \qquad ...(v)$$

From (i), (iii) and (v), we see that the area of the region is

$$2h\left[y_2 + \frac{y_1 + y_3 - 2y_2}{6}\right] = \frac{1}{3}h(y_1 + y_3 + 4y_2).$$

Simpson's rule. Consider the region

$$P_1A_1BP_{2n+1}$$

bounded by a curve $y = f(x)$, X-axis and the two ordinates P_1A and $P_{2n+1}B$.

We divide the interval AB into $2n$ equal parts, n being a sufficiently large positive integer. Let P_1, P_2, P_3, ..., P_{2n+1} be the points on the curve corresponding to the points of division of AB. We replace the arc $P_1P_2P_3$ of the curve by an arc of the parabola through these points. As the points are very close to each other, we can take the area bounded by the arc $P_1P_2P_3$ of the given curve as approximately equal to the area bounded by the parabola through $P_1P_2P_3$. The arcs $P_3P_4P_5$, $P_5P_6P_7$, ..., $P_{2n-1}P_{2n}P_{2n+1}$, are to be similarly replaced by arcs of parabolas.

Applying the result of the lemma to the areas between the ordinates y_1 and y_3, y_3 and y_5, y_5 and y_7, ..., y_{2n-1} and y_{2n+1} we obtain as an approximate value for the whole area

$$\frac{1}{3} h (y_1 + 4y_2 + y_3) + (y_3 + 4y_4 + y_5) + (y_5 + 4y_6 + y_7)$$

$$+ ..... + (y_{2n-1} + 4y_{2n} + y_{2n+1})]$$

$$= \frac{1}{3} h [(y_1 + y_{2n+1}) + 2 (y_3 + y_5 + ... + y_{2n-1})$$

$$+ 4 (y_2 + y_4 + ... + y_{2n})].$$

This is Simpson's rule which may be stated as follows :

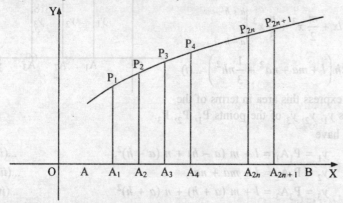

To obtain an approximate value of an area (or of a definite integral), divide it into an even number of strips by drawing equidistant ordinates and multiply one-third of the distance between consecutive ordinates by the sum of

    (i) the first and the last ordinates,

    (ii) twice all the other odd ordinates, and

    (iii) four times all the even ordinates.

EXAMPLES

1. *Obtain an approximate value of, log 2, by calculating the definite integral*

$$\int_1^2 \frac{dx}{x},$$

by Simpson's rule, using eleven ordinates.

We have

$$\int_1^2 \frac{dx}{x} = \log 2.$$

We divide the interval $]1, 2[$ into 10 equal parts.

Let $f(x) = 1/x$. We have

$y_1 = f(1.0) = 1.00000;$ $y_2 = f(1.1) = .90909;$

$y_3 = f(1.2) = .83333;$ $y_4 = f(1.3) = .76923;$

$y_5 = f(1.4) = .71429;$ $y_6 = f(1.5) = .66667;$

$y_7 = f(1.6) = .62500;$ $y_8 = f(1.7) = .58824;$

$y_9 = f(1.8) = .55556;$ $y_{10} = f(1.9) = .52632;$

$y_{11} = f(2.0) = .50000;$

$S_1 =$ Sum of the first and last ordinates $= 1.50000;$

$S_2 =$ Sum of the remaining odd ordinates $= 2.72818;$

$S_3 =$ Sum of the even ordinates $= 3.45955.$

$$\log 2 = \frac{1}{2} \cdot \frac{1}{10} (S_1 + 2S_2 + 4S_3) = \frac{1}{30} (20.79456) = .69315.$$

$\log 2 = .69315.$

Actually, referring to logarithmic tables, we may see that

$\log 2 = .693147.$

2. *Compute* $\int\limits_0^1 \dfrac{tan^{-1} x}{x^{3/2}} \, dx$ *by Simpson's Rule.*

Divide the interval of integration $(0, 1)$ into ten equal parts each of width 0.1. Hence here we have $h = 0.1$. Now find the values of the function $y = (\text{arc tan } x) / x^{3/2} = (\tan^{-1} x) / x^{3/2}$ for each point of subdivision and write them in the following table :

x	$\tan^{-1} x$	$x^{3/2}$	$(\tan^{-1} x) / x^{3/2}$
0.0	0.00000	0.00000	.....
0.1	0.09967	0.03162	$3.15211 = y_1$
0.2	0.19740	0.08944	$2.20707 = y_2$
0.3	0.29146	0.16432	$1.77373 = y_3$
0.4	0.38051	0.25298	$1.50411 = y_4$
0.5	0.46365	0.35355	$0.31141 = y_5$
0.6	0.54042	0.46476	$1.16279 = y_6$
0.7	0.61073	0.58566	$1.04281 = y_7$
0.8	0.67474	0.71554	$0.94298 = y_8$
0.9	0.73282	0.85382	$0.85828 = y_9$
1.0	0.78540	1.00000	$0.78540 = y_{10}$

By Simpson's Rule we have

$$\int_{x=0}^{0+10h} y\, dx = \frac{1}{3} h\, [y_0 + 4\,(y_1 + y_3 + y_5 + y_7 + y_9)$$

$$+ 2\,(y_2 + y_4 + y_6 + y_8) + y_{10}]$$

or $\displaystyle\int_0^1 y\, dx = \frac{1}{3}(0.1)\,[4\,(3.15212 + 1.77373 + 1.31141 + 1.04281 + 0.85828)$

$$2\,(2.20707 + 1.50411 + 1.16279 + 0.94298) + 0.78540]$$

$$= \frac{1}{3}(0.1)\,[4\,(8.13835) + 2\,(5.81695) + 0.78540]$$

$$= \frac{1}{3}(0.1)\,(32.5534 + 11.6339 + 0.7854)$$

$$= \frac{1}{3}(0.1)\,(44.9777) = \frac{1}{3}(4.4927)$$

$$= 1.49909.$$

EXERCISES

1. Find the area of a curve in which successive ordinates at intervals of .2 inch are 3.8, 3.5, 3.2, 2.8, 3.3, 3.6, 4 inches.

2. A curve is drawn through the points

$$(1, 2), (1.5, 2.4), (2, 2.7), (2.5, 2.8), (3, 3), (3.5, 2.6), (4, 2.1).$$

Estimate the area between the curve, the axis of x and the ordinates $x = 1, x = 4$.

3. The velocity of a train which starts from rest is given by the following table, the time being reckoned in minutes from the start and the speed in miles per hour.

Minutes	2	4	6	8	10	12	14	16	18	20
Miles per hour	10	18	25	29	32	20	11	5	2	0

Estimate approximately the total distance run in 20 minutes.

4. A river is 80 feet wide. The depth d in feet at a distance x feet from one bank is given by the following table :

x	0	10	20	30	40	50	60	70	80
d	0	4	7	9	12	15	14	8	3

Find approximately the area of the cross-section.

5. Calculate

$$\int_2^{10} \frac{dx}{1+x}$$

by the Simpson's rule, using nine ordinates.

6. From the formula

$$\frac{\pi}{4} = \int_0^1 \frac{dx}{1+x^2},$$

calculate π, using Simpson's rule with $h = 0.1$.

7. Find an approximate value of π from

$$\int_0^1 \frac{dx}{\sqrt{1-x^2}},$$

using five ordinates.

8. Calculate $\displaystyle\int_4^8 \frac{dx}{x}$, using four equal intervals.

9. Explain Simpson's rule for approximate integration. Use the rule, taking five ordinates, to find an approximation to two decimal places of the value of the integral

$$\int_1^2 \sqrt{x - 1/x} \; dx.$$

10. Given that

$$e^0 = 1, \; e^1 = 2.72, \; e^2 = 7.39, \; e^3 = 20.09, \; e^4 = 54.60;$$

verify Simpson's rule by finding an approximate value of

$$\int_0^4 e^x \; dx,$$

and compare it with the exact value.

11. Prove that

$$\int_a^{a+3h} y \; dx = \frac{3}{8} h \left(y_1 + 3y_2 + 3y_3 + y_4\right),$$

where y is a polynomial of the third degree and y_1, y_2, y_3, y_4 are the values of y corresponding to the values, $a, a+h, a+2h, a+3h$, of x.

Hence obtain an approximate value of

$$\int_0^{0.3} (1 - 8x^3)^{1/2} \; dx.$$

12. Obtain Simpson's rule for three equidistant ordinates, *viz.*,

$$\frac{1}{3} h \left(y_1 + 4y_2 + y_3\right).$$

If, in this method, the middle ordinate y_2 is at unequal distances h, k, from y_1 and y_3 respectively, then show that the formula is

$$\frac{1}{6}(h+k)(y_1+4y_2+y_3)+\frac{1}{6}(h^2-k^2)\left(\frac{y_1-y_2}{h}+\frac{y_2-y_3}{k}\right).$$

ANSWERS

1. 4.03 square inches.   **2.** 7.78.   **3.** 232 / 45 miles.

4. 710 square feet.   **5.** 1.299.   **8.** .693.

9. 0.84.   **10.** 53.87, 54.60. **11.** 0.29159.

EXERCISES ON CHAPTER 7

1. The coordinates of a point on a cycloid are given by $x = a\,(\theta + \sin\theta)$, $y = a\,(1 + \cos\theta)$ and the points corresponding to $\theta = -\pi/2$ and $\theta = \pi/2$ are denoted by P, Q respectively. Calculate the area enclosed by the arc PQ of the cycloid and the straight lines joining P and Q to the origin.

2. Find the area of the smallest portion which is bounded by the curve $r = a\,(\theta + \sin\theta)$ and by a radius vector which is inclined to the initial straight line at a right angle.

3. Prove that the area of either loop of the curve
$$x^4 - 2xya^2 + a^2y^2 = 0$$
is $\frac{2}{3}a^2$.

4. Trace the curve $r\cos\theta = a\sin 3\theta$ and show that the area of a loop is $\frac{1}{8}a^2(9\sqrt{3}-4\pi)$.

5. Prove that the area between the curve
$$r = a\,(\sec\theta + \tan\theta),$$
and its asymptote is equal to $(\pi/2+2)\,a^2$. Also prove that the area of the loop of the curve is $(2-\pi/2)\,a^2$.

6. Show that the curve $r = a\left(1+2\sin\frac{1}{2}\theta\right)$ consists of three loops and find the area of each loop.

7. Find the ratio of the two parts into which the parabola $2a = r\,(1+\cos\theta)$ divides the area of the cardioide $r = 2a\,(1+\cos\theta)$.

8. Prove that the area of the curve
$$4y^2 + x^2\,(x^2 - 6x + 8) = 0$$
is equal to $3\pi/2$.

9. Prove that the area of the curve
$$x^4 - 3ax^3 + a^2\,(2x^2 + y^2) = 0$$
is $\frac{3}{8}\pi a^2$.

10. The loop of the curve $ay^2 = x (x - a)^2$ is cut by the line $x + 2y = a$. Determine the areas of the two parts into which the loop is divided.

11. Determine the area bounded by the parabola

$$x^2 = 4ay + 4a^2,$$

and the line $3x + 4y = 0$.

12. Find the area in the first quadrant bounded by the curves $r = a (1 + \cos \theta)$, $r = a \sin \theta$ and $r = 2a \cos \theta$.

13. O is the pole of the lemniscate $r^2 = a^2 \cos 2\theta$ and PQ is a common tangent to its two loops. Find the area bounded by the line PQ and the OP and OQ of the curve.

14. Show that the area of the successive loops of the curve

$$r = ae^\theta \sin \theta$$

form a geometrical progression whose common ratio is $e^{2\pi}$.

15. Prove that the area common to the two curves

$$r = a \sin \theta, \, r = a \sin 2\theta$$

is $(4\pi - 3\sqrt{3}) \, a^2 / 16$.

16. Trace the curve $r = a \log \theta$, as θ varies from 0 to 1 and show that the area of the region enclosed between the curve and its asymptote is a^2.

17. Prove that the whole area between the four infinite branches of the tractrix

$$x = a \left(\cos t + \frac{1}{2} \log \tan^2 \frac{1}{2} t \right), \, y = a \sin t$$

is πa^2.

18. Show that the area of any closed curve

$$f \left(\frac{x}{m}, \frac{y}{n} \right) = 0,$$

is mn times the area of the curve

$$f(x, y) = 0.$$

Apply this result to find the areas of the following curves :

(i) $(m^2 x^2 + n^2 y^2)^2 = a^2 x^2 + b^2 y^2$.

(ii) $(m^2 x^2 + n^2 y^2)^5 = (a^2 x^3 + b^2 y^3)$.

(iii) $(x^2 + 2y^2)^3 = axy^4$.

ANSWERS

1. $(\pi + 3) \, a^2$.   2. $a^2 (\pi^3 + 6\pi + 48) / 48$.

6. $a^2 (3\pi + 8)$, $\frac{1}{2} a^2 (3\pi - 8)$, $\frac{1}{2} a^2 (3\pi - 8)$.

7. $(9\pi + 16)/(9\pi - 16)$.   **19.** $53a^2/960, 153a^2/320$.

11. $125a^2/24$.   **12.** $a^2 \left(\dfrac{1}{2} + \dfrac{1}{4}\pi - \dfrac{3}{4}\tan^{-1}2 \right)$.

13. $a^2 (3\sqrt{3} - 4)/8$.

18. (i) $(a^2n^2 + b^2m^2)\,\pi/2m^3n^3$.   (ii) $4(a^2n^3 + b^2m^3)/3m^4n^4$.

  (iii) $7\sqrt{2}\,\pi a^2/2^{13}$.

OBJECTIVE QUESTIONS

For each of the following questions, four alternatives are given for the answer. Only one of them is correct. Choose the correct alternative.

1. Quadrature is the process of determining the :

  (a) length of arc of plane curves

  (b) area under plane curves

  (c) intrinsic equation from the polar equation of curve

  (d) None of these.   *(Garhwal, 2002)*

2. The area of the ellipse $\dfrac{x^2}{a^2} + \dfrac{y^2}{b^2} = 1$ is given by :

  (a) ab (b) $\dfrac{1}{4}\pi ab$ (c) $\dfrac{1}{2}\pi ab$ (d) πab.

                                                            (Avadh, 2003)

3. The area bounded by the curve $y = x^3$, the x-axis and the lines $x = 1, x = 4$ is equal to :

  (a) 128   (b) $\dfrac{255}{4}$ (c) $\dfrac{127}{4}$ (d) None of these.

4. The area of the region in the first quadrant bounded by the y-axis and the curves $y = \sin x, y = \cos x$ is :

  (a) $\sqrt{2}$ (b) $\sqrt{2} + 1$ (c) $\sqrt{2} - 1$ (d) $2\sqrt{2} - 1$.

5. The area bounded by the x-axis, the curve $xy = c^2$ and the ordinates $x = a, x = b\ (a < b)$ is :

  (a) $c^2 \log (b/a)$ (b) $c^2 \log (a/b)$

  (c) $c^2 \log ab$ (d) 1.

6. The area of the circle $x^2 + y^2 = r^2$ is :

  (a) πr^2 (b) $\dfrac{\pi}{2}r^2$ (c) πr (d) $\dfrac{\pi}{2}r$.

                                            (Garhwal, 2001; Avadh, 2002)

7. Area bounded by the parabola $y^2 = 4ax$ and its latus rectum is :

  (a) a^2 (b) $\dfrac{2}{3}a^2$ (c) $\dfrac{4}{3}a^2$ (d) $\dfrac{8}{3}a^2$.

8. Area of a loop of the curve $ay^2 = x^2 (a - x)$ is :

(a) $\dfrac{8a^2}{15}$ (b) $\dfrac{4a^2}{15}$ (c) $\dfrac{2a^2}{15}$ (d) $\dfrac{a^2}{15}$.

9. Whole area of the curve $x = a \cos^3 t$, $y = a \sin^3 t$ is :

(a) πab (b) $\dfrac{3}{8} \pi ab$ (c) $\dfrac{5}{8} \pi ab$ (d) $4\pi ab$.

10. Whole area of the curve $r = 2a \cos \theta$ is :

(a) πa^2 (b) $\dfrac{1}{2} \pi a^2$ (c) $2\pi a^2$ (d) $4\pi a^2$.

11. Area of the curve $r^2 = a^2 \cos^2 \theta + b^2 \sin^2 \theta$ is :

(a) $\pi \left(a^2 + \dfrac{1}{2} b^2 \right)$ (b) $\pi (2a^2 + b^2)$

(c) $\dfrac{1}{2} (a^2 + b^2) \pi$ (d) $\pi (a^2 + b^2)$.

12. Area of the limacon $r = a + b \cos \theta$ is :

(a) $\pi \left(a^2 + \dfrac{1}{2} b^2 \right)$ (b) $\pi (2a^2 + b^2)$

(c) $\dfrac{1}{2} (2a^2 + b^2) \pi$ (d) $\pi (a^2 + b^2)$.

13. Area of one loop of the curve $r = a \cos 2\theta$ is :

(a) $\dfrac{1}{2} \pi a^2$ (b) πa^2 (c) $\dfrac{1}{8} \pi a^2$ (d) $\dfrac{1}{4} \pi a^2$.

14. Area of a loop of $r^2 = a^2 \sin 2\theta$ is :

(a) a^2 (b) $\dfrac{1}{2} a^2$ (c) $\dfrac{1}{4} a^2$ (d) $\dfrac{1}{8} a^2$.

15. Area of cardioid $r = a (1 - \cos \theta)$ is :

(a) πa^2 (b) $\dfrac{1}{2} \pi a^2$ (c) $\dfrac{3}{2} \pi a^2$ (d) $\dfrac{5}{2} \pi a^2$.

ANSWERS

1. (b)	**2.** (d)	**3.** (b)	**4.** (c)	**5.** (a)
6. (a)	**7.** (d)	**8.** (a)	**9.** (b)	**10.** (a)
11. (c)	**12.** (a)	**13.** (c)	**14.** (b)	**15.** (c)

9

Rectification. Lengths of Plane Curves

9.1. Introduction. In this chapter, we shall be concerned with the determination of the lengths of arcs of plane curves whose equations are given in the Cartesian, Parametric cartesian or Polar form. The process is known as *Rectification*.

It is known to the reader that in order to obtain analytical expressions for an area, we first proved a corresponding formula giving the derivation of the area function. For example, we have shown that $dA/dx = y$, $dA/d\theta = \frac{1}{2}r^2$. The same thing has to be done in order to determine the lengths of curves. These formulae for the derivatives of the arcs have already been proved in Chapter XIII of the author's *Differential Calculus*. Here we will only refer to them and will not reproduce their proofs.

9.2. Cartesian Equations $y = f(x)$. *The length of the arc of the curve $y = f(x)$ included between two points whose abscissae are a and b is*

$$\int_a^b \sqrt{1 + \left(\frac{dy}{dx}\right)^2}\, dx = \int_a^b \sqrt{1 + f'^2(x)}\, dx.$$

Let AB be two points with abscissae a, b on the curve $y = f(x)$.

If 's' denotes the length of the arc of the curve included between a fixed point A and a variable point P whose abscissa is x so that it is a function of x, we have

$$\frac{ds}{dx} = \sqrt{1 + \left(\frac{dy}{dx}\right)^2}$$

$$\Rightarrow \int_a^b \sqrt{1 + \left(\frac{dy}{dx}\right)^2}\, dx = \int_a^b \frac{ds}{dx}\, dx = |s|_a^b$$

= value of, s, for x equal to b – value of, s, for x equal to a

= Arc AB – 0 = Arc AB.

Hence the result.

9.3. Other Expressions for lengths of arcs. From the formulae

$$\frac{ds}{dy} = \sqrt{1 + \left(\frac{dx}{dy}\right)^2} \; ;$$

$$\frac{ds}{dt} = \sqrt{\left(\frac{dx}{dt}\right)^2 + \left(\frac{dy}{dt}\right)^2} \; ;$$

$$\frac{ds}{d\theta} = \sqrt{r^2 + \left(\frac{dr}{d\theta}\right)^2} \; ;$$

proved in Differential Calculus, we obtain the following results for the determination of the lengths of arcs :

9.31. Cartesian Equations $x = f(y)$. *The length of the arc of the curve* $x = f(y)$, *included between two points whose ordinates are c, d is*

$$\int_c^d \sqrt{1 + \left(\frac{dx}{dy}\right)^2} \; dy = \int_c^d \sqrt{1 + f'^2(y)} \; dy.$$

9.32. Parametric Cartesian Equations $x = f(t), y = \varphi(t)$. *The length of the arc of the curve* $x = f(t), y = \varphi(t)$ *included between two points whose parametric values are* α, β *is*

$$\int_\alpha^\beta \sqrt{\left(\frac{dx}{dt}\right)^2 + \left(\frac{dy}{dt}\right)^2} \; d\theta = \int_\alpha^\beta \sqrt{f'^2(t) + \varphi'^2(t)} \; dt.$$

9.33. Polar Equations $r = f(\theta)$. *The length of the arc of the curve* $r = f(\theta)$ *included between two points whose vectorial angles are* α, β *is*

$$\int_\alpha^\beta \sqrt{r^2 + \left(\frac{dr}{d\theta}\right)^2} \; d\theta = \int_\alpha^\beta \sqrt{f^2(\theta) + f'^2(\theta)} \; d\theta.$$

EXAMPLES

1. *Find the length of the arc of the parabola* $x^2 = 4ay$ *measured from the vertex to one extremity of the latus rectum.*

The abscissa of the extremity L of the latus rectum is $2a$.

Now, $y = \dfrac{x^2}{4a}$

$\Rightarrow \dfrac{dy}{dx} = \dfrac{x}{2a}$.

$\therefore$ The required length

$$= \int_0^{2a} \sqrt{1 + \left(\frac{dy}{dx}\right)^2} \; dx$$

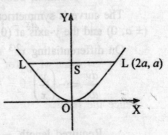

$$= \frac{1}{2a} \int_0^{2a} \sqrt{4a^2 + x^2}\, dx$$

$$= \frac{1}{2a} \left| \frac{x\sqrt{x^2 + 4a^2}}{2} + 2a^2 \sinh^{-1} \frac{x}{2a} \right|_0^{2a}$$

$$= \frac{1}{2a} [2\sqrt{2}\, a^2 + 2a^2 \sinh^{-1} 1]$$

$$= a\,[\sqrt{2} + \log(1 + \sqrt{2})], \text{ for, } \sinh^{-1} x = \log[x + \sqrt{1 + x^2}].$$

2. *Find the length of the curve* $y = \log\{(e^x - 1)/(e^x + 1)\}$ *from* $x = 1$
to $x = 2$.   *(Kanpur, 1997; Rewa, 1998; Bilaspur, 1996;*
Sagar, 1997, 2000; Jabalpur, 1998; Ravishankar, 1999S;
Vikram, 2001; Kumaon, 1996, 99; Rohilkhand, 1998; Agra, 2001)

$$y = \log(e^x - 1) - \log(e^x + 1)$$

$$\Rightarrow \quad \frac{dy}{dx} = \frac{e^x}{e^x - 1} - \frac{e^x}{e^x + 1} = \frac{2e^x}{(e^{2x} - 1)}.$$

$$\therefore \quad \text{Required length} = \int_1^2 \left[1 + \frac{4e^{2x}}{(e^{2x} - 1)^2} \right]^{1/2} dx$$

$$= \int_1^2 \frac{e^{2x} + 1}{e^{2x} - 1}\, dx = \int_1^2 \left(\frac{e^x + e^{-x}}{e^x - e^{-x}} \right) dx$$

$$= \left[\log(e^x - e^{-x}) \right]_1^2, \text{ (By putting } e^x - e^{-x} = t.)$$

$$= \log \frac{e^2 - e^{-2}}{e - e^{-1}} = \log(e + 1/e).$$

3. *Find the whole length of the astroid* $x^{2/3} + y^{2/3} = a^{2/3}$.
(Rohilkhand, 2000, 02; Garhwal, 1999; Sagar, 1998;
Kumaon, 2000; Jiwaji, 2000; Bilaspur, 1998; Indore, 2000)

The curve is symmetrical about both the axes and crosses the x-axis at
$(\pm a, 0)$ and the y-axis at $(0, \pm a)$.

On differentiating $x^{2/3} + y^{2/3} = a^{2/3}$, we have

$$\frac{dy}{dx} = -\left(\frac{y}{x} \right)^{1/3}$$

$$\therefore \quad \text{Required length} = 4 \int_0^a \left[1 + \left(\frac{y}{x} \right)^{2/3} \right]^{1/2} dx$$

$$= 4 \int_0^a \left[\frac{x^{2/3} + y^{2/3}}{x^{2/3}} \right]^{1/2} dx$$

$$= 4 \int_0^a \frac{a^{1/3}}{x^{1/3}} dx = 4a^{1/3} \times \frac{3}{2} \left[x^{2/3} \right]_0^a$$

$$= 6a^{1/3} \cdot a^{2/3} = 6a.$$

4. *Show that the length of the curve* $x^2 = a^2 \left(1 - e^{y/a} \right)$ *measured from* $(0, 0)$ *to* (x, y) *is* $a \log \left(\dfrac{a+x}{a-x} \right) - x.$

The given curve is $x^2 = a^2 \left(1 - e^{y/a} \right)$

or $e^{y/a} = \dfrac{(a^2 - x^2)}{a^2}$

or $y = a \log \left(\dfrac{a^2 - x^2}{a^2} \right)$

$$\therefore \quad \frac{dy}{dx} = a \cdot \frac{1}{(a^2 - x^2)/a^2} (-2x)$$

$$= \frac{-2x}{a^2 - x^2}.$$

Hence the required length

$$= \int_0^x \sqrt{1 + \left(\frac{dy}{dx} \right)^2} \, dx$$

$$= \int_0^x \left[1 + \frac{4a^2 x^2}{(a^2 - x^2)^2} \right]^{1/2} dx$$

$$= \int_0^x \frac{a^2 + x^2}{a^2 - x^2} dx = \int_0^x \left(-1 + \frac{2a^2}{a^2 - x^2} \right) dx$$

$$= \left[-x - 2a^2 \cdot \frac{1}{2a} \log \frac{a-x}{a+x} \right]_0^x$$

$$= -a + a \log \frac{a+x}{a-x}.$$

5. *Find the whole length of the curve* $x^2 (a^2 - x^2) = 8a^2 y^2.$

The given curve is symmetrical about both the axes and it also crosses the x-axis at $x = 0$ and $\pm a$. The curve contains two loops. The limits for x are from 0 to a.

$$\therefore \text{ The required length} = 4 \int_0^a \sqrt{1 + \left(\frac{dy}{dx}\right)^2}\, dx.$$

But the equation of given curve is $8a^2 y^2 = a^2 x^2 - x^4$

or $\qquad 16a^2 y \dfrac{dy}{dx} = 2a^2 x - 4x^3$

$$\therefore \qquad \frac{dy}{dx} = \frac{2a^2 x}{16a^2 y} - \frac{4x^3}{16a^2 y}$$

$$= \frac{x}{8y} - \frac{x^3}{4a^2 y}$$

$$\therefore \qquad \left(\frac{dy}{dx}\right)^2 = \frac{x^2}{64y^2} + \frac{x^6}{16a^4 y^2} - \frac{2x^4}{32a^2 y^2}$$

$$= \frac{a^4 x^2 + 4x^6 - 4a^2 x^4}{64 a^4 y^2}$$

$$= \frac{x^2 (a^4 + 4x^4 - 4a^2 x^2)}{8a^2 x^2 (a^2 - x^2)}$$

$$= \frac{(a^2 - 2x^2)^2}{8a^2 (a^2 - x^2)}$$

$$1 + \left(\frac{dy}{dx}\right)^2 = 1 + \frac{(a^2 - 2x^2)^2}{8a^2 (a^2 - x^2)}$$

$$= \frac{(3a^2 - 2x^2)^2}{8a^2 (a^2 - x^2)}.$$

The required length is

$$= 4 \int_0^a \left[\frac{(3a^2 - 2x^2)^2}{8a^2 (a^2 - x^2)}\right]^{1/2} dx$$

$$= \frac{4}{2\sqrt{2}\, a} \int_0^a \frac{(3a^2 - 2x^2)}{\sqrt{(a^2 - x^2)^{1/2}}}\, dx$$

$$= \frac{\sqrt{2}}{a} \int_0^a \left[\frac{2(a^2 - x^2)}{\sqrt{a^2 - x^2}} + \frac{a^2}{\sqrt{a^2 - x^2}}\right] dx$$

$$= \frac{2\sqrt{2}}{a} \int_0^a \left[\sqrt{a^2 - x^2}\, dx + \sqrt{2}\, a \int_0^a \frac{dx}{\sqrt{a^2 - x^2}}\right]$$

$$= \frac{2\sqrt{2}}{a}\left[\frac{1}{2}x\sqrt{a^2-x^2}+\frac{1}{2}a^2\sin^{-1}\frac{x}{a}\right]_0^a + \sqrt{2}\,a\left[\sin^{-1}\frac{x}{a}\right]_0^a$$

$$= \frac{2\sqrt{2}}{a}\cdot\frac{1}{2}a^2\sin^{-1}1 + \sqrt{2}\,a\,\sin^{-1}1$$

$$= 2\sqrt{2}\,a\cdot\frac{\pi}{2} = \pi a\sqrt{2}.$$

6. *Find the perimeter of the loop of the curve* $9ay^2 = (x-2a)(x-5a)^2$.

The loop lies between the limits $x = 2a$ and $x = 5a$. The curve is symmetrical about the x-axis and, therefore, the perimeter of the loop is double of the length of its part lying about the x-axis.

For any point on the arc lying above X-axis, we have

$$y = -\frac{(x-5a)\sqrt{x-2a}}{3\sqrt{a}}$$

$$\frac{dy}{dx} = -\frac{\sqrt{x-2a}+\dfrac{x-5a}{2\sqrt{x-2a}}}{3\sqrt{a}}$$

$$= -\frac{x-3a}{2\sqrt{a}\sqrt{x-2a}}$$

∴ The required perimeter

$$= 2\int_{2a}^{5a}\sqrt{1+\left(\frac{dy}{dx}\right)^2}\,dx$$

$$= 2\int_{2a}^{5a}\sqrt{1+\frac{(x-3a)^2}{4a(x-2a)}}\,dx$$

$$= 2\int_{2a}^{5a}\frac{x-a}{2\sqrt{a}\sqrt{x-2a}}\,dx$$

$$= \frac{1}{\sqrt{a}}\int_{2a}^{5a}\frac{x-2a+a}{\sqrt{x-2a}}\,dx$$

$$= \frac{1}{\sqrt{a}}\left|\frac{2}{3}(x-2a)^{2/3}+2a\sqrt{x-2a}\right|_{2a}^{5a}$$

$$= 4\sqrt{3}\,a.$$

7. *Rectify the curve* $x = a(\theta + \sin\theta)$, $y = a(1-\cos\theta)$.

(Bhopal, 1995; Jabalpur, 2000; Avadh, 2002)

As a point moves from one end A' to other end A of the one arc, the parameter θ increases from – π to π. The parameter θ is 0 for the vertex O. As the arc is symmetrical about OY,

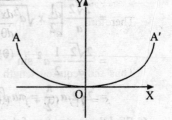

$$\text{arc } AOA' = 2 \text{ arc } OA.$$

We have

$$\frac{dx}{d\theta} = a(1 + \cos\theta), \quad \frac{dy}{d\theta} = a\sin\theta.$$

$$\therefore \quad \sqrt{\left(\frac{dx}{d\theta}\right)^2 + \left(\frac{dy}{d\theta}\right)^2} = \sqrt{2a^2(1 + \cos\theta)}$$

$$= \sqrt{4a^2\cos^2\frac{\theta}{2}} = 2a\cos\frac{\theta}{2}$$

$$\therefore \quad \text{The required arc} = 2\int_0^\pi 2a\cos\frac{\theta}{2}\, d\theta$$

$$= 2\left| 4a\sin\frac{\theta}{2} \right|_0^\pi = 8a.$$

Note. Here we take $\sqrt{4a^2\cos^2(\theta/2)} = 2a\cos(\theta/2)$, and not $-2a\cos(\theta/2)$ as $\cos(\theta/2)$ remains positive when θ increases from 0 to π.

8. *Show that the length of an arc of the curve* $x\sin\theta + y\cos\theta = f'(\theta)$, $x\sin\theta - y\cos\theta = f''(\theta)$ *is given by* $s = f(\theta) + f''(\theta) + c$.

(Kumaon, 1994)

The given relations are

$$x\sin\theta + y\cos\theta = f'(\theta) \qquad\qquad ...(i)$$

$$x\sin\theta + y\cos\theta = f''(\theta) \qquad\qquad ...(ii)$$

Multiplying (*i*) by sin θ and (*ii*) by cos θ and adding, we have

$$x = f'(\theta)\sin\theta + f''(\theta)\cos\theta \qquad\qquad ...(iii)$$

Similarly, multiplying (*i*) by cos θ and (*ii*) by sin θ and subtracting, we get

$$y = f'(\theta)\cos\theta - f''(\theta)\sin\theta \qquad\qquad ...(iv)$$

From (*ii*) and (*iv*), we get

$$\frac{dx}{d\theta} = f''(\theta)\sin\theta + f'(\theta)\cos\theta - f''(\theta)\sin\theta + f'''(\theta)\cos\theta$$

$$= -\sin\theta[f'(\theta) + f'''(\theta)].$$

Therefore, $\dfrac{ds}{d\theta} = \sqrt{\left(\dfrac{dx}{d\theta}\right)^2 + \left(\dfrac{dy}{d\theta}\right)^2}$

$$= f'(\theta) + f'''(\theta).$$

Thus the required length is

$$s = \int [f'(\theta) + f'''(\theta)]\, d\theta + c$$

$$= f(\theta) + f''(\theta) + c.$$

9. *Find the perimeter of the cardioid $r = a\,(1 - \cos\theta)$.*

(Rohilkhand, 2003)

The curve is symmetrical about the initial line, and, therefore, its perimeter is double the length of the arc of the curve lying above the same.

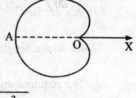

Now $\dfrac{dr}{d\theta} = a\sin\theta.$

$\therefore \quad \sqrt{r^2 + \left(\dfrac{dr}{d\theta}\right)^2} = \sqrt{a^2(1-\cos\theta)^2 + a^2\sin^2\theta}$

$$= \sqrt{2a^2(1-\cos\theta)} = 2a\sin(\theta/2)$$

$\therefore$ The required perimeter

$$= 2\int_0^\pi 2a\sin\frac{\theta}{2}\,d\theta = 2\left| -4a\cos\frac{\theta}{2}\right|_0^\pi = 8a.$$

10. *Prove that the cardioid $r = a\,(1 - \cos\theta)$ is divided by the line $4r\cos\theta = 3a$ into two parts, such that the lengths of the arcs on either side of this line are equal.*

The given curve and straight line are

$r = a\,(1 + \cos\theta)$, and $4r\cos\theta = 3a$, respectively.

These curves cut one another at B and C.

Thereby

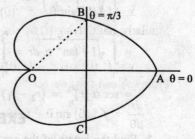

$$\frac{3a}{4\cos\theta} = a\,(1 + \cos\theta)$$

or $4\cos^2\theta + 4\cos\theta - 3 = 0$

$\therefore \quad \cos\theta = \dfrac{1}{2}$ or $\theta = \dfrac{\pi}{3},$

the value $\cos\theta = -\dfrac{3}{2}$ is inadmissible.

The arc BAC is to be shown equal to the arc BOC.

Now $r = a\,(1 + \cos\theta),\ \dfrac{dr}{d\theta} = -a\sin\theta$

$\therefore\quad \dfrac{ds}{d\theta} = \sqrt{a^2\,(1 + \cos\theta)^2 + a^2\sin^2\theta} = 2a\cos\dfrac{\theta}{2}.$

Therefore the length of the arc AB

$$= 2a\int_0^{\pi/3}\cos\dfrac{\theta}{2}\,d\theta = 4a\left[\sin\dfrac{\theta}{2}\right]_0^{\pi/3}$$

$$= 4a\cdot\dfrac{1}{2} = 2a.$$

Hence arc BAC = 2 arc AB = $4a$.

Also, whole length $= 2\int_0^{\pi} 2a\cos\dfrac{\theta}{2}\,d\theta$

$$= 8a\left[\sin\dfrac{\theta}{2}\right]_0^{\pi} = 8a.$$

Therefore the arc BOC = whole length − arc BAC

$$= 8a - 4a = 4a.$$

11. *Find the length of the arc of the equiangular spiral $r = ae^{\theta\cot\alpha}$ between the points for which the radii vectors are r_1 and r_2.*

We have

$$\dfrac{dr}{d\theta} = a\cot\alpha\cdot e^{\theta\cot\alpha} = r\cot\alpha$$

$$\therefore\quad r\dfrac{d\theta}{dr} = \dfrac{1}{\cot\alpha} = \tan\alpha.$$

Hence the required arc length

$$= \int_{r_1}^{r_2}\sqrt{1 + \left(r\dfrac{d\theta}{dr}\right)^2}\,dr$$

$$= \int_{r_1}^{r_2}\sqrt{1 + \tan^2\alpha}\,dr = \int_{r_1}^{r_2}\sec\alpha\,dr$$

$$= \sec\alpha\,[r]_{r_1}^{r_2} = (r_2 - r_1)\sec\alpha.$$

EXERCISES

1. Find the length of the arc of the curve $y = \log\sec x$ from $x = 0$ to $x = \pi/3$. *(Kanpur, 2003)*

2. Find the length of the arc of the curve
$$y = \log \tanh (x/2)$$
from $x = 1$ to $x = 2$.

3. Find the length of the arc of the parabola $y^2 = 4ax$ cut off by its latus rectum. *(Kumaon, 2001)*

4. Find the length of the arc of the catenary
$$y = c \cosh (x/c)$$
measured from the vertex $(0, c)$ to any point (x, y).

5. Prove that the length of the arc of the curve
$$x = a \sin 2\theta (1 + \cos 2\theta),$$
$$y = a \cos 2\theta (1 - \cos 2\theta),$$
measured from $(0, 0)$ to (x, y) is equal to $\frac{4}{3} a \sin 3\theta$.

6. Show that the length s of the curve,
$$x^{2/3} + y^{2/3} = a^{2/3},$$
measured from $(0, a)$ to the point (x, y) is given by $s = \frac{3}{2} \sqrt[3]{a}\, x^2$.

7. A curve is given by the equations
$$x = a (\cos \theta + \theta \sin \theta), y = a (\sin \theta - \theta \cos \theta);$$
find the length of the arc from $\theta = 0$ to $\theta = \alpha$.

8. Show that the arc of the upper half of the curve
$$r = a (1 - \cos \theta)$$
is bisected by $\theta = 2\pi/3$. *(Kumaon, 2003)*

9. Find the length of an arc of the curve
$$r = ae^{\theta \cot \alpha}$$
taking $s = 0$ when $\theta = 0$.

10. Find the length of the curve $r = a \cos^3 (\theta/3)$.

11. Find the length of the loop of the curve $r = a (\theta^2 - 1)$.

12. Show that the length of the loop of the curve
$$3ay^2 = x (x - a)^2 \text{ is } 4a/\sqrt{3}.$$

13. Prove that the whole length of the curve
$$x^2 (a^2 - x^2) = 8a^2y^2 \text{ is } \pi a\sqrt{2}.$$

14. Find the length of the arc of the curve
$$x = t^2 \cos t, y = t^2 \sin t$$
from the origin to the point t.

15. Sketch the curve $y = -\log (1 - x^2)$, and show that the length of the arc measured from the origin to the point whose abscissa is x, is
$$\log [(1 + x)/(1 - x)] - x.$$

16. Show that the length of an arc of the epi-cycloid

$$x = (a + b)\cos\theta - b\cos\frac{a+b}{b}\theta, \ y = (a + b)\sin\theta - b\sin\frac{a+b}{b}\theta$$

is given by $s = \dfrac{4b\,(a+b)}{2}\cos\dfrac{a\theta}{2b}$, s being measured from the point at which $\theta = \pi b / a$.

17. Find the length of the arc of the curve $y = x\,(2 - x)$ as x varies from 0 to 2.

18. Prove that the loop of the curve

$$x = t^2, \ y = t - \frac{1}{3}t^3$$

is of length $4\sqrt{3}$.

19. Prove that the length of the arc of the hyperbolic spiral $r\theta = a$, taken from the point $r = a$ to $r = 2a$, is

$$a\left[\sqrt{5} - \sqrt{2} + \log\frac{2+\sqrt{8}}{1+\sqrt{5}}\right].$$

20. Find the length of the arc of the parabola

$$l/r = 1 + \cos\theta$$

cut off by its latus rectum.

21. Show that the length of the arc of the curve given by

$$x = a\,(3\sin\theta - \sin^3\theta), \ y = a\cos^3\theta$$

measured from $(0, a)$ to any point (x, y) is $\dfrac{3}{2}a\,(\theta + \sin\theta\cos\theta)$.

22. Find the length of the curve

$$x = e^\theta\sin\theta, \ y = e^\theta\cos\theta$$

from $\theta = 0$ to $\theta = \pi / 2$.

23. Show that the length of the curve

$$x = e^\theta\,[\sin(\theta/2) + 2\cos(\theta/2)],$$
$$y = e^\theta\,[\cos(\theta/2) - 2\sin(\theta/2)]$$

measured from $\theta = 0$ to $\theta = \pi$ is $5\,(e^\pi - 1)/2$.

24. If 's' be the length of the arc of the curve

$$x = a\,(\theta + \sin\theta\cos\theta), \ y = a\,(1 + \sin\theta)^2$$

measured from the point $\theta = -\pi/2$ to a point θ, show that s^4 varies as y^3.

25. Trace the curve

$$x = a\,(\theta - \sin\theta), \ y = a\,(1 - \cos\theta),$$

as θ varies from 0 to 2π and show that the point $\theta = \dfrac{2}{3}\pi$ divides it in the ratio $1 : 3$.

26. Find the perimeter of the cardioid $r = a\,(1 + \cos\theta)$.

(*Kanpur, 2001, 02; Ravishankar, 1996, 97, 2000*)

ANSWERS

1. $\log(2 + \sqrt{3})$.

2. $\log[(e^2 + 1)/e]$.

3. $2a[\sqrt{2} + \log(1 + \sqrt{2})]$.

4. $c \sinh(x/c)$.

6. $6a$.

7. $\frac{1}{2}a\alpha^2$.

9. $a \sec \alpha \, (e^{\theta \cot \alpha} - 1)$.

10. $\frac{3}{2}a\pi$.

11. $8a/3$.

14. $\frac{1}{3}[(4 + t^2)^{3/2} - 8]$.

17. $\frac{1}{2}\log(2 + \sqrt{5}) + \sqrt{5}$.

20. $l[\sqrt{2} + \log(1 + \sqrt{2})]$.

22. $\sqrt{2}\,(e^{\pi/2} - 1)$.

26. $8a$.

9.4. Intrinsic Equations of a Curve

Def. *If, s, denotes the length of the arc of a curve measured from some fixed point A to a variable point P, and ψ denotes the angle between the tangents at A and P, then a relation between, s, and, ψ, is called an* **Intrinsic Equation** *of the curve.*

Also, s and ψ are called the **intrinsic co-ordinates.**

The name *'Intrinsic'* arises from the fact that s and ψ for a point depend only upon the *form* of the curve and not on its *position* in the plane, so that they are inherently associated with the curve.

Intrinsic co-ordinates of a point on a curve will not change if the curve changes its position in the plane. This is not the case for the ordinary cartesian or polar co-ordinates.

9.41. Derivation of Intrinsic Equations from Cartesian Equations.

Let $y = f(x)$ be the cartesian equation of a given curve.

We suppose that the abscissa of the fixed point A is a and the tangent at A is parallel to the x-axis. Let P (x, y) be any variable point on the curve. Let arc AP $= s$. Let the tangent at P make angle ψ with the x-axis. We have

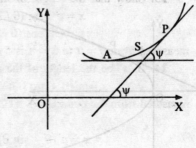

$$s = \int_a^x \sqrt{1 + f'^2(x)}\, dx, \quad \text{...(i)}$$

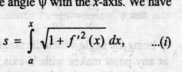

$$\tan \psi = f'(x). \quad \text{...(ii)}$$

Eliminating x between (*i*) and (*ii*), we obtain the required intrinsic equation.

EXAMPLES

1. *Obtain the intrinsic equation of the catenary*

$$y = a \cosh (x / a),$$

taking the vertex $(0, a)$ as the fixed point.

The tangent at A $(0, a)$ is parallel to X-axis.

We have

$$s = \int_0^x \sqrt{1 + \left(\frac{dy}{dx}\right)^2}\, dx$$

$$= \int_0^x \cosh \frac{x}{a}\, dx$$

$$= \left| a \sinh \frac{x}{a} \right|_0^x$$

$$= a \sinh \frac{x}{a} \qquad \qquad …(i)$$

Also, $\quad \tan \psi = \dfrac{dy}{dx} = \sinh \dfrac{x}{a} \qquad …(ii)$

From (i) and (ii), we obtain

$$s = a \tan \psi,$$

as the required intrinsic equation of the given curve.

2. *Find the intrinsic equation of the parabola $y^2 = 4ax$; origin being taken as the fixed point.*

Let P (x, y) be a point on the curve. Y-axis is the tangent at O. Let arc OP $= s$.

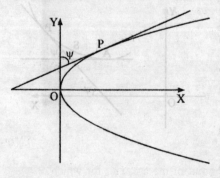

From the given equation, we have

$$\frac{dy}{dx} = \frac{2a}{y}$$

$$\therefore \quad \tan \psi = \frac{dx}{dy} = \frac{y}{2a} \qquad …(i)$$

ψ being the angle which the tangent at any point makes with Y-axis.

Also,

$$s = \int_0^y \sqrt{1 + \left(\frac{dx}{dy}\right)^2}\; dy$$

$$= \frac{1}{2}\int_0^y \sqrt{4a^2 + y^2}\; dy$$

$$= \frac{1}{2a}\left[\frac{y\sqrt{4a^2 + y^2}}{2} + \frac{4a}{2}\log\frac{[y + \sqrt{y^2 + 4a^2}]}{2a}\right] \qquad ...(ii)$$

Eliminating y from (i) and (ii), we get

$$s = a\,[\tan\psi\,\sec\psi + \log(\tan\psi + \sec\psi)],$$

as the required intrinsic equation.

3. *Find the intrinsic equation of the astroid $x^{2/3} + y^{2/3} = a^{2/3}$, when s is measured from (i) the vertex, (ii) the cusp on the x-axis.*

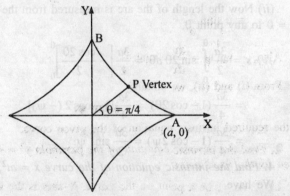

The given curve is

$$x^{2/3} + y^{2/3} = a^{2/3}.$$

The parametric coordinates of this curve may be considered as $x = a\cos^3\theta$, $y = a\sin^3\theta$.

$$\therefore \quad \frac{dx}{d\theta} = -3a\cos^2\theta\sin\theta, \quad \frac{dy}{d\theta} = 3a\sin^2\theta$$

then $\quad \dfrac{dy}{dx} = \tan\psi = -\tan\theta$

$$\therefore \quad \theta = -\psi. \qquad\qquad\qquad ...(i)$$

(i) The vertex P is the middle point of the arc, *i.e.*, for which $\theta = \dfrac{\pi}{4}$

or $\psi = -\dfrac{\pi}{4}$.

Now

s = length of arc from the vertex to any point

$$= \int_{\pi/4}^{\theta} \sqrt{\left(\frac{dx}{d\theta}\right)^2 + \left(\frac{dy}{d\theta}\right)^2}\, d\theta$$

$$= 3a \int_{\pi/4}^{\theta} \cos\theta \sin\theta\, d\theta$$

$$= \frac{3a}{2} \int_{\pi/4}^{\theta} \sin 2\theta\, d\theta$$

$$= \frac{3a}{2}\left[\frac{-\cos 2\theta}{2}\right]_{\pi/4}^{\theta} = -\frac{3a}{2}\cos 2\theta$$

$$\therefore\quad s = \frac{-3a}{2}\cos 2\psi.$$

(*ii*) Now the length of the arc is measured from the cusp A, for which $\theta = 0$ to any point θ.

$$\therefore\quad s = \frac{3a}{2}\int_{0}^{\theta} \sin 2\theta\, d\theta = \frac{3a}{2}\left[-\frac{\cos 2\theta}{2}\right]_{0}^{\theta}$$

$$= \frac{3a}{4}(1 - \cos 2\theta) = \frac{3a}{4}[1 - \cos 2(-\psi)]$$

$$= \frac{3a}{4}(1 - \cos 2\psi) = \frac{3a}{2}\sin^2\psi.$$

4. *Find the intrinsic equation of the curve* $x = at^2$, $y = 2at$.

We have

$$\frac{dx}{dt} = 2at \text{ and } \frac{dy}{dt} = 2a$$

$$\therefore\quad \frac{dy}{dx} = \frac{2a}{2at} = \frac{1}{t} = \tan\psi$$

$$\therefore\quad t = \cot\psi \qquad\qquad\qquad ...(i)$$

Now $\displaystyle s = \int_{0}^{t} \sqrt{\left(\frac{dx}{dy}\right)^2 + \left(\frac{dy}{dt}\right)^2}\, dt$

$$= \int_{0}^{t} \sqrt{4a^2t^2 + 4a^2}\, dt$$

$$= 2a \int_{0}^{t} \sqrt{1 + t^2}\, dt$$

$$= 2a \left[\frac{1}{2} t \sqrt{1+t^2} + \frac{1}{2} \log \{t + \sqrt{1+t^2}\} \right]_0^t$$

$$= 2a \left[\frac{1}{2} t \sqrt{1+t^2} + \frac{1}{2} \log \{t + \sqrt{1+t^2}\} \right]$$

$$= 2a \left[\frac{1}{2} \cot \psi \sqrt{1 + \cot^2 \psi} + \frac{1}{2} \log (\cot \psi + \csc \psi) \right] \quad \text{[From (i)]}$$

$$= 2a \, [\cot \psi \, \csc \psi + \log (\cot \psi + \csc \psi)].$$

5. *Obtain the intrinsic equation of the cycloid*

$$x = a \, (\theta + \sin \theta), \; y = a \, (1 - \cos \theta),$$

he fixed point being the origin.   *(Agra, 2001)*

(Refer Figure of Example 7, page 325.)

X-axis is the tangent at the fixed point O. Let, P (θ) be a variable point n the cycloid. We have

$$\frac{dx}{d\theta} = a \, (1 + \cos \theta), \; \frac{dy}{d\theta} = a \sin \theta.$$

$$\therefore \quad \tan \psi = \frac{dy}{dx} = \frac{\sin \theta}{1 + \cos \theta} = \frac{2 \sin \dfrac{\theta}{2} \cos \dfrac{\theta}{2}}{2 \cos^2 \dfrac{\theta}{2}} = \tan \frac{\theta}{2},$$

$$\Rightarrow \quad \psi = \frac{\theta}{2}. \quad \quad \text{...(i)}$$

Also, $\quad s = \displaystyle\int_0^\theta \sqrt{\left(\frac{dx}{d\theta}\right)^2 + \left(\frac{dy}{d\theta}\right)^2} \; d\theta$

$$= 2a \int_0^\theta \cos \frac{\theta}{2} \, d\theta = 4a \left| \sin \frac{\theta}{2} \right|_0^\theta = 4a \sin \frac{\theta}{2} \quad \text{...(ii)}$$

From (i) and (ii), we obtain

$$s = 4a \sin \psi,$$

s the required intrinsic equation of the cycloid.

EXERCISES

1. Show that the intrinsic equation of the semi-cubical parabola

$$ay^2 = x^3,$$

aking its cusp as the fixed point is

$$27s = 8a \, (\sec^3 \psi - 1). \quad \quad (Avadh, \, 2003)$$

2. Show that the intrinsic equation of the astroid

$$x^{2/3} + y^{2/3} = a^{2/3},$$

aking $(a, 0)$ as the fixed point is

$$s = 3/2a \sin^2 \psi.$$

9.42. Derivation of Intrinsic Equations from Polar Equations.

Let $r = f(\theta)$ be the polar equation of a given curve. Let the vectorial angle of the fixed point A be α. We suppose that the tangent at A is parallel to the initial line. We take any point P on the curve whose vectorial angle is θ. Let arc AP = s.

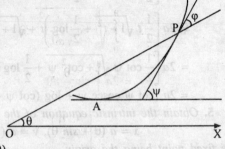

We have

$$\tan \varphi = r \frac{d\theta}{dr} = \frac{f(\theta)}{f'(\theta)} \qquad ...(i)$$

φ being the angle between the radius vector and the tangent.

Also $\psi = \theta + \varphi.$ $\qquad ...(ii)$

$$s = \int_{\alpha}^{\theta} \sqrt{r^2 + \left(\frac{dr}{d\theta}\right)^2}\, d\theta$$

$$= \int_{\alpha}^{\theta} \sqrt{f^2(\theta) + f'^2(\theta)}\, d\theta \qquad ...(iii)$$

Eliminating θ and φ from (i), (ii), (iii), we obtain the required intrinsic equation.

EXAMPLES

1. *Obtain the intrinsic equation of cardioid*

$$r = a\,(1 - \cos\theta),$$

taking pole as the fixed point. (*Ravishankar, 1994; Bhopal, 1997*)

(Refer Figure of Example 9, page 327.)

Initial line is the tangent at the pole.

We have

$$\frac{dr}{d\theta} = a \sin\theta$$

$$\therefore \quad \tan\varphi = r \frac{d\theta}{dr} = \frac{1 - \cos\theta}{\sin\theta}$$

$$= \frac{2\sin^2\dfrac{\theta}{2}}{2\sin\dfrac{\theta}{2}\cos\dfrac{\theta}{2}} = \tan\frac{\theta}{2},$$

$$\Rightarrow \quad \varphi = \frac{\theta}{2}.$$

Again, $\quad \psi = \varphi + \theta = \dfrac{3\theta}{2}$ ...(i)

Also, $\quad s = \displaystyle\int_0^\theta \sqrt{r^2 + \left(\dfrac{dr}{d\theta}\right)^2}\; d\theta$

$\qquad\qquad = 2a \displaystyle\int_0^\theta \sin\dfrac{\theta}{2}\; d\theta$

$\qquad\qquad = -4a \left| \cos\dfrac{\theta}{2} \right|_0^\theta = 4a\left[1 - \cos\dfrac{\theta}{2}\right]$ ...(ii)

From (i) and (ii), we obtain

$$s = 4a\left[1 - \cos\dfrac{\psi}{3}\right]$$

as the required intrinsic equation.

2. *Show that in parabola* $\dfrac{2a}{r} = 1 + \cos\theta$, $\dfrac{ds}{d\psi} = 2a\, cosec^3\, \psi$.

We have

$$r = \dfrac{2a}{(1 + \cos\theta)} = a\, sec^2\, \dfrac{\theta}{2}$$

then $\quad \dfrac{dr}{d\theta} = \dfrac{2a\sin\theta}{(1+\cos\theta)^2} = \dfrac{4a \sin\dfrac{\theta}{2}\cos\dfrac{\theta}{2}}{4\cos^4\dfrac{\theta}{2}}$

$\qquad\qquad = a\, sec^2\, \dfrac{\theta}{2}\, \tan\dfrac{\theta}{2}.$

Now, $\quad \tan\phi = r\, \dfrac{d\theta}{dr} = \dfrac{a\, sec^2\, \dfrac{\theta}{2}}{a\, sec^2\, \dfrac{\theta}{2}\, \tan\dfrac{\theta}{2}}$

$\qquad\qquad = \cot\dfrac{\theta}{2} = \tan\left(\dfrac{\pi}{2} - \dfrac{\theta}{2}\right)$

$\therefore \qquad \phi = \dfrac{\pi}{2} - \dfrac{\theta}{2}$

then $\quad \psi = \theta + \phi = \theta + \dfrac{\pi}{2} - \dfrac{\theta}{2} = \dfrac{\pi}{2} + \dfrac{\theta}{2}$

hence $\quad \dfrac{d\psi}{d\theta} = \dfrac{1}{2}$ ...(i)

Now, we have

$$\frac{d\psi}{d\theta} = \sqrt{r^2 + \left(\frac{dr}{d\theta}\right)^2}$$

$$= \sqrt{a^2 \sec^4 \frac{\theta}{2} + a^2 \sec^4 \frac{\theta}{2} \tan^2 \frac{\theta}{2}}$$

$$= a \sec^3 \frac{\theta}{2} \qquad\qquad\qquad ...(ii)$$

Therefore,

$$\frac{ds}{d\psi} = \frac{ds}{d\theta} \cdot \frac{d\theta}{d\psi} = \frac{a \sec^2 \dfrac{\theta}{2}}{1/2}$$

$$= 2a \sec^3 \frac{\theta}{2} = 2a \sec^3 \left(\psi - \frac{\pi}{2}\right)$$

$$= 2a \operatorname{cosec}^3 \psi.$$

Ex. Show that the intrinsic equation of the cardioid

$$r = a\,(1 + \cos\,\theta)$$

is $s = 4a \sin \dfrac{1}{3} \psi$, taking $\theta = 0$ as the fixed point.

9.5. Rectification of ellipse. $x = a \cos\,\theta,\ y = b \sin\,\theta.$

We have

$$\left(\frac{dx}{d\theta}\right)^2 + \left(\frac{dy}{d\theta}\right)^2 = a^2 \sin^2 \theta + b^2 \cos^2 \theta$$

$$= a^2 \sin^2 \theta + a^2\,(1 - e^2) \cos^2 \theta$$

$$= a^2\,(1 - e^2 \cos^2 \theta);$$

e being the eccentricity of the ellipse. Thus the length of the ellipse is given by

$$4a \int\limits_{0}^{\pi/2} \sqrt{1 - e^2 \cos^2 \theta}\ d\theta.$$

Now, it is not possible to express this integral in terms of a combination of a finite number of algebraic, logarithmic, exponential, trigonometric or inverse trigonometric functions. This can be formulated in terms of a new type of functions known as *Elliptic Functions* only. We may, however, proceed as follows :

Now by binomial theorem, we have

$$*(1 - e^2 \cos^2 \theta)^{1/2} = 1 - \frac{1}{2} e^2 \cos^2 \theta - \frac{1}{8} e^4 \cos^4 \theta - \frac{1}{16} e^6 \cos^6 \theta - ...$$

$$\therefore \int_0^{\pi/2} \sqrt{1 - e^2 \cos^2 \theta} \, d\theta$$

$$= 1 - \frac{1}{2} e^2 \cdot \frac{1}{2} \cdot \frac{\pi}{2} - \frac{1}{8} e^4 \cdot \frac{3 \cdot 1 \cdot \pi}{4 \cdot 2 \cdot 2} - \frac{1}{16} e^6 \cdot \frac{5 \cdot 3 \cdot 1 \cdot \pi}{6 \cdot 4 \cdot 2 \cdot 2} - .....$$

$$= 1 - \frac{1}{8} e^2 \pi - \frac{3}{128} e^4 \pi - \frac{5}{512} e^6 \pi - .....$$

Thus we can find the length of the ellipse up to any number of decimal places.

EXERCISES ON CHAPTER 9

1. Find the length of the cardioid $r = a (1 - \cos \theta)$, lying outside the circle $r = a \cos \theta$.

2. Show that the length of a loop of the curve
$$r = a (1 + \cos 2\theta)$$
is $\frac{2}{3} \sqrt{3} [2\sqrt{3} + \log (\sqrt{3} + 2)] a$.

3. Show that the point $\theta = \pi/6$ divides the arc of the curve
$$x = a \cos^3 \theta, \, y = a \sin^3 \theta,$$
lying in the first quadrant in the ratio $1 : 3$.

4. Find the length of the curve defined by the equations
$$x \cos \theta = a \cos (\tan \theta - \theta),$$
$$y \cos \theta = a \sin (\tan \theta - \theta),$$
between the points for which $\theta = 0$ and $\theta = \alpha < \frac{1}{2} \pi$.

5. Show that the length of the curve whose equation is
$$4 (x^2 + y^2) - a^2 = 3a^{4/3} y^{2/3}$$
is equal to $6a$.

$$\left[\text{**Hint.** It may be shown that } \left(\frac{ds}{dy} \right)^2 = \frac{a^{4/3}}{4y^{2/3} (a^{2/3} - y^{2/3})}. \right]$$

---

* It may be remembered that the theorem *the integral of a sum is equal to the sum of the integrals* may not be true in the case of the sum of an infinite series. In the present case, however, this is true but the justification thereof is beyond the scope of this book.

6. Trace the curve
$$x = a\left(\sin\theta + \frac{1}{3}\sin 3\theta\right), \quad y = a\left(\cos\theta - \frac{1}{3}\cos 3\theta\right)$$
and show that its length is $8a$.

7. Trace the curve
$$x = a\,(\theta + \cos\theta\sin\theta - \sin\theta), \quad y = a\,(\cos^2\theta - \cos\theta)$$
and find the length of its one span which is obtained as θ varies from 0 to 2π.

8. Find the length of the arc of the curve $y = e^x$ measured from $x = 0$ to $x = 1$.

9. Find the length of the arc of the curve $r = a / \theta^2$, as θ ranges from 1 to 2.

10. Find the length of the arc and the area cut off by $y = mx$ from the curve $y^3 = ax^2$.

11. If s be the length of the curve
$$r = a\tanh\frac{1}{2}\theta,$$
between the origin and $\theta = 2\pi$, and Δ be the area under the curve between the same two points, prove that
$$\Delta = a\,(s - a\pi).$$

12. If 's' be the length of the curve
$$a\theta = \sqrt{r^2 - a^2} - a\sec^{-1}(r/a)$$
enclosed between the points $r = a$ and $r = 2a$ and, A the area of the sector subtended by it at the pole, then $\sqrt{3}\,A = as$.

13. A curve is given by
$$x = a\sin\theta - b\sin 2\theta, \quad y = a\cos\theta - b\cos 2\theta;$$
show that its perimeter is equal to that of an ellipse with semi-axes $a + 2b$, $a - 2b$.

14. Show that the intrinsic equation of the curve
$$x = e^\theta\sin\theta, \quad y = e^\theta\cos\theta$$
is $se^{(-\pi/4)} + \sqrt{2} = \sqrt{2}\,(\cosh\psi - \sinh\psi)$,
where $\theta = \pi/4$ is the fixed point.

15. Find the intrinsic equation of the curve $y = \log x$, taking the point $(1, 0)$ as the fixed point.

ANSWERS

1. $4a\sqrt{3}$.   4. $\dfrac{1}{2}a\tan^2\alpha$.   7. $a\left(4\sqrt{3} + \dfrac{2}{3}\pi\right)$.

8. $\sqrt{e^2+1} - \log[(1+\sqrt{1+e^2})/(\sqrt{2}+1)] - (\sqrt{2}-1)$.

9. $\dfrac{1}{4}a\,[2\sqrt{5} - \sqrt{2} + \log\{(\sqrt{2}-1)/(\sqrt{5}-2)\}]$.

10. $\dfrac{a}{27m^3}[(4m^2+9)^{3/2} - 8m^3]$, $\dfrac{a^2}{10m^5}$.

15. $s = \dfrac{\sqrt{2}}{\cos\psi - \sin\psi} - \sqrt{2} + \log(\sqrt{2}+1) - \log\dfrac{\sqrt{2} + \cos\psi - \sin\psi}{\cos\psi + \sin\psi}$.

OBJECTIVE QUESTIONS

For each of the following questions, four alternatives are given for the answer. Only one of them is correct. Choose the correct alternative.

1. Rectification is the process of evaluating the :

   (a) double integrals

   (b) multiple integrals

   (c) the length of arcs of plane curves

   (d) the area under plane curves.

2. The arc length of the curve $y = f(x)$ lying between two points for which $x = a$ and $x = b$ ($b > a$) is given by :

   (a) $\displaystyle\int_a^b y\,dx$ (b) $\pi\displaystyle\int_a^b y^2\,dx$

   (c) $\displaystyle\int_a^b \sqrt{1+\left(\dfrac{dy}{dx}\right)^2}\,dx$ (d) $\displaystyle\int_a^b \sqrt{1+\left(\dfrac{dx}{dy}\right)^2}\,dx$.

3. The length of the arc of the parabola $x^2 = 4ay$ from the vertex to one extremity of the latus rectum is given by :

   (a) $\displaystyle\int_0^{2a} \sqrt{1+\dfrac{x^2}{4a^2}}\,dx$ (b) $\displaystyle\int_0^{2a} \sqrt{1+\dfrac{4a^2}{x^2}}\,dx$

   (c) $\displaystyle\int_0^{a} \sqrt{\dfrac{1+y}{a}}\,dx$ (d) $\displaystyle\int_0^{a} \sqrt{1+\dfrac{x^2}{4a^2}}\,dx$.

4. The length of the arc of the curve $y = \log\sec x$ between $x = 0$ and $x = \pi/6$ is equal to :

   (a) $\log 3$ (b) $2\log 3$ (c) $\dfrac{1}{2}\log 3$ (d) None of these.

5. The perimeter of the curve $r = 2\cos\theta$ is :

   (a) $\dfrac{1}{2}\pi$ (b) π (c) $\dfrac{3}{2}\pi$ (d) 2π.

6. Whole length of the curve $x = a \cos^3 t$, $y = a \sin^3 t$ is :

   (a) $2a$ (b) $4a$ (c) $6a$ (d) $8a$.

7. Length of the arc of the curve $x = e^\theta \sin \theta$, $y = e^\theta \cos \theta$ from $\theta = 0$
   to $\theta = \pi / 2$ is :

   (a) $e^{\pi/2}$ (b) $\sqrt{2} \, (e^{\pi/2} - 1)$

   (c) $\sqrt{2} \, (e^{\pi/2} + 1)$ (d) $\dfrac{e^{\pi/2}}{\sqrt{2}}$.

8. Perimeter of the cardioid $r = a \, (1 + \cos \theta)$ is :

   (a) $2a$ (b) $4a$ (c) $6a$ (d) $8a$.

                                                        (*Avadh, 2003*)

9. Intrinsic equation of a curve is a relation between :

   (a) r and θ (b) x and y (c) s and ψ (d) x and ψ.

                                        (*Avadh, 2002; Rohilkhand, 2001*)

10. Intrinsic equation of $y = a \log \sec (x / a)$ is :

    (a) $s = a \log (\sec \psi + \tan \psi)$ (b) $9s = 4a \, (\sec^3 \psi - 1)$
    (c) $27s = 8a \, (\operatorname{cosec}^3 \psi - 1)$ (d) None of these.

11. Intrinsic equation of the catenary $y = c \cosh \left(\dfrac{x}{a} \right)$ is :

    (a) $s = a \log (\sec \psi + \tan \psi)$ (b) $s = a \tan \psi$
    (c) $9s = 4a \, (\sec^3 \psi - 1)$ (d) None of these.

12. Intrinsic equation of $y^3 = ax^2$ is :

    (a) $s = a \log (\sec \psi + \tan \psi)$ (b) $s = a \tan \psi$
    (c) $9s = 4a \, (\sec^3 \psi - 1)$ (d) None of these.

ANSWERS

1. (c)	2. (c)	3. (a)	4. (c)
5. (d)	6. (c)	7. (b)	8. (d)
9. (c)	10. (a)	11. (b)	12. (d)

10

Volumes and Surfaces of Revolution

10.1. Let AB be an arc of a curve and let CD be a straight line which does not intersect the curve.

Draw AL and BM perpendiculars to the line CD.

A solid will be obtained if the region ALMBA revolves about the line CD. This solid is said to be obtained by the revolution of the arc AB about the line CD.

In this chapter we shall learn how to obtain the volume of this solid and also the area of its surface.

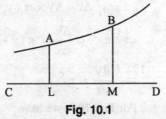

Fig. 10.1

The line CD about which the curve rotates is called the *axis of revolution.*

To start with, we take X-axis as axis of revolution, and obtain expressions for the volume and the surface of the solid. Later on, we shall obtain expressions for the volume and the surface when any line is the axis of revolution.

10.2. Volume of a solid of revolution. *To show that the volume obtained by revolving about X-axis the arc of the curve $y = f(x)$, intercepted between the points whose abscissae are a, b is*

$$\int_a^b \pi y^2 \, dx, \ i.e., \ \int_a^b \pi [f(x)]^2 \, dx;$$

it being assumed that the arc does not cut X-axis.

Let G, H, be points on the curve $y = f(x)$ with abscissae a and b. Let $P(x, y)$ be a variable point on the curve. Let V be the volume of the solid

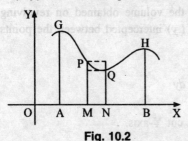

Fig. 10.2

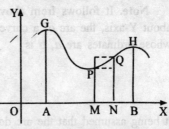

Fig. 10.3

343

obtained by revolving the arc GP about X-axis so that V is a function of x. We take another point

$$Q\ (x + \Delta x,\ y + \Delta y)$$

on the curve so near P that, as a point moves on the curve from P to Q, its ordinate either constantly increases as in Fig. 10.2 or constantly decreases as in Fig. 10.3. Complete the rectangles NP, MQ.

Now ΔV, which is the volume obtained by revolving the arc PQ, lies between the volumes of the two discs obtained by revolving the two rectangles NP, MQ about X-axis.

For Fig. 10.2, we have

$$\pi y^2\ \Delta x < \Delta V < \pi\ (y + \Delta y)^2\ \Delta x$$

$$\Rightarrow \quad \pi y^2 < \frac{\Delta V}{\Delta x} < \pi\ (y + \Delta y)^2$$

$$\Rightarrow \quad \frac{d V}{dx} = \pi y^2.$$

For Fig. 10.3, we have

$$\pi\ (y + \Delta y)^2\ \Delta x < \Delta V < \pi y^2\ \Delta x$$

$$\Rightarrow \quad \pi\ (y + \Delta y)^2 < \frac{\Delta V}{\Delta x} < \pi y^2$$

$$\Rightarrow \quad \frac{d V}{dx} = \pi y^2,\ \text{as before.}$$

Thus $\displaystyle\int_a^b \pi y^2\ dx = \int_a^b \frac{d V}{dx}\ dx = \left|\ V\ \right|_a^b$

= value of V for x equal to b – value of V for x equal to a

= the value of V for x equal to $b - 0$

= the volume of the solid obtained by revolving the arc GH about X-axis.

Note. It follows from above that the volume obtained on revolving about Y-axis, the arc of a curve $x = f\ (y)$ intercepted between the points whose ordinates are a, b is

$$\int_a^b \pi x^2\ dy$$

it being assumed that the arc does not cut Y-axis.

EXAMPLES

1. *Find the volume of the solid obtained by revolving the ellipse* $x^2/a^2 + y^2/b^2 = 1$ *about the axis of x.* (*Kanpur, 2001; Vikram, 1997; Bhopal, 2000; Indore, 1998, 99; Bilaspur, 1999*)

It is easy to see that the solid obtained by revolving the arc ABA' about X-axis is the same as the solid obtained by revolving the whole ellipse. Also, the volume of the solid is double the volume of the solid obtained by revolving the arc AB. The required volume, therefore,

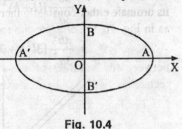

Fig. 10.4

$$= 2\pi \int_0^a y^2 dx = 2\pi \frac{b^2}{a^2} \int_0^a (a^2 - x^2)\, dx$$

$$= 2\pi \frac{b^2}{a^2} \left| a^2 x - \frac{x^3}{3} \right|_0^a = \frac{4}{3} \pi a b^2.$$

2. *If the hyperbola* $\dfrac{x^2}{a^2} - \dfrac{y^2}{b^2} = 1$ *revolves about the x-axis, show that the volume included between the surface thus generated, the cone generated by the asymptote and two planes perpendicular to the axis, of x, at a distance h apart, is equal to that of a circular cylinder of height h and radius b.*

The equation of the hyperbola is $\dfrac{x^2}{a^2} - \dfrac{y^2}{b^2} = 1.$

The equation of asymptotes is

$$\frac{x^2}{a^2} - \frac{y^2}{b^2} = 0$$

or $\qquad x = \pm \dfrac{b}{a} x.$

OK is an asymptote which is $y = \dfrac{b}{a} x.$

Let us take two perpendicular planes $x = l$ and $x = l + h$ from the origin which are at a distance h.

The volume of the part of the cone generated by asymptote between the planes $x = l$ and $x = l + h$

$$= \int_l^{l+h} \pi y^2\, dx = \pi \int_l^{l+h} \frac{b^2}{a^2} x^2\, dx$$

$$= \frac{\pi b^2}{3a^2}\left[\frac{x^3}{3}\right]_l^{l+h}$$

$$= \frac{\pi b^2}{3a^2}[(l+h)^3 - l^3]$$

$$= \frac{\pi b^2}{3a^2}[3l^2 h + 3lh^2 + h^3]. \qquad ...(i)$$

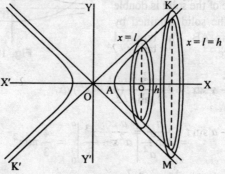

Fig. 10.5

Now the volume of the portion of the solid generated by the hyperbola between two planes

$$= \int_l^{l+h} \pi y^2 \, dx \text{ for the curve } \frac{x^2}{a^2} - \frac{y^2}{b^2} = 1$$

$$= \int_l^{l+h} b^2 \pi \left(\frac{x^2}{a^2} - 1\right) dx$$

$$= \frac{\pi b^2}{a^2}\int_l^{l+h} (x^2 - a^2)\, dx = \frac{\pi b^2}{a^2}\left[\frac{x^3}{3} - a^2 x\right]_l^{l+h}$$

$$= \frac{\pi b^2}{3a^2}[(l+h)^3 - 3a^2(l+h) - l^2 + 3a^2 l]$$

$$= \frac{\pi b^2}{3a^2}[3l^2 h + 3lh^2 + h^3 + 3a^2 h]. \qquad ...(ii)$$

The required volume

$$= (i) - (ii) = \frac{\pi b^2}{3a^2}(3a^2 h)$$

$$= \pi b^2 h$$

= volume of the cylinder of radius b and height h.

3. *Find the volume of the solid generated by the revolution of the tractrix* $x = a \cos t + \dfrac{1}{2} a \log \tan^2 t/2$, $y = a \sin t$ *about its asymptote.*

(Rohilkhand, 1993, 99)

The asymptote is x-axis, *i.e.*, $y = 0$ for the curve. The required volume

$$= 2 \int_0^{\pi/2} \pi y^2 \frac{dx}{dt} dt.$$

We have

$$x = a \cos t + \frac{a}{2} \log \tan^2 t/2$$

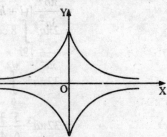

Fig. 10.6

$$\therefore \quad \frac{dx}{dt} = -a \sin t + \frac{2a \sec^2 t/2}{2 \tan t/2}$$

$$= -a \sin t + \frac{a}{\sin t} = \frac{a \cos^2 t}{\sin t}$$

$$\therefore \quad \text{Volume} = 2\pi \int_0^{\pi/2} a^2 \sin^2 t \cdot \frac{a \cos^2 t}{\sin t} dt$$

$$= 2\pi a^3 \int_0^{\pi/2} \sin t \cos^2 t \, dt$$

$$= 2\pi a^3 \cdot \frac{\Gamma 1 \cdot \Gamma\left(\dfrac{3}{2}\right)}{2\Gamma\left(\dfrac{5}{2}\right)} = \frac{2}{3} \pi a^3.$$

4. *Find the volume of the solid obtained by revolving one arc of the cycloid*

$$x = a\,(\theta + \sin \theta), \; y = a\,(1 + \cos \theta)$$

about X-axis.

(Kumaon, 2002)

The volume of the solid obtained by revolving the arc A'BA is double the volume of the solid obtained by revolving the arc AB. As a point moves from B to A, the value of the parameter θ increases from 0 to π. Therefore the required volume

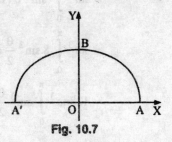

Fig. 10.7

$$= 2\pi \int_0^{\pi a} y^2 \, dx, \text{ where } OA = \pi a.$$

Changing the variable x to θ, we see that the volume

$$= 2\pi \int_0^\pi a^2 (1 + \cos\theta)^2 \, a \, (1 + \cos\theta) \, d\theta$$

$$= 2\pi a^3 \int_0^\pi 8 \cos^6 \frac{\theta}{2} \, d\theta$$

$$= 32\pi a^3 \int_0^{\pi/2} \cos^6 \varphi \, d\varphi, \text{ where } \varphi = \frac{\theta}{2};$$

$$= 32\pi a^3 \cdot \frac{5}{6} \cdot \frac{3}{4} \cdot \frac{1}{2} \cdot \frac{\pi}{2} = 5\pi^2 a^3.$$

5. *Find the volume of the solid obtained by revolving the cardioide*
$r = a \, (1 + \cos\theta)$ *about the initial line.*

(*Agra, 2001; Rohilkhand, 2002; Kumaon, 2000; Jiwaji, 1997;*
Sagar, 1996; Rewa, 1997; Bilaspur, 2000)

The required volume

$$= \pi \int_0^{2a} y^2 \, dx, \text{ for } OA = 2a.$$

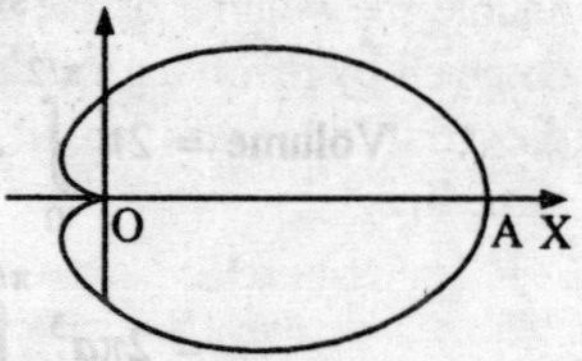

We change the variables x and y to θ.

We have

$$x = r \cos\theta = a \cos\theta \, (1 + \cos\theta)$$

$$y = r \sin\theta = a \sin\theta \, (1 + \cos\theta)$$

$$\therefore \qquad dx = -a \, (\sin\theta + 2 \sin\theta \cos\theta) \, d\theta.$$

Also, $\quad \theta = \pi$ when $x = 0$ and $\theta = 0$, when $x = 2a$.

Fig. 10.8

$$\therefore \quad V = -\pi \int_\pi^0 a^2 \sin^2\theta \, (1 + \cos\theta)^2 \, a \sin\theta \, (1 + 2\cos\theta) \, d\theta$$

$$= \pi a^2 \int_0^\pi \sin^3\theta \, (1 + \cos\theta)^2 \, (1 + 2\cos\theta) \, d\theta$$

$$= \pi a^3 \int_0^\pi 8 \sin^3\frac{\theta}{2} \cos^3\frac{\theta}{2} \cdot 4 \cos^4\frac{\theta}{2} \left(4 \cos^2\frac{\theta}{2} - 1\right) d\theta$$

$$= 128\pi a^3 \int_0^\pi \sin^3\frac{\theta}{2} \cos^9\frac{\theta}{2} \, d\theta - 32\pi a^3 \int_0^\pi \sin^3\frac{\theta}{2} \cos^7\frac{\theta}{2} \, d\theta$$

$$- 32\pi a^3 \int_0^{\pi/2} \sin^3\frac{\theta}{2} \cos^7\frac{\theta}{2} \, d\theta$$

$$= 256\pi a^3 \int_0^{\pi/2} \sin^3 \varphi \cos^9 \varphi \, d\varphi$$

$$- 64\pi a^3 \int_0^{\pi/2} \sin^3 \varphi \cos^7 \varphi \, d\varphi, \text{ where } \varphi = \theta/2$$

$$= 256\pi a^3 \frac{2 \cdot 8 \cdot 6 \cdot 4 \cdot 2}{12 \cdot 10 \cdot 8 \cdot 6 \cdot 4 \cdot 2} - 64\pi a^3 \frac{2 \cdot 6 \cdot 4 \cdot 2}{10 \cdot 8 \cdot 6 \cdot 4 \cdot 2}$$

$$= \frac{64\pi a^3}{25} - \frac{8\pi a^3}{5} = \frac{8\pi a^3}{5}.$$

6. *Find the volume of the solid obtained by revolving the lemniscate* $r^2 = a^2 \cos 2\theta$ *about the initial line.*

The volume of the solid obtained by revolving the whole curve about the initial line is double the volume of the solid obtained by revolving the arc in the first quadrant about the same line.

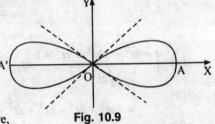

Fig. 10.9

The required volume, therefore,

$$= 2\pi \int_0^a y^2 \, dx \text{ for } OA = a.$$

We change the variables x and y to θ. We have

$$x = r \cos \theta = a \sqrt{\cos 2\theta} \cos \theta$$

$$\Rightarrow \quad dx = \left(-a \sqrt{\cos 2\theta} \cdot \sin \theta - \frac{a \sin 2\theta}{\sqrt{\cos 2\theta}} \cos \theta \right) d\theta$$

$$= -a \frac{\sin 3\theta}{\sqrt{\cos 2\theta}} \, d\theta.$$

Also,

$$y^2 = r^2 \sin^2 \theta = a^2 \cos 2\theta \sin^2 \theta.$$

Again $\theta = \pi/4$ when $x = 0$ and $\theta = 0$ when $x = a$.

$$\therefore \quad \text{Volume} = -2\pi a \int_{\pi/4}^0 a^2 \cos 2\theta \sin^2 \theta \frac{\sin 3\theta}{\sqrt{\cos 2\theta}} \, d\theta$$

$$= 2\pi a^3 \int_0^{\pi/4} \sin^2 \theta \sin 3\theta \sqrt{\cos 2\theta} \, d\theta$$

$$= 2\pi a^3 \int_0^{\pi/4} \sin^2 \theta \, (3 \sin \theta - 4 \sin^3 \theta) \sqrt{\cos 2\theta} \, d\theta.$$

We put

$$\cos \theta = t \implies -\sin \theta \, d\theta = dt.$$

$$\therefore \quad \text{Volume} = -2\pi a^3 \int_1^{\sqrt{1/2}} (1 - t^2)(4t^2 - 1) \cdot \sqrt{2t^2 - 1} \, dt.$$

We write

$$(1 - t^2)(4t^2 - 1) \sqrt{2t^2 - 1} = \frac{(1 - t^2)(4t^2 - 1)(2t^2 - 1)}{\sqrt{2t^2 - 1}}$$

$$= \frac{-8t^6 + 14t^4 - 7t^2 + 1}{\sqrt{2t^2 - 1}}.$$

Let $\displaystyle \int \frac{-8t^6 + 14t^4 - 7t^2 + 1}{\sqrt{2t^2 - 1}} \, dt$

$$= (at^5 + bt^4 + ct^3 + dt^2 + et + f) \sqrt{2t^2 - 1} + g \int \frac{dt}{\sqrt{2t^2 - 1}}.$$

Differentiating and multiplying with $\sqrt{2t^2 - 1}$, we obtain

$$-8t^6 + 14t^4 - 7t^2 + 1 = (5at^4 + 4bt^3 + 3ct^2 + 2dt + e)(2t^2 - 1)$$
$$+ 2t \, (at^5 + bt^4 + ct^3 + dt^2 + et + f) + g.$$

Equating the coefficients of like powers of t, we get

$$12a = -8; \qquad 10b = 0; \qquad 8c - 5a = 14;$$
$$6d - 4b = 0; \qquad 4e - 3c = -7; \qquad -2d + 2f = 0;$$
$$-e + g = 1.$$

$$\therefore \quad a = \frac{2}{3}, \, b = 0, \, c = \frac{4}{3}, \, d = 0, \, e = -\frac{3}{4}, \, f = 0, \, g = \frac{1}{4}.$$

$$\therefore \quad \int_1^{\sqrt{1/2}} \frac{-8t^6 + 14t^4 - 7t^2 + 1}{\sqrt{2t^2 - 1}} \, dt$$

$$= \left| \left(-\frac{2}{3} t^5 + \frac{4}{3} t^3 - \frac{3}{4} t \right) \sqrt{2t^2 - 1} \right|_1^{\sqrt{1/2}} + \frac{1}{4} \int_1^{\sqrt{1/2}} \frac{dt}{\sqrt{2t^2 - 1}}$$

$$= \left| \left(-\frac{2}{3} t^5 + \frac{4}{3} t^3 - \frac{3}{4} t \right) \sqrt{2t^2 - 1} \right|_1^{\sqrt{1/2}}$$

$$+ \frac{1}{4} \left| \frac{\log[\sqrt{2}\, t + \sqrt{2t^2 - 1}]}{\sqrt{2}} \right|_{1}^{\sqrt{1/2}}$$

$$= \frac{1}{12} - \frac{1}{4\sqrt{2}} \log(\sqrt{2} + 1).$$

$$\therefore \quad V = \frac{\pi a^3}{2} \left[\frac{1}{\sqrt{2}} \log(\sqrt{2} + 1) - \frac{1}{3} \right].$$

EXERCISES

1. The loop of the curve $2ay^2 = x(x - a)^2$ revolves about X-axis; find the volume of the solid so generated.

2. Find the volume of the solid obtained by revolving the loop of the curve $a^2y^2 = x^2(2a - x)(x - a)$ about X-axis.

3. Find the area enclosed by the curve $xy^2 = 4(2 - x)$ and Y-axis and also the volume of the solid formed by the revolution of the curve through four right angles about the X-axis.

4. Prove that the volume of the solid generated by the revolution of an ellipse round its minor axis, is a mean proportional between that generated by the revolution of the ellipse and of its auxiliary circle round the major axis.

5. Find the volume of the spindle shaped solid generated by revolving the hypocycloid $x^{2/3} + y^{2/3} = a^{2/3}$ about X-axis.

(Vikram, 1995; Ravishankar, 1998, 2000)

6. Prove that the volume of the solid generated by the revolution of the curve $y = a^3/(a^2 + x^2)$ about its asymptote is $\pi^2 a^3/2$.

7. Show that the volume of the solid obtained by revolving the area included between the curves $y^2 = x^3$ and $x^2 = y^3$ about X-axis is $5\pi/28$.

8. Find the volume formed by the revolution of the loop of the curve $y^2 = x^2(a - x)/(a + x)$ about the X-axis. *(Kanpur, 2002)*

9. Prove that the volume of the reel formed by the revolution of the cycloid $x = a(\theta + \sin\theta)$, $y = a(1 - \cos\theta)$ about the X-axis is $\pi^2 a^3$.

10. Show that the volume of the solid generated by the revolution of the cycloid

$$x = a(\theta + \sin\theta),\ y = a(1 - \cos\theta)$$

about the y-axis is $\pi a^3 \left(\frac{3}{2}\pi^2 - \frac{3}{2} \right)$.

11. Find the volume generated by the portion of the arc

$$y = \sqrt{1 + x^2},$$

lying between $x = 0$ and $x = 4$, as it revolves about the axis of x.

12. Trace the curve $y = e^x \sin x$ as x varies from 0 to π and show that the volume of the solid obtained by revolving it about X-axis is $\pi(e^{2\pi} - 1)/8$.

13. Trace the curves $y = \sin x$ and $y = \cos x$ as x varies from 0 to $\pi/2$ and show that the volume of the solid obtained by revolving about X-axis the region enclosed by them and the X-axis is $\pi (\pi - 2)/4$.

14. Find the volume of the solid generated by rotating completely about X-axis the area enclosed between $y^2 = x^3 + 5x$ and the lines $x = 2$ and $x = 4$.

15. Find the volume generated by the revolution of an arc of the catenary

$$y = c \cosh \frac{x}{c},$$

about the axis of x between $x = a$ and $x = b$.

16. Show that the volume of the solid obtained by revolving about X-axis the area enclosed by the parabola $y^2 = 4ax$ and its evolute

$$27ay^2 = 4 (x - 2a)^3$$

is $80\pi a^3$.

17. The figure bounded by a parabola and the tangents at the extremities of its latus rectum revolves about the axis of the parabola; show that the volume of the solid thus obtained is $2a^3\pi/3$; $4a$ being the latus rectum of the parabola.

18. Find the volume generated by $y = x \sin mx$, as the area lying between $x = 0$ and $x = 2\pi/m$ revolves about X-axis.

19. The loop of the curve $r = a \cos 3\theta$ lying between $\theta = -\pi/6$ and $\theta = \pi/6$ revolves about the initial line; show that the volume of the solid thus obtained is $19\pi a^3/960$.

20. Prove that the volume generated by the revolution about the initial line of the limacon $r = a + b \cos \theta$, $a > b$, is $4\pi a (a^2 + b^2)/3$.

ANSWERS

1. $\pi a^3/24$.   **2.** $23a^3\pi/60$.   **3.** $4\pi, 4\pi^2$.

5. $32\pi a^3/105$.   **8.** $\dfrac{2}{3}\pi a^3 \log (8/e^2)$.   **11.** $76\pi/3$.

14. 90π.   **15.** $\left[\dfrac{\pi c^2}{4}\left(2x + \sinh \dfrac{2x}{c}\right)\right]_a^b$.

18. $\pi^2 (8\pi^2 - 3)/6m^3$.

10.3. Any axis of revolution. We interpret the result obtained in § 10.2 in the following manner :

y, is the length of the perpendicular PM of a point on the curve from the axis of revolution, M being the foot of this perpendicular; x denotes the distance of the foot of the perpendicular M from a fixed point O on the axis, a and b are the distances from the fixed point O of the feet A, B of the perpendicular from the extreme ends G, H of the given arc.

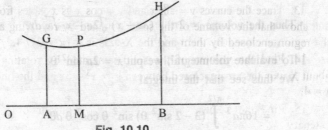

Fig. 10.10

From this we deduce that the volume obtained by revolving the arc GH about the line AB is

$$\int_{OA}^{OP} \pi \, (MP^2) \, d \, (OM).$$

EXAMPLES

1. *Find the volume of the solid obtained by the revolution of the cissoid*

$$y^2 \, (2a - x) = x^3$$

about its asymptote.

The line $x = 2a$ is the asymptote of the curve. The perpendicular distance MP of any point P (x, y) on the curve from the asymptote is

$$2a - x.$$

We take the point A, where the asymptote meets the X-axis as the fixed point on the axis of revolution. By symmetry, the volume of the solid obtained by revolving the whole curve about the asymptote is double of the volume obtained by revolving the part of it lying in the first quadrant.

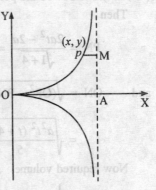

Fig. 10.11

The required volume

$$= 2\pi \int_{0}^{\infty} (MP)^2 \, d \, (AM) = 2\pi \int_{0}^{\infty} (2a - x)^2 \, dy.$$

We change the independent variable from y to x.

Since $\quad y = \dfrac{x^{3/2}}{\sqrt{2a - x}}$

we have, $\quad dy = \dfrac{(3a - x) \sqrt{x} \sqrt{2a - x}}{(2a - x)^2} \, dx.$

Thus the volume $= 2\pi \int\limits_0^{2a} (3a - x) \sqrt{2a - x} \sqrt{x}\, dx.$

To evaluate the integral, we put $x = 2a \sin^2 \theta.$

We thus see that the integral

$$= 16\pi a^3 \int\limits_0^{\pi/2} (3 - 2 \sin^2 \theta) \sin^2 \theta \cos^2 \theta\, d\theta$$

$$= 16\pi a^3 \left[3 \int\limits_0^{\pi/2} \sin^2 \theta \cos^2 \theta\, d\theta - 2 \int\limits_0^{\pi/2} \sin^4 \theta \cos^2 \theta\, d\theta \right]$$

$$= 16\pi a^3 \left[\frac{3 \cdot 1 \cdot 1}{4 \cdot 2} \cdot \frac{\pi}{2} - 2 \cdot \frac{3 \cdot 1}{6 \cdot 4 \cdot 2} \cdot \frac{\pi}{2} \right] = 2\pi^2 a^3.$$

2. *The area cut off from the parabola* $y^2 = 4ax$ *by the chord joining the vertex to an end of the latus rectum is rotated through four right angles about the chord. Find the volume of the solid so formed.*

The equation of the line OB is $y = 2x.$ Let the coordinates of P be $(at^2, 2at)$ and PN be the perpendicular upon OB.

Then

$$PN = \frac{2at^2 - 2a}{\sqrt{1 + 4}} = \frac{2at(t - 1)}{\sqrt{5}}$$

and $ON = \sqrt{(OP^2 - PN^2)} = \sqrt{(at^2)^2 + (2at)^2 - \frac{4}{5} a^2 (t^2 - t)^2}$

$$= \sqrt{\frac{a^2 t^2 (t + 4)^2}{5}} = \frac{at(t + 4)}{\sqrt{5}}.$$

Now required volume

$$= \int\limits_0^1 \pi\, PN^2 \frac{d\,(ON)}{dt}\, dt$$

$$= \pi \int\limits_0^1 \frac{4a^2 t^2 (t - 1)^2}{5} \cdot \frac{2at + 4a}{\sqrt{5}}\, dt$$

$$= \frac{8\pi a^3}{5\sqrt{5}} \int\limits_0^1 t^2 (t - 1)^2 (t + 2)\, dt$$

$$= \frac{8\pi a^3}{5\sqrt{5}} \left[\frac{t^6}{6} - \frac{3t^4}{4} + \frac{2t^3}{3} \right]_0^1$$

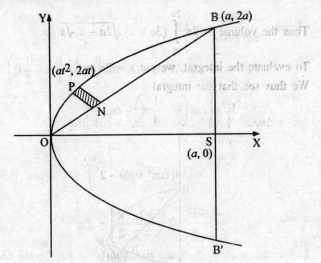

Fig. 10.12

$$= \frac{8\pi a^3}{5\sqrt{5}}\left[\frac{1}{6}-\frac{3}{4}+\frac{2}{3}\right] = \frac{8\pi a^3}{5\sqrt{5}}\cdot\frac{1}{12}$$

$$= \frac{2\pi a^3}{15\sqrt{5}} = \frac{2\sqrt{5}}{75}\pi a^3.$$

3. *A quadrant of a circle of radius a revolves about its chord. Show that the volume of the spindle generated is*

$$\frac{\pi}{6\sqrt{2}}(10-3\pi)\,a^3.$$

The equation of the circle is $x^2 + y^2 = a^2$.

Let P be any point on the arc AB, which is quadrant of the circle. Let there be an angle θ which is $\angle POA$. PM is perpendicular on AN.

Now in $\triangle OPA$

$$AP^2 = OA^2 + OP^2 - 2OA\cdot OP\cos\theta$$

$$= a^2 + a^2 - 2a\cdot a\cos\theta = 2a^2(1-\cos\theta)$$

$$= 4a^2\sin^2\frac{\theta}{2}.$$

$$\therefore \qquad AP = 2a\sin(\theta/2).$$

But $\angle PAM = \dfrac{1}{2}\angle POB$ (can be proved easily by geometry)

$$= \frac{1}{2}\left(\frac{1}{2}\pi-\theta\right) = \frac{1}{4}\pi - \frac{1}{2}\theta.$$

Hence $\quad \dfrac{\text{PM}}{\sin \text{PAM}} = \text{AP}$

or $\quad\quad \text{PM} = \text{AP} \sin \text{APM} = 2a \sin \dfrac{\theta}{2} \cos \left(\dfrac{1}{4} \pi - \dfrac{1}{2} \theta \right)$

$$= a \left[\cos \left(\theta - \dfrac{1}{4} \pi \right) - \cos \dfrac{\pi}{4} \right]$$

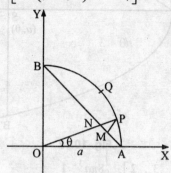

Fig. 10.13

and $\quad\quad \text{AM} = \text{AP} \cos \text{PAM} = 2a \sin \dfrac{\theta}{2} \cos \left(\dfrac{\pi}{4} - \dfrac{\theta}{2} \right)$

$$= a \left[\sin \dfrac{\pi}{4} + \sin \left(\theta - \dfrac{\pi}{4} \right) \right]$$

The solid obtained after revolution will have limits 0 to $\pi / 2$.

$$\dfrac{d\,(\text{AM})}{d\theta} = \dfrac{d \left[a \left\{ \sin \dfrac{\pi}{4} + \sin \left(\theta - \dfrac{\pi}{4} \right) \right\} \right]}{d\theta}$$

The required volume

$$= \pi \int\limits_{0}^{\pi/2} \text{PM}^2 \, \dfrac{d\,(\text{AM})}{d\theta} \, d\theta$$

$$= \pi \int\limits_{0}^{\pi/2} a^3 \left[\cos \left(\theta - \dfrac{\pi}{4} \right) - \cos \dfrac{\pi}{4} \right]^2 \cdot \cos \left(\theta - \dfrac{\pi}{4} \right) d\theta$$

$$= \pi a^3 \int\limits_{0}^{\pi/2} \dfrac{1}{2\sqrt{2}} \left[(\cos \theta + \sin \theta) - 1 \right]^2 (\cos \theta + \sin \theta) \, d\theta$$

$$= \dfrac{\pi a^3}{2\sqrt{2}} \int\limits_{0}^{\pi/2} \left[(\cos \theta + \sin \theta)^2 + 1 - 2 (\cos \theta + \sin \theta) \right] (\cos \theta + \sin \theta) \, d\theta$$

$$= \frac{\pi a^3}{2\sqrt{2}} \int_0^{\pi/2} [(\cos\theta + \sin\theta)^3 + (\cos\theta + \sin\theta) - 2(\cos\theta + \sin\theta)^2]\, d\theta$$

$$= \frac{\pi a^3}{2\sqrt{2}} \int_0^{\pi/2} [\cos^3\theta + 3\cos^2\theta \sin\theta + 3\cos\theta \sin^2\theta$$

$$+ \sin^3\theta + \cos\theta + \sin\theta - 2 - 4\sin\theta\cos\theta]\, d\theta$$

$$= \frac{\pi a^3}{2\sqrt{2}} \left[\int_0^{\pi/2} \cos^3\theta\, d\theta + 3\int_0^{\pi/2} \cos^2\theta \sin\theta\, d\theta \right.$$

$$+ 3\int_0^{\pi/2} \cos\theta \sin^2\theta\, d\theta + \int_0^{\pi/2} \sin^3\theta\, d\theta$$

$$\left. + \int_0^{\pi/2} \cos\theta\, d\theta + \int_0^{\pi/2} \sin\theta\, d\theta - 2\int_0^{\pi/2} d\theta - 4\int_0^{\pi/2} \sin\theta\cos\theta\, d\theta \right]$$

$$= \frac{\pi a^3}{2\sqrt{2}} \left\{ 2 \cdot \frac{\Gamma 2 \cdot \Gamma\frac{1}{2}}{2\Gamma\frac{5}{2}} + 6 \cdot \left[\frac{\Gamma\frac{3}{2}\cdot\Gamma 1}{\Gamma\frac{5}{2}}\right]_0^\pi + 2 \cdot \frac{\Gamma 1 \cdot \Gamma\frac{1}{2}}{\frac{3}{2}} - 4 \cdot \left[\frac{\sin^2\theta}{2}\right]_0^\pi - \pi \right\}$$

$$= \frac{\pi a^3}{2\sqrt{2}} \left[\frac{4}{3} + 3\cdot\frac{2}{3} + 2\cdot\frac{2}{1} - \frac{5}{2} - \pi \right]$$

$$= \frac{\pi}{2}\frac{a^3}{\sqrt{2}}\left(\frac{10}{3} - \pi\right) = \frac{\pi}{6\sqrt{2}}(10 - 3\pi)\, a^3.$$

4. *The smaller segment of the ellipse*

$$\frac{x^2}{a^2} + \frac{y^2}{b^2} = 1,$$

cut off by the chord

$$\frac{x}{a} + \frac{y}{b} = 1,$$

revolves completely about this chord. Show that the volume generated is

$$\frac{1}{6}\pi(10 - 3\pi)\, a^2 b^2 (a^2 + b^2)^{-1/2}.$$

The given chord $x/a + y/b = 1$ joins the points A, B.

Take any point

$$\text{P } (a\cos\theta, b\sin\theta)$$

on the ellipse.

The length of the perpendicular MP is

$$\frac{ab\,(\cos\theta + \sin\theta - 1)}{\sqrt{a^2 + b^2}};$$

We take the point A as the point fixed on the axis of revolution AB. We now require the length AM.

Now $AM^2 = AP^2 - PM^2$

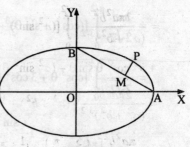

Fig. 10.14

$$= (a\cos\theta - a)^2 + (b\sin\theta)^2 - \frac{a^2 b^2\,(\cos\theta + \sin\theta - 1)^2}{a^2 + b^2}$$

$$= a^2\,(\cos\theta - 1)^2 + b^2 \sin^2\theta$$

$$\qquad - \frac{a^2 b^2}{a^2 + b^2}\,[(\cos\theta - 1)^2 + \sin^2\theta + 2\sin\theta\,(\cos\theta - 1)]$$

$$= \frac{a^4\,(\cos\theta - 1)^2 + b^4 \sin^2\theta - 2a^2 b^2 \sin\theta\,(\cos\theta - 1)}{a^2 + b^2}$$

$$= \frac{[a^2\,(\cos\theta - 1) - b^2 \sin\theta]^2}{a^2 + b^2}$$

$$\Rightarrow \quad AM = \frac{a^2\,(1 - \cos\theta) + b^2 \sin\theta}{\sqrt{a^2 + b^2}}$$

$$\Rightarrow d\,(AM) = \frac{a^2 \sin\theta + b^2 \cos\theta}{\sqrt{a^2 + b^2}}\,d\theta.$$

Thus the required volume is

$$= \pi \int_0^{AB} (MP)^2\, d\,(AM)$$

$$= \pi \int_0^{\pi/2} \frac{a^2 b^2\,(\cos\theta + \sin\theta - 1)^2}{(a^2 + b^2)} \cdot \frac{a^2 \sin\theta + b^2 \cos\theta}{\sqrt{a^2 + b^2}}\, d\theta$$

$$= \frac{\pi a^2 b^2}{(a^2 + b^2)^{3/2}} \int_0^{\pi/2} (a^2 \sin\theta + b^2 \cos\theta)$$

$$\times (2 + 2\sin\theta\cos\theta - 2\sin\theta - 2\cos\theta)\, d\theta$$

$$= \frac{2\pi a^2 b^2}{(a^2 + b^2)^{3/2}} \int\limits_{0}^{\pi/2} [(a^2 \sin\theta + b^2 \cos\theta) + a^2 \sin^2\theta \cos\theta$$

$$+ b^2 \cos^2\theta \sin\theta - (a^2 \sin^2\theta + b^2 \cos^2\theta) - (a^2 + b^2)\sin\theta\cos\theta]\, d\theta$$

$$= \frac{2\pi a^2 b^2}{(a^2 + b^2)^{3/2}} \left[(a^2 + b^2) + \frac{a^2}{3} + \frac{b^2}{3} - \left(\frac{a^2\pi}{4} + \frac{b^2\pi}{4} \right) - \frac{(a^2 + b^2)}{2} \right]$$

$$= \frac{\pi a^2 b^2}{\sqrt{a^2 + b^2}} \left(\frac{5}{3} - \frac{\pi}{2} \right) = \frac{1}{6}\pi (10 - 3\pi)\, a^2 b^2 (a^2 + b^2)^{-1/2}.$$

5. *The loop of the curve* $2ay^2 = x (x - a)^2$ *revolves about the straight line* $y = a$; *find the volume of the solid generated.*   (Kumaon, 2003)

The loop of the curve lies between the limits $x = 0$, $x = a$.

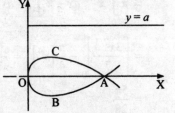

The volume obtained by revolving the loop about $y = a$ is the difference of the two volumes obtained by revolving the arcs OBA and OCA about it.

For any point on the arc OBA

$$y = \frac{\sqrt{x}\,(x - a)}{\sqrt{2a}} = -\frac{\sqrt{x}\,(a - x)}{\sqrt{2a}}.$$

Fig. 10.15

For any point on the arc OCA

$$y = -\frac{\sqrt{x}\,(x - a)}{\sqrt{2a}} = \frac{\sqrt{x}\,(a - x)}{\sqrt{2a}}.$$

The volume obtained by revolving the arc OBA

$$= \pi \int\limits_{0}^{a} \left[a + \frac{\sqrt{x}\,(a - x)}{\sqrt{2a}} \right]^2 dx.$$

The volume obtained by revolving the arc OCA

$$= \pi \int\limits_{0}^{a} \left[a - \frac{\sqrt{x}\,(a - x)}{\sqrt{2a}} \right]^2 dx.$$

The required volume which is the difference of the above two volumes

$$= \frac{4ax}{\sqrt{2a}} \int\limits_{0}^{a} \sqrt{x}\,(a - x)\, dx$$

$$= \frac{4a\pi}{\sqrt{2a}} \left| \frac{2}{3}ax^{3/2} - \frac{2}{5}x^{5/2} \right|_{0}^{a} = \frac{8\sqrt{2}\,\pi a^3}{15}.$$

6. *The area included between the curves* $y^2 = x^3$ *and* $x^2 = y^3$ *is rotated about the x-axis. Find the volume of the solid generated.*

The required volume = volume of the solid generated by the area OLPK

— volume of the solid generated by the area OLPT

$$= \pi \int y_1^2 \, dx - \pi \int y_2^2 \, dx$$

where y_1 stands for the second curve and y_2 for the first curve; $y_2^2 = x^3$ and $x^2 = y_i^3$ limits are 0 to 1 which are obtained after solving the equations of the curves for x

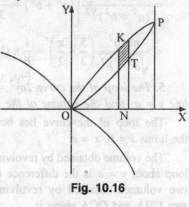

Fig. 10.16

$$= \pi \int_0^1 x^{4/3} \, dx - \pi \int_0^1 x^3 \, dx$$

$$= \left[\frac{3x^{7/3}}{7} \right]_0^1 - \frac{\pi}{4} \left[x^4 \right]_0^1 = \frac{3\pi}{7} - \frac{\pi}{4}$$

$$= \frac{5\pi}{28}.$$

7. *Show that if the area lying within the cardioid* $r = 2a (1 + \cos \theta)$ *and without the parabola* $r (1 + \cos \theta) = 2a$ *revolves about the initial line the volume generated is* $18\pi a^3$.

The first curve is cardioid, *i.e.*, $r = 2a (1 + \cos \theta)$ and second curve is parabola $r (1 + \cos \theta) = 2a$.

Solving for θ, we have

$$2a (1 + \cos \theta)^2 = 2a$$

or $\qquad \cos^2 \theta + 2 \cos \theta = 0$

or $\qquad \cos \theta (\cos \theta + 2) = 0.$

Therefore $\cos \theta = 0$, *i.e.*, $\theta = \dfrac{\pi}{2}$ or $-\dfrac{\pi}{2}$

which is evident from the figure as OK is $\theta = -\dfrac{\pi}{2}$ and OB is $\theta = \dfrac{\pi}{2}$.

Now the shaded area OBA is revolved about the initial line OX.

The required volume = volume generated by the cardioid between 0 and $\pi / 2$

— volume generated by the parabola between 0 and $\pi/2$

$$= \int_0^{\pi/2} \frac{2}{3} \pi r_1^3 \sin \theta \, d\theta - \int_0^{\pi/2} \frac{2}{3} \pi r_2^3 \sin \theta \, d\theta$$

where r_1 is taken for the cardioid, *i.e.*, $r_1 = 2a (1 + \cos \theta)$ and r_2 for the parabola, *i.e.*, $r_2 (1 + \cos \theta) = 2a$.

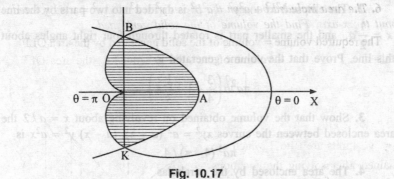

Fig. 10.17

Then the volume

$$= \frac{2}{3} \pi \int_{0}^{\pi/2} (r_1^3 \sin \theta - r_2^3 \sin \theta) \, d\theta$$

$$= \frac{2}{3} \pi \int_{0}^{\pi/2} [8a^3 (1 + \cos \theta)^3 \sin \theta - 8a^3 (1 - \cos \theta)^{-3} \sin \theta] \, d\theta$$

$$= \frac{2}{3} \pi \cdot 8a^3 \int_{0}^{\pi/2} \left[(1 + \cos \theta)^3 - \frac{1}{(1 + \cos \theta)^3} \right] \cdot \sin \theta \, d\theta$$

[Put $\cos \theta = t$, then $- \sin \theta \, d\theta = dt$.]

$$= \frac{2}{3} \pi \, 8a^3 \int_{0}^{1} \left[(1 + t)^3 - \frac{1}{(1 + t)^3} \right] dt$$

$$= \frac{16\pi a^3}{3} \left[\frac{(1 + t)^4}{4} + \frac{1}{2(1 + t)^2} \right]_{0}^{1}$$

$$= \frac{16\pi a^3}{3} \left(\frac{16}{4} + \frac{1}{8} - \frac{1}{4} - \frac{1}{2} \right)$$

$$= \frac{16\pi a^3}{3} \cdot \frac{27}{8} = 18\pi a^3.$$

EXERCISES

1. A figure is bounded by the axis of y and the arc of the ellipse $b^2x^2 + a^2y^2 = a^2b^2$ on which x is negative. A solid is generated by the revolution of this figure about the line $x = - 2a$; prove that its volume is

$$2\pi \left(\pi - \frac{14}{3} \right) a^2 b.$$

2. The ellipse $b^2x^2 + a^2y^2 = a^2b^2$ is divided into two parts by the line $x = \dfrac{1}{2}a$, and the smaller part is rotated through four right angles about this line. Prove that the volume generated is

$$\pi a^2 b\left(\frac{3}{4}\sqrt{3} - \frac{1}{3}\pi\right).$$

3. Show that the volume obtained on revolving about $x = a/2$ the area enclosed between the curves $xy^2 = a^2(a-x)$, $(a-x)y^2 = a^2x$ is

$$\pi a^3(4-\pi)/4.$$

4. The area enclosed by the parabolas

$$x^2 = 4ay \text{ and } x^2 = 4a(2a-y)$$

revolves about the line $y = a$; find the volume of the solid so generated.

5. The ellipse $x^2/a^2 + y^2/b^2 = 1$, $(a > b)$ revolves about the tangent at one extremity of its minor axis; show that the volume of the solid obtained is $2\pi^2 ab^2$.

6. Find the volume of the solid generated by the revolution of the curve

$$(a-x)y^2 = a^2x$$

about its asymptote.   (*Sagar, 1998; Rewa, 1998*)

7. Show that the volume of the spindle formed by revolving the arc of the parabola $y^2 = 4ax$ joining the vertex to one extremity of the latus rectum, about the tangent at the extremity is $7\sqrt{2}\pi a^2/60$.

8. Find the volume of the spindle formed by the revolution of a parabolic arc about the line joining the vertex to one extremity of the latus rectum.

9. A surface is formed by the revolution of the curve $y = x^y e^{-x}$ about the axis of x; show that the volume enclosed by the part of the surface which corresponds to the positive values of x is $3\pi/4$.

10. Show that the volume of the solid generated by the revolution of the curve $r = a + b\sec\theta$ about its asymptote is

$$2\pi a^2\left(\frac{2}{3}a + \frac{1}{2}b\pi\right).$$

ANSWERS

4. $32\pi a^3/15$.   **6.** $\dfrac{1}{2}\pi^2 a^3$.   **8.** $(2/15\sqrt{5})\pi a^3$.

10.4. Area of the surface of the frustum of a cone. We can easily see that the area of the surface of right circular cone, the radius of whose circular base is r, and whose slant height is l, is πrl.

If we tear a right circular cone along one of its generators, we get a circular sector whose radius OA is equal to the slant height and whose arc AB is equal to the circumference of the circular base of the cone.

The area of this sector and, therefore, also the surface of the cone is equal to $\pi r l$.

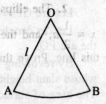

Fig. 10.18

If α be the semi-vertical angle of the cone, we have $r/l = \sin \alpha$. Therefore the surface of the cone is also equal to $\pi l^2 \sin \alpha$.

Consider, now, the frustum CABD of a cone VAB. Let the radii O'A, and OC of its circular bases be r_1 and r_2 respectively and let its slant height CA be l_1. *The area of the surface of this frustum*

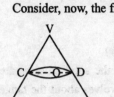

Fig. 10.19

$$= \pi (AV^2 - CV^2) \sin \alpha$$
$$= \pi (AV - CV)(AV \sin \alpha + CV \sin \alpha)$$
$$= \pi AC (O'A + OC)$$
$$= \pi l (r_1 + r_2)$$
$$= \pi \times slant\ height$$
$$\times\ sum\ of\ the\ radii\ of\ the\ two\ bases.$$

10.5. Surface of revolution. *To show that the area of the surface of the solid obtained on revolving about x-axis, the arc of the curve $y = f(x)$ intercepted between the points whose abscissae are a, b is,*

$$\int_a^b 2\pi y \frac{ds}{dx} dx = 2\pi \int_a^b f(x) \sqrt{1 + f'^2(x)}\ dx.$$

Let G $[a, f(a)]$ be a fixed point and P (x, y), a variable point on the arc. Let H be the point $[b, f(b)]$. Let σ be the area of the surface of the solid obtained by revolving the area GP about x-axis so that, σ is a function of x.

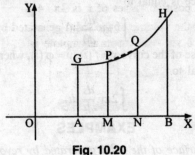

Fig. 10.20

We take a point

$$Q (x + \Delta x, y + \Delta y)$$

on the curve near P

Let arc GP = s and arc PQ = Δs.

Let $\Delta\sigma$ denote the area of the surface of the solid obtained by revolving the arc PQ.

By revolving the chord PQ about x-axis, we get a frustum of the cone whose slant height is PQ and the radii of whose circular ends are MP, NQ. The area of surface of this frustum

$$= \pi \, (PM + QN) \, PQ = \pi \, (\, y + y + \Delta y) \, PQ.$$

Let it be denoted by $\Delta\Sigma$.

We take it as an axiom that

$$\lim \frac{\Delta\Sigma}{\Delta x} = \lim \frac{\Delta\sigma}{\Delta x} \Leftrightarrow \frac{d\Sigma}{dx} = \frac{d\sigma}{dx}.$$

Now $\dfrac{\Delta\Sigma}{\Delta x} = \pi \, (2y + \Delta y) \dfrac{PQ}{\Delta x}$

$$= \pi \, (2y + \Delta y) \frac{\text{chord PQ}}{\text{arc PQ}} \cdot \frac{\text{arc PQ}}{\Delta x}.$$

In the limit, we have

$$\frac{d\Sigma}{dx} = 2\pi y \cdot 1 \cdot \frac{ds}{dx} = 2\pi y \, \frac{ds}{dx},$$

$$\therefore \quad \frac{d\sigma}{dx} = 2\pi y \, \frac{ds}{dx}.$$

Now, $\displaystyle\int_a^b 2\pi y \, \frac{ds}{dx} \, dx = \int_a^b \frac{d\sigma}{dx} \, dx = \left| \, \sigma \, \right|_a^b$

= the value of σ for x equal to b – the value of σ for x equal to a

= Area of the surface obtained by revolving the arc GH.

Note. Taking s as the independent variable, we see that the surface $= \int 2\pi y \, ds$. In the case of a polar curve $r = f(\theta)$, where θ is the independent variable, the surface is equal to

$$\int 2\pi y \, \frac{ds}{d\theta} \, d\theta.$$

Also, in the case of the curve $x = f(t)$, $y = \varphi(t)$, where t is the parameter, the surface is equal to

$$\int 2\pi y \, \frac{ds}{dt} \, dt.$$

EXAMPLES

1. *Find the surface of the solid generated by revolution of the curve* $x^2 + 4y^2 = 16$ *about the x-axis.*   (Garhwal, 1993; Ravishankar, 1999)

The equation of the curve is

$$\frac{x^2}{16} + \frac{y^2}{4} = 1.$$

Now, differentiating it, we get

$$\frac{x}{8} + \frac{y}{2}\frac{dy}{dx} = 0 \text{ or } \frac{dy}{dx} = -\frac{x}{4y}$$

$$\therefore \quad \frac{ds}{dx} = \sqrt{1 + \left(\frac{dy}{dx}\right)^2} = \sqrt{1 + \frac{x^2}{16y^2}}$$

$$= \frac{\sqrt{16y^2 + x^2}}{4y} = \frac{\sqrt{64 - 4x^2 + x^2}}{4y}$$

$$= \frac{1}{2}\sqrt{\frac{64 - 3x^2}{16 - x^2}}.$$

The required surface generated by the curve about x-axis

$$= 2\pi \int_{-4}^{4} y\frac{ds}{dx}\cdot dx$$

$$= 2x \int_{-4}^{4} y\cdot\frac{1}{2}\frac{\sqrt{64 - 3x^2}}{2y}\,dx$$

$$= \frac{\pi}{2}\int_{-4}^{4}\sqrt{64 - 3x^2}\,dx$$

$$= \frac{\pi\sqrt{3}}{2}\int_{-4}^{4}\sqrt{\frac{64}{3} - x^2}\,dx$$

$$= \frac{\pi\sqrt{3}}{2}\left[\frac{1}{2}x\sqrt{\frac{64}{3} - x^2} + \frac{1}{2}\cdot\frac{64}{3}\sin^{-1}\frac{x\sqrt{3}}{8}\right]_{-4}^{4}$$

$$= \frac{\pi\sqrt{3}}{2}\left[2\sqrt{\frac{64}{3} - 16} + \frac{32}{3}\sin^{-1}\frac{\sqrt{3}}{2}\right.$$

$$\left. + 2\sqrt{\frac{64}{3} - 16} + \frac{32}{3}\sin^{-1}\frac{\sqrt{3}}{2}\right]$$

$$= \frac{\pi\sqrt{3}}{2}\left[\frac{16}{\sqrt{3}} + \frac{64}{3}\cdot\frac{\pi}{3}\right]$$

$$= \frac{1}{2}\left[16\pi + \frac{64\pi^2\sqrt{2}}{9}\right] = 8\pi + \frac{32\sqrt{3}}{9}\pi^2.$$

2. *Find the surface of the solid generated by the revolution of the astroid* $x^{2/3} + y^{2/3} = a^{2/3}$ *about the x-axis.*

(*Agra, 2001; Ravishankar, 1998; Indore, 1995*)

The limits for x are 0 to a.

The required surface

$$= 2\pi \int_0^a 2y \cdot \frac{ds}{dx}\, dx$$

$$= 4\pi \int_0^a (a^{2/3} - x^{2/3})^{3/2} \sqrt{1 + \left(\frac{dy}{dx}\right)^2}\, dx$$

$$= 4\pi \int_0^a (a^{2/3} - x^{2/3})^{3/2} \sqrt{1 + \frac{y^{2/3}}{x^{2/3}}}\, dx$$

$$= 4\pi \int_0^a (a^{2/3} - x^{2/3})^{3/2} \sqrt{\frac{x^{2/3} + y^{2/3}}{x^{2/3}}}\, dx$$

$$= 4\pi \int_0^a (a^{2/3} - x^{2/3})^{3/2}\, a^{1/3}\, x^{-1/3}\, dx$$

$$[\text{Put } x = a \sin^3 \theta,\ dx = 3a \sin^2 \theta \cos \theta\, d\theta]$$

$$= 4\pi a^{1/3} \int_0^{\pi/2} (a^{2/3} - a^{2/3} \sin^2 \theta)^{3/2} (a \sin \theta)^{-1/3} \cdot 3a \sin^2 \theta \cos \theta\, d\theta$$

$$= 12\pi a^{1/3} \cdot a^2 \cdot a^{-1/3} \int_0^{\pi/2} \cos^4 \theta \sin \theta\, d\theta$$

$$= 12\pi a^2\, \frac{\Gamma \frac{5}{2} \cdot \Gamma 1}{\Gamma \frac{7}{2}} = \frac{12\pi a^2}{5}.$$

3. *Find the surface generated by the revolution of an arc of the catenary* $y = c \cosh \frac{x}{c}$ *about the axis of x.* (*Kumaon, 1998*)

The equation of the given curve is $y = c \cosh \frac{x}{c}$.

Differentiating, we get

$$\frac{dy}{dx} = \sinh \frac{x}{c}$$

$$\frac{ds}{dx} = \sqrt{1 + \sinh^2 \frac{x}{c}} = \cosh \frac{x}{c}.$$

If the arc be measured from the vertex (where $x = 0$) to any point (x, y) then the required surface

$$= 2\pi \int_0^x y \frac{ds}{dx} dx$$

$$= 2\pi \int_0^x c \cosh \frac{x}{c} \cdot \cosh \frac{x}{c} dx$$

$$= 2\pi c \int_0^x \cosh^2 \frac{x}{c} dx$$

$$= \pi c \int_0^x \left[1 + \cosh \left(\frac{2x}{c} \right) \right] dx$$

$$= \pi c \left[x + \frac{c}{2} \sinh \left(\frac{2x}{c} \right) \right]_0^x$$

$$= \pi c \left[x + \frac{c}{2} \sinh \left(\frac{2x}{c} \right) \right].$$

4. *Find the surface of the solid formed by revolving the cardioide*

$$r = a \, (1 + \cos \theta)$$

about the initial line.

(*Kumaon, 2001; Ravishankar, 1995; Indore, 1996*)

The required surface

$$= \int_0^\pi 2\pi y \frac{ds}{d\theta} d\theta.$$

Now $\quad y = r \sin \theta = a \sin \theta \, (1 + \cos \theta)$

$$\frac{ds}{d\theta} = \sqrt{r^2 + \left(\frac{dr}{d\theta} \right)^2}$$

$$= \sqrt{a^2 (1 + \cos \theta)^2 + a^2 \sin^2 \theta}$$

$$= 2a \cos \frac{\theta}{2}.$$

$\therefore \quad$ Surface $= \int_0^\pi 2\pi a \sin \theta \, (1 + \cos \theta) \, 2a \cos \frac{\theta}{2} \, d\theta$

$$= 4\pi a^2 \int_0^\pi \sin \theta \, (1 + \cos \theta) \cos \frac{\theta}{2} \, d\theta$$

$$= 4\pi a^2 \int_0^{\pi} 2 \sin\frac{\theta}{2} \cos\frac{\theta}{2} \cdot 2 \cos^2\frac{\theta}{2} \cdot \cos\frac{\theta}{2} \, d\theta$$

$$= 32\pi a^2 \int_0^{\pi/2} \sin\varphi \cos^4\varphi \, d\varphi, \text{ where } \varphi = \frac{\theta}{2},$$

$$= 32\pi a^2 \left| -\frac{\cos^5\varphi}{5} \right|_0^{\pi/2} = \frac{32}{5}\pi a^2.$$

5. *Find the surface of the solid generated by the revolution of the lemniscate $r^2 = a^2 \cos 2\theta$ about the initial line.*

There are two loops in the curve. For the upper half of the loop on the right, θ varies from 0 to $\pi/4$.

The equation of the curve is

$$r^2 = a^2 \cos 2\theta.$$

Differentiating, we get

$$2r\frac{dr}{d\theta} = -2a^2 \sin 2\theta$$

or

$$\frac{dr}{d\theta} = -\frac{a^2 \sin 2\theta}{r}$$

$$\therefore \quad \frac{ds}{d\theta} = \sqrt{r^2 + \left(\frac{dr}{d\theta}\right)^2}$$

$$= \sqrt{a^2 \cos 2\theta + \frac{a^4 \sin^2 2\theta}{r^2}}$$

$$= a\sqrt{\cos 2\theta + \frac{\sin^2 2\theta}{\cos 2\theta}}$$

$$= \frac{a}{\sqrt{\cos 2\theta}}.$$

∴ The required surface

$$= 2 \times \text{surface generated by one loop}$$

$$= 2 \times 2\pi \int_0^{\pi/4} y \frac{ds}{d\theta} \cdot d\theta$$

$$= 4\pi \int_0^{\pi/4} r \sin\theta \cdot \frac{a}{\sqrt{\cos 2\theta}} \, d\theta$$

$$= 4\pi \int_0^{\pi/4} a\sqrt{\cos 2\theta}\, \sin\theta\, \frac{a}{\sqrt{\cos 2\theta}}\, d\theta$$

$$= 4\pi a^2 \int_0^{\pi/4} \sin\theta\, d\theta = 4\pi a^2 \left[-\cos\theta\right]_0^{\pi/4}$$

$$= 4\pi a^2 \left(1 - \frac{1}{\sqrt{2}}\right).$$

6. *Prove that the surface generated by the revolution of the tractrix*

$x = a\cos t + \dfrac{a}{2}\log\tan^2\dfrac{t}{2}$, $y = a\sin t$ *about its asymptote is equal to the surface of sphere of radius* a. *(Rohilkhand, 2001)*

Here $x = a\cos t + \dfrac{a}{2}\log\tan^2\dfrac{t}{2}$

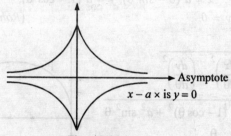

Asymptote

$x - a \times$ is $y = 0$

Fig. 10.21

$$\frac{dx}{dt} = -a\sin t + \frac{a}{2}\cdot\frac{2\tan\dfrac{t}{2}\sec^2\dfrac{t}{2}\cdot\dfrac{1}{2}}{\tan^2\dfrac{t}{2}}$$

$$= -a\sin t + \frac{a}{2\sin\dfrac{t}{2}\cos\dfrac{t}{2}} = \frac{a\cos^2 t}{\sin t}$$

$$y = a\sin t, \quad \frac{dy}{dt} = a\cos t.$$

Therefore

$$\frac{ds}{dt} = \sqrt{\left(\frac{dx}{dt}\right)^2 + \left(\frac{dy}{dt}\right)^2}$$

$$= a\sqrt{\frac{\cos^4 t}{\sin^2 t} + \cos^2 t}$$

$$= \frac{a\cos t}{\sin t} = a\cot t.$$

The required surface

$$= 2 \times 2\pi \int_0^{\pi/2} y \frac{ds}{dt} dt$$

$$= 4\pi \int_0^{\pi/2} a \sin t \cdot a \cot t \, dt$$

$$= 4\pi a^2 \int_0^{\pi/2} \cos t \, dt$$

$$= 4\pi a^2 \left[\sin t \right]_0^{\pi/2} = 4\pi a^2.$$

7. *Evaluate the surface area of the solid generated by revolving the cycloid*

$$x = a\,(\theta - \sin\,\theta),\ y = a\,(1 - \cos\,\theta),$$

about the line $y = 0$.   (Rohilkhand, 2001)

We have

$$\frac{ds}{d\theta} = \sqrt{\left(\frac{dx}{d\theta}\right)^2 + \left(\frac{dy}{d\theta}\right)^2}$$

$$= \sqrt{a^2\,(1 - \cos\theta)^2 + a^2 \sin^2 \theta}$$

$$= 2a \sin \frac{\theta}{2}.$$

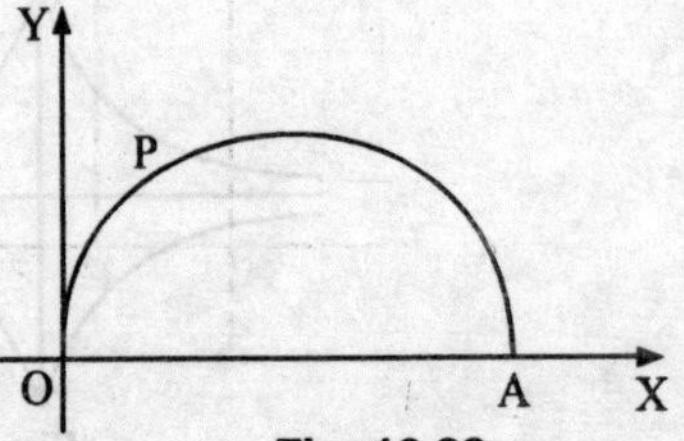

Fig. 10.22

For the part OPA, θ varies from 0 to 2π.

The required surface

$$= \int_0^{2\pi} 2\pi y \frac{ds}{d\theta} \cdot d\theta$$

$$= \int_0^{2\pi} 2\pi a\,(1 - \cos\theta) \cdot 2a \sin \frac{\theta}{2}\, d\theta$$

$$= 8\pi a^2 \int_0^{2\pi} \sin^3 \frac{\theta}{2}\, d\theta$$

$$= 16\pi a^2 \int_0^{\pi} \sin^3 \varphi\, d\varphi, \text{ where } \frac{\theta}{2} = \varphi$$

$$= 32\pi a^2 \int_0^{\pi/2} \sin^3 \varphi\, d\varphi = 32\pi a^2 \cdot \frac{2}{3} = \frac{64\pi a^2}{3}.$$

10.6. Theorems of Pappus.

10.61. Volume of Revolution.
If a closed plane curve revolves about a straight line in its plane, (the straight line not intersecting the curve), then the volume of the solid of revolution thus formed is obtained on multiplying the area of the region enclosed by the curve with the length of the path described by the centroid of the region.

We take x-axis as the axis of revolution. Suppose that the curve is such that every line parallel to y-axis and lying between the co-ordinates $x = a$, $x = b$ of two points A, B meets the curve in two and only two points P_1, P_2.

Let $MP_1 = y_1$, and $MP_2 = y_2$ so that y_1, y_2 are functions of x; x varying between a and b.

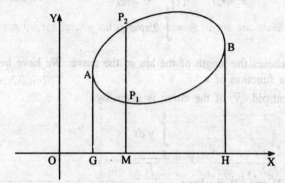

Fig. 10.23

Now the volume, V, of the solid of revolution is given by

$$V = \pi \int_a^b y_2^2 \, dx - \pi \int_a^b y_1^2 \, dx$$

$$= \pi \int_a^b (y_2^2 - y_1^2) \, dx \qquad \qquad \text{...(1)}$$

Also the ordinate, $\bar{y}$, of the centroid of the region is given by

$$\bar{y} = \frac{\displaystyle\int_a^b \frac{1}{2}(y_1 + y_2)(y_2 - y_1)\, dx}{A}$$

$$= \frac{1}{2} \frac{\displaystyle\int_a^b (y_2^2 - y_1^2)\, dx}{A} \qquad \qquad \text{...(2)}$$

A, being the area of the region.

From (1) and (2), we have

$$V = 2\pi\bar{y}A$$

so that the result follows; $2\pi\bar{y}$ being the length of the path described by the centroid.

10.7. Surface of Revolution. *If a closed plane curve revolves about a straight line in its plane (the straight line not intersecting the curve), then the surface of the solid of revolution thus formed is obtained on multiplying the length of the curve with that of the path described by the centroid of the curve.*

We take x-axis as the axis of revolution.   [Refer Fig. 10.23, above]

The surface, S, of the solid of revolution is given by

$$S = \int_0^l 2\pi y \, ds, \qquad \qquad ...(1)$$

where, l, denotes the length of the arc of the curve. We have here looked upon y as a function of s.

The centroid, $\bar{y}$ of the curve is given by

$$\bar{y} = \frac{\int_0^l y \, ds}{l}. \qquad \qquad ...(2)$$

From (1) and (2), we have

$$S = 2\pi\bar{y}l,$$

so that the result follows; $2\pi\bar{y}$ being the length of the path described by the centroid.

EXERCISES

1. Find the surface of a sphere of radius a.

                                              (*Agra, 2000; Bilaspur, 1997*)

2. Find the surface of the solid generated by revolving the arc of the parabola $y^2 = 4ax$ bounded by its latus rectum about x-axis.

                                              (*Rohilkhand, 2002*)

3. The part of the parabola $y^2 = 4ax$ bounded by the latus rectum revolves about the tangent at the vertex; find the area of the curved surface of the reel thus generated.

4. Find the surface of the solid generated by the revolution of the astroid

$$x = a \cos^2 t, \, y = a \sin^2 t,$$

about the axis of x.   (*Kumaon, 2000*)

5. Find the surface of the solid obtained by revolving the cardioide $r = a (1 - \cos \theta)$ about the initial line.

6. Find the area of the surface of revolution formed by revolving the curve $r = 2a \cos \theta$ about the initial line.

7. Show that the ratio of the areas of the surface formed by the rotation of the arc of the cycloid

$$x = a \, (\theta + \sin \theta), \; y = a \, (1 + \cos \theta)$$

between two consecutive cusps about the axis of x to the area enclosed by the cycloid and the axis of x is $64 / 9$.

8. The arc of the curve $8a^2y^2 = x^2 \, (a^2 - 2x^2)$, in the first quadrant, revolves about the axes of X and Y and generates the surfaces A and B. Show that the surface of A is to the surface of B as $3\sqrt{2}$ is to 2, and that the volume of B is that of a right cylinder standing on a circular base of radius $\dfrac{1}{4} a$ and of altitude equal to the length of the arc.

9. Prove that the surface of the solid obtained by revolving the ellipse $b^2x^2 + a^2y^2 = a^2b^2$ about the axis of x is

$$2\pi ab \, [\sqrt{1 - e^2} + (1 / e) \sin^{-1} e]$$

e, being the eccentricity of the ellipse.

10. An arc of a circle of radius a revolves about its chord. If the length of the arc is $2a\alpha$, $(\alpha < \pi / 2)$, show that the area of the surface generated is $4\pi a^2 \, (\sin \alpha - \alpha \cos \alpha)$.

11. Show that the surface of the solid obtained by revolving the arc of the curve $y = \sin x$ from $x = 0$ to $x = \pi$ about x-axis is

$$\pi^2 \, [\sqrt{2} + \log (1 + \sqrt{2})].$$

ANSWERS

1. $4a^2\pi$. **2.** $8a^2\pi \, (2\sqrt{2} - 1) / 3$.

3. $a^2\pi \, [3\sqrt{2} - \log (\sqrt{2} + 1)]$.

4. $12\pi a^2 / 5$. **5.** $32\pi a^2 / 5$. **6.** $4\pi a^2$.

EXERCISES ON CHAPTER X

1. Prove that the surface and the volume of the solid generated by the revolution, about the x-axis, of the loop of the curve

$$x = t^2, \; y = t - \frac{1}{3} t^3$$

are respectively 3π and $3\pi / 4$.

2. The figure bounded by a quadrant of a circle of radius a and the tangents at its extremities revolves about one of these tangents; prove that (*i*) the volume of the solid thus generated is

$$(10 - 3\pi)\,\pi a^3 / 6.$$

(*ii*) the area of the curved surface so generated is

$$\pi\,(\pi - 2)\,a^2.$$

3. The arc of the cycloid

$$x = a\,(\theta - \sin \theta),\ y = a\,(1 - \cos \theta)$$

joining the points $(0, 0)$, $(a\pi, 2a)$ revolves about its chord; show that the surface of the solid obtained is

$$\frac{32a^2\pi\,(\pi - 2)}{3\sqrt{\pi^2 + 4}}.$$

4. Show that the volume generated by the revolution of the loop of the curve $x^2y^2 = a\,(x - a)\,(x - b)^2$ about the *x*-axis is

$$\pi a \left[\frac{1}{2}\,a^2 + 2ab - \frac{5}{3}\,b^2 + b\,(2a + b)\,\log\,(b / a) \right].$$

5. A solid spheroid formed by the revolution of the ellipse $b^2x^2 + a^2y^2 = a^2b^2$ about the major axis has a cylindrical hole of circular section, having the major axis drilled through it. Prove that the volume of the solid which remains is $4\pi b^2 l^3 / 3a^2$, where $2l$ is the length of the hole.

6. Show that the surface of the solid obtained by revolving the arc of the curve $y = c \cosh\,(x / c)$ joining $(0, c)$ to (x, y) about *x*-axis is

$$\pi c \left(x + c \sinh \frac{x}{c} \cosh \frac{x}{c} \right).$$

7. The arc of the ellipse $x^2 / a^2 + y^2 / b^2 = 1$ lying in the first quadrant revolves about the line $y = b$, show that the volume of the solid thus obtained is

$$\left(\frac{5}{3} - \frac{1}{2}\,\pi \right) \pi ab^2.$$

8. Determine the volume generated by revolving the curve

$$y^2 = b^2 \log\,(a / x),$$

lying between $x = a$ and $x = b$ about the axis of *x*, where $b < a < 0$.

9. Show that the volume of the solid formed by revolving one loop of the curve

$$r^2 = a^2 \cos 2\theta$$

about the line $\theta = \frac{1}{2}\,\pi$ is $\pi^2 a^3 / 4\sqrt{2}$.

10. Show that the area of the surface of the solid generated by revolving the tractrix

$$x = a \,(u - \tanh u), \; y = a \,\text{sech} \; u$$

about OX is equal to the area of the surface of a sphere of radius a.

11. The region enclosed by the curve $y = \tanh x$, its asymptote $y = 1$, and y-axis revolves about the asymptote; show that the volume of the solid generated is $\pi \log (4 / e)$.

12. Show that the curve $r = a \,(1 + 2 \cos \theta)$ consists of an outer and an inner loop. If the area of the inner loop is rotated through two right angles about the initial line show that the volume of the solid so formed is $\pi / 12$.

13. The arc of the cardioide $r = a \,(1 + \cos \theta)$, specified by $-\pi / 2 \le \theta \le \pi / 2$, is rotated about the line $\theta = 0$; prove that the volume and the area of the surface of revolution generated are respectively

$$\frac{5}{2} a^3 \pi \; \text{and} \; \frac{4}{5} (8 - \sqrt{2}) \, a^2 \pi.$$

14. The arc of the cardioide $r = a \,(1 + \cos \theta)$ included between $-\pi / 2 \le \theta \le \pi / 2$, is rotated about the line $\theta = \pi / 2$; find the area of the surface generated.

ANSWERS

8. $\pi b^2 \,[a - b - b \log (a / b)]$.   14. $48\sqrt{2} \pi a^2 / 5$.

MISCELLANEOUS EXERCISE III

1. Prove that the area between the curve $y = c \cosh (x / c)$, the axis of x, and the ordinates of two points on the curve varies as the length of the intervening arc.

2. Show that the coordinates of a point on the curve

$$y^2 \,(a + x) = x^2 \,(3a - x)$$

may be taken as

$$x = a \sin 3\theta \, \text{cosec} \, \theta, \; y = a \sin 3\theta \sec \theta,$$

and prove that the area of the loop of the curve and the area between the curve and its asymptote are both equal to $3\sqrt{3}a^2$. Find also the volume generated by the loop when the curve revolves about the axis of x.

3. In an astroid prove that a tangent divides the portion of the curve between two ends into arcs whose lengths are to each other as the segments of the portion of the tangent intercepted by the axes.

4. A $(0, a)$ and P (x, y) are two points on the curve whose equation is $y = a \cosh (x / a)$ and s is the length of the arc AP. If the curve makes a complete revolution about the x-axis, prove that the area S of the curved surface bounded by planes through A and P perpendicular to X-axis and the corresponding volume V are given by

$$aS = 2V = \pi a \,(ax + sy).$$

5. Find the length of the arc of the curve

$$6xy = x^4 + 3$$

between the points where $x = 1$ and $x = 4$; find also the area of curved surface generated when this portion of the curve is given a complete turn about OY.

6. Show that if, s, is the arc of the curve

$$9y^2 = x \,(3 - x)^2$$

measured from the origin to the point (x, y), then

$$3s^2 = 3y^2 + 4x^2.$$

The perimeter of the loop of the curve is S, its area is A and maximum breadth is B; prove that

$$A = \frac{3}{10} BS.$$

7. Find the length of the arc of the curve

$$25a^3xy^2 = (x^3 + 5a^3)^2,$$

measured from $x = a$ to $x = 4a$.

8. Find the sum of the areas of all the loops included between $y = e^{-kx} \sin px$ and $y = 0$.

9. Find the area A bounded by the curve

$$y = a \left(\sin x + \frac{1}{3} \sin 3x + \frac{1}{5} \sin 5x \right),$$

and the axis of x between the limits 0 and π; and the volume V obtained by rotating the area about the axis of x. Prove that $4V = \pi^2 aA$.

10. Prove that area of a parabolic segment is two-third of that of the triangle formed by the base and the tangents at its extremities.

11. If A be the area of the segment of a parabola cut off by a focal chord of length c, show that the latus rectum is $36A^2 / c^3$.

12. Show that the area of the loop of the curve

$$x^5 + 2a^2x^2y - a^3y^2 = 0$$

is $32a^2 / 105$.

13. Show that the area of the loop of the curve

$$r = 3 \operatorname{cosec} \theta - 5$$

   is

$$12 - 30 \log 3 + 25\left(\frac{1}{2}\pi - \tan^{-1}\frac{3}{4}\right)$$

14. Find the volume and the surface of the solid formed by the revolution about the initial line of the curve

$$r^2 = a^2 \cos^2 \theta + b^2 \sin^2 \theta. \qquad (a^2 > b^2)$$

15. The part of the ellipse $x^2/a^2 + y^2/b^2 = 1$, cut off by a latus rectum, revolves about the tangent at the nearer end; find the volume of the reel thus formed.

16. Find the volume generated by revolving about OX the areas bounded by the following loci :

   (i) $x^2 + y^2 = 25$; $3x - 4y = 0$, $y = 0$; lying in the first quadrant.

   (ii) $y^2 = 4ax$, $x^2 + y^2 - 12a^2 = 0$.

17. Show that the volume of the solid generated by revolving about X-axis the region bounded by $y = \log x$, $y = 0$ and $x = 2$ is $2\pi (1 - \log 2)^2$.

18. Draw a rough sketch of the curve whose polar equation is

$$r = a (2 \cos \theta + \cos 3\theta).$$

   Show that the radius vector has maximum values $3a$ and $a/3\sqrt{3}$ and that the area of the larger loop of the curve is

$$\left(\frac{5}{6}\pi + \frac{3}{4}\sqrt{3}\right)a^2$$

   and the area of a smaller loop is

$$\left(\frac{5}{24}\pi - \frac{3}{8}\sqrt{3}\right)a^2.$$

19. Trace the curve $y^4 - 2axy^2 + x^4 = 0$ and show that the area of the curve and the volume generated by revolving it round the axis of x are respectively

$$\frac{\pi}{2\sqrt{2}}a^2 \text{ and } \frac{2\pi}{3}a^3.$$

20. If $r = a (\sec \theta - \cos \theta)$, find the area between the curve and the straight line $r = a \sec \theta$.

21. Show that the area of the loop of the curve

$$x = a\sqrt{1 - t^2}, \quad y = at\sqrt{1 - t^2}$$

   is $2a^2/3$; square root is to be taken with positive sign.

22. Find the area of the region which is defined by the inequalities $x^2 + y^2 \leq 9, y^2 \leq 8x$.

23. Find the intrinsic equation of the curve
$$\sqrt{x} + \sqrt{y} = \sqrt{a},$$
taking $(a, 0)$ as the fixed point.

24. Show that the perimeter of the limacon $r = a + b \cos \theta$ is the same as that of the ellipse whose semi-axes are $a + b$ and $a - b$.

25. The curve
$$y = \frac{h}{\sqrt{\pi}} \cdot e^{-h^2 x^2}$$
is rotated round the axis of y; show that the volume of revolution is $\sqrt{\pi} / h$.

26. Show that the intrinsic equation of the tractrix
$$x = a \cos t + a \log \tan \frac{1}{2} t, \quad y = a \sin t,$$
taking $t = \pi / 2$ as the fixed point is $s = a \log \cos \psi$.

27. Show that the intrinsic equation of the curve
$$y = a \log \sec \left(\frac{x}{a} \right),$$
is
$$s = a \log (\tan \psi + \cos \psi).$$

28. Find the intrinsic equation of the equiangular spiral
$$r = a e^{\theta \cot \alpha}$$
taking $(a, 0)$ as the fixed point.

29. Find the cartesian parametric representation of the cardioide $r = a (1 + \cos \theta)$ when the length of the arc measured from $\theta = 0$ is used as parameter.

30. The lemniscate $r^2 = a^2 \cos 2\theta$ revolves about a tangent at the pole; show that the volume and the surface of the solid generated are respectively $\frac{1}{4} \pi^2 a^3$ and $4\pi a^2$.

31. Show that the volume generated by the revolution of the loop of the curve
$$r \cos \theta = a \cos 2\theta$$
about the initial line is
$$2\pi a^3 \left(\log_e 2 - \frac{2}{3} \right).$$

32. Show that the area of the loop is equal to the area between the infinite branch and the asymptote of the curve

$$x^7 + y^7 = 7ax^3y^3.$$

33. Trace the curve $x^4 = ay^3 - axy^2$ and show that the area of its loop is $a^2/210$.

34. Show that the area of either of the loops of the curve

$$y^4 - 2c^2y^2 + a^2x^2 = 0$$

is $4\sqrt{2}c^3/3a$.

35. In the curve

$$x = a\left(\cos\varphi + \log\tan\frac{1}{2}\varphi\right), \quad y = a\sin\varphi$$

if 's' denotes the length of the arc measured from the axis of y, prove that, as $x \to \infty$

$$\lim (s - x) = a (1 - \log 2).$$

36. Find the whole area included between the curve

$$x^2y^2 = a^2 (x^2 + y^2)$$

and its asymptotes.

37. Find the whole area contained between the curve

$$x^2 (x^2 + y^2) = a^2 (y^2 - x^2)$$

and its asymptotes.

38. If for a curve

$$x \sin\theta + y \cos\theta = f'(\theta)$$
$$x \cos\theta - y \sin\theta = f''(\theta)$$

show that

$$s = f(\theta) + f''(\theta) + c.$$

ANSWERS

2. $a^3 \log (256/e^3)$.

5. $87/8; (255 + 8 \log 2)/4$.

7. $67a/10$.

8. $p (e^{k\pi/p} + 1)/(p^2 + k^2)(e^{k\pi/p} - 1)$.

9. $518a^2/525; 259\pi^2a^3/450$.

14. $\pi\left[\dfrac{b^2a}{2} + \dfrac{a^3}{3} + \dfrac{b^4}{4\sqrt{a^2 - b^2}} \log \dfrac{2a^2 - b^2 + 2a\sqrt{a^2 - b^2}}{b^2}\right];$

$\pi\left[a^2 + \dfrac{b^4}{\sqrt{a^4 - b^4}} \log \dfrac{a^2 + \sqrt{a^4 - b^4}}{b^2}\right].$

15. $(2b\pi/3a)[6a^2b - b^3 - 3ab\sqrt{a^2 - b^2} - 3a^3 \sin^{-1}(b/a)]$.

16. $50\pi/3, \dfrac{8}{3}(6\sqrt{3}-5)\pi a^3$.   20. $3a^2\pi/4$.

22. $2\left(\dfrac{\sqrt{2}}{3}+\dfrac{9\pi}{4}-\dfrac{9}{2}\sin^{-1}\dfrac{1}{3}\right)$.

23. $s = \dfrac{a}{2}-\dfrac{a}{2}\cdot\dfrac{\cos\psi-\sin\psi}{(\cos\psi+\sin\psi)^2}+\dfrac{\sqrt{2}a}{4}\log(1+\sqrt{2})$

$$-\dfrac{\sqrt{2}a}{4}\sinh^{-1}\dfrac{\cos\psi-\sin\psi}{\cos\psi+\sin\psi}.$$

28. $s = a\sec\alpha\,(e^{\psi\cot\alpha}-1)$.

29. $x = 2a\left[1-\dfrac{s^2}{8a^2}\right]\left[1-\dfrac{s^2}{16a^2}\right],\ y = s\left[1-\dfrac{s^2}{16a^2}\right]^{-3/2}$.

36. $4a^2$.   37. $a^3\,(\pi+2)$.

OBJECTIVE QUESTIONS

For each of the following questions, four alternatives are given for the answer. Only one of them is correct. Choose the correct alternative.

1. The volume generated by revolving about the x-axis an area bounded by the curve $y = f(x)$ and the two ordinates $x = a$ and $x = b$ is given by :

(a) $\displaystyle\int_a^b y^2\,dx$ (b) $\dfrac{1}{2}\displaystyle\int_a^b y^2\,dx$

(c) $\dfrac{1}{2}\pi\displaystyle\int_a^b y^2\,dx$ (d) $\pi\displaystyle\int_a^b y^2\,dx$.

(*Garhwal, 2002; Rohilkhand, 2002*)

2. The volume of the solid generated by revolving the ellipse $x^2/a^2 + y^2/b^2 = 1$ about the initial line is :

(a) $\dfrac{1}{3}\pi ab^2$ (b) $\dfrac{2}{3}\pi ab^2$ (c) πab^2 (d) $\dfrac{4}{3}\pi ab^2$.

3. The volume of the solid generated by revolution of the loop of the curve $y^2 = x^2\,(a-x)$ about the x-axis is :

(a) $\dfrac{4}{3}\pi a^4$ (b) $\dfrac{3}{4}\pi a^4$ (c) $\dfrac{1}{12}\pi a^4$ (d) πa^4.

4. The volume of the reel formed by revolving the part of the parabola $y^2 = 4ax$ cut off by the latus rectum about the tangent at the vertex is :

(a) $\dfrac{1}{5}\pi a^3$ (b) $\dfrac{2}{5}\pi a^3$ (c) $\dfrac{4}{5}\pi a^3$ (d) $\dfrac{2}{3}\pi a^3$.

5. The volume of the solid generated by the revolution about the initial line of the area bounded by the curve $r = f(\theta)$ and the radii vectors $x = a$ and $x = b$ is given by :

(a) $2\pi \int_{\alpha}^{\beta} r^3 \sin^3 \theta \, d\theta$

(b) $\frac{2}{3}\pi \int_{\alpha}^{\beta} r \sin \theta \, d\theta$

(c) $\frac{2}{3}\pi \int_{\alpha}^{\beta} r^3 \sin \theta \, d\theta$

(d) $\frac{2}{3}\pi \int_{\alpha}^{\beta} r^3 \sin^3 \theta \, d\theta.$

6. The area of the surface generated by revolving about the x-axis an area bounded by the curve $y = f(x)$, the x-axis and two ordinates $x = a$ and $x = b$ is given by :

(a) $2\pi \int_{a}^{b} y \, dx$

(b) $2\pi \int_{x=a}^{x=b} y^2 \, ds$

(c) $2\pi \int_{x=a}^{x=b} y \, ds$

(d) $\pi^2 \int_{x=a}^{x=b} y \, ds.$

(Rohilkhand, 2003)

7. Area of the surface of a cone whose semi-vertical angle is α and base a circle of radius r is :

(a) $\pi r^2 \sin \alpha$ (b) $\pi r^2 \csc \alpha$ (c) $\pi r^2 \cos \alpha$ (d) $\pi r^2.$

8. Surface area of the segment of a sphere of radius a and height h is :

(a) πah (b) $\frac{1}{2} \pi ah$ (c) $2\pi ah$ (d) None of these.

9. Surface of the solid formed by the revolution about x-axis of the loop of the curve $x = t^2$, $y = \left(t - \frac{1}{3}t^3\right)$ is :

(a) π (b) 3π (c) 5π (d) $7\pi.$

10. Area of the surface of revolution formed by revolving the curve $r = 2a \cos \theta$ about the initial line is :

(a) $4\pi a^2$ (b) $2\pi a^2$ (c) πa^2 (d) $\frac{4}{3}\pi a^2.$

ANSWERS

1. (d)   2. (d)   3. (c)   4. (c)   5. (c)
6. (c)   7. (b)   8. (c)   9. (b)   10. (a)

11

Centre of Gravity. Moment of Inertia

11.1. Introduction. In chapters 8, 9, and 10 we were concerned with the applications of Integral Calculus to **Geometry** inasmuch as we dealt with the determination of the three types of geometrical magnitudes, *viz.*, *Lengths*, *Areas* and *Volumes*. In this chapter we shall be concerned with applications to **Mechanics** and in this regard consider the concepts of *Centre of Gravity* (C.G.) and *Moment of Inertia* (M.I.).

The notion of centre of gravity of a rigid material system is of importance inasmuch as we often find it useful to replace both in Statics as well as in Dynamics a given rigid system by a single particle whose position coincides with that of the C.G. and whose mass is the same as that of the given system. In view of the fact that we have only been concerned in this book with ordinary integrals and not with double, triple integrals, etc., we are not in a position to develop general formulae for the C.G. of *arbitrary* systems and shall as such consider only special types of systems.

The notion of *Moment of Inertia about a given line of a rigid material system* is of importance in the study of Dynamics of rigid bodies. In this case also, we shall be considering only a few special types of systems.

11.2. Centre of Gravity. A given rigid material system may involve a Discrete or a Continuous distribution of matter. For a discrete distribution, it is proved in Statics that if we have a system of n particles with weights

$$w_1, w_2, \ldots, w_r, \ldots, w_n$$

on a plane with coordinates

$$(x_1, y_1), (x_2, y_2), \ldots, (x_r, y_r), \ldots, (x_n, y_n)$$

then the C.G. $(\bar{x}, \bar{y})$ of the system is given by

$$\bar{x} = \frac{\sum\limits_{r=1}^{n} w_r x_r}{\sum\limits_{r=1}^{n} w_r}, \quad \bar{y} = \frac{\sum\limits_{r=1}^{n} w_r y_r}{\sum\limits_{r=1}^{n} w_r}. \qquad \ldots(1)$$

In case gravity at each of the points is the same and is denoted by g so that

$$w_r = m_r g,$$

382

m_r denoting the mass of the particle with weight w_r, we have

$$\bar{x} = \frac{\sum\limits_{r=1}^{n} m_r x_r}{\sum\limits_{r=1}^{n} m_r}, \quad \bar{y} = \frac{\sum\limits_{r=1}^{n} m_r y_r}{\sum\limits_{r=1}^{n} m_r}. \qquad ...(2)$$

Because of the relations (2), the centre of gravity is also often referred to as *Centre of Mass* or *Centre of Inertia*.

We shall now proceed to adopt the above formulae for the C.G. of a finite discrete distribution of matter to that of continuous distributions.

It will be seen that the C.G. of a continuous distribution of matter will be obtained through the limiting process from that of a discrete distribution. The process will consist in *replacing* the given continuous distribution by an appropriately selected finite system of particles and to have recourse to a limiting process.

11.3. Centre of gravity of a continuous distribution of matter.

11.31. Centre of gravity of a uniform plane curve. Consider a portion of a curve $y = f(x)$ intercepted between points A and B with abscissae a and b. Actually we have to imagine a thin rigid wire in the form of this arc.

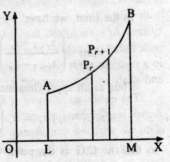

Fig. 11.1

Draw AL, BM $\perp$ OX and divide the interval $[a, b]$ and the corresponding line segment LM into n equal parts each of length h so that we obtain points with abscissae

$$a, a + h, \ldots, a + (r-1) h, a + rh, \ldots, a + nh$$

which we may re-write as

$$x_0, x_1, \ldots, x_{r-1}, x_r, \ldots, x_n.$$

Erect ordinates at these points of division meeting the arc AB at points

$$P_0 = A, P_1, P_2, \ldots, P_{r-1}, P_r, \ldots, P_n = B.$$

We write

$$y_r = f(x_r) = f(a + rh).$$

Let

$$\text{arc } AP_r = s_r.$$

We replace the arc $P_r P_{r+1}$ by a particle of equal mass $\rho\,(s_{r+1} - s_r)$ at its initial point P_r; ρ being the density, *i.e.*, the mass per unit length. Thus we obtain a system of n particles with masses

$$\rho\,(s_1 - s_0), \ldots, \rho\,(s_{r+1} - s_r), \ldots, \rho\,(s_n - s_{n-1})$$

at points with coordinates

$$(x_0, y_0), \ldots, (x_r, y_r), \ldots, (x_{n-1}, y_{n-1})$$

and the C.G. of this system is the point with coordinates

$$\left[\frac{\Sigma \rho (s_{r+1} - s_r) x_r}{\Sigma \rho (s_{r+1} - s_r)}, \frac{\Sigma \rho (s_{r+1} - s_r) y_r}{\Sigma \rho (s_{r+1} - s_r)} \right]$$

or

$$\left[\frac{\Sigma (s_{r+1} - s_r) x_r}{\Sigma (s_{r+1} - s_r)}, \frac{\Sigma (s_{r+1} - s_r) y_r}{\Sigma (s_{r+1} - s_r)} \right]$$

summation extending from $r = 0$ to $n - 1$.

The denominator in each case is l which denotes the length of the complete arc.

We write

$$(s_{r+1} - s_r) x_r = x_r \left(\frac{s_{r+1} - s_r}{x_{r+1} - x_r} \right)(x_{r+1} - x_r) = x_r \frac{s_{r+1} - s_r}{x_{r+1} - x_r} \cdot h.$$

In the limit, we have

$$\lim_{x_{r+1} \to x_r} \left(\frac{s_{r+1} - s_r}{x_{r+1} - x_r} \right) = \left(\frac{ds}{dx} \right)_{x = x_r}$$

Thus as an approximation we write

$$(s_{r+1} - s_r) x_r = x_r \left(\frac{ds}{dx} \right)_{x = x_r} \cdot h$$

so that the C.G. is the point with coordinates

$$\left[h \sum_{r=0}^{n-1} x_r \frac{\left(\frac{ds}{dx} \right)_{x = x_r}}{l}, \; h \sum_{r=0}^{n-1} y_r \frac{\left(\frac{ds}{dy} \right)_{y = y_r}}{l} \right]$$

By the fundamental theorem of Integral Calculus, we see that these expressions tend to the limits

$$\frac{\int_a^b x \frac{ds}{dx} dx}{l}, \; \frac{\int_a^b y \frac{ds}{dy} dy}{l}$$

which we take as the co-ordinates of the C.G. of the given curve.

Note 1. It may be seen that if we amend the above procedure by locating the mass of the arc $P_r P_{r+1}$ at the point P_{r+1} instead of at P_r, we shall obtain the same limits as obtained above.

Note 2. If we write $x \dfrac{ds}{dx} = \phi(x)$, and $y \dfrac{ds}{dy} = \psi(x)$,

we see that

$$h \sum_{r=0}^{n-1} x_r \left(\frac{ds}{dx}\right)_r = h \sum_{r=0}^{n-1} \phi(a+rh)$$

$$h \sum_{r=0}^{n-1} y_r \left(\frac{ds}{dy}\right)_r = h \sum_{r=0}^{n-1} \psi(a+rh)$$

so that we obtain expressions which are exactly of the same form as we were concerned with in the formulation of the fundamental theorem of Integral Calculus.

11.32. Centre of gravity of a uniform plane area. Consider the plane area bounded by a curve $y = f(x)$, x-axis and the two ordinates $x = a$, $x = b$. Actually we have to imagine a thin plane lamina bounded as given.

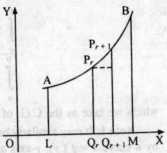

Fig. 11.2

We divide the segment LM into n equal segments each of length h by points with abscissae,

$$a, a+h, \ldots\ldots, a+rh, \ldots\ldots, a+nh = b$$

which we may re-write as

$$x_0, x_1, \ldots\ldots, x_r, \ldots\ldots, x_n$$

and erect ordinates at these points meeting the curve at points

$$A = P_0, P_1, \ldots\ldots, P_r, \ldots\ldots, P_n = B$$

respectively. We write $y_r = f(x_r) = f(a+rh)$, and replace the area below $P_r P_{r+1}$ by the rectangle $P_r Q_{r+1}$ with area

$$hy_r$$

and C.G. at point

$$\left[\frac{1}{2}(x_r + x_{r+1}), \frac{1}{2}y_r\right].$$

Again we replace this rectangle by a particle of mass ρhy_r at point

$$\left[\frac{1}{2}(x_r + x_{r+1}), \frac{1}{2}y_r\right]$$

so that we obtain n particles with C.G.

$$\left[\frac{\Sigma \rho hy_r \cdot \frac{1}{2}(x_r + x_{r+1})}{\Sigma \rho hy_r}, \frac{\Sigma \rho hy_r \cdot \frac{1}{2}y_r}{\Sigma \rho hy_r}\right].$$

We have when $n \to \infty$ and $h \to 0$,

$$\lim \Sigma \, hy_r = \int_a^b y \, dx$$

$$\lim \Sigma \, hy_r \cdot \frac{1}{2}(x_r + x_{r+1}) = \int_a^b yx \, dx$$

$$\lim \Sigma \frac{1}{2} hy_r^{\,2} = \frac{1}{2} \int_a^b y^2 \, dx.$$

Thus in the limit we obtain a point with co-ordinates

$$\frac{\displaystyle\int_a^b xy \, dx}{\displaystyle\int_a^b y \, dx}, \quad \frac{\dfrac{1}{2}\displaystyle\int_a^b y^2 \, dx}{\displaystyle\int_a^b y \, dx}$$

which we take as the C.G. of the given area or the given lamina.

Note 1. It may similarly be shown that the C.G. of a plane area bounded by a curve $x = f(y)$, y-axis and the two ordinates $y = c$, $y = d$ is

$$\frac{\dfrac{1}{2}\displaystyle\int_c^d x^2 \, dy}{\displaystyle\int_c^d x \, dy}, \quad \frac{\displaystyle\int_c^d yx \, dy}{\displaystyle\int_c^d x \, dy}.$$

Note 2. Centre of gravity of a sectorial area. Consider a sectorial area bounded by a curve $r = f(\theta)$ and two radii vectors

$$\theta = \alpha, \ \theta = \beta.$$

We divide the angle AOB into n equal parts; each part being equal to say h. Let OP_r, OP_{r+1} be two lines through O making angles $\alpha + hr$, $\alpha + h(r+1)$ respectively with OX.

We have $OP_r = f(\alpha + hr)$.

We replace the area bounded by the arc $P_r P_{r+1}$ by that of the triangle $OP_r P_{r+1}$. The C.G. of the triangle $OP_r P_{r+1}$ is a

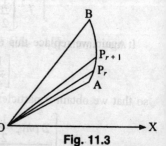

Fig. 11.3

point on the median through O. We replace the same by the point on OP_r at a distance $\frac{2}{3} OP_r$ from O. Finally we replace the area bounded by the arc

$P_r P_{r+1}$ by a particle of mass equal to that of the triangle at a point on OP_r
at a distance equal to $\frac{2}{3} OP_r$ from O.

Thus we have a mass

$$\frac{1}{2} OP_r . OP_{r+1} \sin h$$

at the point with co-ordinates

$$\frac{2}{3} OP_r \cos(\alpha + hr), \quad \frac{2}{3} OP_r \sin(\alpha + hr)$$

i.e., at the point with co-ordinates

$$\frac{2}{3} f(\alpha + hr) \cos(\alpha + hr), \quad \frac{2}{3} f(\alpha + hr) \sin(\alpha + hr).$$

Thus the abscissa of the C.G. of the system of n particles is

$$\frac{\Sigma \rho \frac{1}{2} f(\alpha + hr) f(\alpha + \overline{hr+1}) \sin h \cdot \frac{2}{3} f(\alpha + hr) \cos(\alpha + hr)}{\Sigma \rho \frac{1}{2} f(\alpha + hr) f(\alpha + \overline{hr+1}) \sin h}$$

... ...

We re-write this as an approximation

$$\frac{\frac{2}{3} \Sigma f^3(\alpha + hr) \cos(\alpha + hr)}{\Sigma f^2(\alpha + hr) h},$$

which in the limit becomes

$$\frac{\frac{2}{3} \int_\alpha^\beta f^3(\theta) \cos \theta \, d\theta}{\int_\alpha^\beta f^2(\theta) \, d\theta} = \frac{\frac{2}{3} \int_\alpha^\beta r^3 \cos \theta \, d\theta}{\int_\alpha^\beta r^2 \, d\theta}.$$

It may similarly be seen that the ordinate of the C.G. is

$$\frac{\frac{2}{3} \int_\alpha^\beta r^3 \sin \theta \, d\theta}{\int_\alpha^\beta r^2 \, d\theta}.$$

11.33. Centre of gravity of a volume of Revolution. Let a curve $y = f(x)$
intercepted between two points with abscissae a and b revolve about x-axis.

We have to find the position of the C.G. of the solid thus obtained. By considerations of symmetry, it is obvious that C.G. lies on x-axis.

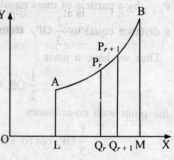

Fig. 11.4

We divide LM into n equal parts each of length h and thus obtain parts with abscissae

$$a, a + h, ..., a + rh, ..., a + nh = b$$

which we may denote by

$$x_0, x_1, ..., x_r, ..., x_n$$

respectively. Let the ordinates through these points meet the curve at points

$$P_0 = A, P_1, ..., P_r, ..., P_n = B.$$

The ordinate of $P_r = f(a + rh) = y_r$, say.

Consider the part of the volume obtained on revolving the arc $P_r P_{r+1}$ by that obtained on revolving the rectangle $P_r Q_{r+1}$ about x-axis. This latter volume is

$$\rho \pi h y_r^2$$

with its C.G. at the mid-point of $Q_r Q_{r+1}$ whose abscissa is $\frac{1}{2}(x_r + x_{r+1})$.

Again we replace this latter volume by a particle of equal mass at the mid-point of $Q_r Q_{r+1}$. The abscissa of the C.G. of this system of n particles is

$$\dfrac{\sum\limits_{r=0}^{n-1} \rho \pi h y_r^2 \cdot \frac{1}{2}(x_r + x_{r+1})}{\sum\limits_{r=1}^{n-1} \rho \pi h y_r^2}.$$

In the limit when $n \to \infty$ and $h \to 0$ we obtain

$$\dfrac{\displaystyle\int_a^b xy^2\, dx}{\displaystyle\int_a^b y^2\, dx}$$

which is the required abscissa.

11.34. Centre of gravity of a surface of revolution. (Refer Fig. 11.4, previous article).

We find the C.G. of the surface of revolution obtained on revolving the arc AB about x-axis.

We replace the part of the surface generated by the arc $P_r P_{r+1}$ by that generated by the chord $P_r P_{r+1}$ whose area as shown in § 9.5 is

$$\pi (y_r + y_{r+1})\, P_r P_{r+1}.$$

Its C.G. is at the mid-point $Q_r Q_{r+1}$. Again, we replace this surface by a particle of equal mass at the mid-point of $Q_r Q_{r+1}$. The centre of gravity of this system of particles is a point on x-axis with abscissa

$$\frac{\Sigma \rho\pi (y_r + y_{r+1}) \, P_r \, P_{r+1} \cdot \frac{1}{2}(x_r + x_{r+1})}{\Sigma \rho\pi (y_r + y_{r+1}) \, P_r \, P_{r+1}}$$

which may be taken as

$$\frac{\sum\limits_{r=0}^{n-1} h\,(y_r + y_{r+1})\left(\dfrac{ds}{dx}\right)_{x=x_r} \dfrac{1}{2}(x_r + x_{r+1})}{\sum\limits_{r=0}^{n-1} h\,(y_r + y_{r+1})\left(\dfrac{ds}{dx}\right)_{x=x_r}}$$

which, in the limit, gives

$$\frac{\int\limits_a^b xy\,\dfrac{ds}{dx}\,dx}{\int\limits_a^b y\,\dfrac{ds}{dx}\,dx}.$$

EXAMPLES

1. *Find the centre of gravity of the arc of the curve*
$$x = a\,\sin^3\theta,\ y = a\,\cos^3\theta$$

lying in the first quadrant.

We have (§ 11.31)

$$\bar{x} = \frac{\int\limits_0^a x\,\dfrac{ds}{dx}\,dx}{\int\limits_0^a \dfrac{ds}{dx}\,dx};\quad \bar{y} = \frac{\int\limits_0^a y\,\dfrac{ds}{dx}\,dx}{\int\limits_0^a \dfrac{ds}{dx}\,dx}.$$

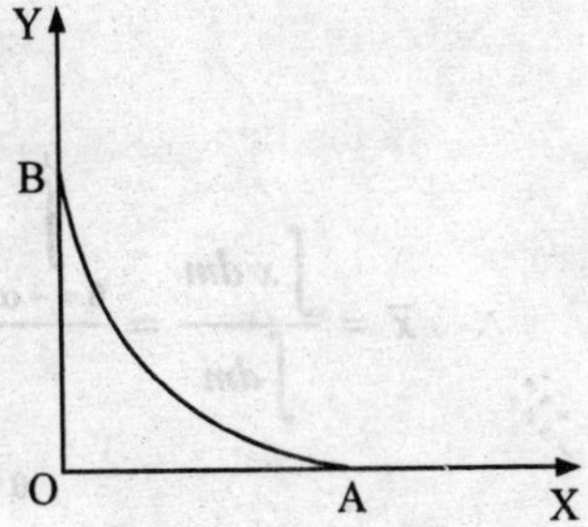

Fig. 11.5

Also

$$\int\limits_0^a x\,\frac{ds}{dx}\,dx = \int\limits_0^{\pi/2} x\,\frac{ds}{dx}\cdot\frac{dx}{d\theta}\,d\theta$$

$$= \int\limits_0^{\pi/2} x\,\frac{ds}{d\theta}\,d\theta = \frac{3a^2}{5}$$

$$\int\limits_0^a \frac{ds}{dx}\,dx = \int\limits_0^{\pi/2} \frac{ds}{dx}\frac{dx}{d\theta}\,d\theta = \int\limits_0^{\pi/2} \frac{ds}{d\theta}\,d\theta = \frac{3a}{2}$$

$$\therefore \quad \bar{x} = \frac{2a}{5}.$$

We may similarly show that

$$\bar{y} = \frac{2a}{5}.$$

2. *Find the C.G. of a circular arc subtending an angle* 2α *at the centre.*

We are to find the C.G. of the arc ACB, where $\angle$ AOB $= 2\alpha$ (given). Take the central radius OC as the initial line, then $\angle$ AOC $= \angle$ BOC $= \alpha$.

Thus OC is the line of symmetry, hence $\bar{y} = 0$, where $(\bar{x}, \bar{y})$ is the required C.G. of the circular arc ACB.

Take two neighbouring points P (r, θ) and Q $(r + \delta r, \theta + \delta\theta)$ on the curve. Let arc PQ $= \delta s$, then $\delta s = a\delta\theta$, where a is the radius of the circular arc. If (x, y) be the cartesian coordinates of P, then $x = a \cos\theta$ and $y = a \sin\theta$, so the C.G. of the elementary arc PQ is $(a \cos\theta, a \sin\theta)$.

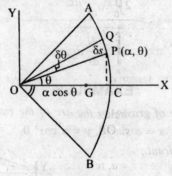

Fig. 11.6

$$\therefore \quad \bar{x} = \frac{\int x\, dm}{\int dm} = \frac{\displaystyle\int_{\theta=-\alpha}^{\alpha} a\cos\theta \cdot a\, d\theta}{\displaystyle\int_{\theta=-\alpha}^{\alpha} a\, d\theta} = a \frac{\displaystyle\int_{-\alpha}^{\alpha} \cos\theta\, d\theta}{\displaystyle\int_{-\alpha}^{\alpha} d\theta}$$

$$= \frac{a \left[\sin\theta\right]_{-\alpha}^{\alpha}}{\left[\theta\right]_{-\alpha}^{\alpha}} = \frac{a\,(\sin\alpha + \sin\alpha)}{(\alpha + \alpha)} = \frac{a \sin\alpha}{\alpha}.$$

Hence the required centre of gravity G lies on the central radius OC, such that OG $= \dfrac{a \sin\alpha}{\alpha}$.

3. *Find the centre of gravity of a uniform lamina bounded by the co-ordinate axes and the arc of the ellipse*

$$\frac{x^2}{a^2} + \frac{y^2}{b^2} = 1$$

in the first quadrant.

We have (§ 11.32)

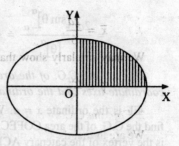

Fig. 11.7

$$\bar{x} = \frac{\displaystyle\int_0^a xy\,dx}{\displaystyle\int_0^a y\,dx} = \frac{\displaystyle\int_0^a x \cdot \frac{b}{a}\sqrt{a^2 - x^2}\,dx}{\displaystyle\int_0^a \frac{b}{a}\sqrt{a^2 - x^2}\,dx} = \frac{4a}{3\pi}.$$

$$\bar{y} = \frac{\dfrac{1}{2}\displaystyle\int_0^a y^2\,dx}{\displaystyle\int_0^a y\,dx} = \frac{\dfrac{1}{2}\displaystyle\int_0^a \frac{b^2}{a^2}(a^2 - x^2)\,dx}{\displaystyle\int_0^a \frac{b}{a}\sqrt{a^2 - x^2}\,dx} = \frac{4b}{3\pi}.$$

4. *Find C.G. of the sector of a circle subtending an angle 2α at the centre of the circle.*

AOB is the sector of the circle subtending an angle 2α at the centre. OX is the bisector of $\angle$ AOB.

Equation of the curve is $r = a$, referred to O as pole and OX as initial line, a being the radius of the circle.

OX is the line of symmetry. Hence the C.G. of the sector lies on OX. Hence $\bar{y} = 0$.

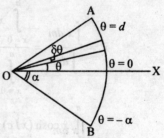

Fig. 11.8

And $\quad \bar{x} = \dfrac{2}{3} \cdot \dfrac{\displaystyle\int_{-\alpha}^{\alpha} r^3 \cos\theta\,d\theta}{\displaystyle\int_{-\alpha}^{\alpha} r^2\,d\theta},$

$\quad\quad\quad = \dfrac{2}{3} \cdot a \dfrac{\displaystyle\int_{-\alpha}^{\alpha} \cos\theta\,d\theta}{\displaystyle\int_{-\alpha}^{\alpha} d\theta},$ $\quad [\because\ r = a]$

$$= \frac{2a}{3} \cdot \frac{[\sin \theta]_{-\alpha}^{\alpha}}{[\theta]_{-\alpha}^{\alpha}} = \frac{2a}{3} \cdot \frac{\sin \alpha}{\alpha}.$$

5. *Find the C.G. of the area between the curve* $y = c \cosh(x/c)$, *the coordinate axes and the ordinate* $x = a$.

EF is the ordinate $x = a$. We are to find the C.G. of the area COFEC, where C is the vertex of the catenary ACB and OF is the directrix of the catenary.

Take two neighbouring points $P(x, y)$ and $Q(x + \delta x, y + \delta y)$ on the arc CE of the catenary.

From P and Q draw PN and QM perpendiculars to x axis.

Then area PNMQ is the elementary area. Its area $= y\delta x$ and mass $= \delta m = \rho \cdot y \delta x$, where ρ is the mass per unit area.

Also the C.G. of the area is $\left(x, \dfrac{1}{2} y \right)$.

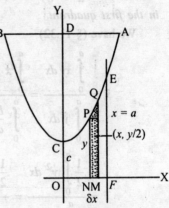

Fig. 11.9

If $(\bar{x}, \bar{y})$ be the required C.G., then

$$\bar{x} = \frac{\displaystyle\int x \, dm}{\displaystyle\int dm} = \frac{\displaystyle\int_{x=0}^{a} x \cdot \rho y \, dx}{\displaystyle\int_{x=0}^{a} \rho y \, dx}, \text{ where } y = c \cosh(x/c)$$

$$= \frac{\displaystyle\int_0^a x \cosh(x/c) \, dx}{\displaystyle\int_0^a \cosh(x/c) \, dx} = \frac{\left[cx \sinh(x/c) \right]_0^a - c \displaystyle\int_0^a \sinh(x/c) \, dx}{\left[c \sinh(x/c) \right]_0^a}$$

$$= \frac{ca \sinh(a/c) - c^2 \left[\cosh(x/c) \right]_0^a}{c \sinh(a/c)}$$

$$= \frac{a \sinh(a/c) - c \cosh(a/c) + c}{\sinh(a/c)}$$

$$= a - c \coth(a/c) + c \, \text{cosech}(a/c).$$

And

$$\bar{y} = \frac{\int y \, dm}{\int dm} = \frac{\displaystyle\int_{x=0}^{a} \frac{1}{2} y \cdot \rho y \, dx}{\displaystyle\int_{x=0}^{a} \rho y \, dx}, \quad \text{where } y = c \cosh (x/c)$$

$$= \frac{1}{2} c \cdot \frac{\displaystyle\int_{0}^{a} \cosh^2 (x/c) \, dx}{\displaystyle\int_{0}^{a} \cosh (x/c) \, dx} = \frac{1}{4} c \cdot \frac{\displaystyle\int_{0}^{a} [\cosh (2x/c) + 1] \, dx}{\big[c \sinh (x/c) \big]_{0}^{a}}$$

$$= \frac{1}{4} c \cdot \frac{\left[\dfrac{1}{2} c \sinh (2x/c) + x \right]_{0}^{a}}{c \sinh (a/c)} = \frac{1}{4} \cdot \frac{\left[\dfrac{1}{2} c \sinh (2a/c) + a \right]}{\sinh (a/c)}$$

$$= \frac{1}{4} [c \cosh (a/c) + a \operatorname{cosech} (a/c)],$$

$$[\because \ \sinh (2a/c) = 2 \sinh (a/c) \cosh (a/c)]$$

Hence $\bar{x} = a - c \coth (a/c) + \operatorname{cosech} (a/c)$

and $\bar{y} = \dfrac{1}{4} [c \cosh (a/c) + a \operatorname{cosech} (a/c)].$

6. *Find the position of the centroid of the area of cardioid* $r = a(1 + \cos \theta)$.

Since the curve is symmetrical about the initial line, so $\bar{y} = 0$. Also for the whole cardioid θ varies from $-\pi$ to π.

Take two neighbouring points $P(r, \theta)$ and $Q(r + \delta r, \theta + \delta \theta)$ on the curve. Then elementary area is the sector POQ. Its area $= \dfrac{1}{2} r^2 \, \delta \theta$ and x-coordinate of its C.G. is

$$\frac{2}{3} r \cos \theta.$$

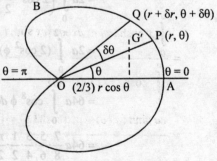

Fig. 11.10

$\therefore$ $\bar{x}$, the x-coordinate of the C.G. of the cardioid is given by

$$\bar{x} = \frac{\int x \, dm}{\int dm} = \frac{\displaystyle\int_{\theta=-\pi}^{\pi} \frac{2}{3} r \cos\theta \cdot \frac{1}{2} r^2 \, d\theta}{\displaystyle\int_{\theta=-\pi}^{\pi} \frac{1}{2} r^2 \, d\theta} = \frac{\displaystyle\int_{-\pi}^{\pi} \frac{2}{3} r^3 \cos\theta \, d\theta}{\displaystyle\int_{-\pi}^{\pi} r^2 \, d\theta}$$

$$= \frac{2}{3} \cdot \frac{\displaystyle\int_{0}^{\pi} a^3 (1+\cos\theta)^3 \cos\theta \, d\theta}{\displaystyle\int_{0}^{\pi} a^2 (1+\cos\theta)^2 \, d\theta},$$

$$\left[\because \int_{-a}^{a} f(x) \, dx = 2 \int_{0}^{a} f(x) \, dx, \text{ if } f(x) = f(-x) \right]$$

$$= \frac{2a}{3} \cdot \frac{\displaystyle\int_{0}^{\pi} (1+\cos\theta)^3 \cos\theta \, d\theta}{\displaystyle\int_{0}^{\pi} (1+\cos\theta)^2 \, d\theta} \qquad \qquad \dots($$

Numerator of $\bar{x} = 2a \int_{0}^{\pi} (1+\cos\theta)^3 \cos\theta \, d\theta$

$$= 2a \int_{0}^{\pi} \left(2\cos^2 \frac{1}{2}\theta \right)^3 \left(2\cos^2 \frac{1}{2}\theta - 1 \right) d\theta$$

$$= 2a \int_{0}^{\pi/2} (2\cos^2 \phi)^3 (2\cos^2 \phi - 1) \, 2 \, d\phi, \text{ putting } \theta = 2\phi$$

$$= 64a \int_{0}^{\pi/2} \cos^8 \phi \, d\phi - 32a \int_{0}^{\pi/2} \cos^6 \phi \, d\phi$$

$$= 64a \, \frac{7}{8} \cdot \frac{5}{6} \cdot \frac{3}{4} \cdot \frac{1}{2} \cdot \frac{\pi}{2} - 32a \, \frac{5}{6} \cdot \frac{3}{4} \cdot \frac{1}{2} \cdot \frac{\pi}{2} = \frac{15\pi a}{4}.$$

And denominator of $\bar{x} = 3 \int_{0}^{\pi} (1+\cos\theta)^2 \, d\theta = 12 \int_{0}^{\pi} \cos^4 \frac{1}{2}\theta \, d\theta$

$$= 12 \int_{0}^{\pi/2} \cos^4 \phi \cdot 2 \, d\phi, \text{ putting } \theta = 2\phi$$

$$= 24 \cdot \frac{3}{4} \cdot \frac{1}{2} \cdot \frac{\pi}{2} = \frac{9\pi}{2}.$$

$$\therefore \quad \text{From } (i), \quad \bar{x} = \frac{15\pi a/4}{9\pi/2} = \frac{5a}{6}.$$

Hence the required C.G. is given by $\bar{x} = \dfrac{5}{6}a$, $\bar{y} = 0$.

7. *Find the C.G. of a zone of a sphere.*

Let the spherical zone BDD'B' be generated by the revolution of the arc BD of the generating circle whose radius is a (say). OA is the central radius. Take the centre O as origin and the axes as shown in the Fig. 11.11. Then the equation of generating circle is

$$x^2 + y^2 = a^2. \qquad ...(i)$$

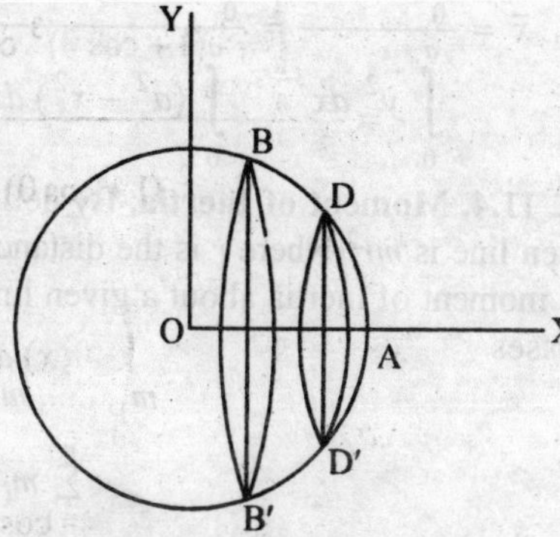

From (i), on differentiating we get

$$2x + 2y \frac{dy}{dx} = 0 \text{ or } \frac{dy}{dx} = -\frac{x}{y}.$$

Fig. 11.11

$$\therefore \quad \frac{ds}{dx} = \sqrt{1 + \left(\frac{dy}{dx}\right)^2} = \sqrt{1 + \frac{x^2}{y^2}} = \sqrt{\frac{x^2 + y^2}{y^2}} = \sqrt{\frac{a^2}{y^2}}, \quad [\text{From } (i)]$$

$$ds = (a / y) \, dx.$$

Also let C and E be the centres of the plane ends of zone. Let OC = b and OE = c.

Then if $(\bar{x}, \bar{y})$ be the required C.G. of the spherical zone, then from symmetry $\bar{y} = 0$ and

$$\bar{x} = \frac{\int x \, dm}{\int dm} = \frac{\displaystyle\int_{x=b}^{c} x \cdot 2\pi y \, ds}{\displaystyle\int_{x=b}^{c} 2\pi y \, ds} = \frac{\displaystyle\int_{b}^{c} xy \frac{a}{y} \, dx}{\displaystyle\int_{b}^{c} y \cdot \frac{a}{y} \, dx}, \qquad [\text{From } (i)]$$

$$= \frac{\left[\dfrac{1}{2} x^2\right]_b^c}{[x]_b^c} = \frac{\dfrac{1}{2}(c^2 - b^2)}{(c - b)} = \frac{1}{2}(c + b).$$

$\therefore$ The required C.G. is the mid-point of CE, *i.e.*, C.G. of the zone bisects its height.

8. *Find the C.G. of a uniform solid hemisphere of radius a.*

We can regard the hemisphere as generated
by revolving through x-axis the arc of the circle
$x^2 + y^2 = a^2$ lying in the first quadrant.

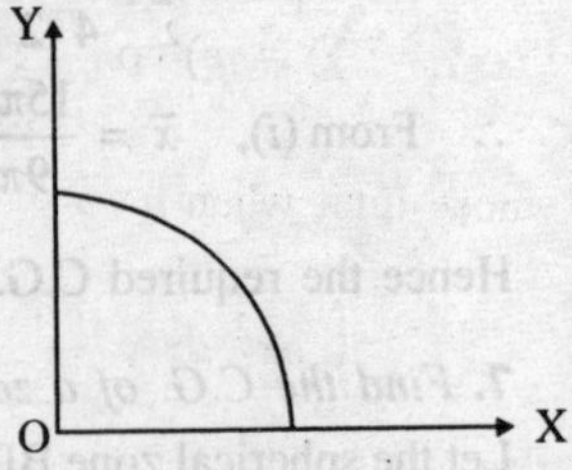

We have

$$\bar{x} = \frac{\displaystyle\int_0^a xy^2\, dx}{\displaystyle\int_0^a y^2\, dx} = \frac{\displaystyle\int_0^a x(a^2 - x^2)\, dx}{\displaystyle\int_0^a (a^2 - x^2)\, dx} = \frac{3a}{8}.$$

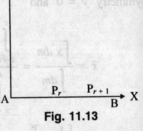

Fig. 11.12

11.4. Moment of Inertia. By definition, the particle of mass about any
given line is mr^2 where r is the distance of the particle from the line. Again
the moment of inertia about a given line of a finite number of particles with
masses

$$m_1, \ldots, m_i, \ldots, m_n$$

is

$$\sum_{i=1}^{n} m_i r_i^2$$

where

$$r_1, \ldots, r_i, \ldots, r_n$$

are the distances of the particles from the given line.

The moment of inertia of a continuous distribution of matter is obtained
through a limiting process. The process will be indicated by the following
examples.

EXAMPLES

1. *Find the moment of inertia of a thin uniform rod of length 2a about
the line through its one extremity perpendicular to the rod.*

Let AB be the rod. We take A as origin
and AB as x-axis. We require moment of inertia
about the line AY through A perpendicular to
AB.

We divide AB into n equal parts each of
length h by points

$$A = P_0, P_1, \ldots, P_r, \ldots, P_n = B$$

we have $AP_r = \dfrac{2a}{n} r = hr$.

Fig. 11.13

We replace the part $P_r P_{r+1}$ of the rod by a particle at P_r of mass equal
to that of the part. If ρ be the density of the rod, the mass of this particle
is

$$\rho h$$

so that the moment of inertia about AY is

$$(hr)^2\, \rho h.$$

The moment of inertia of the system of particles is, therefore,

$$\sum_{r=0}^{n-1} (hr)^2 \, \rho h = \frac{1}{n} \sum_{r=0}^{n-1} \rho \left(\frac{r}{n}\right)^2$$

whose limit when $n \to \infty$ and $h \to 0$ and $nh = 2a$ is

$$\int_0^{2a} \rho x^2 \, dx = \frac{8a^3}{3} \rho = M \frac{4a^2}{3}$$

where M denotes the mass of the whole rod.

Ex. Show that the M.I. of a uniform thin rod of length $2a$ and mass M about the line through its middle point perpendicular to the rod is

$$Ma^2 / 3.$$

2. *Find the moment of inertia of a thin uniform circular disc of radius a about any diameter thereof.*

We take the given diameter as x-axis and the centre O as origin.

We divide the diameter AB into n equal parts each of length h and through the points of division draw $\perp$ AB. We replace the part of the disc contained between the ordinates through Q_r and Q_{r+1} by a rod of length $2y_r$ whose moment of inertia about OX is

$$2\rho y_r h \cdot \frac{y_r^2}{3}$$

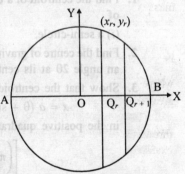

Fig. 11.14

so that the moment of inertia of the system of rods about OX is

$$\sum_{r=0}^{n-1} 2\rho y_r h \cdot \frac{y_r^2}{3}.$$

We have $y_r = f(-a + hr)$, where $f(x) = \sqrt{a^2 - x^2}$.

When $n \to \infty$, $h \to 0$, we obtain in the limit

$$\int_{-a}^{+a} \frac{2\rho}{3} (a^2 - x^2)^{3/2} \, dx = \frac{\rho \pi a^4}{4} = \frac{Ma^2}{4}$$

where M is the mass of the disc.

Ex. Show that the moment of inertia of a uniform circular disc of mass M and radius a about the line through its centre perpendicular to its plane is $Ma^2 / 2$.

3. *Find the moment of inertia of a uniform solid sphere of radius a about the diameter.*

Dividing the diameter into n equal parts and drawing through the point of division planes perpendicular to the axis and replacing each part of the sphere bound between two consecutive planes by a thin circular disc we may see that the required moment of inertia is

$$= \int_{-a}^{+a} \pi\rho \, (a^2 - x^2) \frac{1}{2} (a^2 - x^2) \, dx$$

$$= \frac{8\rho\pi a^5}{15} = \frac{2a^2}{5} \cdot \frac{4a^2}{3} \rho = \frac{2a^2}{5} M$$

where M is the mass of sphere.

EXERCISES ON CHAPTER 11

1. Find the centroid of a uniform circular wire of radius a in the form of
   (*i*) a semi-circle.   (*ii*) quadrant of a circle.

2. Find the centre of gravity of the arc of a circle of radius a subtending an angle 2θ at its centre.

3. Show that the centroid of the arc of the cycloid
$$x = a \, (\theta + \sin \theta), \; y = a \, (1 - \cos \theta)$$
in the positive quadrant is
$$\left[\left(\pi - \frac{4}{3} \right) a, \; \frac{2}{3} a \right].$$

4. Find the centre of gravity of the arc of the parabola $y^2 = 4ax$ bounded by the vertex and an extremity $(a, 2a)$ of its latus rectum.

5. Show that the centre of gravity of the arc of the catenary
$$y = c \cosh \frac{x}{c}$$
included between its vertex $(0, c)$ and a point (x, y) is
$$\left[x - \frac{c\,(y - c)}{s}, \; \frac{y}{2} + \frac{cx}{2s} \right]$$
where s is the length of the arc.

6. Find the centroid of a plane lamina bounded by x-axis and the part of the ellipse $x^2 / a^2 + y^2 / b^2 = 1$ for which y is positive.

7. Show that the centroid of the area bounded by the parabola $x^2 = 4ay$, x-axis and the ordinate $x = b$ is
$$\left(\frac{3}{4} b, \; \frac{3}{40} \cdot \frac{b^2}{a} \right).$$

8. Show that the centroid of the area bounded by the cardioid $r = a (1 + \cos \theta)$ is on the initial line at a distance $\dfrac{5}{6} a$ from the pole.

9. What are the coordinates of the C.G. of the area under one arc of the sine curve $y = \sin x$?

10. Determine the C.G. of the area bounded by the parabolas $y^2 = ax$ and $x^2 = by$.

11. Find the centre of gravity of the area in the first quadrant bounded by the axes and the curve

$$y = 2 + x - x^2.$$

12. A flat thin plate of uniform density is bounded by the two curves $y = x^2, y = -x^2$ and the line $x = 2$. Find the coordinates of its C.G.

13. Show that the centroid of the area bounded by the loop of the curve

$$y^2 (a + x) = x^2 (a - x)$$

is $\dfrac{1}{3} a (3\pi - 8)/(4 - \pi)$.

14. Show that the abscissa of the C.G. of the area of one loop of $r^2 = a^2 \cos 2\theta$ is $\dfrac{1}{8} \pi a \sqrt{2}$.

15. Where is the C.G. of the solid formed by revolving about x-axis the area bounded by the lines $y = 0, x = \pi / 4$ and the curve $y = \sin x$?

16. Find the C.G. of the solid formed by the revolution about x-axis of the parabola $y^2 = 4ax$ cut off by the ordinate $x = b$.

17. Find the centroid of

 (i) surface, (ii) volume

 of the solid formed by the revolution of $r = a (1 + \cos \theta)$ about the initial line.

18. Find the centroid of

 (i) hemispherical surface, (ii) curved surface

 of a right circular cone.

19. A quadrant of the ellipse $x^2 / a^2 + y^2 / b^2 = 1$ revolves about the major axis; find the C.G. of the solid thus obtained.

20. Find the moment of inertia about the y-axis of a uniform lamina of density ρ bounded by those parts of the x-axis and the curve $y = \cos x$ which lie between $x = -\pi / 2$ and $x = \pi / 2$.

21. Find the moment of inertia about x-axis of the solid obtained by revolving $x^2 / a^2 + y^2 / b^2 = 1$ about x-axis.

22. Find the moment of inertia of a uniform solid right cylinder of height h and radius r about its axis.

23. Find the moment of inertia of a thin uniform hollow sphere of radius a about and diameter thereof.

ANSWERS

1. (i) $\bar{x} = 0$, $\bar{y} = 2a/\pi$.   (ii) $(2\sqrt{2}\,a/\pi, 2\sqrt{2}\,a/\pi)$.

2. At a distance $a \sin \theta / \theta$ from the centre on the bisecting radius

4. $\left[\dfrac{a}{4} \cdot \dfrac{3\sqrt{2} - \log(1 + \sqrt{2})}{\sqrt{2} + \log(1 + \sqrt{2})}, \dfrac{4a}{3} \dfrac{\sqrt{8} - 1}{\sqrt{2} + \log(1 + \sqrt{2})} \right]$.

6. $(0, 4b/3\pi)$.   **9.** $\left(\dfrac{\pi}{2}, \dfrac{\pi}{8} \right)$.

10. $\left(\dfrac{9}{20} a^{1/3} b^{5/3}, \dfrac{9}{20} a^{2/3} b^{1/3} \right)$.   **11.** $\left(\dfrac{4}{5}, \dfrac{24}{25} \right)$.

12. $\left(\dfrac{3}{2}, 0 \right)$.   **15.** $\bar{x} = (\pi^2 - 4\pi + 8)/8\,(\pi - 2)$.

16. $\bar{x} = \dfrac{2}{3} b$.   **17.** (i) $\bar{x} = \dfrac{50}{63} a$. (ii) $\dfrac{4}{5} a$.

18. (i) At the mid-point of the bisecting radius.

(ii) At the point dividing the axis in the ratio 2 : 1.

19. $\bar{x} = 3a/8$.   **20.** $\dfrac{1}{2} \rho(\pi^2 - 8)$.

21. $2b^2 M/5$, where M is the mass of the solid.

22. $\dfrac{1}{2} M r^2$, where M is the mass and r the radius of the base.

23. $\dfrac{1}{3} M a^2$, where M is the mass and a the radius of the base.

OBJECTIVE QUESTIONS

For each of the following questions, four alternatives are given for th *answer. Only one of them is correct. Choose the correct alternative.*

1. Distance of C.G. of the sector of a circle subtending an angle 2 at the centre, from the centre is :

(a) $\dfrac{2a}{3}$ (b) $\dfrac{2a}{3} \sin \alpha$ (c) $\dfrac{2a}{3} \cos \alpha$ (d) $\dfrac{2a}{3} \cdot \dfrac{\sin \alpha}{\alpha}$

2. Distance of the C.G. of a uniform circular disc from the centre is

(a) $\dfrac{2a}{3}$ (b) $\dfrac{4a}{3}$ (c) $\dfrac{4a}{3\pi}$ (d) $\dfrac{2a}{3\pi}$.

3. Distance of the C.G. of a solid uniform hemisphere of radius a from the centre is :

   (a) $\dfrac{4a}{3\pi}$ (b) $\dfrac{3a}{8}$ (c) $\dfrac{a}{2}$ (d) a.

4. C.G. of a thin hemispherical shell divides the central radius in the ratio :

   (a) $1:1$ (b) $1:2$ (c) $2:1$ (d) $1:3$.

5. Moment of inertia of a circular plate about a line perpendicular to the plate through the centre is :

   (a) Ma^2 (b) $\dfrac{1}{2}Ma^2$ (c) $\dfrac{1}{3}Ma^2$ (d) $\dfrac{1}{4}Ma^2$.

ANSWERS

1. (d)   2. (c)   3. (b)   4. (a)   5. (b)

SOME MISCELLANEOUS TOPICS

SOME MISCELLANEOUS TOPICS

12

Multiple Integrals

12.1. Multiple Integrals. The process of integration for one variable can be extended to the functions of more than one variable. The generalization of definite integrals is known as *multiple integral.* *(Ajmer, 1998)*

12.2. Double Integral. The notation $\iint_S f(x, y)\, ds$ is used to denote the double integral, over the region S, of the $f(x, y)$.

Consider the region S, as covered by a grid of lines parallel to x-axis and y-axis, which is bounded above by the curve $y = f_2(x)$ and below by $y = f_1(x)$, on the left by the line $x = a$ and on the right by $x = b$. These parallel lines divide the plane into small portions of areas

$$\delta S = \delta x\, \delta y = \delta y\, \delta x.$$

Some of them lie completely within the given regions, some entirely outside and some are intersected by the boundary of the region.

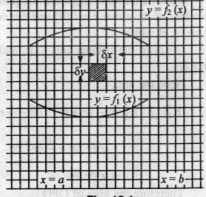

Fig. 12.1

We take account of those portions which lie inside the region and partly inside the region. Although we may discard portions partly inside the region together with the portions outside the region.

Now, we also consider (x_r, y_r), any point lying in δS_r.

Then the total sum

$$S_n = \delta S_1 + \delta S_2 + \delta S_3 + \ldots + \delta S_r + \ldots = \sum_{r=1}^{n} f(x_r, y_r)\, \delta S_r.$$

Let the maximum linear dimensions of each portion of areas approach zero, and n increases indefinitely then, the sum S_n will approach a limit, namely the double integral $\iint_S f(x, y)\, ds$ and the value of this limit is given by

$$\iint_S f(x, \dot{y}) \, ds = \int\limits_a^b \left[\int\limits_{f_1(x)}^{f_2(x)} f(x, y) \, dy \right] dx.$$

Also $$\iint_S f(x, y) \, ds = \int\limits_c^d \left[\int\limits_{f_1(y)}^{f_2(y)} f(x, y) \, dx \right] dy.$$

12.21. Working Method

(i) We integrate with respect to y, x is to be regarded as constant and evaluate the result between the limits $y = f_1(x)$ and $y = f_2(x)$.

(ii) Then we integrate the result of (i) with respect to x between the limits $x = a$ and $x = b$.

Note 1. We treat x as a constant while we perform the y integration.

Note 2. Sometimes it shall be convenient to start with the integration, treating y as a constant.

12.22. Double Integration for polar curves. OP and OQ are two radii vectors of the curve $r = f(\theta)$ and the coordinates of P and Q be (r, θ) and $(r + \delta r, \theta + \delta\theta)$.

We draw the circular arcs K_1L_1 and K_2L_2 with centre O and radii r and $r + \delta r$.

Now the area

$$K_1L_1K_2L_2 = \frac{1}{2}(r + \delta r)^2 \, \delta\theta - \frac{1}{2}r^2 \, \delta\theta$$

$$= r \, \delta r \, \delta\theta + \frac{1}{2}\delta r^2 \, \delta\theta$$

$$= r \, \delta r \, \delta\theta.$$

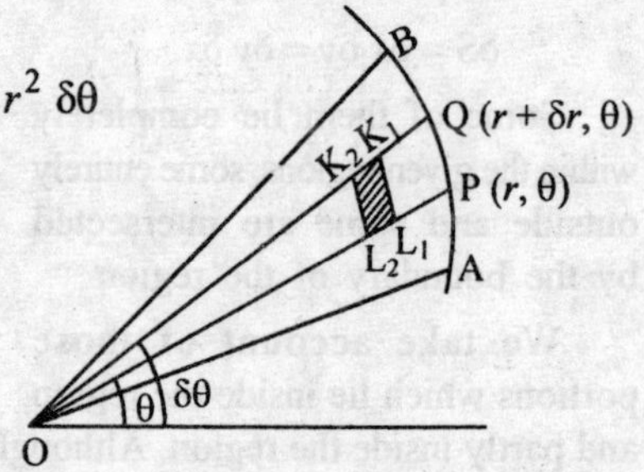

Therefore the area of OPQ

$$= \lim_{\delta r \to 0} [\Sigma r \, \delta r \, \delta\theta]$$

$$= \lim_{\delta r \to 0} [\Sigma r \, \delta r] \, \delta\theta$$

$$= \left[\int\limits_0^{f(\theta)} r \, dr \right] \delta\theta.$$

Fig. 12.2

Hence the area OAB

$$= \lim_{\delta r \to 0} \sum \left[\int\limits_0^{f(\theta)} r \, dr \right] \delta\theta$$

$$= \int\limits_{\theta = \alpha}^{\theta = \beta} \left[\int\limits_0^{f(\theta)} r \, dr \right] d\theta$$

where α and β are the vectorial angles of A and B.

Then $\displaystyle\int_{\alpha}^{\beta} \int_{0}^{f(\theta)} r\, d\theta\, dr$

is defined as the area of the region in polar form.

EXAMPLES

1. *Evaluate* $\displaystyle\int_{0}^{\pi} \int_{0}^{x} \sin y\, dy\, dx.$

We have

$$I = \int_{0}^{\pi} \left[\int_{0}^{x} \sin y\, dy \right] dx$$

$$= \int_{0}^{\pi} \left[-\cos y \right]_{0}^{x} dx, \text{ treating } x \text{ as constant}$$

$$= -\int_{0}^{\pi} (\cos x - \cos 0)\, dx$$

$$= -\int_{0}^{\pi} \cos x\, dx + \int_{0}^{\pi} dx$$

$$= -\left[\sin x \right]_{0}^{\pi} + \left[x \right]_{0}^{\pi} = \pi.$$

2. *Evaluate* $\displaystyle\int_{1}^{\log 8} \int_{0}^{\log y} e^{x+y}\, dx\, dy.$

We have

$$I = \int_{1}^{\log 8} \left[\int_{0}^{\log y} (e^x\, dx) \right] e^y\, dy$$

$$= \int_{1}^{\log 8} \left[e^x \right]_{0}^{\log y} e^y\, dy$$

$$= \int_{1}^{\log 8} e^y\, (e^{\log y} - e^0)\, dy$$

$$= \int_{1}^{\log 8} e^y\, (y - 1)\, dy$$

$$= \left[e^y \cdot y - 2e^y \right]_1^{\log 8}$$

$$= e^{\log 8} \cdot \log 8 - e - 2e^{\log 8} + 2e$$

$$= 8 \log 8 - 16 + e.$$

3. *Evaluate* $\displaystyle \int_1^{\sqrt{2}} \int_{-\sqrt{4-2y^2}}^{\sqrt{4-2y^2}} y \, dx \, dy.$

We have

$$I = \int_1^{\sqrt{2}} \left[\int_{-\sqrt{4-2y^2}}^{\sqrt{4-2y^2}} dx \right] y \, dy$$

$$= \int_0^{\sqrt{2}} \left[x \right]_{-(4-2y^2)^{1/2}}^{(4-2y^2)^{1/2}} y \, dy$$

$$= \int_0^{\sqrt{2}} 2\sqrt{4-2y^2} \; y \, dy$$

$$= -\frac{1}{2} \int_4^0 \sqrt{t} \, dt$$

$$\text{[By putting } 4 - 2y^2 = t, \; -4y \, dy = dt]$$

$$= -\frac{1}{2} \cdot \frac{2}{3} \left[t^{3/2} \right]_4^0 = \frac{1}{3} \cdot 8 = \frac{8}{3}.$$

4. *Evaluate* : $\displaystyle \int_0^1 \int_0^1 \frac{dx \, dy}{\sqrt{(1-x^2)} \; \sqrt{(1-y^2)}}.$　　　　*(Bhopal, 1999)*

$$\int_0^1 \int_0^1 \frac{dx \, dy}{\sqrt{(1-x^2)} \; \sqrt{(1-y^2)}}$$

$$= \int_0^1 \frac{1}{\sqrt{(1-y^2)}} \left[\int_0^1 \frac{dx}{\sqrt{(1-x^2)}} \right] dy$$

$$= \int_0^1 \frac{1}{\sqrt{(1-y^2)}} \left[\sin^{-1} x \right]_0^1 dy$$

$$= \frac{\pi}{2} \int_0^1 \frac{dy}{\sqrt{(1-y^2)}} = \frac{\pi}{2} \left[\sin^{-1} y \right]_0^{\pi/2} = \frac{\pi^2}{4}.$$

5. *Evaluate* :

$$\int_0^1 dx \int_0^{\sqrt{(1-x^2)}} \sqrt{(1-x^2-y^2)}\, dy. \qquad \textit{(Ravishankar, 1997)}$$

$$I = \int_0^1 \frac{1}{2}\left[y\sqrt{(1-x^2-y^2)} + (1-x^2)\sin^{-1}\frac{y}{\sqrt{1-x^2}} \right]_0^{\sqrt{(1-x^2)}} dx$$

$$= \frac{1}{2}\int_0^1 [0 + (1-x^2)\sin^{-1}(1)]\, dx$$

$$= \frac{\pi}{4}\int_0^1 (1-x^2)\, dx = \frac{\pi}{4}\left[x - \frac{x^3}{3} \right]_0^1$$

$$= \frac{\pi}{4}\left[\left(1 - \frac{1}{3}\right) - 0 \right] = \frac{\pi}{6}.$$

6. *Evaluate* $\iint_A xy\, dx\, dy$ *over the positive quadrant of the circle* $x^2 + y^2 = a^2$.

Here the region of integration is positive quadrant of circle $x^2 + y^2 = a^2$, where x varies from 0 to a and y varies from 0 to $\sqrt{(a^2 - x^2)}$.

Hence $\iint_A xy\, dx\, dy$

$$= \int_0^a \int_0^{\sqrt{a^2-x^2}} xy\, dx\, dy$$

$$= \int_0^a \left[\int_0^{\sqrt{a^2-x^2}} y\, dy \right] x\, dx$$

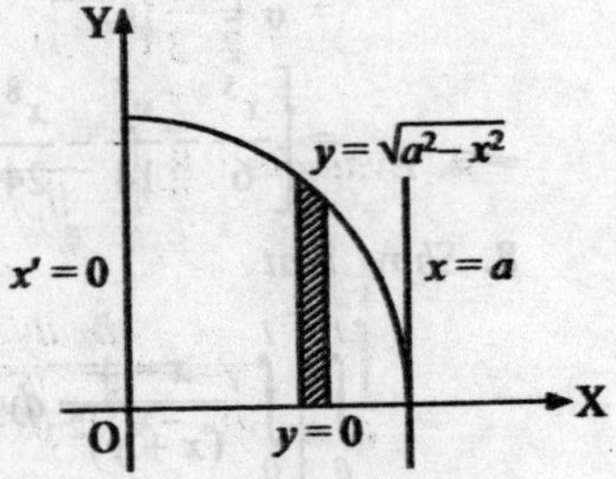

Fig. 12.3

$$= \int_0^a \left[\frac{y^2}{2} \right]_0^{\sqrt{a^2-x^2}} x\, dx$$

$$= \frac{1}{2}\int_0^a x(a^2 - x^2)\, dx$$

$$= \frac{1}{2}\left[\frac{a^2 x^2}{2} - \frac{x^4}{4} \right]_0^a = \frac{1}{8}a^4.$$

7. *Evaluate* $\iint xy \, (x + y) \, dx \, dy$ *over the area between* $y = x^2$ *and* $y = x$.

(Ravishankar, 2000; Bilaspur, 2000)

The area is bounded by the curves

$$y = f_1 \, (x) = x^2, \quad y = f_2 \, (x) = x.$$

When $f_1 \, (x) = f_2 \, (x)$, $x^2 = x$,

i.e., $x \, (x - 1) = 0$

or $x = 0, x = 1$.

i.e., the area of integration is bounded by

$$y = x^2, \ y = x, \ x = 0, \ x = 1.$$

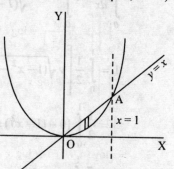

Fig. 12.4

$$\therefore \quad \iint_A xy \, (x + y) \, dx \, dy$$

$$= \int_0^1 \left[\int_{x^2}^x xy \, (x + y) \, dy \right] dx$$

$$= \int_0^1 \left[\int_{x^2}^x (x^2 y + xy^2) \, dy \right] dx$$

$$= \int_0^1 \left[\frac{x^2 y^2}{2} + \frac{xy^3}{3} \right]_{x^2}^x dx$$

$$= \int_0^1 \left[\frac{5x^4}{6} - \frac{x^6}{2} - \frac{x^7}{3} \right] dx$$

$$= \left[\frac{x^5}{6} - \frac{x^7}{14} - \frac{x^8}{24} \right]_0^1 = \left[\frac{1}{6} - \frac{1}{14} - \frac{1}{24} \right] = \frac{3}{56}.$$

8. *Show that*

$$\int_0^1 \left[\int_0^1 \frac{x - y}{(x + y)^2} \, dy \right] dx \neq \int_0^1 \left[\int_0^1 \frac{x - y}{(x + y)^2} \, dx \right] dy.$$

(Indore, 1998; Garhwal, 2002)

We have

$$\text{L.H.S.} = \int_0^1 \left[\int_0^1 \frac{2x - (x + y)}{(x + y)^2} \, dy \right] dx$$

$$= \int_0^1 \left[\int_0^1 \left\{ \frac{2x}{(x + y)^2} - \frac{1}{x + y} \right\} dy \right] dx$$

$$= \int_0^1 \left[-\frac{2x}{x+y} - \log(x+y) \right]_0^1 dx$$

$$= \int_0^1 \left[\left\{ -2\frac{x}{x+1} - \log(x+1) + 2 + \log x \right\} \right] dx$$

$$= \int_0^1 \left[\frac{2}{x+1} + \log x - \log(x+1) \right] dx$$

$$= \left[2\log(x+1) + (x\log x - x) - \{x\log(x+1) - x + \log(x+1)\} \right]_0^1$$

$$= \left[\log(x+1) + x\log x - x\log(x+1) \right]_0^1$$

$$= (\log 2 - \log 2) - \lim_{x \to 0} x\log x = 0. \qquad \qquad ...(i)$$

Again,

$$\text{R.H.S.} = \int_0^1 \left[\int_0^1 \frac{x-y}{(x+y)^2} dx \right] dy$$

$$= \int_0^1 \left[\int_0^1 \frac{(x+y) - 2y}{(x+y)^2} dx \right] dy$$

$$= \int_0^1 \left[\int_0^1 \left\{ \frac{1}{x+y} - \frac{2y}{(2+y)^2} \right\} dx \right] dy$$

$$= \int_0^1 \left[\log(x+y) + \frac{2y}{x+y} \right]_0^1 dy$$

$$= \int_0^1 \left[\log(1+y) + \frac{2y}{1+y} - \log y - 2 \right] dy$$

$$= \int_0^1 \left[\log(1+y) - \log y - \frac{2}{1+y} \right] dy$$

$$= \left[\{ y\log(1-y) - y + \log(1+y) \} - (y\log y - y) \right.$$
$$\left. - 2\log(1+y) \right]_0^1$$

$$= \left[y\log(1+y) - y\log y + 3\log(1+y) \right]_0^1$$

$$= \log 2 + 3\log 2 = 4\log 2. \qquad \qquad ...(ii)$$

From (i) and (ii), we conclude that the given integrals are not equal.

9. *Evaluate* $\displaystyle\int_0^\pi \int_0^{a\theta} r^3 \, d\theta \, dr.$

We have

$$I = \int_0^\pi \int_0^{a\theta} r^3 \, d\theta \, dr$$

$$= \int_0^\pi \left[\int_0^{a\theta} r^3 \, dr \right] d\theta$$

$$= \int_0^\pi \left[\frac{r^4}{4} \right]_0^{a\theta} d\theta$$

$$= \frac{1}{4} \int_0^\pi a^4 \theta^4 \, d\theta$$

$$= \frac{a^4}{4} \left[\frac{\theta^5}{5} \right]_0^\pi = \frac{a^4 \pi^5}{20}.$$

10. *Evaluate* $\displaystyle\int_0^\pi \int_0^{a\,(1+\cos\theta)} r^3 \sin\theta \cos\theta \, d\theta \, dr.$

We have

$$I = \int_0^\pi \sin\theta \cos\theta \left[\int_0^{a\,(1+\cos\theta)} r^3 \, dr \right] d\theta$$

$$= \int_0^\pi \sin\theta \cos\theta \left[\frac{r^4}{4} \right]_0^{a\,(1+\cos\theta)} d\theta$$

$$= \frac{a^4}{4} \int_0^\pi (1+\cos\theta)^4 \sin\theta \cos\theta \, d\theta.$$

Putting $1 + \cos\theta = t$ and $-\sin\theta \, d\theta = dt$, we get

$$= \frac{a^4}{4} \int_2^0 t^4 \, (t-1)\,(-dt)$$

$$= \frac{a^4}{4} \int_0^2 (t^5 - t^4) \, dt = \frac{16}{15} a^4.$$

11. *Evaluate* $\iint_A r^2 \sin\theta \, d\theta \, dr$ *over the area of cardioid*

$$r = a (1 + \cos\theta)$$

above the initial line.

The region of integration A can be covered by radial strips whose ends are at $r = 0$, $r = a (1 + \cos\theta)$.

The strips lie between $\theta = 0$ and $\theta = \pi$.

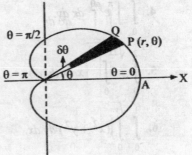

Fig. 12.5

Thus $\iint_A r^2 \sin\theta \, d\theta \, dr$

$$= \int_0^\pi \int_0^{a(1+\cos\theta)} r^2 \sin\theta \, d\theta \, dr$$

$$= \int_0^\pi \sin\theta \left[\int_0^{a(1+\cos\theta)} r^2 \, dr \right] d\theta$$

$$= \int_0^\pi \sin\theta \left[\frac{r^3}{3} \right]_0^{a(1+\cos\theta)} d\theta$$

$$= \frac{a^3}{3} \int_0^\pi (1+\cos\theta)^3 \sin\theta \, d\theta$$

$$= \frac{16a^3}{3} \int_0^\pi \cos^7 \frac{\theta}{2} \sin\frac{\theta}{2} \, d\theta$$

$$= \frac{16}{3} a^3 \int_0^{\pi/2} \sin\phi \cos^7 \phi \cdot 2 \, d\phi \qquad \left[\text{Putting } \frac{\theta}{2} = \phi. \right]$$

$$= 2 \times \frac{16}{3} a^3 \left[\frac{-\cos^8 \phi}{8} \right]_0^{\pi/2} = \frac{4}{3} a^3.$$

EXERCISES

Evaluate the following double integrals :

1. $\int_1^2 \int_0^{3y} y \, dy \, dx.$ **(Sagar, 1996; Jabalpur, 1999)**

2. $\int_0^2 \int_0^x \frac{1}{x^2 + y^2} \, dx \, dy.$

3. $\displaystyle\int_0^1 \int_0^{\sqrt{1+x^2}} \frac{1}{1+x^2}\, dx\, dy.$

4. $\displaystyle\int_0^x \int_0^{x^2} e^{y/x}\, dx\, dy.$

5. $\displaystyle\int_0^2 \int_0^{\sqrt{2x-x^2}} x\, dx\, dy.$ (*Vikram, 2000*)

6. $\displaystyle\int_0^1 \int_0^{\sqrt{y}} (x^2 + y^2)\, dy\, dx.$

7. $\displaystyle\int_0^1 \int_0^{\sqrt{1+x^2}} \frac{1}{1+x^2+y^2}\, dx\, dy.$ (*Jiwaji, 1997; Jabalpur, 2000; Ajmer, 1996; Rohilkhand, 2001, 02, 03*)

8. $\displaystyle\int_0^{\pi/2} \int_0^{\pi/2} \cos(x+y)\, dy\, dx.$ (*Jabalpur, 1993; Garhwal, 1996*)

9. $\displaystyle\int_0^a \int_0^{\sqrt{a^2-y^2}} \sqrt{a^2 - x^2 - y^2}\, dy\, dx.$

(*Rohilkhand, 2000; Bilaspur, 1993*)

10. $\displaystyle\int_0^\pi \int_0^{a\sin\theta} r\, d\theta\, dr.$

11. $\displaystyle\int_0^{\pi/2} \int_0^{a\cos\theta} r\sin\theta\, d\theta\, dr.$

12. $\displaystyle\int_0^{\pi/2} \int_0^a r^n \sin^n \theta \cos\theta\, d\theta\, dr,$ for $n+1>0$.

13. $\displaystyle\iint \frac{r\, d\theta\, dr}{\sqrt{a^2+r^2}}$ over one loop of $r^2 = a^2 \cos 2\theta$.

14. $\displaystyle\iint r^2\, d\theta\, dr$ over the area of the circle $r = a\cos\theta$.

15. Evaluate $\displaystyle\iint x^2 y^2\, dx\, dy$ over the region $x^2 + y^2 \le 1$.

(*Indore, 1997*)

16. Evaluate $\iint_A (x^2 + y^2)\, dx\, dy$ over the region bounded by $x = 0$, $y = 0$, $x + y = 1$.

17. Evaluate $\iint_A \dfrac{xy}{\sqrt{1-y^2}}\, dx\, dy$, where the region of integration is the positive quadrant of the circle $x^2 + y^2 = 1$. *(Jabalpur, 1994)*

18. Evaluate $\iint xy\, dx\, dy$ over the region in the positive quadrant for which $x + y \leq 1$. *(Ravishankar, 1996; Jabalpur, 1997)*

ANSWERS

1. 7; **2.** $\dfrac{1}{4} \log 2$; **3.** $\log(1+\sqrt{2})$; **4.** $\dfrac{1}{2}$;

5. $\dfrac{\pi}{2}$; **6.** $\dfrac{3}{35}$; **7.** $\dfrac{\pi}{4} \log(1+\sqrt{2})$; **8.** -2;

9. $\dfrac{\pi a^3}{6}$; **10.** $\dfrac{\pi a^2}{4}$; **11.** $\dfrac{a^2}{6}$;

12. $\dfrac{a^{n+1}}{(n+1)^2}$; **13.** $\left(2 - \dfrac{\pi}{2}\right) a$; **14.** $\dfrac{\pi a^3}{9}$; **15.** $\dfrac{\pi}{24}$;

16. $\dfrac{1}{6}$; **17.** $\dfrac{1}{6}$; **18.** $\dfrac{1}{24}$.

12.3. Applications of Double Integration

(i) Area of a region

The area of a region of the xy-plane,

$$A = \iint dx\, dy = \iint dy\, dx$$

with proper limits of integration to be provided.

We have already discussed that the area

$$A = \int_a^b \int_{f_1(x)}^{f_2(x)} dy\, dx,$$

when the integrations are carried out in order of first y and then x.

(ii) Volume of the solids

Volume is given by the formula

$$V = \int_a^b \int_{f_1(x)}^{f_2(x)} f(x, y)\, dy\, dx.$$

This expression for V is called a repeated integral since it is an integral of an integral.

If $Z = f(x, y)$

then volume $V = \iint Z\, dx\, dy$ with suitable limits.

(iii) Volumes of the solids of revolution

Consider an area S bounded by curves whose equations are given in polar coordinates, this be rotated about the polar axis. We consider it divided into elements of area $\delta_1 S, \delta_2 S, \ldots ,$ $\delta_n S$. When S is rotated, the element of area will generate a ring shaped element of volume $2\pi R\, \delta S$ where R is the distance from the polar axis to any point (r, θ),

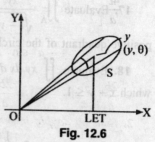

Fig. 12.6

Then the required volume of revolution is the limit of sum of all such elements.

Now, $R = r \sin \theta$.

Therefore the area of the ring shaped element formed by this rotation is $r\, \delta r\, \delta\theta$ and volume is $2\pi r \sin \theta \cdot \delta r\, \delta\theta$. Adding all such elements and taking the limit of their sum, we get

$$V = \int_{\alpha}^{\beta} \int_{r_1}^{r_2} 2\pi r^2 \sin \theta\, dr\, d\theta,$$

where r_1 and r_2 are the values of r for a fixed θ upon the bounding curves and α and β are the smallest and largest values of θ for points on boundary.

Note. If the area is rotated about the line $\theta = \pi / 2$, then $R = r \cos \theta$ and then

$$\text{Volume } V = \int_{\alpha}^{\beta} \int_{r_1}^{r_2} 2\pi r^2 \sin \theta\, dr\, d\theta.$$

EXAMPLES

1. *Find by double integration the area of the ellipse* $\dfrac{x^2}{a^2} + \dfrac{y^2}{b^2} = 1.$

Required area of the ellipse = 4 (area of the quadrant OABO of the ellipse)

where $y = f(x) = \dfrac{b}{a}\sqrt{a^2 - x^2}$ is the equation of the ellipse.

$$= 4 \int_{a}^{a} \left[y\right]_0^{f(x)} dx = 4 \int_0^{a} f(x)\, dx$$

$$= 4 \int_0^a \frac{b}{a} \sqrt{a^2 - x^2} \, dx$$

$$= \frac{4b}{a} \left[\frac{1}{2} x \sqrt{a^2 - x^2} \right.$$

$$\left. + \frac{1}{2} a^2 \sin^{-1} \left(\frac{x}{a} \right) \right]_0^a$$

$$= \frac{2b}{a} [a^2 \sin^{-1}(1)] = \frac{2b}{a} \cdot a^2 \cdot \frac{\pi}{2} = \pi ab.$$

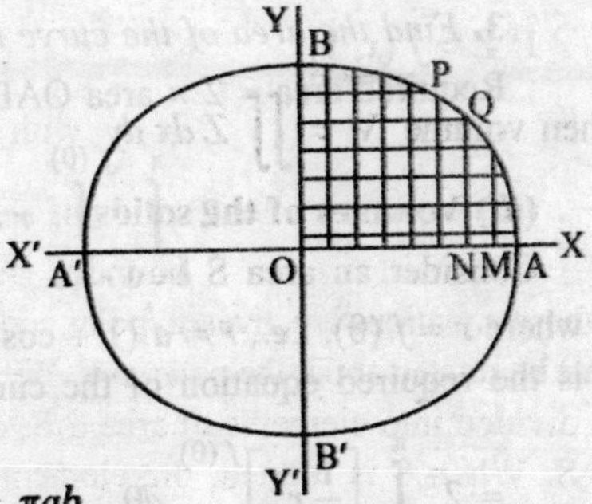

Fig. 12.7

2. *Find by double integration the whole area of the curve*

$$a^2 x^2 = y^3 (2a - y).$$

Required area = 2 × area OAB

$$= 2 \int_{y=0}^{2a} \int_{x=0}^{f(y)} dx \, dy$$

where $x = f(y)$, *i.e.*, $x = y^{3/2} \sqrt{2a - y} / a$ is the
equation of the curve.

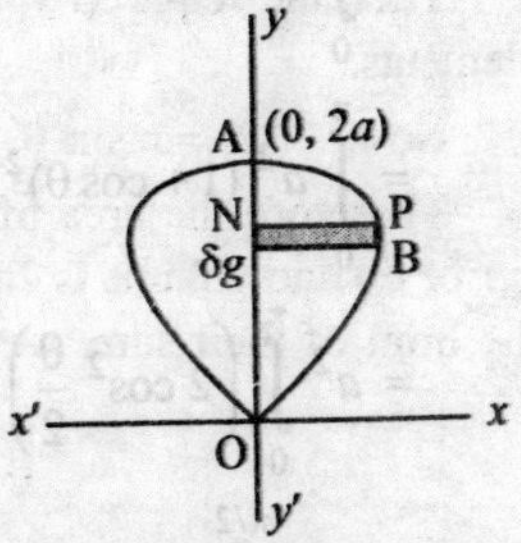

∴ The required area

Fig. 12.8

$$= 2 \int_{y=0}^{2a} [x]_0^{f(y)} \, dy = 2 \int_0^{2a} f(y) \, dy$$

$$= 2 \int_0^{2a} \frac{y^{3/2} \sqrt{2a - y}}{a} \, dy$$

$$= \frac{2}{a} \int_0^{\pi/2} (2a \sin^2 \theta)^{3/2} \sqrt{2a - 2a \sin^2 \theta} \, 4a \sin \theta \cos \theta \, d\theta$$

[Putting $y = 2a \sin^2 \theta$]

$$= 32a^2 \int_0^{\pi/2} \sin^4 \theta \cos^2 \theta \, d\theta$$

$$= 32a^2 \frac{\Gamma\left(\frac{5}{2}\right) \Gamma\left(\frac{3}{2}\right)}{2\Gamma(4)}$$

$$= 32a^2 \cdot \frac{\frac{3}{2} \cdot \frac{1}{2} \sqrt{\pi} \cdot \frac{1}{2} \sqrt{\pi}}{2 \cdot 3 \cdot 2 \cdot 1} = \pi a^2.$$

3. *Find the area of the curve* $r = a\,(1 + \cos\theta)$, *by double integration.*

Required area = 2 × area OABO

$$= 2 \int_{\theta=0}^{\pi} \int_{r=0}^{f(\theta)} r\,d\theta\,dr$$

where $r = f(\theta)$, i.e., $r = a\,(1 + \cos\theta)$
is the required equation of the curve

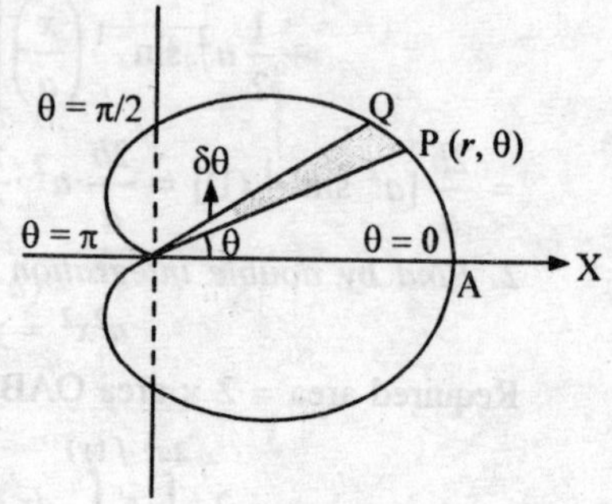

$$= 2 \int_{\theta=0}^{\pi} \left[\frac{1}{2}r^2\right]_{r=0}^{f(\theta)} d\theta$$

$$= \int_{0}^{\pi} [f(\theta)]^2\,d\theta$$

$$= \int_{0}^{\pi} a^2\,(1+\cos\theta)^2\,d\theta$$

$$= a^2 \int_{0}^{\pi} \left(2\cos^2\frac{\theta}{2}\right)^2 d\theta = 4a^2 \int_{0}^{\pi} \cos^4\frac{\theta}{2}\,d\theta$$

$$= 8a^2 \int_{0}^{\pi/2} \cos^4\phi\,d\phi, \text{ putting } \theta = 2\phi$$

$$= 8a^2 \cdot \frac{3}{4}\cdot\frac{1}{2}\cdot\frac{1}{2}\,\pi = \frac{3}{2}\,a^2\pi.$$

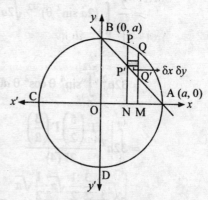

Fig. 12.9

4. *Find by double integration the area of the region enclosed by curves* $x^2 + y^2 = a^2$, $x + y = a$ *in the first quadrant.*

The curve $x^2 + y^2 = a^2$ is a circle
with centre $(0, 0)$ and radius a.

The equation $x + y = a$ or
$\dfrac{x}{a} + \dfrac{y}{a} = 1$ represents a straight line
which cuts off intercepts a and a
from positive directions of x and y
axes.

Hence the points of intersection
of $x^2 + y^2 = a^2$ and $x + y = a$ are
A $(a, 0)$ and B $(0, a)$ respectively. So
the area under consideration is the
area AQPBP′Q′A.

Fig. 12.10

∴ The required area

$$= \int\limits_{x=0}^{a} \int\limits_{y=\text{P'N}}^{\text{PN}} dx\, dy$$

where $\text{PN} = \sqrt{a^2 - x^2}$ and $\text{P'N} = (a - x)$

$$= \int\limits_{x=0}^{a} \int\limits_{y=(a-x)}^{\sqrt{a^2-x^2}} dx\, dy = \int\limits_{0}^{a} [y]_{(a-x)}^{(a^2-x^2)^{1/2}} dx$$

$$= \int\limits_{0}^{a} \left[\sqrt{a^2 - x^2} - (a - x) \right] dx$$

$$= \left[\frac{1}{2} x \sqrt{a^2 - x^2} + \frac{1}{2} a^2 \sin^{-1}\left(\frac{x}{a}\right) - ax + \frac{1}{2} x^2 \right]_{0}^{a}$$

$$= \left[\frac{1}{2} a^2 \left(\frac{\pi}{2}\right) - a^2 + \frac{1}{2} a^2 \right] = \frac{1}{2} a^2 \left(\frac{1}{2} \pi - 1\right)$$

$$= \frac{1}{4} a^2 (\pi - 2).$$

5. *Show by double integration that the area between the parabolas* $y^2 = 4ax$ *and* $x^2 = 4ay$ *is* $\dfrac{16}{3} a^2$.

As in figure the area is bounded by

$$y = \frac{x^2}{4a}, \ y = \sqrt{4ax}, \ x = 0 \text{ and } x = 4a.$$

Therefore,

$$\text{Area} = \int\limits_{0}^{4a} \int\limits_{x^2/4a}^{\sqrt{4ax}} dx\, dy$$

$$= \int\limits_{0}^{4a} [y]_{x^2/4a}^{\sqrt{4ax}} dx$$

$$= \int\limits_{0}^{4a} \left[\sqrt{4ax} - \frac{x^2}{4a} \right] dx$$

$$= \left[\sqrt{4a}\, \frac{x^{3/2}}{3/2} - \frac{x^3}{12a} \right]_{0}^{4a} = \frac{16}{3} a^2.$$

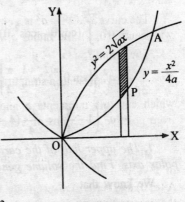

Fig. 12.11

6. *Show by double integration that the area lying inside the circle* $r = a \sin \theta$ *and outside the cardioid* $r = a (1 - \cos \theta)$ *is* $\dfrac{a^2}{4} (4 - \pi)$.

The shaded region in the figure is the required area. Take an elementary area $r \, \delta\theta \, \delta r$.

The required area $= \displaystyle\iint r \, d\theta \, dr$, the limits of integration are $r = OP$ to OQ, *i.e.*, from $a (1 - \cos \theta)$ to $a \sin \theta$ and $\theta = 0$ to $\dfrac{\pi}{2}$.

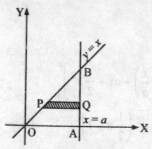

Fig. 12.12

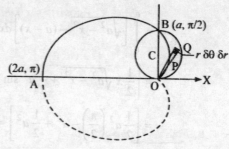

Fig. 12.13

Hence the required area

$$= \int_{0}^{\pi/2} \int_{a(1-\cos\theta)}^{a\sin\theta} r \, d\theta \, dr$$

$$= \int_{0}^{\pi/2} \left[\frac{r^2}{2} \right]_{a(1-\cos\theta)}^{a\sin\theta} d\theta$$

$$= a^2 \int_{0}^{\pi/2} (\cos\theta - \cos^2\theta) \, d\theta$$

$$= a^2 \left\{ \left[\sin\theta \right]_{0}^{\pi/2} - \frac{1}{2} \cdot \frac{\pi}{2} \right\}$$

$$= a^2 \left(1 - \frac{\pi}{4} \right) = \frac{a^2}{4} (4 - \pi).$$

7. *The upper half of the cardioid* $r = a (1 + \cos \theta)$ *rotates about the polar axis. Find the volume generated.*

We know that

$$V = \int_{\alpha}^{\beta} \int_{r_1}^{r_2} 2\pi r^2 \sin\theta \, d\theta \, dr.$$

Limits for r are 0 to $a(1 + \cos \theta)$ and for θ are 0 to π.

Now,

$$V = 2\pi \int_0^\pi \int_0^{a(1+\cos \theta)} r^2 \sin \theta \, d\theta \, dr$$

$$= \frac{2\pi}{3} \int_0^\pi \left[r^3 \right]_0^{a(1+\cos \theta)} \sin \theta \, d\theta$$

$$= \frac{2\pi a^3}{3} \int_0^\pi (1+\cos \theta)^3 \sin \theta \, d\theta$$

$$= \frac{2\pi a^3}{3} \left[-\frac{(1+\cos \theta)^4}{4} \right]_0^\pi$$

$$= \frac{8}{3} \pi a^3.$$

8. Find the volume of

$$\frac{x^2}{a^2} + \frac{y^2}{b^2} + \frac{z^2}{c^2} = 1.$$

Let us consider a section by the plane $z = 0$ which becomes

$$\frac{x^2}{a^2} + \frac{y^2}{b^2} = 1.$$

The limits of y are 0 to $\dfrac{b\sqrt{a^2 - x^2}}{a}$.

Therefore

$$V = 8 \int_0^a \int_0^{\frac{b}{a}\sqrt{a^2 - x^2}} c\sqrt{1 - \frac{x^2}{a^2} - \frac{y^2}{b^2}} \, dx \, dy.$$

Put $\dfrac{y}{b} = \sqrt{1 - \dfrac{x^2}{a^2}} \sin \theta$ then the limits are 0 to $\dfrac{\pi}{2}$.

Hence

$$V = 8 \int_0^a cb \int_0^{\pi/2} \left(1 - \frac{x^2}{a^2} \right) \cos^2 \theta \, d\theta \, dx$$

$$= 8 \int_0^a \int_0^{\pi/2} cb \left(1 - \frac{x^2}{a^2} \right) \left(\frac{1 + \cos 2\theta}{2} \right) d\theta \, dx$$

$$= \frac{8}{2} \int_0^a cb \left(1 - \frac{x^2}{a^2}\right) \left[\theta + \frac{\sin 2\theta}{2}\right]_0^{\pi/2} dx$$

$$= 8bc \int_0^a \left(1 - \frac{x^2}{a^2}\right) \frac{\pi}{4} dx$$

$$= 2\pi bc \int_0^a \left(1 - \frac{x^2}{a^2}\right) dx$$

$$= 2\pi bc \left[x - \frac{x^3}{3a^2}\right]_0^a$$

$$= \frac{4}{3} \pi abc. \qquad \text{[Prov(y)]}$$

9. *Find the volume of the solid whose base is in the xy-plane and is the triangle bounded by the x-axis, the line y = x and the line x = 1 while the top of the solid is in the plane z = x + y + 1.*

Now the volume of the elementary strip of altitude z is

$$dV = z \, dy \, dx$$

$$= (x + y + 1) \, dy \, dx.$$

For any x between 0 and 1, y varies from $y = 0$, $y = x$. Therefore

$$V = \int_0^1 \int_0^x (x + y + 1) \, dy \, dx$$

$$= \int_0^1 \left[xy + \frac{y^2}{2} + y\right]_{y=0}^{y=x} dx$$

$$= \int_0^1 \left[\frac{3x^2}{2} + x\right] dx = \left[\frac{3x^3}{6} + \frac{x^2}{2}\right]_0^1 = 1.$$

10. *Find the area of the surface of $x^2 + z^2 = a^2$, that lies inside the cylinder $x^2 + y^2 = a^2$.*

Here surface is $z^2 = a^2 - x^2$ ...(i)

$$\therefore \quad 2z \frac{\partial z}{\partial x} = -2x \text{ or } \frac{\partial z}{\partial x} = \frac{x}{z}. \text{ Also } \frac{\partial z}{\partial y} = 0.$$

Also the projection of the given surface on the plane $z = 0$ is $x^2 = a^2$, so the limits of x for the first quadrant are from 0 to a.

Also for the cylinder $x^2 + y^2 = a^2$, we have $y^2 = a^2 - x^2$.

∴   The required surface

$$= \iint \sqrt{1 + \left(\frac{\partial z}{\partial x}\right)^2 + \left(\frac{\partial z}{\partial y}\right)^2} \, dx \, dy$$

$$= 8 \int_{x=a}^{a} \int_{y=0}^{\sqrt{a^2-x^2}} \sqrt{1 + \left(-\frac{x}{z}\right)^2 + (0)^2} \, dx \, dy$$

$$= 8 \int_{x=a}^{a} \int_{y=0}^{\sqrt{a^2-x^2}} \left(\frac{z^2+x^2}{z^2}\right) \, dx \, dy$$

$$= 8 \int_{x=a}^{a} \int_{y=0}^{\sqrt{a^2-x^2}} \sqrt{\frac{a^2}{a^2-x^2}} \, dx \, dy \qquad \text{[From (i)]}$$

$$= 8a \int_{x=a}^{a} \int_{y=0}^{\sqrt{a^2-x^2}} \frac{1}{\sqrt{a^2-x^2}} \, dx \, dy$$

$$= 8a^2, \text{ on integrating.}$$

EXERCISES

1. Find by double integration the area of the region bounded by $y = 4x - x^2$ and $y = x$. *(Ajmer, 1997)*

2. Find the area of the region bounded by quadrant of $x^2 + y^2 = a^2$ and $x + y = a$.

3. Find by double integration the area of the region bounded by $y^2 = x$ and $y = x$.

4. Find the area of the loop of the curve $r = a\theta \cos \theta$ between $\theta = 0$ and $\theta = \pi / 2$ by double integration.

5. Find the area of the curve $r^2 = a^2 \cos 2\theta$ by double integration.

6. Show by double integration that the area lying inside the cardioid $r = a (1 + \cos \theta)$ and outside the circle $r = a$ is $\frac{1}{4} a^2 (\pi + 8)$.

7. Find the volume bounded by the paraboloid $x^2 + y^2 = z$ and the plane $z = 4$.

8. Find the volume bounded by the paraboloid $4x^2 + y^2 = 4z$ and the plane $z = 2$.

9. Find the volume bounded by the coordinate planes and the plane $\frac{x}{a} + \frac{y}{b} + \frac{z}{c} = 1$.

10. Find the area of the surface $z^2 = 2xy$ included between planes $x = 0$, $x = a$, $y = 0$, $y = b$.

ANSWERS

1. $\dfrac{9}{2}$;   2. $\dfrac{1}{4}(\pi - 2)\,a^2$;   3. $\dfrac{1}{10}$;   4. $\dfrac{\pi a^2}{96}(\pi^2 - 6)$;

5. a^2;   7. 8π;   8. 4π;   9. $abc\,/\,6$;

10. $\dfrac{2}{3}\sqrt{2}\,\sqrt{ab}\,(a+b)$.

12.4. Change of order of Integration

If the limits of x and y are constant $\displaystyle\iint (x,\,y)\,dx\,dy$ can be integrated in either order, but if the limits of y are functions of x, then the new limits of x as function of y are to be determined. The best method is by geometrical consideration.

The following examples will make the procedure clear.

EXAMPLES

1. *Change the order of integration in*

$$\int\limits_{0}^{2a}\int\limits_{x^2/4a}^{3a-x} F(x,\,y)\,dx\,dy.$$

(Sagar, 2001; Bilaspur, 1995; Jiwaji, 1998; 2003; Jabalpur, 1999; Vikram, 2001; Gorakhpur, 2000)

Here the limits are

$$x^2 = 4ay \text{ and } y = 3a - x$$

i.e., $x^2 = 4ay$ and $x + y = 3a$ and also $x = 0$ and $x = 2a$.

The integral is extended to area OAB. We consider shaded strip.

Now the integral is broken into two parts which are corresponding to the area OAL and the triangle BLA.

Hence we have

$$\int\limits_{0}^{2a}\int\limits_{x^2/4a}^{2a-x} F(x,\,y)\,dx\,dy$$

$$= \int\limits_{0}^{a}\int\limits_{0}^{2\sqrt{ay}} F(x,\,y)\,dy\,dx$$

$$+ \int\limits_{0}^{3a}\int\limits_{0}^{3a-y} F(x,\,y)\,dy\,dx.$$

Since $x^2 = 4ay$, i.e., $x = 2\sqrt{ay}$.

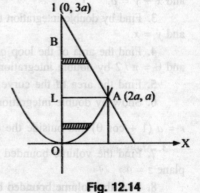

Fig. 12.14

2. *Change the order of integration in*

$$\int_{0}^{a} \int_{\sqrt{a^2-x^2}}^{x+2a} \phi(x, y)\, dx\, dy.$$

Here the limits are $y = \sqrt{a^2 - x^2}$ and $y = x + 2a$ and $x = 0$ and $x = a$.

Now, $y = \sqrt{a^2 - x^2}$, i.e., $x^2 + y^2 = a^2$ is a circle and the straight line $y = x + 2a$ and the limits of x are given by the straight lines $x = 0$ and $x = a$.

The integral extends to all points in the space bounded by the axis of y, the circle with centre O, and L the straight line ML.

We draw BN, KP perpendiculars to AM.

Now the order of integration is to be changed. For this we consider parallel strips which are shaded.

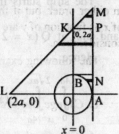

Fig. 12.15

The integral is broken into three parts.

1st part is BAN, bounded by the lines $x = 0$, $x = a$ and the circle.

2nd part is KPNB, bounded by the lines $y = a$, $y = 2a$ and $x = 0$, $x = a$.

3rd part is triangle KPM, bounded by the lines $y = 2a$, $y = x + 2a$ and $x = a$.

Hence
$$\int_{0}^{a} \int_{\sqrt{a^2-x^2}}^{x+2a} \phi(x, y)\, dx\, dy$$

$$= \int_{0}^{a} \int_{\sqrt{a^2-y^2}}^{a} \phi(x, y)\, dy\, dx + \int_{0}^{2a} \int_{0}^{a} \phi(x, y)\, dx\, dy$$

$$+ \int_{2a}^{3a} \int_{y-2a}^{a} \phi(x, y)\, dy\, dx.$$

3. *Show that*

$$\int_{0}^{4a} \int_{x^2/4a}^{2\sqrt{ax}} f(x, y)\, dx\, dy = \int_{0}^{4a} \int_{x^2/4a}^{2\sqrt{ax}} f(x, y)\, dy\, dx.$$

(Bilaspur, 1994; Ravishankar, 1995)

Obviously the integral is bounded by the curves $y = \dfrac{x^2}{4a}$ or $x^2 = 4ay$, $y = 2\sqrt{ax}$ or $y^2 = 4ax$, $x = 0$, $x = 4a$.

Here $x^2 = 4ay$ and $y^2 = 4ax$ represent parabolas with vertex at origin intersecting at A $(x = 4a)$.

The line $x = 0$ is y-axis and $x = 4a$ is parallel to y-axis at a distance $4a$, *i.e.*, it passes from the point of intersection of two parabolas.

Draw a strip PQ parallel to x-axis.

The strip starts from $P\left(x = \dfrac{y^2}{4a}\right)$

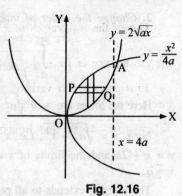

Fig. 12.16

and ends at $Q(x = 2\sqrt{ay})$. The strip may start from $y = 0$ to $y = 4a$.

Hence

$$\int\limits_{0}^{4a} \int\limits_{x^2/4a}^{2\sqrt{ax}} f(x,\ y)\ dx\ dy = \int\limits_{0}^{4a} \int\limits_{y^2/4a}^{2\sqrt{ay}} f(x,\ y)\ dy\ dx.$$

4. *Change the order of integration in the integral*

$$\int\limits_{0}^{a} \int\limits_{\sqrt{ax-x^2}}^{\sqrt{ax}} f(x,\ y)\ dx\ dy.$$

(*Bhopal, 1994, 95; Sagar, 1995; Bilaspur, 1999*)

The region of integration is bounded by the circle $x^2 + y^2 = ax$, parabola $y^2 = ax$, lines $x = 0$ and $x = a$.

In figure this region of integration as shown by OLPMACO.

The strips parallel to x-axis change their character at the highest point C of the circle. Through the highest point C draw a tangent LM (which is parallel to x-axis).

The region is clearly divided into three parts, namely

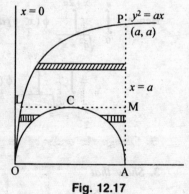

Fig. 12.17

OLC, CMA and LPM.

The equation of the circle is

$$x^2 - ax + y^2 = 0.$$

$$\therefore \quad x = \frac{1}{2}[a \pm \sqrt{a^2 - 4y^2}].$$

Out of the two values of x the lesser one is $\frac{1}{2}[a - \sqrt{a^2 - 4y^2}]$ and

the greater one is $[a \pm \sqrt{a^2 - 4y^2}]$.

In region OLC, x varies from parabola $y^2 = ax$ to nearer point on the circle $x^2 + y^2 - ax = 0$. So limits of x in terms of y are y^2/a to $\frac{1}{2}[a - \sqrt{a^2 - 4y^2}]$, and limits of y are from 0 to $\frac{1}{2}a$ as point C is $\left(\frac{1}{2}a, \frac{1}{2}a\right)$.

In region CMA, limits of x in terms of y are from $\frac{1}{2}[a + \sqrt{a^2 - 4y^2}]$

to a, and limits of y are from 0 to $\frac{1}{2}a$.

Again in region LPM, the strip has its extremities on $y^2 = ax$ and $x = a$.

Hence limits of x are from y^2/a to a, and limits of y are from $\frac{1}{2}a$ to a as

point P is (a, a). Hence the given integral

$$\int_0^{\frac{1}{2}a} \int_{y^2/a}^{\frac{1}{2}[a - \sqrt{a^2 - 4y^2}]} f(x, y) \, dy \, dx$$

$$+ \int_0^{\frac{1}{2}a} \int_{\frac{1}{2}[a + \sqrt{a^2 - 4y^2}]}^{a} f(x, y) \, dy \, dx$$

$$+ \int_{\frac{1}{2}a}^{a} \int_{y^2/a}^{a} f(x, y) \, dy \, dx.$$

5. *Change the order of integration in the double integral*

$$\int_0^{a \cos \alpha} \int_{x \tan \alpha}^{\sqrt{a^2 - x^2}} f(x, y) \, dx \, dy.$$

(Jabalpur, 2000; Vikram, 2002; Ravishankar, 1994; Bilaspur, 2000; Jiwaji, 1995, 97, 99; Bhoj, 1999; Kumaon, 2002; Avadh, 1997, 99)

The region of integration is bounded by the line $y = x \tan \alpha$, the circle $y^2 = a^2 - x^2$, i.e., $x^2 + y^2 = a^2$, the y-axis, $x = 0$ and line $x = a \cos \alpha$. Clearly, the region of integration is OAB.

The strips parallel to x-axis change their character at A $(a \cos \alpha, a \sin \alpha)$. Thus the region is divided into two parts namely OAL and LAB.

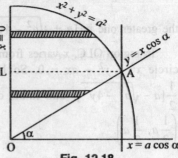

Fig. 12.18

In the region OAL, the strip parallel to x-axis has its extremities on $x = 0$ and $y = x \tan \alpha$. Hence limits of x are from 0 to $y \cot \alpha$. As the point A is $(a \cos \alpha, a \sin \alpha)$, the limits of y are from 0 to $a \sin \alpha$.

Again in the region LAB, the strip parallel to x-axis has its extremities on $x = 0$ and circle $x^2 + y^2 = a^2$. Hence limits of x are from 0 to $\sqrt{a^2 - y^2}$. The limits of y are clearly from $a \sin \alpha$ to a.

Hence, we have

$$\int_0^{a \sin \alpha} \int_{x \tan \alpha}^{\sqrt{a^2 - x^2}} f(x, y) \, dx \, dy$$

$$= \int_0^{a \cos \alpha} \int_0^{y \cot \alpha} f(x, y) \, dy \, dx + \int_{a \sin \alpha}^{a} \int_0^{\sqrt{a^2 - y^2}} f(x, y) \, dy \, dx.$$

To verify the above result when $f(x, y) = 1$. In this case the integral

becomes $\displaystyle\int_0^{a \cos \alpha} \int_{x \tan \alpha}^{\sqrt{a^2 - x^2}} x \, dy$ and represents the area of the vector of the

circle of radius a, the angle of sector BOA $= \dfrac{1}{2} \pi - \alpha$. Hence the result

should be $\dfrac{1}{2} a^2 \left(\dfrac{1}{2} \pi - \alpha \right)$. Also transformed integral is

$$\int_0^{a \sin \alpha} \int_0^{y \cot \alpha} dy \, dx + \int_{a \sin \alpha}^{a} \int_0^{\sqrt{a^2 - y^2}} dy \, dx$$

$$= \int_0^{a \sin \alpha} y \cot \alpha \, dy + \int_{a \sin \alpha}^{a} \sqrt{a^2 - y^2} \, dy$$

$$= \left[\frac{1}{2} y^2 \cot \alpha \right]_a^{a \sin \alpha} + \left[\frac{1}{2} y \sqrt{a^2 - y^2} + \frac{1}{2} a^2 \sin^{-1} (y/a) \right]_{a \sin \alpha}^{a}$$

$$= \frac{1}{2} a^2 \sin \alpha \cos \alpha + \frac{1}{2} a^2 \left[\frac{1}{2} \pi - \sin \alpha \cos \alpha - a^2 \alpha \right]$$

$$= \frac{1}{2} a^2 \left(\frac{1}{2} \pi - \alpha \right).$$

This verifies the result.

6. *Change the order of integration in*

$$\int_0^a \int_{\frac{1}{2}\sqrt{a^2 - x^2}}^{\sqrt{a^2 - x^2}} V \, dx \, dy.$$

V being a function of x and y.

The region of integration is bounded by $y = \frac{1}{2} \sqrt{a^2 - x^2}$, i.e., $x^2 + 4y^2$ $= a^2$ (an ellipse), the circle $x^2 + y^2 = a^2$, $x = 0$ (y-axis) and line $x = a$, the positive quadrant. Clearly the region of integration is ABC.

The strip parallel to x-axis changes its character at B where $y = \frac{1}{2} a$.

Hence the region is divided into two parts namely ABM and BCM.

The strip parallel to x-axis, in the region ABM, has its extremities on the ellipse $x^2 + 4y^2 = a^2$ and the circle $x^2 + y^2 = a^2$. Hence limits of x are from $\sqrt{a^2 - 4y^2}$ to $\sqrt{a^2 - y^2}$. Limits of y are from 0 to $\frac{1}{2} a$ as B is the point $\left(0, \frac{1}{2} a \right)$.

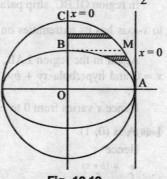

Fig. 12.19

In the region BCM, a strip parallel to x-axis has its extremities on $x = 0$ and the circle $x^2 + y^2 = a^2$. Hence limits of x are from 0 to $\sqrt{a^2 - y^2}$.

Also limits of y are from $\frac{1}{2} a$ to a. Hence

$$\int_0^a \int_{\frac{1}{2}\sqrt{a^2 - x^2}}^{a\sqrt{a^2 - x^2}} V \, dx \, dy$$

$$= \int_0^{\frac{1}{2} a} \int_{\sqrt{a^2 - 4y^2}}^{\sqrt{a^2 - y^2}} V \, dx \, dy + \int_{\frac{1}{2} a}^{a} \int_0^{\sqrt{a^2 - y^2}} V \, dy \, dx.$$

7. *Change the order of integration in*

$$\int\limits_{0}^{a} \int\limits_{0}^{b/(b+x)} \phi(x,\ y)\ dx\ dy.$$

The region of integration is bounded by $y = 0$ (*x*-axis), $y = \dfrac{b}{b+x}$, i.e.,

$xy + by - b = 0$ (rectangular hyperbola), $x = 0$ (*y*-axis) and the line $x = a$.

Clearly the region is OABC. The strip parallel to *x*-axis changes its character at

$$\mathrm{B}\left(a,\ \frac{b}{a+b}\right).$$

Hence the region is divided into two parts namely OLBC and LAB.

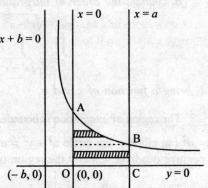

In region OLBC, strip parallel

Fig. 12.20

to *x*-axis has its extremities on $x = 0$, $x = a$ and y varies from 0 to $\dfrac{b}{a+b}$.

Again in the region LAB, strip parallel to *x*-axis has its extremities on $x = 0$ and hyperbola $xy + by - b = 0$.

Hence x varies from 0 to $\dfrac{b(1-y)}{y}$. Also limits of y are from $\dfrac{b}{a+b}$ to 1 as A is (0, 1).

Hence

$$\int\limits_{0}^{a} \int\limits_{0}^{a/(b+x)} \phi(x,\ y)\ dx\ dy$$

$$= \int\limits_{0}^{b/(a+b)} \phi(x,\ y)\ dy\ dx + \int\limits_{b/(a+b)}^{1} \int\limits_{b/(i-y)/y} \phi(x,\ y)\ dy\ dx.$$

8. *Change the order of integration in*

$$\int\limits_{0}^{\infty} \int\limits_{0}^{\infty} \frac{e^{-y}}{y}\ dx\ dy,$$

and hence find its value.

(*Indore, 1994, 98; Sagar, 1997, 2000; Jiwaji, 1998; Vikram, 1999; Jabalpur, 1995, 2001; Ravishankar, 1996; Bhopal, 2002; Kumaon, 2001; Avadh, 1996, 98*)

The region of integration is bounded by lines $y = x$, $x = 0$ (y-axis) and an infinite boundary.

Take strips parallel to x-axis to change the order of integration.

The extremities of the strip lie on $x = 0$ and $y = x$.

Hence limits of x are from 0 to y and limits of y are from 0 to ∞.

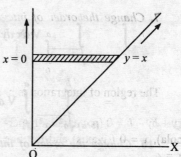

Fig. 12.21

$$\therefore \int_0^\infty \int_x^\infty \frac{e^{-y}}{y}\, dx\, dy = \int_0^\infty \int_0^y \frac{e^{-y}}{y}\, dy\, dx$$

$$= \int_0^\infty \frac{e^{-y}}{y} \cdot [x]_0^y\, dy$$

$$= \int_0^\infty e^{-y}\, dy$$

$$= \left[-e^{-y} \right]_0^\infty = 1.$$

9. *Change the order of integration in the integral*

$$\int_c^a \int_{(b/a)\sqrt{a^2 - x^2}}^b V\, dx\, dy$$

where c is less than a.

The region of integration is bounded by the ellipse $y = \dfrac{b}{a}\sqrt{a^2 - x^2}$,

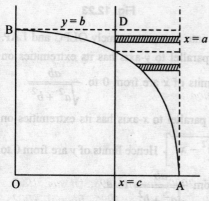

Fig. 12.22

i.e., $\dfrac{x^2}{a^2} + \dfrac{y^2}{b^2} = 1$, limits $y = b$, $x = c$ and $x = a$.

Thus ACDEA is the region of integration.

Strips parallel to x-axis change their character at

$$E\left(c,\ \frac{b}{a}\sqrt{a^2 - c^2} \right).$$

Hence the region is divided into two parts namely DCLE and AEL. We therefore have

$$\int\limits_{c}^{a} \int\limits_{(b/a)\sqrt{a^2-x^2}}^{b} V \, dx \, dy$$

$$= \int\limits_{(b/a)\sqrt{a^2-c^2}}^{b} \int\limits_{c}^{a} V \, dy \, dx + \int\limits_{0}^{(b/a)\sqrt{a^2-c^2}} \int\limits_{(a/b)\sqrt{a^2-y^2}}^{a} V \, dy \, dx.$$

10. *Change the order of integration in*

$$\int\limits_{0}^{ab/\sqrt{a^2+b^2}} \int\limits_{a}^{(a/b)\sqrt{b^2-y^2}} f(x, y) \, dy \, dx.$$

The region of integration is given by

$$x = 0, \quad x = \frac{a}{b}\sqrt{b^2 - y^2}, \text{ ellipse } \frac{x^2}{a^2} + \frac{y^2}{b^2} = 1,$$

$$y = 0, \text{ } (x\text{-axis}) \text{ and } y = \frac{ab}{\sqrt{a^2 + b^2}}.$$

Hence to change the order of integration we will have to consider strips parallel to the axis of *y*.

Clearly the region of integration is OAPC. The strip parallel to the axis of *y* changes its character at

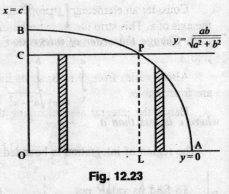

Fig. 12.23

$$P\left(\frac{ab}{\sqrt{a^2 + b^2}}, \frac{ab}{\sqrt{a^2 + b^2}}\right).$$

The region is therefore divided into two parts namely OLPC and LAP. In the region OLPC, the strip parallel to *y*-axis has its extremities on

$$y = 0 \text{ and } y = \frac{ab}{\sqrt{a^2 + b^2}}. \text{ Also limits of } x \text{ are from 0 to } \frac{ab}{\sqrt{a^2 + b^2}}.$$

Again in the region LAP, strip parallel to *x*-axis has its extremities on

$$y = 0 \text{ and } \frac{x^2}{a^2} + \frac{y^2}{b^2} = 1 \left[y = \frac{b}{a}\sqrt{a^2 - x^2} \right]. \text{ Hence limits of } y \text{ are from 0 to}$$

$$\frac{b}{a}\sqrt{a^2 - x^2} \text{ and limits of } x \text{ are from } \frac{ab}{\sqrt{a^2 + b^2}} \text{ to } a.$$

$$\therefore \quad \int_0^{ab/\sqrt{a^2+b^2}} \int_0^{(a/b)\sqrt{b^2-y^2}} f(x, y)\, dy\, dx$$

$$= \int_0^{ab/\sqrt{a^2+b^2}} \int_0^{ab/\sqrt{a^2-b^2}} f(x, y)\, dx\, dy$$

$$+ \int_{ab/\sqrt{a^2+b^2}}^{a} \int_0^{(a/b)\sqrt{a^2-x^2}} f(x, y)\, dx\, dy.$$

11. *Change the order of integration in* $\displaystyle \int_0^a \int_0^x \frac{f'(y)\, dy}{\sqrt{(a-x)(x-y)}}$ *and*

hence find its value.

The region of integration is bounded by
$y = 0$, $y = x$, $x = 0$ and $x = a$.

Thus OAB is the region of integration.

Consider an elementary strip parallel to
the axis of x. This strip has its extremities on
$y = x$ and $x = a$. Hence limits of x are from
y to a.

Also y varies from O to B; so its limits
are from 0 to a.

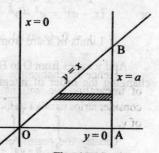

Fig. 12.24

Hence the integral after changing the order of integration is

$$= \int_0^a \int_y^a \frac{f'(y)\, dy\, dx}{\sqrt{(a-x)(x-y)}}.$$

To find its value, put

$$x = a\sin^2\theta + y\cos^2\theta,\quad dx = 2(a-y)\sin\theta\cos\theta\, d\theta,$$

$$a - x = (a-y)\cos^2\theta,\quad x - y = (a-y)\sin^2\theta.$$

When $x = y$, $\sin^2\theta = 0$, *i.e.*, $\theta = 0$ and when $x = a$, $\cos^2\theta = 0$,
i.e., $x = \pi/2$.

Now, $\displaystyle \int_y^a \frac{dx}{\sqrt{(a-x)(x-y)}} = \int_0^{\pi/2} \frac{2(a-y)\sin\theta\cos\theta\, d\theta}{(a-y)\sin\theta\cos\theta} = 2\int_0^{\pi/2} d\theta = \pi.$

$\therefore$ Given integral $= \displaystyle \int_0^a \pi f'(y)\, dy = \pi\big[f(y)\big]_0^a = \pi[f(a) - f(0)].$

12. *Change the order of integration in*

$$\int_0^{2a} \int_0^{\sqrt{2ax-x^2}} \frac{\phi'(y)(x^2+y^2)\,x\,dx\,dy}{\sqrt{4a^2x^2-(x^2+y^2)^2}}.$$

and hence find its value.

The region of integration is bounded by x-axis ($y=0$), circle $x^2+y^2=2ax$, $x=0$ and $x=2a$. Thus OABO is the region of integration.

To change the order of integration consider a strip parallel to the axis of x.

This strip has both its extremities on the circle

$$x^2+y^2=2ax$$

or $(x-a)^2 = a^2 - y^2.$

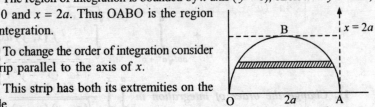

Fig. 12.25

$\therefore$ Limits of x are from $a-\sqrt{a^2-x^2}$ to $a+\sqrt{a^2-y^2}$.

And y varies from O to B, *i.e.*, from 0 to a. Hence the given integral after changing the order of integration becomes

$$\int_0^a \int_{a-\sqrt{a^2-y^2}}^{a+\sqrt{a^2-y^2}} \frac{\phi'(y)(x^2+y^2)\,x\,dy\,dx}{\sqrt{4a^2x^2-(x^2+y^2)^2}}.$$

To find its value : Put $x^2=z$, $2x\,dx=dz$.

Let z_1 and z_2 be limits of z. Now let us first consider the integral

$$\int_{a-\sqrt{a^2-y^2}}^{a+\sqrt{a^2-y^2}} \frac{(x^2+y^2)\,x\,dx}{\sqrt{4a^2x^2-(x^2+y^2)^2}}$$

$$= \frac{1}{2}\int_{z_1}^{z_2} \frac{(y^2+z)\,dz}{\sqrt{4a^2z-(z+y^2)^2}}$$

$$= \frac{1}{2}\int_{z_1}^{z_2} \frac{(y^2+z)\,dz}{\sqrt{4a^2(a^2-y^2)-(z+y^2-2a^2)^2}}$$

$$= \frac{1}{2}\int_{z_1}^{z_2} \frac{(y^2+z-2a^2)+2a^2}{\sqrt{4a^2(a^2-y^2)-(y^2+z-2a^2)^2}}$$

$$= \frac{1}{2} \int\limits_{z_1}^{z_2} \frac{(y^2 + z - 2a^2)\, dz}{\sqrt{4a^2(a^2 - y^2) - (y^2 + z - 2a^2)^2}}$$

$$+ a^2 \int\limits_{z_1}^{z_2} \frac{dz}{\sqrt{4a^2(a^2 - y^2) - (y^2 + z - 2a^2)^2}}$$

$$= \frac{1}{2} \left[\sqrt{4a^2(a^2 - y^2) - (y^2 + z - 2a^2)^2} \right.$$

$$\left. + a^2 \sin^{-1} \frac{y^2 + z - 2a}{\sqrt{4a^2(a^2 - y^2)}} \right]_{z_2}^{z_1}$$

$$= \frac{1}{2} \left[\sqrt{4a^2(a^2 - y^2) - (y^2 + x^2 - 2a^2)^2} \right.$$

$$\left. + a^2 \sin^{-1} \frac{x^2 + y^2 - 2a}{\sqrt{4a^2(a^2 - y^2)}} \right]_{a - \sqrt{a^2 - y^2}}^{a + \sqrt{a^2 - y^2}}$$

Putting x^2 for z

$$= 0 + a^2 [\sin^{-1}(1) - \sin^{-1}(-1)] = a^2 (\pi/2 + \pi/2) = a^2 \pi.$$

Hence the given integral

$$= \int\limits_0^a a^2 \pi \phi'(y)\, dy = a^2 \pi \left[\phi(y)\right]_0^a = a^2 \pi [\phi(a) - \phi(0)].$$

13. *Change the order of integration in*

$$\int\limits_0^{\pi/2} \int\limits_{a \cos\theta}^{a(1+\cos\theta)} f(r, \theta)\, r\, dr\, d\theta + \int\limits_{\pi/2}^{\pi} \int\limits_0^{a(1+\cos\theta)} f(r, \theta)\, r\, dr\, d\theta.$$

The region of integration is bounded by the half circle $r = a \cos\theta$, upper half of the cardioid $r = a(1 + \cos\theta)$ and the initial line. Thus OLABBQCMO is the region of integration. Now to change the order of integration consider elementary circular arcs (lines LM and PQ) about the pole O as a centre. These arcs change their character at A. Hence the region is divided into two parts, namely OLACMO and ABQC.

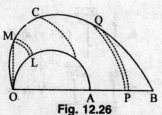

Fig. 12.26

In the region OLACMO, the extremities of the arc LM lie on $r = a \cos\theta$

and $r = a(1 + \cos\theta)$. Hence θ varies from $\cos^{-1}(r/a)$ to $\cos^{-1}\dfrac{r-a}{a}$.
Also r varies from 0 to a as OA = a.

In the region ABQC, the extremities of the arc PQ lie on $\theta = 0$ and cardioid $r = a\,(1 + \cos\theta)$. Hence θ varies from 0 to $\cos^{-1}\dfrac{r-a}{a}$, and r varies from a to $2a$ as OB = $2a$.

Hence the given integral is equal to

$$\int_0^a \int_{\cos^{-1}(r/a)}^{\cos^{-1}\{(r-a)/a\}} f(r,\theta)\,r\,dr\,d\theta + \int_0^{2a} \int_0^{\cos^{-1}\{(r-a)/a\}} f(r,\theta)\,r\,dr\,d\theta.$$

EXERCISES

1. Change the order of integration in the double integral

$$\int_0^a \int_0^x f(x,y)\,dx\,dy.$$

Change the order of integration in the following integrals :

2. $\displaystyle\int_a^b \int_a^x f(x,y)\,dx\,dy.$ *(Indore, 2002)*

3. $\displaystyle\int_0^a \int_{mx}^{lx} V(x,y)\,dx\,dy.$ *(Bhopal, 1998, 99; Jabalpur, 1997)*

4. $\displaystyle\int_0^a \int_x^{a^2/x} f(x,y)\,dx\,dy.$ *(Bilaspur, 1998; Jiwaji, 1996; Sagar, 1999; Ravishankar, 2003)*

5. $\displaystyle\int_0^b \int_0^{\sqrt{a^2-x^2}} f(x,y)\,dx\,dy.$

6. $\displaystyle\int_0^3 \int_1^{\sqrt{4-y}} (x+y)\,dy\,dx.$ *(Vikram, 1998)*

7. $\displaystyle\int_0^{2a} \int_{\sqrt{2ax-x^2}}^{\sqrt{2ax}} V\,dx\,dy.$ *(Ravishankar, 1994S, 2001; Rewa, 1999; Vikram, 1995, 2000; Avadh, 1994)*

8. $\displaystyle\int_0^a \int_{\frac{1}{2}\sqrt{a^2-x^2}}^{\sqrt{a^2-x^2}} V\,dx\,dy.$

Evaluate the following integrals by changing the order of integration :

9. $\displaystyle\int_{0}^{a/2}\int_{x^2/a}^{x-x^2/a} V\,dx\,dy.$ (*Gorakhpur, 2003*)

10. $\displaystyle\int_{0}^{a/2}\int_{0}^{\sqrt{a^2-x^2}} f(x,y)\,dx\,dy.$

11. $\displaystyle\int_{0}^{1}\int_{x}^{x(2-x)} f(x,y)\,dx\,dy.$

12. $\displaystyle\int_{0}^{\pi/3}\int_{0}^{2a\cos\theta} f(r,\theta)\,r\,d\theta\,dr.$

13. $\displaystyle\int_{1}^{2}\int_{1}^{x^2} (x^2+y^2)\,dx\,dy.$

14. $\displaystyle\int_{0}^{1}\int_{x}^{\sqrt{2-x^2}} \frac{x\,dx\,dy}{\sqrt{x^2+y^2}}.$

(*Indore, 1996, 99, 2002; Ravishankar, 2002; Kumaon, 2000*)

15. If $n \geq 0$, show that

$$\int_{a}^{b}\int_{a}^{y} (y-x)^n\, f(x)\,dy\,dx = \frac{1}{n+y}\int_{a}^{b} (b-x)^{n+1}\, f(x)\,dx.$$

[**Hint.** Change the order of integration.]

ANSWERS

1. $\displaystyle\int_{0}^{a}\int_{y}^{a} f(x,y)\,dy\,dx;$ 2. $\displaystyle\int_{a}^{b}\int_{y}^{b} f(x,y)\,dy\,dx;$

3. $\displaystyle\int_{0}^{ma}\int_{y/l}^{y/m} V(x,y)\,dy\,dx + \int_{ma}^{la}\int_{y/c}^{a} V(x,y)\,dy\,dx;$

4. $\displaystyle\int_{0}^{a}\int_{0}^{y} f(x,y)\,dy\,dx + \int_{a}^{\infty}\int_{0}^{a^2/y} f(x,y)\,dy\,dx;$

5. $\displaystyle\int_{0}^{a}\int_{0}^{\sqrt{a^2-y^2}} f(x,y)\,dy\,dx;$ 6. $\displaystyle\int_{1}^{2}\int_{0}^{4-x^2} f(x,y)\,dx\,dy;$

7. $\displaystyle\int_0^a \int_{y^2/2a}^{a-\sqrt{a^2-y^2}} V\,dy\,dx + \int_0^a \int_{a+\sqrt{a^2-y^2}}^{2a} V\,dy\,dx + \int_a^{2a} \int_{y^2/2a}^{2a} V\,dy\,dx;$

8. $\displaystyle\int_0^{\frac{1}{2}a} \int_{\sqrt{a^2-4y^2}}^{\frac{1}{2}a\sqrt{a^2-y^2}} V\,dy\,dx + \int_{\frac{1}{2}a}^a \int_0^{\sqrt{a^2-y^2}} V\,dy\,dx;$

9. $\displaystyle\int_0^{a/4} \int_{\frac{1}{2}[a-\sqrt{a^2-4ay}]}^{\sqrt{ay}} V\,dy\,dx;$ 10. $\displaystyle\int_0^a \int_0^{\sqrt{a^2-y^2}} f(x,y)\,dy\,dx;$

11. $\displaystyle\int_0^1 \int_{1-\sqrt{1-y}}^{y} f(x,y)\,dy\,dx;$ 12. $\displaystyle\int_0^{2a} \int_0^{\cos^{-1}(r/2a)} f(r,\theta)\,r\,dr\,d\theta;$

13. $9\dfrac{61}{105};$ 14. $1 - \dfrac{\sqrt{2}}{2}.$

12.5. Change of the variable in a multiple integral. Sometimes it becomes easier to evaluate definite integrals by changing one system of variables to another system of variables; such as cartesian coordinates system to polar coordinates system.

Let us consider the transformation of

$$\iint_S f(x,\,y)\,dx\,dy, \qquad\qquad ...(i)$$

when the variables are changed from x and y to u and v by the relations

$$x = \phi\,(u,\,v),\; y = \psi\,(u,\,v) \qquad\qquad ...(ii)$$

Let these relations transform the function $f(x,\,y)$ to $f_1\,(u,\,v)$. To express $dx\,dy$ in terms of new variables $u,\,v$ we proceed as follows :

First solve equations (ii) for $u,\,v$ to get

$$u = f_1\,(x,\,y) \text{ and } v = f_2\,(x,\,y) \qquad\qquad ...(iii)$$

Then $u = $ constant and $v = $ constant form two systems of curves in the xy-plane. Divide the region S into elementary areas by the curve $u = $ constant, $u + \delta u = $ constant, $v = $ constant and $v + \delta v = $ constant.

Let P be the intersection of u = constant and v = constant, and Q is the intersection of $u + \delta u = $ constant and $v + \delta v = $ constant.

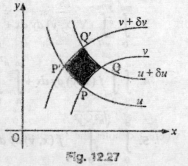

Fig. 12.27

Thus if P is the point (x, y), so that $x = \phi(u, v)$, $y = \psi(u, v)$ then, Q is the point

$$[\phi(u + \delta u, v), \psi(u + \delta u, v)].$$

Now using Taylor's theorem to the first order of approximation, we obtain

$$\phi(u + \delta u, v) = \phi(u, v) + \frac{\partial \phi}{\partial u} \partial u$$

and $$\psi(u + \delta u, v) = \psi(u, v) + \frac{\partial \psi}{\partial u} \partial u.$$

Therefore the coordinates of Q are

$$\left(x + \frac{\partial x}{\partial u} \partial u, \; y + \frac{\partial y}{\partial u} \partial u \right).$$

Similarly, P′ is the point

$$\left(x + \frac{\partial x}{\partial v} \partial v, \; y + \frac{\partial y}{\partial v} \partial v \right)$$

and Q′ is the point

$$\left(x + \frac{\partial x}{\partial u} \partial u + \frac{\partial x}{\partial v} \partial v, \; y + \frac{\partial y}{\partial u} \partial u + \frac{\partial y}{\partial v} \partial v \right).$$

Therefore, to the first order of approximation PQQ′P′ will be a parallelogram and its area would be double that of the triangle PQP′.

Hence the elementary area PQP′Q′ = $[2 \times \Delta\, PQP']$

$$= 2 \times \frac{1}{2} \begin{vmatrix} x & y & 1 \\ x + \dfrac{\partial x}{\partial u} \partial u & y + \dfrac{\partial y}{\partial u} \partial u & 1 \\ x + \dfrac{\partial x}{\partial v} \partial v & y + \dfrac{\partial y}{\partial v} \partial v & 1 \end{vmatrix}$$

$$= \begin{vmatrix} x & y & 1 \\ \dfrac{\partial x}{\partial u} \partial u & \dfrac{\partial y}{\partial u} \partial u & 0 \\ \dfrac{\partial x}{\partial v} \partial v & \dfrac{\partial y}{\partial v} \partial v & 0 \end{vmatrix} = \begin{vmatrix} \dfrac{\partial x}{\partial u} & \dfrac{\partial y}{\partial u} \\ \dfrac{\partial x}{\partial v} & \dfrac{\partial y}{\partial v} \end{vmatrix} \cdot \partial u\, \partial v$$

$$= \frac{\partial(x, y)}{\partial(u, v)} \cdot \partial u\, \partial v \qquad\qquad ...(iv)$$

$$= J\, \partial u\, \partial v$$

where J denotes the Jacobian of (x, y) with respect to u, v.

Thus, if the whole region S be divided into elementary areas by the system of curves f_1 = constant and f_2 = constant, then we have

$$\lim \Sigma f(x, y) \, \partial S = \lim \Sigma F(u, v) \, |J| \cdot \partial u \, \partial v$$

i.e., $$\int \int_S f(x, y) \, dx \, dy = \iint_S F(u, v) |J| \, du \, dv \qquad \ldots(v)$$

From this it is clear that $dx \, dy$ is replaced by $|J| \, du \, dv$, where

$$J = \frac{\partial(x, y)}{\partial(u, v)} = \begin{vmatrix} \dfrac{\partial x}{\partial u} & \dfrac{\partial y}{\partial u} \\ \dfrac{\partial x}{\partial v} & \dfrac{\partial y}{\partial v} \end{vmatrix}.$$

The limits of integration in (v), with respect to u and v are changed in such a way that they define the region S in the xy-plane.

EXAMPLES

1. Transform $\displaystyle\int_0^a \int_0^{a-x} V \, dx \, dy$ **by the substitution** $x + y = u, y = uv,$ **and** V **being a function of** $x, y.$

Let $V = f(u, v)$.

Then

$$\frac{\partial(x, y)}{\partial(u, v)} = \begin{vmatrix} \dfrac{\partial x}{\partial u} & \dfrac{\partial x}{\partial v} \\ \dfrac{\partial y}{\partial u} & \dfrac{\partial y}{\partial v} \end{vmatrix}$$

Now, $x + y = u, \ y = uv$

or $x + uv = u$, i.e., $x = u - uv$

and $y = uv.$

Hence $\dfrac{\partial x}{\partial u} = 1 - v, \ \dfrac{\partial x}{\partial v} = -u, \ \dfrac{\partial y}{\partial u} = v, \ \dfrac{\partial y}{\partial v} = u$

$\therefore \quad \dfrac{\partial(x, y)}{\partial(u, v)} = \begin{vmatrix} 1-v & -u \\ v & u \end{vmatrix} = u.$

Now the limits for y are

$$y = 0, \ y = a - x$$

and the limits for x are

$$x = 0, \ x = a.$$

Now the limits for u

from $u = uv, u = 0$ when $y = 0$

and $y = x + y = x + a - x = a.$

Similarly $v = \dfrac{y}{u} = \dfrac{y}{x + y}.$

If $y = 0$, $v = 0$

$$y = a - x, \quad v = \frac{a - x}{a}.$$

Also for $x = 0$, $v = 1$, for $x = a$, $v = 0$.

Hence

$$\int_0^a \int_0^{a-x} V \, dx \, dy = \int_0^a \int_0^1 V' \, u \, du \, dv.$$

2. *Transform to polar coordinates and integrate*

$$\iint \sqrt{\frac{1 - x^2 - y^2}{1 + x^2 + y^2}} \, dx \, dy$$

the integral being extended over all positive values of x and y subject to
$x^2 + y^2 \le 1$.

Put $x = r \cos \theta$, $y = r \sin \theta$, then

$$\frac{\partial (x, y)}{\partial (r, \theta)} = \begin{vmatrix} \dfrac{\partial x}{\partial r} & \dfrac{\partial x}{\partial \theta} \\ \dfrac{\partial y}{\partial r} & \dfrac{\partial y}{\partial \theta} \end{vmatrix} = \begin{vmatrix} \cos \theta & r \sin \theta \\ \sin \theta & r \cos \theta \end{vmatrix} = r.$$

Therefore $dx \, dy = r \, d\theta \, dr$ and limits of r are from 0 to 1 and those of θ from 0 to $\pi / 2$.

Hence $I = \displaystyle\iint \sqrt{\frac{1 - x^2 - y^2}{1 + x^2 + y^2}} \, dx \, dy$

$$= \int_0^{\pi/2} \int_0^1 \sqrt{\frac{1 - r^2}{1 + r^2}} \, r \, d\theta \, dr$$

$$= \frac{\pi}{2} \int_0^1 \sqrt{\frac{1 - r^2}{1 + r^2}} \, r \, dr.$$

Now suppose $r^2 = \cos \phi$, $2r \, dr = - \sin \phi \, d\phi$.

$$I = \frac{\pi}{2} \int_{\pi/2}^0 \frac{1}{2} \sqrt{\frac{1 - \cos \phi}{1 + \cos \phi}} \, (- \sin \phi) \, d\phi$$

$$= \frac{\pi}{4} \int_0^{\pi/2} (1 - \cos \phi) \, d\phi$$

$$= \frac{\pi}{4} \left[\phi - \sin \phi \right]_0^{\pi/2} = \frac{\pi}{4} \left(\frac{\pi}{2} - 1 \right).$$

3. *Transform the double integral* $\iint x^{m-1} y^{n-1} \, dx \, dy$ *by the formulae*

x + y = u, y = uv, *showing that transformed result is*

$$\iint u^{m+n-1} (1-v)^{m-1} v^{n-1} \, du \, dv.$$

We have $x = u - y, \; y = uv$

$$\frac{dx}{du} = 1, \; \frac{dy}{dv} = u,$$

$\therefore$ $dx \, dy = \dfrac{dx}{du} \cdot \dfrac{dy}{dv} \, du \, dv = u \, du \, dv.$

Also $x = u - y = u - uv = u\,(1 - v).$

$\therefore$ $x^{m-1} y^{n-1} = u^{m-1} (1-v)^{m-1} (uv)^{n-1}$

$$= u^{m+n-2} (1-v)^{m-1} v^{n-1}.$$

$\therefore$ $\iint x^{m-1} y^{n-1} \, dx \, dy$

$$= \iint u^{m+n-2} (1-v)^{m-1} v^{n-1} u \, du \, dv$$

$$= \iint u^{m+n-1} (1-v)^{m-1} v^{n-1} \, du \, dv.$$

4. *Evaluate* $\displaystyle\int_0^{\pi/2} \int_0^{\pi/2} \sin x \, \sin^{-1} (\sin x \sin y) \, dx \, dy.$

Let $\sin x \sin y = \sin \theta.$

Then $\sin x \cos y \, dy = \cos \theta \, d\theta$, keeping x constant.

When $y = 0, \sin \theta = 0, i.e., \theta = 0.$

and when $y = \pi/2, \sin \theta = \sin x, i.e., \theta = x.$

Hence θ varies from 0 to x.

$\therefore$ Given integral

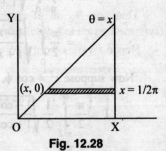

Fig. 12.28

$$\int_0^{\pi/2} \int_0^x \sin x \cdot \theta \, dx \cdot \frac{\cos \theta}{\cos y \sin x} \, d\theta$$

$$= \int_0^{\pi/2} \int_0^x \frac{\theta \cos \theta \sin x \, dx \, d\theta}{\sqrt{\sin^2 x - \sin^2 \theta}}$$

$$= \int_0^{\pi/2} \int_0^x \frac{\theta \cos \theta \sin x \, dx \, d\theta}{\sqrt{\cos^2 \theta - \cos^2 x}}$$

$$= \int_0^{\pi/2} \frac{\theta \cos \theta \sin x \, dx \, d\theta}{\sqrt{\cos^2 \theta - \cos^2 x}}.$$

Changing the order of integration with the help of the figure

$$= \int_0^{\pi/2} \theta \cos\theta \left[-\sin^{-1} \frac{\cos x}{\cos\theta} \right]_0^{\pi/2} d\theta$$

$$= \frac{1}{2} \pi \int_0^{\pi/2} \theta \cos\theta \, d\theta$$

$$= \frac{1}{2} \pi \left[(\theta \sin\theta)_0^{\pi/2} - \int_0^{\pi/2} \sin\theta \, d\theta \right]$$

$$= \frac{1}{2} \pi \left(\frac{1}{2} \pi - 1 \right).$$

5. *Transform the integral* $\displaystyle\int_0^\infty \int_0^\infty e^{(ax^2 + bx^2)} x^{2m-1} y^{2n-1} \, dx \, dy$, *to polar*

coordinates and deduce that

$$\int_0^{\pi/2} \frac{\cos^{2m-1}\theta \sin^{2n-1}\theta}{(a\cos^2\theta + b\sin^2\theta)^{m+n}} d\theta = \frac{B(m,n)}{2a^m b^n}.$$

For polar transformation, we have

$$x = r\cos\theta, \quad y = r\sin\theta$$

$$dx \, dy = r \, d\theta \, dr$$

$$e^{-(ax^2 + by^2)} = e^{-r^2 (a\cos^2\theta + b\sin^2\theta)}$$

$$x^{2m-1} y^{2n-1} = r^{2m+2n-2} \cos^{2m-1}\theta \sin^{2n-1}\theta.$$

Now x varies from 0 to $+\infty$ and y also varies from 0 to $+\infty$.

Thus the region of integration includes the whole positive octant (supposed extended upto infinity).

Hence r varies from 0 to ∞ and θ varies from 0 to $\pi/2$.

$\therefore$ Given integral

$$\int_0^{\pi/2} \int_0^\infty e^{-r^2 (a\cos^2\theta + b\sin^2\theta)}$$

$$\times r^{2m+2n-2} \cos^{2m-1}\theta \sin^{2n-1}\theta \, d\theta \, dr$$

which is the transformed integral. Put $r^2 = t$, then integral

$$= \int_0^{\pi/2} \int_0^\infty e^{-t(a\cos^2\theta + b\sin^2\theta)} t^{m+n-1} \cos^{2m-1}\theta \sin^{2n-1}\theta \, d\theta \, dt$$

$$= \int_0^{\pi/2} \frac{\Gamma(m+n)}{(a\cos^2\theta + b\sin^2\theta)^{m+n}} \cos^{2m-1}\theta \sin^{2n-1}\theta \, d\theta$$

$$= \frac{1}{2}\Gamma(m+n) \int_0^{\pi/2} \frac{\cos^{2m-1}\theta \sin^{2n-1}\theta}{(a\cos^2\theta + b\sin^2\theta)^{m+n}} \, d\theta. \qquad ...(1)$$

Also $\displaystyle\int_0^\infty \int_0^\infty e^{(ax^2+by^2)} x^{2m-1} y^{2n-1} \, dx \, dy$

$$= \int_0^\infty e^{-ax^2} x^{2m-1} \, dx \int_0^\infty e^{-by^2} y^{2n-1} \, dy$$

$$= \frac{1}{4}\int_0^\infty e^{-\xi} \left(\frac{\xi}{a}\right)^{m-1} \frac{d\xi}{a} \cdot \frac{1}{2}\int_0^\infty e^{-\eta} \left(\frac{\eta}{b}\right)^{n-1} \frac{d\eta}{b}$$

$$\left[\text{Putting } ax^2 = \xi, \ x = \left(\frac{\xi}{a}\right)^{1/2} \text{ and } by^2 = \eta, \ y = \left(\frac{\eta}{b}\right)\right]$$

$$= \frac{1}{2a^m}\int_0^\infty e^{-\xi} \xi^{m-1} \, d\xi \cdot \frac{1}{2b^n}\int_0^\infty e^{-\eta} \eta^{n-1} \, d\eta$$

$$= \frac{1}{4a^m b^n} \Gamma(m)\Gamma(n). \qquad ...(2)$$

Hence (1) and (2) are the values of the same integral; equating them, we get

$$\frac{1}{2}\Gamma(m+n) \int_0^{\pi/2} \frac{\cos^{2m-1}\theta \sin^{2n-1}\theta \, d\theta}{(a\cos^2\theta + b\sin^2\theta)^{m+n}}$$

$$= \frac{1}{4a^m b^n} \Gamma(m)\Gamma(n)$$

$$\therefore \quad \int_0^{\pi/2} \frac{\cos^{2m-1}\theta \sin^{2n-1}\theta \, d\theta}{(a\cos^2\theta + b\sin^2\theta)^{m+n}} = \frac{\Gamma(m)\Gamma(n)}{a^m b^n \, \Gamma(m+n)}$$

$$= \frac{B(m,n)}{a^m b^n}$$

as $\quad B(m,n) = \dfrac{\Gamma(m)\Gamma(n)}{\Gamma(m+n)}$.

6. *Show by polar transformation, that*

$$c \int_0^{c\,tan\,\alpha/\sqrt{2}} \int_0^{c\,tan\,\alpha/\sqrt{2}} \frac{dx\,dy}{(x^2+y^2+c^2)^{3/2}} \; tan^{-1}\left[\frac{sin^2\,\alpha}{2\,cos\,\alpha}\right].$$

The polar transformation formulae are

$$x = r \cos\theta, \; y = r \sin\theta.$$

$$\therefore \quad dx\,dy = r\,d\theta\,dr.$$

Thus

$$c \int_0^{c\,tan\,\alpha/\sqrt{2}} \int_0^{c\,tan\,\alpha/\sqrt{2}} \frac{dx\,dy}{(x^2+y^2+c^2y)^{3/2}}$$

$$= c \iint \frac{r\,d\theta\,dr}{(r^2+c^2)^{3/2}}$$

and the limits of r and θ can be determined by the following geometrical consideration :

The region of integration is the square bounded by

$$x = 0, \; x = \frac{c \tan\alpha}{\sqrt{2}},$$

$$y = 0, \; y = \frac{c \tan\alpha}{\sqrt{2}}.$$

Diagonal OC makes an angle $\pi/4$ with the side OA.

The region is the sum of the triangles OAC and OBC.

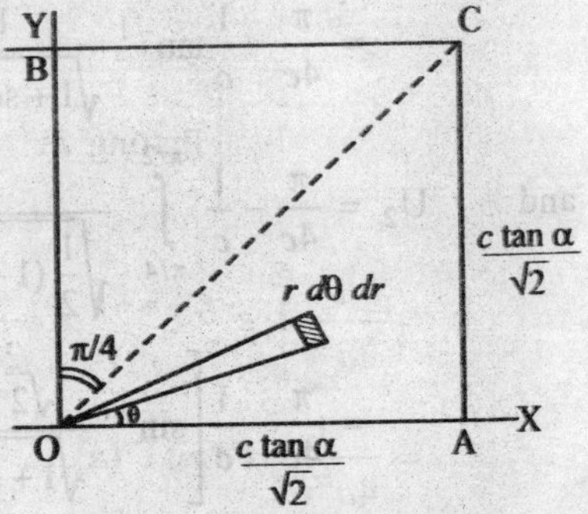

Fig. 12.29

Hence the given integral

$$= c \int_0^{\pi/4} \int_0^{(c\,sec\,\theta\,tan\,\alpha)/\sqrt{2}} \frac{r\,d\theta\,dr}{(r^2+c^2)^{3/2}}$$

$$+ c \int_{\pi/4}^{\pi/2} \int_0^{(c\,cosec\,\theta\,tan\,\alpha)/2} \frac{r\,d\theta\,dr}{(r^2+c^2)^{3/2}}$$

$$= c\,(U_1 + U_2) \text{ say} \qquad\qquad ...(1)$$

where

$$U_1 = \int_0^{\pi/4} \left[\frac{(c^2+r^2)^{-1/2}}{-1/2}\right]_0^{(c\,sec\,\theta\,tan\,\alpha)/\sqrt{2}}$$

$$= \int_0^{\pi/4} \left[\frac{1}{c} - \frac{1}{\sqrt{\frac{1}{2}c^2\,sec^2\,\theta\,tan^2\,\alpha+c^2}}\right]$$

$$= \frac{\pi}{4c} - \frac{1}{c} \int_0^{\pi/4} \frac{\cos\theta \, d\theta}{\sqrt{\frac{1}{2}\tan^2\alpha + \cos^2\theta}}$$

$$= \frac{\pi}{4c} - \frac{1}{c} \int_0^{\pi/4} \frac{\cos\theta \, d\theta}{\sqrt{\frac{1}{2}(\sec^2\alpha - 1) + (1 - \sin^2\theta)}}$$

$$= \frac{\pi}{4c} - \frac{1}{c} \int_0^{\pi/4} \frac{\cos\theta \, d\theta}{\sqrt{\frac{1}{2}(1 + \sec^2\alpha) - \sin^2\theta}}$$

$$= \frac{\pi}{4c} - \frac{1}{c} \left[\sin^{-1} \frac{\sin\theta\sqrt{2}}{\sqrt{1 + \sec^2\alpha}} \right]_0^{\pi/4}$$

$$= \frac{\pi}{4c} - \frac{1}{c} \sin^{-1} \frac{1}{\sqrt{1 + \sec^2\alpha}} = \frac{\pi}{4c} - \frac{1}{c} \tan^{-1}(\cos\alpha)$$

and
$$U_2 = \frac{\pi}{4c} - \frac{1}{c} \int_{\pi/4}^{\pi/2} \frac{\sin\theta \, d\theta}{\sqrt{\frac{1}{2}(1 + \sec^2\alpha) - \cos^2\theta}}$$

$$= \frac{\pi}{4c} - \frac{1}{c} \left[\sin^{-1} \frac{\sqrt{2}\cos\theta}{\sqrt{1 + \sec^2\alpha}} \right]_{\pi/4}^{\pi/2}$$

$$= \frac{\pi}{4c} - \frac{1}{c} \left[0 - \sin^{-1} \frac{1}{\sqrt{1 + \sec^2\alpha}} \right]$$

$$= \frac{\pi}{4c} - \frac{1}{c} \tan^{-1}(\cos\alpha).$$

Hence putting in (1), we have :

Given integral

$$= c\left[\frac{\pi}{4c} - \frac{1}{c}\tan^{-1}(\cos\alpha) + \frac{\pi}{4c} - \frac{1}{c}\tan^{-1}(\cos\alpha) \right]$$

$$= \frac{\pi}{2} - \tan^{-1}(\cos\alpha) - \tan^{-1}(\cos\alpha)$$

$$= \cot^{-1}(\cos\alpha) - \tan^{-1}(\cos\alpha)$$

$$= \tan^{-1}(\sec\alpha) - \tan^{-1}(\cos\alpha)$$

$$= \tan^{-1} \frac{\sec \alpha - \cos \alpha}{1 + \sec \alpha \cos \alpha}$$

$$= \tan^{-1} \frac{1 - \cos^2 \alpha}{2 \cos \alpha} = \tan^{-1} \left(\frac{\sin^2 \alpha}{2 \cos \alpha} \right).$$

EXERCISES

1. Show that if $x = a \sin \theta \cos \phi$, $y = b \sin \theta \sin \phi$, the integral

$$\iint_A \left(\frac{x^2}{a^2} + \frac{y^2}{b^2} \right) dx \, dy$$

is transformed to $\displaystyle\iint_A ab \sin^3 \theta \cos \theta \, d\theta \, d\phi$.

2. Change the following integrals into polar coordinates and show that

(i) $\displaystyle\int_0^a \int_y^a \frac{1}{x^2 + y^2} \, dy \, dx = \frac{\pi a}{4}$;

(ii) $\displaystyle\int_0^1 \int_x^{\sqrt{2x - x^2}} (x^2 + y^2) \, dx \, dy = \frac{3\pi}{8} - 1$;

(iii) $\displaystyle\int_0^a \int_0^{\sqrt{a^2 - x^2}} y \sqrt{x^2 + y^2} \, dx \, dy = \frac{\pi a^5}{20}$.

(Sagar, 2001; Bilaspur, 1996; Ravishankar, 1998)

3. By using the transformation $x + y = u$, $y = uv$; show that

$$\int_0^1 \int_0^{1-x} e^{y/(x+y)} \, dx \, dy = \frac{1}{2}(e - 1).$$

4. Find the area enclosed by the parabolas $y^2 = 4ax$, $y^2 = 4bx$, $x^2 = 4cy$, $x^2 = 4dy$.

5. Transform the integral $\displaystyle\int_0^1 \int_x^{1/x} V \, dx \, dy$, by the substitutions $u = 1 + x$

and $v = xy$.

6. Show that $\displaystyle\int_0^\infty \int_0^\infty e^{-(x^2 + y^2)} \, dx \, dy = \int_0^\infty \int_0^\infty e^{-r^2} r \, dr \cdot \frac{dt}{1 + t^2}$ where $y = tx$, $x^2 + y^2 = r^2$. Hence evaluate the integral.

7. Show that

$$\int_0^c \int_0^{c-x} V \, dx \, dy = \int_0^1 \int_0^c V' \, u \, dv \, du, \text{ where } x + y = u \text{ and } y = uv.$$

8. Transform the integral $\iiint (x + y + z)^n \, xyz \, dx \, dy \, dz$ taken over the volume bounded by $x = 0$, $y = 0$, $z = 0$ and $x + y + z = 1$ by the substitution $u = x + y + z$, $uv = y + z$, $uvw = z$. Hence or otherwise calculate its value.

9. Find the value of $\displaystyle\int_0^a \int_0^b \frac{dx \, dy}{(c^2 + x^2 + y^2)^{3/2}}$ by transforming to polars.

ANSWERS

4. $\dfrac{16}{3}(b - a)(d - c)$, if $a < b; c < d$; **5.** $\displaystyle\int_0^2 \int_{(4-u)^2}^1 \frac{V'}{u - 1} \, du \, dv$;

6. $\dfrac{\pi}{4}$; **8.** $\dfrac{1}{120(n+6)}$;

9. $\dfrac{1}{c} \tan^{-1} \dfrac{ab}{c\sqrt{a^2 + b^2 + c^2}}$.

12.6. Triple Integrals. Let $f(x, y, z)$ be a function of three independent variables x, y and z defined at every point of a three-dimensional region V. Divide the region V into n elementary volumes δV_1, δV_2, ..., δV_n and let (x_r, y_r, z_r) be any point inside the rth sub-division δV_r. Find the sum

$$\sum_{r=1}^{n} f(x_r, y_r, z_r) \, \delta V_r.$$

Then $\displaystyle\iiint_V f(x, y, z) \, dV = \lim_{\substack{n \to \infty \\ \delta V_r \to 0}} \sum_{r=1}^{n} f(x_r, y_r, z_r) \, \delta V_r.$

To extend definition of repeated integrals for triple integrals, consider a function $f(x, y, z)$ and keep x and y constant and integrate with respect to z between limits in general depending upon x and y. This would reduce $f(x, y, z)$ to a function of x and y only. Thus, let

$$\phi(x, y) = \int_{z_1(x,y)}^{z_2(x,y)} f(x, y, z) \, dz.$$

Then in $\phi(x, y)$ we can keep x constant and integrate with respect to y between limits in general depending upon x this leads to a function of x alone, say

$$\psi(x) = \int_{y_1(x)}^{y_2(x)} \phi(x, y)\, dy.$$

Finally $\psi(x)$ is integrated with respect to x assuming that the limits for x are from a to b. Thus

$$\iiint_V f(x, y, z)\, dV = \int_a^b \int_{y_1(x)}^{y_2(x)} f(x, y, z)\, dx\, dy\, dz$$

$$= \int_a^b \left[\int_{y_1(x)}^{y_2(x)} \left\{ \int_{z_1(x, y)}^{z_2(x, y)} f(x, y, z)\, dz \right\} dy \right] dx.$$

If we put $f(x, y, z) = 1$, then the volume

$$V = \iiint_V dV = \int_b^a \int_{y_1(x)}^{y_2(x)} \int_{z_1(x, y)}^{z_2(x, y)} dx\, dy\, dz.$$

EXAMPLES

1. *Evaluate the integral*

$$\int_0^1 \int_0^{1-x} \int_0^{1-x-y} \frac{dx\, dy\, dz}{(x + y + z + 1)^3}. \qquad \text{(Ravishankar, 1993)}$$

Let

$$I = \int_0^1 \int_0^{1-x} \int_0^{1-x-y} \frac{dx\, dy\, dz}{(x + y + z + 1)^3}$$

$$= \int_0^1 \int_0^{1-x} \left[-\frac{1}{2} \frac{1}{(x + y + z + 1)^2} \right]_0^{1-x-y} dx\, dy$$

$$= -\frac{1}{2} \int_0^1 \int_0^{1-x} \left[\frac{1}{4} - \frac{1}{(x + y + 1)^2} \right] dx\, dy$$

$$= -\frac{1}{2} \int_0^1 \left[\frac{1}{4} y + \frac{1}{x + y + 1} \right]_0^{1-x} dx$$

$$= -\frac{1}{2} \int_0^1 \left[\frac{1}{4}(1 - x) + \frac{1}{2} - \frac{1}{x + 1} \right] dx$$

$$= -\frac{1}{2} \int_0^1 \left(\frac{3}{4} - \frac{1}{4} x - \frac{1}{x + 1} \right) dx$$

$$= -\frac{1}{2}\left[\frac{3}{4}x - \frac{1}{8}x^2 - \log(x+1)\right]_0^1$$

$$= \frac{1}{2}\left(\log 2 - \frac{5}{8}\right).$$

2. *Evaluate* $\displaystyle\int_0^4 \int_0^{2\sqrt{z}} \int_0^{\sqrt{4z-x^2}} dz\, dx\, dy.$

We have

$$I = \int_0^4 \int_0^{2\sqrt{z}} [z]_0^{(4z-x^2)^{1/2}} dz\, dx$$

$$= \int_0^4 \int_0^{2\sqrt{z}} \sqrt{4z - x^2}\, dz\, dx$$

$$= \int_0^4 \left[\frac{1}{2}x\sqrt{4z-x^2} + \frac{1}{2}\cdot 4z\sin^{-1}\left(\frac{x}{\sqrt{4}\,z}\right)\right]_0^{2\sqrt{z}} dz$$

$$= \int_0^4 \left[\frac{1}{2}\cdot 2\sqrt{z}\sqrt{4z-4z} + \frac{1}{2}\cdot 4z\sin^{-1}(1)\right] dz$$

$$= \int_0^4 \pi z\, dx = \pi\left[\frac{1}{2}z^2\right]_0^4 = 8\pi.$$

3. *Evaluate* $\displaystyle\iiint_V (x^2 + y^2 + z^2)\, dx\, dy\, dz$ *where V is the volume of the cube bounded by the coordinate planes and the planes* $x = y = z = a.$

Here a column parallel to z-axis is bounded by the planes $z = 0$ and $z = a.$

Here the region S above which the volume V stands is the region in the xy-plane bounded by the lines $x = 0$, $x = a$, $y = 0$, $y = a.$

Hence the given integral

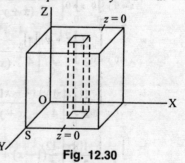

Fig. 12.30

$$= \int_0^a \int_0^a \int_0^a (x^2 + y^2 + z^2)\, dx\, dy\, dz$$

$$= \int_0^a \int_0^a \left[x^2 z + y^2 z + \frac{z^3}{3}\right]_0^a dx\, dy$$

$$= \int\limits_{0}^{a} \int\limits_{0}^{a} \left(x^2 a + y^2 a + \frac{1}{3} a^3 \right) dx \, dy$$

$$= \int\limits_{0}^{a} \left[x^2 ay + \frac{1}{3} y^3 a + \frac{1}{3} a^3 y \right]_{0}^{a} dx$$

$$= \int\limits_{0}^{a} \left(x^2 a^2 + \frac{1}{3} a^4 + \frac{1}{3} a^4 \right) dx$$

$$= \left[\frac{1}{3} x^2 a^3 + \frac{1}{3} a^4 x + \frac{1}{3} a^4 x \right]_{0}^{a} = a^5.$$

4. *Evaluate* $\iiint_V (2x + y) \, dx \, dy \, dz$, *where V is the closed region bounded by the cylinder* $z = 4 - x^2$ *and the planes* $x = 0, y = 0, y = 2$ *and* $z = 0$.

Here a column parallel to z-axis is bounded by the plane $z = 0$ and the surface $z = 4 - x^2$ of the cylinder.

This cylinder $z = 4 - x^2$ meets the z-axis, $x = 0, y = 0$, at $(0, 0, 4)$ and the x-axis, $y = 0, z = 0$ at $(2, 0, 0)$ in the given region.

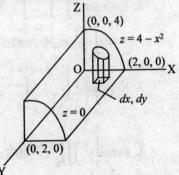

Therefore, it is evident that the limits of integration for z are from 0 to $4 - x^2$, for y from 0 to 2 and for x from 0 to 2.

Hence the given integral

Fig. 12.31

$$= \int\limits_{x=0}^{2} \int\limits_{y=0}^{2} \int\limits_{z=0}^{4-x^2} (2x + y) \, dx \, dy \, dz$$

$$= \int\limits_{x=0}^{2} \int\limits_{y=0}^{2} (2x + y) \left[z \right]_{0}^{4-x^2} dx \, dy$$

$$= \int\limits_{x=0}^{2} \int\limits_{y=0}^{2} (2x + y) (4 - x^2) \, dx \, dy$$

$$= \int\limits_{x=0}^{2} \int\limits_{y=0}^{2} [8x - 2x^3 + (4 - x^2) y] \, dx \, dy$$

$$= \int\limits_{x=0}^{2} \left[8xy - 2x^3 y + \frac{1}{2} (4 - x^2) y^2 \right]_{0}^{2} dx$$

$$= \int_0^2 [16x - 4x^3 + 2(4 - x^2)]\, dx$$

$$= \left[8x^2 - x^4 + 8x - \frac{2}{3}x^3 \right]_0^2$$

$$= \left(32 - 16 + 16 - \frac{16}{3} \right) = \frac{80}{3}.$$

EXERCISES

1. Evaluate $\int_0^a \int_0^x \int_0^{x+y} e^{x+y+z}\, dx\, dy\, dz$ and state precisely what is the region of integration. *(Rewa, 1999)*

2. Evaluate $\int_0^{\log 2} \int_0^x \int_0^{x+\log y} e^{x+y+z}\, dx\, dy\, dz$.

(Ravishankar, 1999S; Jiwaji, 1996; Rewa, 1997; Sagar, 1998)

3. Evaluate $\int_{x=0}^1 \int_{y=0}^{\sqrt{1-x^2}} \int_{z=0}^{\sqrt{1-x^2-y^2}} xyz\, dz\, dy\, dx$.

(Bhopal, 1994)

4. Evaluate $\iiint_V zy^2\, dx\, dy\, dz$, where V is the volume and the sphere $x^2 + y^2 + z^2 = 1$.

5. Evaluate $\iiint_V x^2\, dx\, dy\, dz$ over the region $x = 0, y = 0, z = 0$ and $x + y + z = a$. *(Ajmer, 1998)*

6. Evaluate $\iiint_V dx\, dy\, dz$ over the region V enclosed by the cylinder $x^2 + z^2 = 9$ and the planes $x = 0, y = 0, z = 0, y = 8$.

ANSWERS

1. $\frac{1}{8}(e^4 a - 6e^{2a} + 8e^a - 3)$. Region of integration is the volume enclosed by the planes $x = a, y = 0, y = x, z = 0$ and $z = x + y$.

2. $\frac{3}{8}\log 3 - \frac{19}{9}$; **3.** $\frac{-5}{48}$; **4.** $\frac{\pi}{24}$; **5.** $\frac{1}{6}a^5$; **6.** 18π.

12.7. Dritchlet's Theorem

If V is a region bounded by $x \geq 0$, $y \geq 0$ and $x + y + z \leq 1$, then

$$\iiint_V x^{l-1} y^{m-1} z^{n-1} \, dx \, dy \, dz = \frac{\Gamma(l)\,\Gamma(m)\,\Gamma(n)}{\Gamma(l+m+n+1)}.$$

(*Ajmer, 1998*; *Gorakhpur, 2003*)

The given triple integral may be written as

$$I = \int_0^1 \int_0^{1-x} \int_0^{1-x-y} x^{l-1} y^{m-1} z^{n-1} \, dx \, dy \, dz$$

$$= \int_0^1 \int_0^{1-x} x^{l-1} y^{m-1} \left[\frac{z^n}{n} \right]_0^{1-x-y} \, dx \, dy$$

$$= \frac{1}{n} \int_0^1 \int_0^{1-x} x^{l-1} y^{m-1} (1-x-y)^n \, dx \, dy.$$

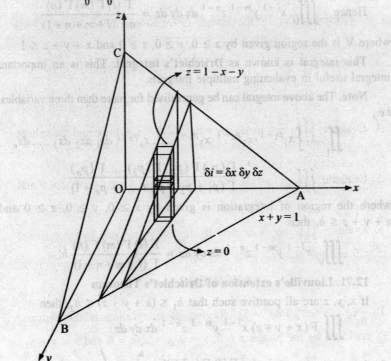

Fig. 12.32

Put $y = (1-x)\,t$, so that $dy = (1-x)\,dt$.

Then

$$I = \frac{1}{n} \int_0^1 \int_0^1 x^{l-1} [(1-x)\,t]^{m-1} - [1-x-(1-x)\,t]^n\,(1-x)\,dx\,dt$$

$$= \frac{1}{n} \int_0^1 x^{l-1}(1-x)^{(m+n-1)-1}\,dx \int_0^1 t^{m-1}(1-t)^{(n+1)-1}\,dt$$

$$= \frac{1}{n}\,B(l, m+n+1)\cdot B(m, n+1)$$

$$= \frac{\Gamma(l)\cdot\Gamma(m+n+1)}{n\,\Gamma(l+m+n+1)}\cdot\frac{\Gamma(m)\,\Gamma(n+1)}{\Gamma(m+n+1)}$$

$$= \frac{\Gamma(l)\cdot\Gamma(m)\,\Gamma(n+1)}{n\,\Gamma(l+m+n+1)} \qquad\qquad [\because\ \Gamma(n+1) = n\,\Gamma(n)]$$

$$= \frac{\Gamma(l)\cdot\Gamma(m)\,\Gamma(n)}{\Gamma(l+m+n+1)}.$$

Hence $\displaystyle \iiint_V x^{l-1}\,y^{m-1}\,z^{n-1}\,dx\,dy\,dz = \frac{\Gamma(l)\,\Gamma(m)\,\Gamma(n)}{n\,\Gamma(l+m+n+1)}$

where V is the region given by $x \geq 0$, $y \geq 0$, $z \geq 0$ and $x + y + z \leq 1$.

This integral is known as **Dritchlet's integral.** This is an important integral useful in evaluating multiple integrals.

Note. The above integral can be generalised for more than three variables, *i.e.*,

$$\iint \cdots \int x_1^{p_1-1}\cdot x_2^{p_2-1}\cdot x_3^{p_3-1} \cdots x_n^{p_n-1}\,dx_1\,dx_2\,dx_3 \cdots dx_n$$

$$= \frac{\Gamma(p_1)\,\Gamma(p_2)\,\Gamma(p_3)\cdots\Gamma(p_n)}{\Gamma(p_1+p_2+p_3+\cdots+p_n+1)}$$

where the region of integration is given by $x \geq 0$, $y \geq 0$, $z \geq 0$ and $x + y + z \leq h$, then

$$\iiint_V x^{l-1}\,y^{m-1}\,z^{n-1}\,dx\,dy\,dz = \frac{\Gamma(l)\,\Gamma(m)\,\Gamma(n)}{\Gamma(l+m+n+1)}\,h.$$

12.71. Liouville's extension of Dritchlet's Theorem

If x, y, z are all positive such that $h_1 \leq (x + y + z) \leq h_2$, then

$$\iiint F(x+y+z)\,x^{l-1}\,y^{m-1}\,z^{n-1}\,dx\,dy\,dz$$

$$= \frac{\Gamma(l)\,\Gamma(m)\,\Gamma(n)}{\Gamma(l+m+n)} \int_{h_1}^{h_2} F(h)\,h^{l+m+n-1}\,dh.$$

We know from Dritchlet's integral

$$u = \iiint x^{l-1} y^{m-1} z^{n-1} \, dx \, dy \, dz$$

$$= \frac{\Gamma(l)\,\Gamma(m)\,\Gamma(n)}{\Gamma(l+m+n+1)} h^{l+m+n}$$

where $x + y + z \leq h$.

If $x + y + z \leq h + \delta h$, then

$$u = \frac{\Gamma(l)\,\Gamma(m)\,\Gamma(n)}{\Gamma(l+m+n+1)} \cdot (h+\partial h)^{l+m+n}.$$

Now if the integral u is extended to all such positive values of the variables which make the sum of all the variables lie between h and $h + \delta h$, then the value of u

$$= \frac{\Gamma(l)\,\Gamma(m)\,\Gamma(n)}{\Gamma(l+m+n+1)} \cdot [(h+\delta h)^{l+m+n} - h^{l+m+n}]$$

$$= \frac{\Gamma(l)\,\Gamma(m)\,\Gamma(n)}{\Gamma(l+m+n+1)} \left[h^{l+m+n} \left\{ 1 + (l+m+n)\frac{\partial h}{h} + \ldots \right\} - h^{l+m+n} \right]$$

$$= \frac{\Gamma(l)\,\Gamma(m)\,\Gamma(n)}{\Gamma(l+m+n+1)} [(l+m+n)\, h^{l+m+n} \, \partial h]$$

neglecting higher powers of ∂h.

Now, let us consider the integral

$$\iiint F(x,y,z)\, x^{l-1} y^{m-1} z^{n-1} \, dx \, dy \, dz$$

where $h_1 \leq (x+y+z) \leq h$.

If $(x+y+z)$ lies between h and $h + \delta h$, then the value of $F(x+y+z)$ differs from that of $F_2(h)$ by a small quantity of the order of δh. Hence neglecting $(\delta h)^2$ etc. the part of the integral which is due to the supposition that the sum of the variables lies between h and $h + \delta h$ is ultimately equal to $\dfrac{\Gamma(l)\,\Gamma(m)\,\Gamma(n)}{\Gamma(l+m+n)} F(h)\, h^{l+m+n-1} \, \partial h$. The whole integral

$$\frac{\Gamma(l)\,\Gamma(m)\,\Gamma(n)}{\Gamma(l+m+n)} \int_{h_1}^{h_2} F(h)\, h^{l+m+n-1} \, dh.$$

The above integral is known as **Liouville's extension to Dritchlet's integral.**

EXAMPLES

1. *Evaluate* $\displaystyle\iiint x^{-1/2} y^{-1/2} z^{-1/2} (1-x-y-z)^{1/2} \, dx \, dy \, dz$ *extended to all positive values of the variables subject to the condition* $x + y + z < 1$.

The given integral

$$= \iiint x^{-1/2}\, y^{-1/2}\, z^{-1/2}\, [1-(x+y+z)]^{1/2}\, dx\, dy\, dz$$

$$= \frac{\Gamma\left(\dfrac{1}{2}\right)\cdot\Gamma\left(\dfrac{1}{2}\right)\cdot\Gamma\left(\dfrac{1}{2}\right)}{\Gamma\left(\dfrac{1}{2}+\dfrac{1}{2}+\dfrac{1}{2}\right)} \int_0^1 h^{1/2+1/2+1/2-1}\,(1-h)^{1/2}\, dh$$

by Liouville's extension to Dritchlet's integral.

$$= \frac{(\sqrt{\pi})^3}{\Gamma\left(\dfrac{3}{2}\right)} \int_0^h h^{1/2}\, dh$$

$$= \frac{2\pi\sqrt{\pi}}{\sqrt{\pi}} \int_0^{\pi/2} \sin\theta\cdot\cos\theta\, 2\sin\theta\cos\theta\, d\theta \qquad [\text{Putting } h = \sin^2\theta]$$

$$= 4\pi \int_0^{\pi/2} \sin^2\theta \cos^2\theta\, d\theta$$

$$= 4\pi\, \frac{\Gamma\left(\dfrac{3}{2}\right)\Gamma\left(\dfrac{3}{2}\right)}{2\,\Gamma(3)} = 2\pi\cdot\frac{\dfrac{1}{2}\sqrt{\pi}\cdot\dfrac{1}{2}\sqrt{\pi}}{2\cdot1} = \frac{1}{4}\pi^2.$$

2. *Find the value of* $\iiint x^{l-1}\, y^{m-1}\, z^{n-1}\, dx\, dy\, dz$ *where* x, y, z *are*

always positive but $\left(\dfrac{x}{a}\right)^p + \left(\dfrac{y}{b}\right)^q + \left(\dfrac{z}{c}\right)^r \geq 1.$ *(Ajmer, 1994)*

Putting $\left(\dfrac{x}{a}\right)^p = u,\ \left(\dfrac{y}{b}\right)^q = v,\ \left(\dfrac{z}{c}\right)^r = w,$ we have

$$x = au^{1/p},\ y = bv^{1/q},\ z = cw^{1/r}.$$

$$\therefore\quad dx = \left(\frac{a}{p}\right)u^{(1/p-1)}\,du,\ dy = \left(\frac{b}{q}\right)v^{(1/q-1)}\,dv,\ dz = \left(\frac{c}{r}\right)w^{(1/r-1)}\,dw$$

$$\therefore\quad \text{The given integral} = \iiint (au^{1/p})^{l-1}\,(bv^{1/q})^{m-1}\,(cw^{1/r})^{n-1}$$

$$\times \left(\frac{a}{p}\right)u^{1/p-1}\cdot\left(\frac{b}{q}\right)v^{1/q-1}\cdot\left(\frac{c}{r}\right)w^{1/r-1}\,du\,dv\,dw$$

where $u + v + w \leq 1$

$$= \frac{a^l b^m c^n}{pqr}\, \frac{\Gamma(l/p)\,\Gamma(m/q)\,\Gamma(n/r)}{\Gamma\left(\dfrac{l}{p}+\dfrac{m}{q}+\dfrac{n}{r}+1\right)}.$$

3. *Evaluate* $\iiint \log (x + y + z)\, dx\, dy\, dz$, *the integral extending over all positive values of x, y, z subject to the condition* $x + y + z < l$.

The given integral

$$= \iiint \log (x + y + z)\, x^{1-1}\, y^{1-1}\, z^{1-1}\, dx\, dy\, dz$$

$$= \frac{\Gamma (1)\,\Gamma (1)\,\Gamma (1)}{\Gamma (1+1+1)} \int_0^1 (\log h)\, h^{1+1+1}\, dh$$

by Liouville's extension to Dritchlet's Theorem.

$$= \frac{1}{2} \int_0^1 h^2 \log h\, dh$$

$$= \frac{1}{2} \left\{ \left[(\log h) \cdot \frac{1}{3} h^3 \right]_0^1 - \int_0^1 \left(\frac{1}{h} \right) \frac{1}{3} h^3\, dh \right\}$$

$$= \frac{1}{2} \left[(0) - \frac{1}{3} \int_0^1 h^2\, dh \right] = -\frac{1}{18}.$$

4. *Show that* $\iiint \dfrac{dx\, dy\, dz}{\sqrt{1 - (x^2 + y^2 + z^2)}} = \dfrac{1}{8} \pi^2$, *the integral being extended to all positive values of the variables for which the expression is real.*

Putting $x^2 = u,\ y^2 = v,\ z^2 = w$, we get

$$x = \sqrt{u},\ y = \sqrt{v},\ z = \sqrt{w},$$

$$dx = \frac{1}{2} u^{-1/2}\, du,\ dy = \frac{1}{2} v^{-1/2}\, dv,\ dz = \frac{1}{2} w^{-1/2}\, dw.$$

Also the expression is real if $x^2 + y^2 + z^2$ or $u + v + w < 1$.

$\therefore$ The given integral

$$= \iiint \frac{(1/2)^3\, u^{1/2-1}\, v^{1/2-1}\, w^{1/2-1}\, du\, dv\, dw}{\sqrt{1 - (u + v + w)}}$$

where $u + v + w < 1$.

$$= \frac{1}{8} \iiint \frac{u^{1/2-1}\, v^{1/2-1}\, w^{1/2-1}}{\sqrt{1 - (u + v + w)}}\, du\, dv\, dw$$

$$= \frac{1}{8} \frac{\Gamma \left(\frac{1}{2} \right) \Gamma \left(\frac{1}{2} \right) \Gamma \left(\frac{1}{2} \right)}{\Gamma \left(\frac{1}{2} + \frac{1}{2} + \frac{1}{2} \right)} \int_0^1 \frac{h^{1/2 + 1/2 + 1/2 - 1}}{\sqrt{1 - h}}\, dh$$

by Liouville's extension to Dritchlet's Theorem.

$$= \frac{1}{8} \cdot \frac{\left\{ \Gamma\left(\frac{1}{2}\right) \right\}^3}{\Gamma\left(\frac{3}{2}\right)} \int_0^h \frac{h^{1/2}}{\sqrt{1-h}}\, dh$$

$$= \frac{1}{8} \cdot \frac{\pi\sqrt{\pi}}{\frac{1}{2}\sqrt{\pi}} \int_0^{\pi/2} \frac{\sin\theta}{\sqrt{1-\sin^2\theta}} \cdot 2\sin\theta\cos\theta\, d\theta \quad [\text{Putting } h = \sin^2\theta]$$

$$= \frac{1}{4} \int_0^{\pi/2} 2\sin^2\theta\, d\theta = \frac{1}{2}\pi \cdot \frac{1}{2} \cdot \frac{\pi}{2} = \frac{\pi^2}{8}.$$

5. *Find the volume of the ellipsoid* $\dfrac{x^2}{a^2} + \dfrac{y^2}{b^2} + \dfrac{z^2}{c^2} = 1.$

The volume in the positive octant will be

$$V = \iiint dx\, dy\, dz.$$

For points within positive octant, $\dfrac{x^2}{a^2} + \dfrac{y^2}{b^2} + \dfrac{z^2}{c^2} \le 1.$

Put $\dfrac{x^2}{a^2} = u$ or $x = a\sqrt{u},\ y = b\sqrt{v},\ z = c\sqrt{w},$

$$\therefore \quad dx = \frac{a}{2} u^{-1/2}\, du,\ dy = \frac{b}{2} v^{-1/2}\, dv,\ dz = \frac{c}{2} w^{-1/2}\, dw$$

$$\therefore \quad V = \frac{abc}{8} \iiint u^{(1/2-1)} v^{(1/2-1)} w^{(1/2-1)}\, du\, dv\, dw$$

where $u + v + w \le 1$

$$= \frac{abc}{8} \cdot \frac{\Gamma\left(\frac{1}{2}\right) \cdot \Gamma\left(\frac{1}{2}\right) \cdot \Gamma\left(\frac{1}{2}\right)}{\Gamma\left(1 + \frac{1}{2} + \frac{1}{2} + \frac{1}{2}\right)}$$

$$= \frac{abc}{8} \frac{(\sqrt{\pi})^3}{\frac{3}{2} \cdot \frac{1}{2} \sqrt{\pi}} = \frac{\pi abc}{6}$$

$$\therefore \quad \text{Total volume} = 8 \times \frac{\pi abc}{6} = \frac{4}{3}\pi abc.$$

EXERCISES

1. Evaluate $\iiint dx\, dy\, dz$, where $\dfrac{x^2}{a^2} + \dfrac{y^2}{b^2} + \dfrac{z^2}{c^2} \leq 1$. *(Ajmer, 1998)*

2. Find the volume enclosed by the surface

$$\left(\frac{x}{a}\right)^{2n} + \left(\frac{y}{b}\right)^{2n} + \left(\frac{z}{c}\right)^{2n} = 1.$$

3. Find the volume of the solid bounded by the coordinate planes and the surface

$$\left(\frac{x}{a}\right)^{1/2} + \left(\frac{y}{b}\right)^{1/2} + \left(\frac{z}{c}\right)^{1/2} = 1.$$

4. Find the volume of the solid surrounded by the surface

$$\left(\frac{x}{a}\right)^{2/3} + \left(\frac{y}{b}\right)^{2/3} + \left(\frac{z}{c}\right)^{2/3} = 1. \quad \textit{(Rohilkhand, 1992)}$$

5. The plane $\dfrac{x}{a} + \dfrac{y}{b} + \dfrac{z}{c} = 1$ meets the axes in A, B and C. Apply Dritchlet's integral to find the volume of the tetrahedron OABC.

6. Evaluate $\iiint xyz \sin(x + y + z)\, dx\, dy\, dz$; the integral being extended to all positive values of the variables subject to the condition $x + y + z \leq \dfrac{\pi}{2}$.

7. Evaluate $\iiint e^{x+y+z}\, dx\, dy\, dz$, taken over positive octant, such that $x + y + z \leq 1$.

8. Prove that $\iiint \dfrac{dx\, dy\, dz}{\sqrt{a^2 - x^2 - y^2 - z^2}} = \dfrac{\pi^2 a^2}{8}$, the integrals being extended to all positive values of the variables for which the expression is real.

9. Evaluate

$$\iiint \sqrt{a^2 b^2 c^2 - b^2 c^2 x^2 - c^2 a^2 y^2 - a^2 b^2 z^2}\, dx\, dy\, dz,$$

taken throughout the ellipsoid $\dfrac{x^2}{a^2} + \dfrac{y^2}{b^2} + \dfrac{z^2}{c^2} = 1$.

ANSWERS

1. $\dfrac{1}{6}\pi abc$; **2.** $\dfrac{1}{6}a^2 b^2 c^2$; **3.** $\dfrac{abc}{90}$; **4.** $\dfrac{4abc\pi}{35}$; **5.** $\dfrac{abc}{6}$;

6. $\dfrac{1}{5!}\left[\dfrac{5}{16}\pi^4 - 15\pi^2 + 120\right]$; **7.** $\dfrac{1}{2}e - 1$; **9.** $\dfrac{\pi^2 a^2 b^2 c^2}{32}$.

EXERCISES ON CHAPTER XII

1. When the region of integration R is the triangle bounded by $y = 0$, $y = x$ and $x = 1$, show that

$$\iint_R (4x^2 - y^2)\, dx\, dy = \frac{1}{3}\left(\frac{\pi}{3} + \frac{\sqrt{3}}{2}\right).$$

2. Evaluate $\iint (x + y)^2\, dx\, dy$ over the area bounded by the ellipse

$$\frac{x^2}{a^2} + \frac{y^2}{b^2} = 1.$$

3. Evaluate $\iint_R dx\, dy$, where R is the positive quadrant of the ellipse

$$\frac{x^2}{a^2} + \frac{y^2}{b^2} = 1.$$

4. Evaluate $\iint_R y\, dx\, dy$, where R is the region bounded by the parabolas $y^2 = 4x$ and $x^2 = 4y$.   (*Ravishankar, 2002*)

5. Evaluate $\iint_R y\, dx\, dy$ over the part R of the plane bounded by the line $y = x$ and the parabola $y = 4x - x^2$.   (*Ravishankar, 2001*)

6. Evaluate $\iint_R \frac{xy}{x^2 + y^2}\, dx\, dy$, where R is the region of integration bounded by $y = x$, $y = 2x$, $x = 2$.   (*Bhoj, 1999*)

7. Change the order of integration in

$$I = \int_0^1 \int_y^1 x^2 \cos(x^2 - xy)\, dy\, dx$$

and hence evaluate it.

8. Transform $\displaystyle\int_0^{\pi/2} \int_0^{\pi/2} \sqrt{\frac{\sin\phi}{\sin\theta}}\, d\phi\, d\theta$ by the substitution $x = \sin\phi\cos\theta$, $y = \sin\phi\sin\theta$, and show that its value is π.

9. Show that

$$\int_{-\infty}^{\infty} \int_{-\infty}^{\infty} \frac{a\, dx\, dy}{(x^2 + y^2 + a^2)^{3/2}(x^2 + y^2 + b^2)^{1/2}} = \frac{2\pi}{a + b}$$

after transforming the integral into polars.

10. Evaluate : $\int_0^2 \int_0^x \int_0^{x+y} e^x (y+2z)\, dx\, dy\, dz.$

(Ravishankar, 2003; Bilaspur, 2000; Indore, 1999; Bhopal, 2000; Jiwaji, 1998; Sagar, 2000)

11. Evaluate :

$\int_1^e \int_0^{\log y} \int_1^x \log z\, dy\, dx\, dz.$ *(Sagar, 1999)*

12. Evaluate $\iiint_V (x+y+z)\, dx\, dy\, dz$ when the region V is bounded by $x+y+z = a\ (a>0)$, $x=0$, $y=0$, $z=0$. *(Jabalpur, 2000)*

13. Evaluate $\iiint_V (x+z)\, dx\, dy\, dz$, where the region of integration V is bounded by the solid $x^2 + y^2 + z^2 \le 1$; $x \ge 0$, $y \ge 0$, $z \ge 0$.

14. Prove that the area in the positive quadrant between the curve $x^n + y^n = a^n$ and the axes is $\dfrac{a^2}{2n} \cdot \dfrac{\{\Gamma(1/n)\}^2}{\Gamma(2/n)}$.

15. If S is a unit sphere with its centre at the origin, then prove that

$$\iiint_S \frac{dx\, dy\, dz}{\sqrt{1 - x^2 - y^2 - z^2}} = \pi^2.$$

16. Evaluate the integral $\iiint x^{l-1} y^{m-1} z^{n-1}\, dx\, dy\, dz$ where x, y, z are always positive but limited by the condition

$$(x/a)^p + (y/b)^q + (z/c)^r \le 1.$$

17. Prove that $I = \iiiint dx\, dy\, dz\, dw$, for all values of the variable for which $x^2 + y^2 + z^2 + w^2$ is not less than a^2 and not greater than b^2 is $\dfrac{\pi^2}{32}(b^4 - a^4)$.

18. Prove that $\iiint \dfrac{dx\, dy\, dz}{(x+y+z+1)^2} = \dfrac{1}{2}\left[\log 2 - \dfrac{5}{8}\right]$ throughout the volume bounded by the coordinate planes and the plane $x+y+z=1$.

ANSWERS

2. $\dfrac{\pi ab(a^2+b^2)}{4}$;   **3.** $\dfrac{1}{4}\pi ab$;   **4.** $\dfrac{48}{5}$;   **5.** $\dfrac{54}{8}$;

6. $\log(5/2)$;   **7.** $\dfrac{1}{2}(1-\cos 1)$;   **10.** $19\left(\dfrac{e^2}{3}+1\right)$;

11. $-\dfrac{3e^2}{4} + 2e + \dfrac{1}{4}$;   12. $\dfrac{a^4}{8}$;   13. $\dfrac{\pi}{8}$;

16. $\dfrac{a^l b^m c^n}{pqr} \cdot \dfrac{\Gamma(l/p)\,\Gamma(m/q)\,\Gamma(n/r)}{\Gamma(1 + l/p + m/q + n/r)}$.

OBJECTIVE QUESTIONS

To each of the following questions, four alternatives are given for the answer. Only one of them is correct. Choose the correct alternative.

1. Value of $\displaystyle\int_1^2 \int_0^{1/2} y\,dy\,dx$ is :

   (a) $7/6$ (b) $1/6$ (c) $2/3$ (d) $7/3$.

   (Avadh, 2002)

2. Value of $\displaystyle\int_1^2 \int_0^{3y} y\,dy\,dx$ is :

   (a) 3 (b) 5 (c) 7 (d) 9.

3. Value of $\displaystyle\int_0^a \int_0^b (x^2 + y^2)\,dx\,dy$ is :

   (a) $ab(a^2 + b^2)$ (b) $\dfrac{1}{3}ab(a^2 + b^2)$

   (c) $\dfrac{1}{2}ab(a^2 + b^2)$ (d) $3ab(a^2 + b^2)$.

4. Value of $\displaystyle\int_0^1 \int_y^{\sqrt{y}} (x^2 + y^2)\,dy\,dx$ is :

   (a) $\dfrac{1}{35}$ (b) $\dfrac{2}{35}$ (c) $\dfrac{3}{35}$ (d) $\dfrac{4}{35}$.

5. Value of $\displaystyle\int_0^{\pi/2} \int_0^{a\cos\theta} r\sin\theta\,d\theta\,dr$ is :

   (a) $\dfrac{1}{6}a^2$ (b) $\dfrac{1}{3}a^2$ (c) $\dfrac{1}{2}a^2$ (d) $\dfrac{5}{6}a^2$.

6. Area lying between the parabola $y = 4x - x^2$ and the line $y = k$ is :

   (a) $\dfrac{1}{2}$ unit   (b) $\dfrac{3}{2}$ unit   (c) $\dfrac{5}{2}$ unit   (d) $\dfrac{9}{2}$ unit.

7. Value of $\int\limits_1^a \int\limits_1^b \dfrac{dx\,dy}{xy}$ is :

(a) $\log(ab)$

(b) $\log(a/b)$

(c) $(\log a)\cdot(\log b)$

(d) $\dfrac{(\log a)}{(\log b)}$.

8. Value of $\int\limits_0^{\pi/2} \int\limits_{\pi/2}^{\pi} \cos(x+y)\,dy\,dx$ is :

(a) 0

(b) 2

(c) – 2

(d) 1.

9. The double integral $\int\limits_0^1 \int\limits_0^1 (x^2 + y^2)\,dx\,dy$ is equal to :

(a) 0

(b) 1

(c) $\dfrac{1}{3}$

(d) $\dfrac{2}{3}$.

10. $\int\limits_0^{\pi/2} \int\limits_0^{\sin\theta} r\,d\theta\,dr$ is equal to :

(a) $\int\limits_0^{\pi/2} \sin\theta\,d\theta$

(b) $\int\limits_0^{\sin\theta} \dfrac{1}{2}\pi r\,dr$

(c) $\int\limits_0^{\pi/2} \dfrac{1}{2}\sin^2\theta\,d\theta$

(d) None of these.

11. The area bounded by the curve $y = \phi(x)$, the x-axis and the lines $x = a$ and $x = b$ $(a < b)$ is given by :

(a) $\int\limits_a^b \int\limits_0^{\phi(x)} y\,dx\,dy$

(b) $\int\limits_a^b \int\limits_0^{\phi(x)} dx\,dy$

(c) $\int\limits_a^b \int\limits_0^{\phi(x)} dx\,dy$

(d) None of these.

12. Which of the following relations is true ?

(a) $\iint\limits_A f(x, y)\,dx\,dy = \iint\limits_A f(r\cos\theta, r\sin\theta)\,d\theta\,dr$

(b) $\iint\limits_A f(x, y)\,dx\,dy = \iint\limits_A f(r\sin\theta, r\cos\theta)\,d\theta\,dr$

(c) $\iint\limits_A f(x, y)\,dx\,dy = \iint\limits_A f(r\cos\theta, r\sin\theta)\,r\,d\theta\,dr$

(d) $\iint\limits_A f(x, y)\,dx\,dy = \iint\limits_A f(r\cos\theta, r\sin\theta)\,r^2\,d\theta\,dr$.

13. The volume of a region represented as :

$a \le x \le b, y_1(x) \le y \le y_2(x), z_2(x, y) \le z \le z_1(x, y)$ is given as :

(a) $\displaystyle\int_a^b \int_{y_1(x)}^{y_2(x)} \int_{z_1(x,y)}^{z_2(x,y)} dx\, dz\, dy$ (b) $\displaystyle\int_a^b \int_{y_1(x)}^{y_2(x)} \int_{z_1(x,y)}^{z_2(x,y)} dx\, dy\, dz$

(c) $\displaystyle\int_a^b \int_{y_1(x)}^{y_2(x)} \int_{z_1(x,y)}^{z_2(x,y)} dz\, dx\, dy$ (d) None of these.

14. The integral $\displaystyle\iint \left(\dfrac{1-x^2-y^2}{1+x^2+y^2}\right) dx\, dy$, extended over all positive

values of x and y such that $x^2 + y^2 \le 1$ can be evaluated by changing the variables x and y by using the substitution :

(a) $x + y = u, xy = v$ (b) $x = r \sin\theta, y = r \cos\theta$

(c) $x = r \cos\theta, y = r \sin\theta$ (d) None of these.

15. If $x = f_1(u, v, w), y = f_2(u, v, w)$ and $z = f_3(u, v, w)$, then $dx\, dy\, dz$ is equal to :

(a) $du\, dv\, dw$ (b) $uvw\, du\, dv\, dw$

(c) $\left| \dfrac{\partial(u, v, w)}{\partial(x, y, z)} \right| du\, dv\, dw$ (d) $\left| \dfrac{\partial(x, y, z)}{\partial(u, v, w)} \right| du\, dv\, dw.$

16. To change a given double integral from Cartesian to polar coordinates; we use the formula :

(a) $dx\, dy = d\theta\, dr$ (b) $dx\, dy = r\, d\theta\, dr$

(c) $dx\, dy = r^2\, d\theta\, dr$ (d) $r\, dx\, dy = d\theta\, dr.$

17. For transformation $x + y = u, y = uv$, the value of $dx\, dy$ is :

(a) $du\, dv$ (b) $u^2\, du\, dv$ (c) $\dfrac{1}{u}\, du\, dv$ (d) $u\, du\, dv.$

18. Value of triple integral $\displaystyle\int_0^1 \int_{y^2}^1 \int_0^{1-x} x\, dy\, dx\, dz$ is :

(a) $\dfrac{4}{35}$ (b) $\dfrac{3}{35}$ (c) $\dfrac{2}{35}$ (d) $\dfrac{1}{35}.$

19. Value of $\displaystyle\int_{-c}^c \int_{-b}^b \int_{-a}^a (x^2 + y^2 + z^2)\, dx\, dy\, dz$ is :

(a) 0 (b) $\dfrac{2}{3} abc\,(a^2 + b^2 + c^2)$

(c) $\dfrac{8}{3} abc\,(a^2 + b^2 + c^2)$ (d) None of these.

20. Dritchlet's theorem :

$$\iint \cdots \int x_1^{m_1-1} x_2^{m_2-1} \cdots x_n^{m_n-1} \, dx_1 \, dx_2 \cdots dx_n$$

$$= \frac{\Gamma(m_1)\,\Gamma(m_2)\cdots\Gamma(m_n)}{\Gamma(m_1+m_2+\cdots+1)}$$

holds to the condition :

(a) $x_1 + x_2 + \cdots + x_n = 1$ (b) $x_1 + x_2 + \cdots + x_n \geq 1$

(c) $x_1 + x_2 + \cdots + x_n \leq 1$ (d) None of these.

21. If x, y, z are all positive such that $h_1 \leq x + y + z \leq h_2$, the value

of $\iiint F(x+y+z)\, x^{l-1}\, y^{m-1}\, z^{n-1} \, dx \, dy \, dz$ is :

(a) $\dfrac{\Gamma(l)\,\Gamma(m)\,\Gamma(n)}{\Gamma(l+m+n)} \displaystyle\int_{h_1}^{h_2} F(u)\, u^{l+m+n-1} \, du$

(b) $\dfrac{\Gamma(l)\,\Gamma(m)\,\Gamma(n)}{\Gamma(l+m+n+1)} \displaystyle\int_{h_1}^{h_2} F(u)\, u^{l+m+n-1} \, du$

(c) $\dfrac{\Gamma(l)\,\Gamma(m)\,\Gamma(n)}{\Gamma(l+m+n)} \displaystyle\int_{h_1}^{h_2} F(u)\, u^{l+m+n} \, du$

(d) $\dfrac{\Gamma(l)\,\Gamma(m)\,\Gamma(n)}{\Gamma(l+m+n+1)} \displaystyle\int_{h_1}^{h_2} F(u)\, u^{l+m+n} \, du.$

22. Value of $\iint x^{2l-1}\, y^{2m-1} \, dx \, dy$ for $x^2 + y^2 \leq c^2$ is :

(a) $c^{l+m}\, \dfrac{\Gamma(l)\,\Gamma(m)}{\Gamma(l+m+1)}$ (b) $\dfrac{c^{2(l+m)}}{4} \cdot \dfrac{\Gamma(l)\,\Gamma(m)}{\Gamma(l+m+1)}$

(c) $\dfrac{c^{2(l+m)}}{4} \cdot \dfrac{\Gamma(l)\,\Gamma(m)}{\Gamma(l+m)}$ (d) $\dfrac{c^{2(l+m)}}{2} \cdot \dfrac{\Gamma(l)\,\Gamma(m)}{\Gamma(l+m+1)}.$

23. The value of $\iiint dx \, dy \, dz$, where $\dfrac{x^2}{a^2} + \dfrac{y^2}{b^2} + \dfrac{z^2}{c^2} \leq 1$ is :

(a) $\dfrac{\pi abc}{6}$ (b) $\dfrac{\pi abc}{3}$ (c) $\dfrac{\pi abc}{2}$ (d) $\pi abc.$

24. Value of $\iint x^{l-1}\, y^{-l}\, e^{x+y} \, dx \, dy$, extended to all positive values

such that $x + y < h$ is :

(a) $\dfrac{\pi}{\sin \pi} (e^h + 1)$ (b) $\dfrac{\pi}{\sin l\pi} e^h$

(c) $\dfrac{\pi}{\sin l\pi} (e^h + 1)$ (d) $\dfrac{\pi}{\sin l\pi} (e^h - 1)$.

25. Area in the +ve quadrant between the curve $x^n + y^n = a^n$ and the axes is :

(a) $\dfrac{a^2}{2n} \dfrac{\Gamma(1/n)^2}{\Gamma(2/n)}$ (b) $\dfrac{a^2}{2n} \dfrac{\Gamma(n^2)}{\Gamma(2/n)}$

(c) $\dfrac{a^2}{2n} \dfrac{\Gamma(n^2)}{\Gamma(n/2)}$ (d) $\dfrac{a^2}{2n} \dfrac{\Gamma(1/n)^2}{\Gamma(n/2)}$.

26. Value of $\iiint e^{x+y+z}\, dx\, dy\, dz$ over positive octant such that $x + y + z \le 1$ is :

(a) $\dfrac{1}{2} e$ (b) $\dfrac{1}{2}(e+2)$

(c) $\dfrac{1}{2}(e-2)$ (d) None of these.

27. Value of $\iint_R \sqrt{x^2 + y^2}\, dx\, dy$ where R is the region in xy-plane bounded by $x^2 + y^2 = 4$ and $x^2 + y^2 = 9$ is :

(a) $\dfrac{19\pi}{6}$ (b) $\dfrac{19\pi}{3}$ (c) $\dfrac{19\pi}{2}$ (d) $\dfrac{19\pi}{4}$.

28. If V is the region given by $x \ge 0,\ y \ge 0,\ z \ge 0$ and $x + y + z \le 1$, then $\iiint_V x^{l-1} y^{m-1} z^{n-1}\, dx\, dy\, dz :$

(a) $\dfrac{\Gamma(l)\,\Gamma(m)\,\Gamma(n)}{\Gamma(l+m+n)}$ (b) $\dfrac{\Gamma(l+m+n)}{\Gamma(l)\,\Gamma(m)\,\Gamma(n)}$

(c) $\dfrac{\Gamma(l)\,\Gamma(m)\,\Gamma(n)}{\Gamma(l+m+n-1)}$ (d) $\dfrac{\Gamma(l)\,\Gamma(m)\,\Gamma(n)}{\Gamma(l+m+n+1)}$.

29. Dritchlet's theorem can be generalised for n variables, where :

(a) $n \le 4$ (b) $n \le 100$

(c) n is any positive integer (d) None of these.

30. Liouville's theorem is an extension of :

(a) Euler's theorem (b) Dritchlet's theorem

(c) Cayley's theorem (d) Lagrange's theorem.

ANSWERS

1. (a)	2. (c)	3. (b)	4. (c)	5. (a)	6. (d)
7. (c)	8. (c)	9. (d)	10. (c)	11. (c)	12. (c)
13. (b)	14. (c)	15. (d)	16. (b)	17. (d)	18. (a)
19. (c)	20. (c)	21. (a)	22. (b)	23. (a)	24. (d)
25. (a)	26. (c)	27. (a)	28. (d)	29. (c)	30. (b)

13

Convergence of Improper Integrals

13.1. Proper Integrals. The definite integral $\int_a^b f(x)\, dx$ is said to be a *proper integral* if the range of integration is finite and the integrand $f(x)$ is bounded. The integral $\int_0^{\pi/2} \sin x\, dx$ is a proper integral. Also $\int_0^1 \dfrac{\sin x}{x}\, dx$

is an example of a proper integral because $\lim\limits_{x \to 0} \dfrac{\sin x}{x} = 1$.

13.2. Improper Integrals. We know that $\int_a^b f(x)\, dx$ exists when $f(x)$ is a single valued continuous function on the closed interval $a \le x \le b$.

These conditions can be relaxed to allow $f(x)$ to have a finite number of points of discontinuity, provided that at these points the abrupt change in the function is finite in amount. This type of behaviour of the function is illustrated in the figure below.

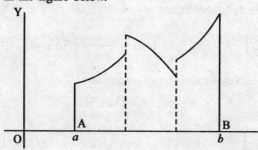

Fig. 13.1

The truth of the theorem follows at once due to the fact that the graph of the integrand is still *sectionally* or *piecewise continuous*, and hence the theorem can be applied to each segment.

Thus, we observe that $\int_a^b f(x)\, dx$ exists even if $f(x)$ has a finite number of finite discontinuities. However, there are two types of behaviour which, in general, must be ruled out. Specifically,

(i) if $f(x)$ becomes infinite at a point within the range of integration, or

(ii) if either of the limits of integration is infinite.

Under these circumstances the definite integral of $f(x)$ may have a finite value, it may be infinite or indeterminate depending upon the function $f(x)$ and the limits a, b. Integrals with one or both of these characteristics are called **improper integrals**.

Definition. If the range of integration (a, b) is not finite or if $f(x)$ is not bounded at one or more points of (a, b) then the integral of $f(x)$ over this range is called an *improper integral*. Thus the integral

$$\int_a^b f(x)\, dx$$

is called an *improper integral*, if

(i) $a = -\infty$ or $b = \infty$ or both, *i.e.*, one or both integration limits are infinite;

(ii) $f(x)$ is unbounded at one or more points of $a \le x \le b$. Such points are called *singularities* of $f(x)$.

Integrals corresponding to (i) and (ii) are called *improper integrals of the first and second kinds* respectively. Integrals with both conditions (i) and (ii) are called *improper integrals of the third kind*.

Examples

(1) $\displaystyle\int_0^\infty \cos x\, dx$ is an improper integral of the first kind.

(2) $\displaystyle\int_0^1 \frac{dx}{x-1}$ is an improper integral of the second kind.

(3) $\displaystyle\int_0^\infty \frac{dx}{(1-x)^2}$ is an improper integral of the third kind.

13.3. Improper integrals of the first kind or infinite integrals.

A definite integral $\displaystyle\int_a^b f(x)\, dx$ in which the range of integration is infinite, *i.e.*, either $b = \infty$ or $a = -\infty$ or both, and the integrand $f(x)$ is bounded, is called an improper integral of the first kind or an infinite integral.

For example $\displaystyle\int_0^\infty \frac{dx}{1+x^2}$, $\displaystyle\int_{-\infty}^0 e^x\, dx$ and $\displaystyle\int_{-\infty}^\infty \frac{dx}{1+x^2}$ are improper integrals of first kind since one or both of the limits are infinite and the integrands are bounded.

In case the interval (a, b) is infinite and the integrand $f(x)$ is bounded, we define

$$(i) \quad \int_a^\infty f(x)\,dx = \lim_{x \to \infty} \int_a^x f(x)\,dx,$$

provided the limit exists finitely, *i.e.*, the limit is equal to a definite real number.

$$(ii) \quad \int_{-\infty}^b f(x)\,dx = \lim_{x \to \infty} \int_{-x}^b f(x)\,dx,$$

provided that the limit exists finitely.

$$(iii) \quad \int_{-\infty}^\infty f(x)\,dx = \lim_{x_1 \to \infty} \int_{-x_1}^c f(x)\,dx + \lim_{x_2 \to \infty} \int_c^{x_2} f(x)\,dx,$$

provided that both these limits exist finitely.

13.4. Improper integrals of the second kind. A definite integral $\int_a^b f(x)\,dx$ in which the range of integration is finite but the integrand $f(x)$ is unbounded at one or more points of the interval $a \le x \le b$, is called an improper integral of the second kind. Thus $\int_1^5 \dfrac{dx}{(x-2)(x-4)}$ and $\int_0^1 \dfrac{1}{x^2}\,dx$ are improper integrals of the second kind.

In this case, we define the values of integral as follows :

(i) If $f(x)$ is unbounded at $x = b$ only, *i.e.*, if $f(x) \to \infty$ as $x \to b$ only, then we define

$$\int_a^b f(x)\,dx = \lim_{\varepsilon \to 0} \int_a^{b-\varepsilon} f(x)\,dx,$$

provided that the limit exists finitely. Here ε is a small positive number.

(ii) If $f(x) \to \infty$ as $x \to a$ only, then we define

$$\int_a^b f(x)\,dx = \lim_{\varepsilon \to 0} \int_{a+\varepsilon}^b f(x)\,dx,$$

provided that the limit exists finitely.

(iii) If $f(x) \to \infty$ as $x \to c$ only, where $a < c < b$, then we define

$$\int_a^b f(x)\,dx = \lim_{\varepsilon \to 0} \int_a^{c-\varepsilon} f(x)\,dx + \lim_{\varepsilon \to 0} \int_{c+\varepsilon'}^b f(x)\,dx,$$

provided that both these limits exist finitely.

(*iv*) If $f(x)$ is unbounded at both the points a and b of the interval (a, b) and is bounded at each other point of this interval, we write

$$\int_a^b f(x)\, dx = \int_a^c f(x)\, dx + \int_c^b f(x)\, dx, \qquad (i)$$

where $a < c < b$ and the value of the integral exists only if each of the integrals on the right hand side exists.

13.5. Convergence of Improper Integrals. *(Garhwal, 2002)*

The integral $\displaystyle\int_a^\infty f(x)\, dx$ is said to *converge* to I, when any positive number ε having been chosen, as small as we please, there is a positive number x, such that

$$\left| I - \int_a^x f(x)\, dx \right| < \varepsilon, \text{ for values of } x \geq \lambda.$$

Thus the integral $\displaystyle\int_a^\infty f(x)\, dx$ in which $f(x)$ is bounded and integrable in the given interval, is said to converge to I, when

$$\lim_{x \to \infty} \int_a^x f(x)\, dx = I.$$

But when the limit is $+\infty$ or $-\infty$, then we say that the integral *diverges* to $+\infty$ or $-\infty$. Also when this limit *oscillates finitely* or *infinitely*, the integral $\displaystyle\int_a^\infty f(x)\, dx$ is said to *oscillate finitely* or *infinitely*.

EXAMPLES

1. *Test the convergence of* $\displaystyle\int_1^\infty \frac{dx}{x^{3/2}}$.

We have

$$\int_1^\infty \frac{dx}{x^{3/2}} = \lim_{x \to \infty} \int_1^x \frac{dx}{x^{3/2}}$$

$$= \lim_{x \to \infty} \int_1^x x^{-3/2}\, dx = \lim_{x \to \infty} \left[\frac{x^{-1/2}}{-1/2} \right]_1^x$$

$$= \lim_{x \to \infty} \left[-\frac{2}{\sqrt{x}} \right]_1^x = \lim_{x \to \infty} \left[-\frac{2}{\sqrt{x}} + 2 \right]$$

$$= 2.$$

Thus the limit exists and is unique and finite; therefore the given integral is convergent and its value is 2.

2. *Test the convergence of* $\displaystyle\int_0^\infty \frac{4a}{x^2 + 4a^2} \, dx.$

We have

$$\int_0^\infty \frac{4a \, dx}{x^2 + 4a^2} = \lim_{x \to \infty} \int_0^x \frac{4a \, dx}{x^2 + (2a)^2}$$

$$= \lim_{x \to \infty} \left[4a \cdot \frac{1}{2a} \tan^{-1} \frac{x}{2a} \right]_0^x = 2 \lim_{x \to \infty} \left[\tan^{-1} \frac{x}{2a} \right]_0^x$$

$$= 2 \lim_{x \to \infty} \left[\tan^{-1} \frac{x}{2a} - 0 \right] = 2 \left[\tan^{-1} \infty \right] = 2 \cdot \frac{\pi}{2}$$

$$= \pi.$$

Thus the limit exists and is unique and finite, therefore, the given integral is convergent.

3. *Test the convergence of*

(i) $\displaystyle\int_{-\infty}^0 e^x \, dx;$ (ii) $\displaystyle\int_{-\infty}^0 e^{-x} \, dx.$ *(Garhwal, 1999)*

(*i*) We have

$$\int_{-\infty}^0 e^x \, dx = \lim_{x \to \infty} \int_{-x}^0 e^x \, dx$$

$$= \lim_{x \to \infty} \left[e^x \right]_{-x}^0 = \lim_{x \to \infty} [1 - e^{-x}]$$

$$= [1 - 0] = 1.$$

Thus the limit exists and is unique and finite; therefore the given integral is convergent.

(*ii*) We have

$$\int_{-\infty}^0 e^{-x} \, dx = \lim_{x \to \infty} \int_{-x}^0 e^{-x} \, dx$$

$$= \lim_{x \to \infty} \left[\frac{e^{-x}}{-1} \right]_{-x}^{0} = - \lim_{x \to \infty} \left[e^0 - e^x \right]$$

$$= \infty.$$

Thus the limit does not exist finitely and therefore the given integral is divergent and hence the integral does not exist.

4. Evaluate $\displaystyle\int_0^1 \frac{dx}{\sqrt{1-x}}.$ *(Garhwal, 1997)*

Here the integrand $\dfrac{1}{\sqrt{1-x}}$ becomes unbounded, *i.e.*, infinite at $x = 1$,

i.e., at the upper limit.

$$\therefore \quad \int_0^1 \frac{dx}{\sqrt{1-x}} = \lim_{\varepsilon \to 0} \int_0^{1-\varepsilon} \frac{dx}{\sqrt{1-x}}$$

$$= \lim_{\varepsilon \to 0} \left[-2\sqrt{1-x} \right]_0^{1-\varepsilon} = \lim_{\varepsilon \to 0} \left[-2\sqrt{\varepsilon} + 2 \right]$$

$$= 2,$$

which is a definite real number. Hence the given integral is convergent and its value is 2.

5. Evaluate $\displaystyle\int_{-1}^1 \frac{dx}{x^2}.$ *(Garhwal, 1998)*

Here the integrand $\dfrac{1}{x^2}$ becomes infinite at $x = 0$ and $-1 < 0 < 1$.

$$\therefore \quad \int_{-1}^1 \frac{dx}{x^2} = \lim_{\varepsilon \to 0} \int_{-1}^{-\varepsilon} \frac{dx}{x^2} + \lim_{\varepsilon' \to 0} \int_{\varepsilon'}^1 \frac{dx}{x^2}$$

$$= \lim_{\varepsilon \to 0} \left[-\frac{1}{x} \right]_{-1}^{-\varepsilon} + \lim_{\varepsilon' \to 0} \left[-\frac{1}{x} \right]_{\varepsilon'}^1$$

$$= \lim_{\varepsilon \to 0} \left[\frac{1}{\varepsilon} - 1 \right] + \lim_{\varepsilon' \to 0} \left[-1 + \frac{1}{\varepsilon'} \right].$$

Since both the limits do not exist finitely, therefore the integral does not exist and is divergent.

EXERCISES

Evaluate the following integrals and discuss their convergence :

1. $\displaystyle\int_1^\infty \frac{dx}{\sqrt{x}};$ **2.** $\displaystyle\int_1^\infty \frac{dx}{x};$

3. $\int\limits_{3}^{\infty} \dfrac{dx}{(x-2)^2};$ **4.** $\int\limits_{0}^{\infty} e^{-mx}\, dx,\ (m>0);$

5. $\int\limits_{-\infty}^{\infty} \dfrac{dx}{1+x^2};$ **6.** $\int\limits_{-\infty}^{0} \sinh x\, dx;$ *(Garhwal, 1999)*

7. $\int\limits_{0}^{\infty} \cos x\, dx;$ **8.** $\int\limits_{0}^{1} \dfrac{dx}{\sqrt{x}};$

9. $\int\limits_{0}^{1} \dfrac{dx}{1-x};$ *(Garhwal, 1998)*   **10.** $\int\limits_{-1}^{1} \dfrac{dx}{x^{2/3}}.$

ANSWERS

1. ∞, divergent;   **2.** ∞, divergent;

3. 1, convergent;   **4.** $\dfrac{1}{m}$, convergent;

5. π, convergent;   **6.** $-\infty$, divergent;

7. oscillates and so not convergent;   **8.** 2, convergent;

9. ∞, divergent;   **10.** 6, convergent.

13.6. Tests for convergence of improper integrals of the first kind.

To test the convergence of improper integrals in which the range of integration is infinite and the integrand is bounded.

If an integral of the form $\int\limits_{a}^{\infty} f(x)\, dx$ or $\int\limits_{-\infty}^{b} f(x)\, dx$ cannot be easily evaluated, its convergence is determined with the help of the tests given in the following articles.

13.6.1. Comparison Test. Let $f(x)$ and $\phi(x)$ be two functions which are bounded and integrable in the interval (a, ∞). Also let $f(x)$ be positive and $|\phi(x)| \le f(x)$ when $x \ge a$. Then, if $\int\limits_{a}^{\infty} f(x)\, dx$ is **convergent**, it follows that

$\int\limits_{a}^{\infty} \phi(x)\, dx$ is also convergent, and that

$$\int\limits_{a}^{\infty} \phi(x)\, dx \le \int\limits_{a}^{\infty} f(x)\, dx$$

and if $|\phi(x)| \ge f(x)$ for all values of x greater than some number $x_0 > a$, and $\displaystyle\int_a^\infty f(x)\,dx$ is **divergent** then

$$\int_a^\infty \phi(x)\,dx \text{ is also } \textbf{divergent.}$$

13.6.2. To test the convergence of $\displaystyle\int_a^\infty \dfrac{dx}{x^n}$, **where** $a > 0$.

(Garhwal, 1995)

We have

$$\int_a^\infty \frac{dx}{x^n} = \lim_{\varepsilon \to 0} \int_a^{1/\varepsilon} \frac{dx}{x^n}$$

$$= \lim_{\varepsilon \to 0} \frac{1}{(1-n)} \Big[x^{1-n} \Big]_a^{1/\varepsilon}$$

$$= \lim_{\varepsilon \to 0} \frac{1}{(1-n)} \Big[\frac{1}{\varepsilon^{1-n}} - a^{1-n} \Big]$$

$$= \frac{a^{1-n}}{n-1}, \text{ when } n > 1,$$

$$= \infty, \quad \text{ if } n < 1.$$

Also, when $n = 1$, we have

$$\int_a^\infty \frac{dx}{x^n} = \lim_{\varepsilon \to 0} \int_a^{1/\varepsilon} \frac{dx}{x}.$$

$$= \lim_{\varepsilon \to 0} \Big[\log \frac{1}{\varepsilon} - \log a \Big] = \infty.$$

Hence when $n > 1$, the integral converges and when $n \leq 1$, the integral diverges.

EXAMPLES

1. *Test the convergence of the integral*

$$\int_0^\infty \frac{\cos x}{1+x^2}\,dx.$$

(Garhwal, 1995; Kanpur, 2002; Gorakhpur, 2002)

We have

$$\phi(x) = \frac{\cos x}{1+x^2}.$$

Let $\qquad f(x) = \dfrac{1}{1+x^2}$.

Now, $\qquad \left| \dfrac{\cos x}{1+x^2} \right| \leq \dfrac{1}{1+x^2}$, since $| \cos x | \leq 1$.

Now, $\qquad \displaystyle\int_0^\infty \dfrac{dx}{1+x^2} = \lim_{\varepsilon \to 0} \int_0^{1/\varepsilon} \dfrac{dx}{1+x^2}$

$$= \lim_{\varepsilon \to 0} \left[\tan^{-1} x \right]_0^{1/\varepsilon} = \lim_{\varepsilon \to 0} \left[\tan^{-1} \dfrac{1}{\varepsilon} - 0 \right]$$

$$= [\tan^{-1} \infty] = \dfrac{\pi}{2}.$$

Hence $\displaystyle\int_0^\infty \dfrac{dx}{1+x^2}$ is convergent.

Then from comparison test, it follows that

$$\int_0^\infty \dfrac{\cos x}{1+x^2}\, dx \quad \text{is also convergent.}$$

2. *Test the convergence of the integral* $\displaystyle\int_a^\infty \dfrac{dx}{x^2 \sqrt{1+x^2}}$.

Here $\dfrac{1}{x^2 \sqrt{1+x^2}} < \dfrac{1}{x^3}$ for $x \geq a$.

Now, $\displaystyle\int_a^\infty \dfrac{dx}{x^3}$ is convergent, as $\displaystyle\int_a^\infty \dfrac{dx}{x^n}$ is convergent when $n > 1$, and here $n = 3$ which is greater than 1.

Hence by comparison test, the given integral is also convergent.

3. *Test the convergence of the integral*

$$\int_\pi^\infty \dfrac{\sin^2 x}{x^2}\, dx. \qquad\qquad (\textit{Garhwal 2004})$$

We have

$\dfrac{\sin^2 x}{x^2} \leq \dfrac{1}{x^2}$ for all $x \geq \pi$, and $\displaystyle\int_\pi^\infty \dfrac{dx}{x^2}$ is convergent. Hence the given integral is also convergent.

4. *Test the convergence of*

$$\int_0^\infty e^{-x} \frac{\sin x}{x} \, dx.$$

We have

$$\int_0^\infty e^{-x} \frac{\sin x}{x} \, dx = \int_0^1 e^{-x} \frac{\sin x}{x} \, dx + \int_1^\infty e^{-x} \frac{\sin x}{x} \, dx.$$

Since $\lim_{x \to 0} e^{-x} \frac{\sin x}{x} = 1$, therefore the integrand $e^{-x} \frac{\sin x}{x}$ is bounded

throughout the finite interval (0, 1). So $\int_0^1 e^{-x} \frac{\sin x}{x} \, dx$ is a proper integral

and therefore it is convergent.

Now, we will check the convergence of $\int_1^\infty e^{-x} \frac{\sin x}{x} \, dx$. Let $f(x)$

$= e^{-x} \frac{\sin x}{x}$. Then $f(x)$ is positive in the interval (1, ∞). Let $\phi(x) = e^{-x}$.

Then $\phi(x)$ is positive in the interval (1, ∞).

We have

$$|f(x)| = \left| e^{-x} \frac{\sin x}{x} \right| = e^{-x} |\sin x| \cdot \frac{1}{x}$$

$\leq e^{-x}$, since $|\sin x| \leq 1$, and $\frac{1}{x} \leq 1$.

Thus $|f(x)| \leq \phi(x)$ throughout the interval (1, ∞).

Hence by comparison test $\int_1^\infty f(x) \, dx$ is convergent if $\int_1^\infty \phi(x) \, dx$ is

convergent.

Now

$$\int_1^\infty \phi(x) \, dx = \int_1^\infty e^{-x} \, dx = \lim_{x \to \infty} \int_1^x e^{-x} \, dx$$

$$= \lim_{x \to \infty} \left[-e^{-x} \right]_1^x = \lim_{x \to \infty} \left[-e^{-x} + e^{-1} \right]$$

$$= 0 + e^{-1} = 1/e;$$

which is a definite finite number. Hence $\int_1^\infty \phi(x) \, dx$ is convergent.

$$\therefore \int_1^\infty f(x)\,dx \text{ is also convergent.}$$

Hence $\int_0^\infty e^{-x}\dfrac{\sin x}{x}\,dx$ is convergent because the sum of two convergent integrals is also convergent.

5. *Show that the integral* $\int_0^\infty e^{-x^2}\,dx$ *is convergent.*

We have

$$\int_0^\infty e^{-x^2}\,dx = \int_0^1 e^{-x^2}\,dx + \int_1^\infty e^{-x^2}\,dx.$$

Obviously $\int_0^1 e^{-x^2}\,dx$ is a proper integral because here the interval of integration $(0, 1)$ is finite and the integrand e^{-x^2} is bounded throughout this interval. Therefore this integral is convergent.

Now, we will discuss the convergence of $\int_1^\infty e^{-x^2}\,dx$ only. Let $f(x) = e^{-x^2}$.

Take $\phi(x) = xe^{-x^2}$ so that $\phi(x)$ is positive throughout the interval $(1, \infty)$. We have $|f(x)| = e^{-x^2} \le xe^{-x^2}$, since $x \ge 1$. Thus $|f(x)| \le \phi(x)$ throughout the interval $(1, \infty)$.

$\therefore$ By comparison test $\int_1^\infty e^{-x^2}\,dx$ is convergent if $\int_1^\infty xe^{-x^2}\,dx$ is convergent.

Now, $\int_1^\infty xe^{-x^2}\,dx = \lim_{x\to\infty} \int_1^x xe^{-x^2}\,dx$

$$= \lim_{x\to\infty}\left[-\frac{1}{2}e^{-x^2}\right]_1^x = \lim_{x\to\infty}\left(-\frac{1}{2}e^{-x^2}+\frac{1}{2}e^{-1}\right)$$

$$= \frac{1}{2}e^{-1}, \text{ which is a definite finite number.}$$

$$\therefore \quad \int_1^\infty x e^{-x^2}\, dx \text{ is convergent and so } \int_1^\infty e^{-x^2}\, dx \text{ is also convergent.}$$

Hence the given integral $\int_0^\infty e^{-x^2}\, dx$ is convergent as it is the sum of two convergent integrals.

13.63. The μ-test. Let $f(x)$ be bounded and integrable in the interval (a, ∞), where $a > 0$.

(a) If there is a number $\mu > 1$, such that $\lim\limits_{x \to \infty} x^\mu f(x)$ exists, then

$$\int_a^\infty f(x)\, dx \text{ is convergent.}$$

(b) If there is a number $\mu \le 1$, such that $\lim\limits_{x \to \infty} x^\mu f(x)$ exists and is

not 0, then the integral $\int_a^\infty f(x)\, dx$ is divergent, and the same is

true if $\lim\limits_{x \to \infty} x^\mu f(x)$ is $+\infty$ or $-\infty$.

EXAMPLES

1. *Examine the convergence of*

$$(i) \quad \int_1^\infty \frac{dx}{x^{1/3}\,(1 + x^{1/2})}, \qquad (ii) \quad \int_0^\infty \frac{x\, dx}{(1 + x)^3}. \qquad \textit{(Garhwal, 1997)}$$

(i) Take $\mu = \dfrac{1}{3} + \dfrac{1}{2} = \dfrac{5}{6}$; then

$$\lim_{x \to \infty} x^\mu f(x) = \lim_{x \to \infty} x^{5/6} \frac{1}{x^{1/3}\,(1 + x^{1/2})} = 1.$$

Since $\mu < 1$ and the above limit is non-zero. Hence from μ-test it follows that the given integral is divergent.

(ii) Take $\mu = 2$. Then, we have

$$\lim_{x \to \infty} x^\mu f(x) = \lim_{x \to \infty} x^2 \cdot \frac{x}{(1 + x)^3} = 1.$$

Since $\mu > 1$, the given integral is convergent.

2. *Test the convergence of the integral*

$$\int_0^\infty \frac{x^{2m}}{1 + x^{2n}}\, dx,$$

where m and n are positive integers.   *(Garhwal, 1994, 99)*

We have

$$\int_0^\infty \frac{x^{2m}}{1+x^{2n}}\,dx = \int_0^a \frac{x^{2m}}{1+x^{2n}}\,dx + \int_a^\infty \frac{x^{2m}}{1+x^{2n}}\,dx, \; a > 0.$$

Here

$$\lim_{x \to \infty} x^\mu f(x) = \lim_{x \to \infty} x^\mu \frac{x^{2m}}{1+x^{2n}}$$

$$= \lim_{x \to \infty} \frac{x^{\mu+2m}}{1+x^{2n}}$$

$$= 1, \text{ if } \mu + 2m = 2n, \text{ i.e., if } \mu = 2\,(n-m).$$

Now since m and n are positive integers, we have

$$\mu > 1, \text{ if } n > m$$

and

$$\mu < 1, \text{ if } n \le m.$$

Hence $\displaystyle\int_a^\infty \frac{x^{2m}}{1+x^{2n}}\,dx$ is convergent if $n > m$ and divergent if $n \le m$.

Also $\displaystyle\int_0^a \frac{x^{2m}}{1+x^{2n}}\,dx$ is convergent, being a proper integral.

It follows that the given integral is convergent if $n > m$ and divergent if $n \le m$.

3. *Examine the convergence of*

$$\int_a^\infty \frac{dx}{x\,(\log x)^{n+1}}, \text{ where } a > 1.$$

Let $\log x = t$ so that $\dfrac{1}{x}\,dx = dt.$

$$\therefore \quad \int_a^\infty \frac{dx}{x\,(\log x)^{n+1}} = \int_{\log a}^\infty \frac{dt}{t^{n+1}}.$$

Let $f(t) = \dfrac{1}{t^{n+1}}$. Then $f(t)$ is bounded in the interval $(\log a, \infty)$. Take $\mu = (n+1) - 0 = n+1$. Then

$$\lim_{t \to \infty} t^\mu f(t) = \lim_{t \to \infty} \frac{t^{n+1}}{t^{n+1}} = \lim_{t \to \infty} 1 = 1; \text{ which is finite and non-zero.}$$

Therefore by μ-test, the given integral is convergent if

$$\mu > 1, \text{ i.e., } n+1 > 1, \text{ i.e., } n > 0$$

and divergent if

$$\mu \le 1, \text{ i.e., } n+1 \le 1, \text{ i.e., } n \le 0.$$

4. *Show that the integral* $\int_{1}^{\infty} x^{n-1} e^{-x}\, dx$ *is convergent.*

(Garhwal, 1998, 2002, 04)

Let $f(x) = x^{n-1} e^{-x}$. Then $f(x)$ is bounded in the interval $(1, \infty)$.
We have

$$\lim_{x \to \infty} x^{\mu} f(x) = \lim_{x \to \infty} \frac{x^{\mu} \cdot x^{n-1}}{e^x}$$

$$= \lim_{x \to \infty} \frac{x^{\mu+n-1}}{1 + x + \frac{x^2}{2!} + \ldots} = 0, \text{ for all values of } \mu \text{ and } n.$$

Taking $\mu > 1$, we see by μ-test that the integral

$$\int_{1}^{\infty} x^{n-1} e^{-x}\, dx$$

is convergent for all values of n.

13.64. Abel's Test. *If* $\int_{a}^{\infty} f(x)\, dx$ *converges and* $\phi(x)$ *is bounded and monotonic for* $x > a$, *then* $\int_{a}^{\infty} f(x) \phi(x)\, dx$ *is convergent.*

13.65. Dirichlet's Test. *If* $f(x)$ *be bounded and monotonic and if* $\lim_{x \to \infty} f(x) = 0$, *then the integral* $\int_{a}^{\infty} f(x) \phi(x)\, dx$ *converges provided* $\left| \int_{a}^{x} \phi(x)\, dx \right|$ *is bounded as* x *takes all finite values.*

EXAMPLES

1. *Test the convergence of*

$$\int_{a}^{\infty} (1 - e^{-x}) \frac{\cos x}{x^2}\, dx, \text{ when } a > 0.$$ (Garhwal, 1998)

Let $f(x) = \frac{\cos x}{x^2}$ and $\phi(x) = 1 - e^{-x}$.

We have $\left| \frac{\cos x}{x^2} \right| \le \frac{1}{x^2}$ as $|\cos x| \le 1$.

Since $\displaystyle\int\limits_{a}^{\infty}\dfrac{1}{x^2}\,dx$ is convergent, therefore by comparison test $\displaystyle\int\limits_{a}^{\infty}\dfrac{\cos x}{x^2}\,dx$

is also convergent.

Again $\phi(x) = 1 - e^{-x}$ is monotonic increasing and bounded function for $x > a$.

Hence by Abel's test $\displaystyle\int\limits_{a}^{\infty}(1 - e^{-x})\dfrac{\cos x}{x^2}\,dx$ is convergent.

2. *Test the convergence of* $\displaystyle\int\limits_{a}^{\infty}e^{-x}\dfrac{\sin x}{x^2}\,dx$ *where $a > 0$.*

(Garhwal, 1999)

Let $f(x) = \dfrac{\sin x}{x^2}$ and $\phi(x) = e^{-x}$. Since $\left|\dfrac{\sin x}{x^2}\right| \le \dfrac{1}{x^2}$ and $\displaystyle\int\limits_{a}^{\infty}\dfrac{1}{x^2}\,dx$

is convergent, therefore by comparison test $\displaystyle\int\limits_{a}^{\infty}\dfrac{\sin x}{x^2}\,dx$, is also convergent.

Again e^{-x} is monotonic decreasing and bounded function for $x > a$.

Hence by Abel's test $\displaystyle\int\limits_{a}^{\infty}e^{-x}\dfrac{\sin x}{x^2}\,dx$ is convergent.

3. *Show that* $\displaystyle\int\limits_{0}^{\infty}\sin x^2\,dx$ *is convergent.*   (Garhwal, 1994)

We have

$$\int\limits_{0}^{\infty}\sin x^2\,dx = \int\limits_{0}^{1}\sin x^2\,dx + \int\limits_{1}^{\infty}\sin x^2\,dx.$$

But $\displaystyle\int\limits_{0}^{1}\sin x^2\,dx$ is a proper integral and hence convergent.

Now we will test the convergence of $\displaystyle\int\limits_{1}^{\infty}\sin x^2\,dx$.

We can write $\displaystyle\int\limits_{1}^{\infty}\sin x^2\,dx = \int\limits_{1}^{\infty}2x\,(\sin x^2)\dfrac{1}{2x}\,dx.$

Let $f(x) = \dfrac{1}{2x}$ and $\phi(x) = 2x \sin x^2$. The function $f(x) = \dfrac{1}{2x}$ is

bounded and monotonic decreasing for all $x \geq 1$ and $\lim\limits_{x \to \infty} \dfrac{1}{2x} = 0$.

Also, $\left| \displaystyle\int_1^x \phi(x)\, dx \right| = \left| \displaystyle\int_1^x 2x \sin x^2\, dx \right|$

$$= |\cos 1^2 - \cos x^2| \leq 2,$$

for all finite values of x.

Hence by Dirichlet's test

$$\int_1^\infty \frac{1}{2x} (\sin x^2) \cdot 2x\, dx, \; i.e., \int_1^\infty \sin x^2\, dx \text{ is convergent.}$$

Since the sum of two convergent integrals is convergent, therefore the

integral $\displaystyle\int_0^\infty \sin x^2\, dx$ is convergent.

4. *Test the convergence of the integral*

$$\int_a^\infty \frac{\sin x}{\sqrt{x}}\, dx, \text{ where } a > 0. \hspace{2cm} \textit{(Garhwal 2004)}$$

Let $f(x) = \dfrac{1}{\sqrt{x}}$ and $\phi(x) = \sin x$. Now $\dfrac{1}{\sqrt{x}}$ is bounded and monotonic

decreasing for all $x \leq a$ and $\lim\limits_{x \to \infty} \dfrac{1}{\sqrt{x}} = 0$.

Also $\left| \displaystyle\int_a^x \phi(x)\, dx \right| = \left| \displaystyle\int_a^x \sin x\, dx \right|$

$$= |\cos a - \cos x| \leq 2,$$

for all finite values of x, as the value of $\cos x$ lies between -1 and 1.

$\therefore \quad \left| \displaystyle\int_a^x \phi(x)\, dx \right|$ is bounded for all finite values of x.

Hence by Dirichlet's test the integral $\displaystyle\int_a^\infty \frac{\sin x}{\sqrt{x}}\, dx$ is convergent.

5. *Show that the integral* $\displaystyle\int_0^\infty \frac{\sin x}{x}\, dx$ *is convergent.*

$$\textit{(Garhwal, 1993, 95, 2002)}$$

We have $\int\limits_{0}^{\infty} \dfrac{\sin x}{x}\, dx = \int\limits_{0}^{a} \dfrac{\sin x}{x}\, dx + \int\limits_{a}^{\infty} \dfrac{\sin x}{x}\, dx$, where $a > 0$.

Since $\lim\limits_{x \to 0} \dfrac{\sin x}{x} = 1$, the integral $\int\limits_{0}^{a} \dfrac{\sin x}{x}\, dx$ is a proper integral and hence convergent.

Now to test the convergence of $\int\limits_{a}^{\infty} \dfrac{\sin x}{x}\, dx$, let $f(x) = 1/x$ and $\phi(x)$ $= \sin x$.

Also $\left| \int\limits_{a}^{x} \phi(x)\, dx \right| = \left| \int\limits_{a}^{x} \sin x\, dx \right|$

$$= |\cos a - \cos x| \leq 2,$$

for all finite values of x.

$\therefore$ $\left| \int\limits_{a}^{x} \phi(x)\, dx \right|$ is bounded for all finite values of x.

Hence by Dirichlet's test the integral

$$\int\limits_{a}^{\infty} \dfrac{\sin x}{x}\, dx \text{ is convergent.}$$

Since the sum of two convergent integrals is convergent, therefore $\int\limits_{0}^{\infty} \dfrac{\sin x}{x}\, dx$ is convergent.

6. *Show that the integral*

$$\int\limits_{0}^{\infty} e^{-ax}\, \dfrac{\sin x}{x}\, dx, a \geq 0 \text{ is convergent. (Garhwal, 2000, 02)}$$

We have

$$\int\limits_{0}^{\infty} e^{-ax}\, \dfrac{\sin x}{x}\, dx = \int\limits_{0}^{\alpha} e^{-ax}\, \dfrac{\sin x}{x}\, dx + \int\limits_{\alpha}^{\infty} e^{-ax}\, \dfrac{\sin x}{x}\, dx,$$

where $\alpha > 0$.

Since $\lim\limits_{x \to 0} e^{-ax}\, \dfrac{\sin x}{x} = 1$, the integral $\int\limits_{0}^{\alpha} e^{-ax}\, \dfrac{\sin x}{x}\, dx$ is a proper integral and hence convergent.

Now we want to test the convergence of

$$\int_{\alpha}^{\infty} e^{-ax} \frac{\sin x}{x} \, dx.$$

Let $f(x) = \dfrac{e^{-ax}}{x}$ and $\phi(x) = \sin x$.

Obviously the function $f(x) = \dfrac{1}{xe^{ax}}$ is bounded and monotonic

decreasing for all $x \geq \alpha$ and $\lim\limits_{x \to \infty} f(x) = \lim\limits_{x \to \infty} \dfrac{1}{xe^{ax}} = 0.$

Moreover $\left| \displaystyle\int_{\alpha}^{x} \phi(x) \, dx \right| = \left| \displaystyle\int_{\alpha}^{x} \sin x \, dx \right|$

$$= |\cos \alpha - \cos x| \leq 2,$$

for all finite values of x.

$\therefore \qquad \left| \displaystyle\int_{\alpha}^{x} \phi(x) \, dx \right|$ is bounded for all finite values of x.

$\therefore$ By Dirichlet's test $\displaystyle\int_{\alpha}^{\infty} e^{-ax} \dfrac{\sin x}{x} \, dx$ is convergent.

Since the sum of two convergent integrals is convergent, therefore

$\displaystyle\int_{0}^{\infty} e^{-ax} \dfrac{\sin x}{x} \, dx$ is convergent.

7. Prove that $\displaystyle\int_{a}^{\infty} \dfrac{\cos \alpha x - \cos \beta x}{x} \, dx$ **is convergent, where** $a > 0$.

(Garhwal, 1997)

We have

$$\int_{a}^{\infty} \frac{\cos \alpha x - \cos \beta x}{x} \, dx = \int_{a}^{\infty} \frac{\cos \alpha x}{x} \, dx - \int_{a}^{\infty} \frac{\cos \beta x}{x} \, dx.$$

The function $f(x) = \dfrac{1}{x}$ is bounded and monotonic decreasing for all

$x \geq a$ and $\lim\limits_{x \to \infty} \dfrac{1}{x} = 0.$

Also $\qquad \left| \int\limits_{a}^{x} \cos \alpha x\, dx \right| = \left| \dfrac{1}{\alpha}(\sin \alpha x - \sin \alpha a) \right| \leq \dfrac{2}{|\alpha|}.$

$\therefore \quad \left| \int\limits_{a}^{x} \cos \alpha x\, dx \right|$ is bounded for all finite values of x.

Similarly $\left| \int\limits_{a}^{x} \cos \beta x\, dx \right|$ is bounded for all finite values of x.

$\therefore$ By Dirichlet's test both the integrals

$$\int\limits_{a}^{\infty} \frac{\cos \alpha x}{x}\, dx \text{ and } \int\limits_{a}^{\infty} \frac{\cos \beta x}{x}\, dx \text{ are convergent.}$$

Hence the given integral is convergent.

13.7. Absolute Convergence. The integral $\int\limits_{a}^{\infty} f(x)\, dx$ will converge if

$\int\limits_{a}^{\infty} |f(x)|\, dx$ converges.

If this condition is satisfied, we say that $\int\limits_{a}^{\infty} f(x)\, dx$ **converges absolutely.**

EXAMPLES

1. *Show that* $\int\limits_{1}^{\infty} \dfrac{\sin x}{x^4}\, dx$ *is absolutely convergent.*

We have

$$\int\limits_{1}^{\infty} \left| \frac{\sin x}{x^4} \right| dx = \lim_{x \to \infty} \int\limits_{1}^{x} \frac{|\sin x|}{|x^4|}\, dx$$

$$\leq \lim_{x \to \infty} \int\limits_{1}^{x} \frac{dx}{x^4}$$

$$= \lim_{x \to \infty} \left[\frac{1}{3} - \frac{1}{3x^3} \right] = \frac{1}{3}.$$

Hence $\int\limits_{1}^{\infty} \left| \dfrac{\sin x}{x^4} \right| dx$ is convergent.

It follows that $\displaystyle\int_1^\infty \dfrac{\sin x}{x^4}\,dx$ is absolutely convergent.

Note. Absolute convergence gives a sufficient but not a necessary condition for the convergence of an infinite integral. The following integral converges but not absolutely.

2. *Test the integral* $\displaystyle\int_0^\infty f(x)\,dx$ *for absolute convergence, where* $f(x)$ *is defined as follows :*

$$f(x) = 1, \text{ for } 0 \le x \le 1$$

$$= 0, \text{ for } n-1 < x \le n - \dfrac{1}{n}$$

$$= (-1)^{n+1}, \text{ for } n - \dfrac{1}{n} < x \le n,$$

where $n = 2, 3, 4, \ldots\ldots$.

We have

$$\int_0^\infty f(x)\,dx = \int_0^1 f(x)\,dx + \int_0^{1\frac{1}{2}} f(x)\,dx + \int_{1\frac{1}{2}}^2 f(x)\,dx + \ldots\ldots$$

$$= \int_0^1 dx + \int_1^{1\frac{1}{2}} 0\,dx - \int_{1\frac{1}{2}}^2 dx + \ldots\ldots$$

$$= 1 - \dfrac{1}{2} + \dfrac{1}{3} - \dfrac{1}{4} + \ldots\ldots$$

Now we know that the series on the right hand side is convergent, its value being $\log_e 2$. Hence the given integral is convergent.

But $\displaystyle\int_0^\infty |f(x)|\,dx = \int_0^1 |f(x)|\,dx + \int_1^{1\frac{1}{2}} |f(x)|\,dx + \int_{1\frac{1}{2}}^2 |f(x)|\,dx + \ldots\ldots$

$$= 1 + \dfrac{1}{2} + \dfrac{1}{3} + \dfrac{1}{4} + \ldots\ldots$$

This series is divergent. Therefore $\displaystyle\int_0^\infty |f(x)|\,dx$ is divergent. It follows that the given integral converges but not absolutely.

3. *Show that* $\displaystyle\int_0^\infty \dfrac{\sin mx}{a^2 + x^2}\,dx$ *converges absolutely.* *(Kanpur, 2002)*

The integral $\int\limits_0^\infty \dfrac{\sin mx}{a^2 + x^2}\, dx$ will be absolutely convergent if

$\int\limits_0^\infty \left| \dfrac{\sin mx}{a^2 + x^2} \right|\, dx$ is convergent.

Let $f(x) = \left| \dfrac{\sin mx}{a^2 + x^2} \right|$. Then $f(x)$ is bounded in the interval $(0, \infty)$. We have

$$f(x) = \left| \dfrac{\sin mx}{a^2 + x^2} \right| = \dfrac{|\sin mx|}{a^2 + x^2} \le \dfrac{1}{a^2 + x^2},$$

since $|\sin mx| \le 1$.

$\therefore$ By comparison test, $\int\limits_0^\infty f(x)\, dx$ is convergent if $\int\limits_0^\infty \dfrac{dx}{a^2 + x^2}$ is convergent.

But $\int\limits_0^\infty \dfrac{dx}{a^2 + x^2} = \lim_{x \to \infty} \int\limits_0^x \dfrac{dx}{a^2 + x^2}$

$$= \lim_{x \to \infty} \left[\frac{1}{a} \tan^{-1} \frac{x}{a} \right]_0^x = \lim_{x \to \infty} \left[\frac{1}{a} \tan^{-1} \frac{x}{a} - 0 \right]$$

$$= \frac{1}{a} \cdot \frac{\pi}{2},$$

which is a definite real number.

$\therefore$ $\int\limits_0^\infty \dfrac{dx}{a^2 + x^2}$ is convergent. Hence $\int\limits_0^\infty f(x)\, dx$ is also convergent and so the given integral is absolutely convergent.

4. *Show that* $\int\limits_0^\infty e^{-a^2 x^2} \cos bx\, dx$ *is absolutely convergent.*

(*Garhwal, 1994*)

$$\int\limits_0^\infty |e^{-a^2 x^2} \cos bx|\, dx < \int\limits_0^\infty |e^{-a^2 x^2}|\, dx, \text{ as } \cos bx \le 1.$$

Now

$$\int\limits_0^\infty e^{-a^2 x^2}\, dx = \int\limits_0^1 e^{-a^2 x^2}\, dx + \int\limits_1^\infty e^{-a^2 x^2}\, dx.$$

The first integral is bounded and the range of integration is finite. Hence it is a proper integral and therefore convergent.

Now for values of $x > 1$, $e^{-a^2x^2} < xe^{-a^2x^2}$, i.e., $f(x) < \phi(x)$ and

hence $\int_1^\infty f(x)\,dx$ will be convergent if $\int_1^\infty \phi(x)\,dx$ is convergent,

i.e., $\lim\limits_{x \to \infty} \int_1^x xe^{-a^2x^2}\,dx$ is finite or

$$\lim_{x \to \infty} -\frac{1}{2a^2}\left[e^{-a^2x^2}\right]_1^x = \lim_{x \to \infty} \frac{1}{2a^2}\left[\frac{1}{e^{a^2}} - \frac{1}{e^{a^2x^2}}\right]$$

$$= \frac{1}{2a^2 e^{a^2}}, \text{ i.e., finite.}$$

Hence $\int_1^\infty e^{-a^2x^2}\,dx$ is also convergent.

Therefore the integral $\int_0^\infty e^{-a^2x^2}\,dx$ being the sum of two convergent integrals is also convergent.

Hence the integral $\int_0^\infty e^{-a^2x^2}\cos bx\,dx$ is absolutely convergent.

EXERCISES

Test the convergence of the following integrals :

1. $\int_1^\infty \dfrac{\cos mx}{x^2 + a^2}\,dx$; (Garhwal, 1998)

2. $\int_0^\infty \dfrac{dx}{x\sqrt{1+x^2}}$;

3. $\int_\pi^\infty \dfrac{\sin x}{x^2}\,dx$;

4. $\int_0^\infty \dfrac{\sin mx}{x^2 + a^2}\,dx$;

5. $\int_2^\infty \dfrac{dx}{\sqrt{x^2 - x - 1}}$;

6. $\int_1^\infty \dfrac{dx}{\sqrt{x^3 + 1}}$;

7. $\int_0^\infty \dfrac{x^{3/2}}{(b^2x^2 + c)}\,dx$;

8. $\int\limits_{0}^{\infty} \dfrac{x^2}{(a^2 + x^2)^2} \, dx;$ *(Lucknow, 1995, 97)*

9. $\int\limits_{0}^{\infty} \dfrac{dx}{(1+x)\sqrt{x}};$ *(Garhwal, 1996)*

10. $\int\limits_{b}^{\infty} \dfrac{x^{3/2} \, dx}{\sqrt{x^4 - a^4}},$ where $b > a$;   11. $\int\limits_{0}^{\infty} \dfrac{\sin x}{x^{3/2}} \, dx;$

12. $\int\limits_{0}^{\infty} \dfrac{dx}{x^{1/3}(1 + x^{1/2})};$

13. $\int\limits_{0}^{\infty} \dfrac{x^{1/2}}{(x^2 + 4)} \, dx;$ *(Garhwal, 1998)*   14. $\int\limits_{0}^{\infty} \dfrac{x}{1 + x^2} \sin x \, dx.$

15. Prove that $\int\limits_{a}^{\infty} \dfrac{\sin mx}{a^2 + x^2} \, dx$ and $\int\limits_{a}^{\infty} \dfrac{\cos mx}{a^2 + x^2} \, dx$ converge absolutely,

when m and a are positive.   *(Garhwal, 1998)*

16. Show that $\int\limits_{a}^{\infty} \dfrac{\sin x}{x^{1+n}} \, dx$ and $\int\limits_{a}^{\infty} \dfrac{\cos x}{x^{1+n}} \, dx$ are absolutely convergent,

when n and a are positive.   *(Garhwal, 1998)*

ANSWERS

1. Convergent;   2. Divergent;   3. Convergent;   4. Convergent;

5. Divergent;   6. Convergent;   7. Divergent;   8. Convergent;

9. Convergent; 10. Divergent;   11. Convergent; 12. Divergent;

13. Divergent;   14. Convergent.

13.8. Tests for convergence of improper integrals of the second kind.

Now we will consider the convergence of the integral $\int\limits_{a}^{b} f(x) \, dx$, when

the range of integration is finite and the integrand $f(x)$ is unbounded at one or more points of the given interval (a, b).

It is sufficient to consider the case when $f(x)$ becomes unbounded at $x = a$ and bounded for other values of x in the interval (a, b). In this case, we have

$$\int\limits_{a}^{b} f(x) \, dx = \lim_{\varepsilon \to 0} \int\limits_{a+\varepsilon}^{b} f(x) \, dx.$$

Below we give a few important tests for the convergence of the above integral.

13.81. Comparison Test. *Let $f(x)$ be positive and $|\phi(x)| \leq f(x)$ in the interval $(a + \varepsilon, b)$. Then $\int_a^b \phi(x)\,dx$ is convergent provided $\int_a^b f(x)\,dx$ is convergent.*

And if $|\phi(x)| \geq f(x)$ for all values of x in $(a + \varepsilon, b)$, then $\int_a^b \phi(x)\,dx$ is divergent provided $\int_a^b f(x)\,dx$ is divergent.

13.82. *To test the convergence of $\int_a^b \dfrac{dx}{(x-a)^n}$.* (Garhwal, 1997, 2000)

We have

$$\int_a^b \frac{dx}{(x-a)^n} = \lim_{\varepsilon \to 0} \int_{a+\varepsilon}^b \frac{dx}{(x-a)^n}$$

$$= \lim_{\varepsilon \to 0} \frac{1}{(1-n)}[(b-a)^{1-n} - \varepsilon^{1-n}]$$

$$= \frac{1}{(1-n)}(b-a)^{1-n}, \text{ if } n < 1,$$

and $\qquad\qquad = \infty, \qquad\qquad \text{ if } n > 1.$

When $n = 1$, we have

$$\int_a^b \frac{dx}{(x-a)} = \lim_{\varepsilon \to 0} \int_{a+\varepsilon}^b \frac{dx}{(x-a)}$$

$$= \lim_{\varepsilon \to 0} [\log(b-a) - \log \varepsilon]$$

$$= \infty.$$

Hence the integral is **convergent if $n < 1$ and divergent if $n \geq 1$.**

EXAMPLES

1. *Test the convergence of the integral $\int_1^2 \dfrac{dx}{\sqrt{x^4 - 1}}$.* (Garhwal, 1999)

In the given integral the integrand $f(x) = \dfrac{1}{\sqrt{x^4 - 1}}$ is unbounded at

the lower limit of integration $x = 1$.

Take $\quad \phi(x) = \dfrac{1}{\sqrt{x^2 - 1}}$.

Then $\quad \lim\limits_{x \to 1} \dfrac{f(x)}{\phi(x)} = \lim\limits_{x \to 1} \left[\dfrac{1}{\sqrt{x^4 - 1}} \sqrt{x^2 - 1} \right]$

$$= \lim\limits_{x \to 1} \dfrac{1}{\sqrt{x^2 - 1}} = \dfrac{1}{\sqrt{2}},$$

which is finite and non-zero.

Therefore by comparison test,

$$\int\limits_1^2 f(x)\, dx \quad \text{and} \quad \int\limits_1^2 \phi(x)\, dx$$

are either both convergent or both divergent.

But $\quad \displaystyle\int\limits_1^2 \phi(x)\, dx = \int\limits_1^2 \dfrac{dx}{\sqrt{x^2 - 1}} = \lim\limits_{\varepsilon \to 0} \int\limits_{1+\varepsilon}^2 \dfrac{dx}{\sqrt{x^2 - 1}}$

$$= \lim\limits_{\varepsilon \to 0} \left[\log\{ x + \sqrt{x^2 - 1} \} \right]_{1+\varepsilon}^2$$

$$= \lim\limits_{\varepsilon \to 0} [\log(2 + \sqrt{3}) - \log\{1 + \varepsilon + \sqrt{\varepsilon^2 + \varepsilon}\}]$$

$$= \log(2 + \sqrt{3}),$$

which is a definite real number.

$\therefore \quad \displaystyle\int\limits_1^2 \phi(x)\, dx$ is convergent.

Hence $\displaystyle\int\limits_1^2 \dfrac{1}{\sqrt{x^4 - 1}}\, dx$ is also convergent.

2. Show that the integral $\displaystyle\int\limits_0^1 \dfrac{dx}{x^{1/3}(1 + x^2)}$ **is convergent.**

In the given integral, the integrand $f(x) = \dfrac{1}{x^{1/3}(1 + x^2)}$ is unbounded

at the lower limit of integration $x = 0$. Take $\phi(x) = \dfrac{1}{x^{1/3}}$.

Then $\quad \lim\limits_{x \to 0} \dfrac{f(x)}{\phi(x)} = \lim\limits_{x \to 0} \dfrac{1}{1+x^2} = 1$, which is finite and non-zero.

∴ By comparison test

$$\int_0^1 f(x)\,dx \quad \text{and} \quad \int_0^1 \phi(x)\,dx$$

either both converge or both diverge. But the comparison integral $\displaystyle\int_0^1 \dfrac{dx}{x^{1/3}}$

is convergent because here $n = 1/3$ which is less than 1. Hence the integral

$\displaystyle\int_0^1 \dfrac{dx}{x^{1/3}\,(1+x^2)}$ is also convergent.

3. Show that the integral $\displaystyle\int_0^1 \dfrac{\sec x}{x}\,dx$ **is divergent.**

In the given integral the integrand $f(x) = \dfrac{\sec x}{x}$ is unbounded at the

lower limit of integration $x = 0$. Take $\phi(x) = \dfrac{1}{x}$.

Then $\quad \lim\limits_{x \to 0} \dfrac{f(x)}{\phi(x)} = \lim\limits_{x \to 0} \left\{ \dfrac{\sec x}{x} \cdot x \right\}$

$$= \lim_{x \to 0} \sec x = 1,$$

which is finite and non-zero.

Therefore, by comparison test,

$$\int_0^1 f(x)\,dx \quad \text{and} \quad \int_0^1 \phi(x)\,dx$$

either both converge or both diverge. But the comparison integral $\displaystyle\int_0^1 \dfrac{1}{x}\,dx$

is divergent because here $n = 1$.

Hence the given integral $\displaystyle\int_0^1 \dfrac{\sec x}{x}\,dx$ is also divergent.

4. Show that $\displaystyle\int_0^1 x^{n-1}\,e^{-x}\,dx$ **is convergent if $n > 0$.**

If $n \geq 1$, then $\int\limits_0^1 x^{n-1} e^{-x} \, dx$ is a proper integral because the integrand $f(x) = x^{n-1} e^{-x}$ is bounded in the interval $(0, 1)$. So the given integral is convergent when $n \geq 1$.

If $0 < n < 1$, the integrand $f(x) = x^{n-1} e^{-x}$ is unbounded at $x = 0$. Take $\phi(x) = x^{n-1}$.

Then $\lim\limits_{x \to 0} \dfrac{f(x)}{\phi(x)} = \lim\limits_{x \to 0} e^{-x} = 1$, which is finite and non-zero.

$\therefore$ By comparison test, $\int\limits_0^1 f(x) \, dx$ and $\int\limits_0^1 \phi(x) \, dx$ either both converge or both diverge.

But $\int\limits_0^1 \phi(x) \, dx = \int\limits_0^1 x^{n-1} \, dx = \lim\limits_{\varepsilon \to 0} \int\limits_\varepsilon^1 x^{n-1} \, dx$

$$= \lim_{\varepsilon \to 0} \left[\frac{x^n}{n} \right]_\varepsilon^1 = \lim_{\varepsilon \to 0} \left[\frac{1}{n} - \frac{\varepsilon^n}{n} \right]$$

$$= \frac{1}{n}, \text{ which is a definite real number.}$$

$\therefore$ $\int\limits_0^1 \phi(x) \, dx$ is convergent.

Hence $\int\limits_0^1 x^{n-1} e^{-x} \, dx$ is also convergent.

5. *Test the convergence of*

$$\int\limits_0^1 \left[\cos(e^{1/x}) + \frac{e^{1/x}}{x} \sin(e^{1/x}) \right] dx.$$

We have

$$\lim_{\varepsilon \to 0} \int\limits_\varepsilon^1 \left[\cos(e^{1/x}) + \frac{e^{1/x}}{x} \sin(e^{1/x}) \right] dx$$

$$= \lim_{\varepsilon \to 0} \left[x \cos(e^{1/x}) \right]_\varepsilon^1$$

$$= \lim_{\varepsilon \to 0} \left[\cos e - \varepsilon \cos(e^{1/\varepsilon}) \right]$$

$$= \cos e,$$

which is a definite real number.

13.83. The μ-test. *Let $f(x)$ be bounded and integrable in the arbitrary interval $(a + \varepsilon, b)$, where $0 < \varepsilon < b - a$.*

If there is a number μ between zero and one such that

$$\lim_{x \to a + 0} (x - a)^{\mu} f(x) \text{ exists, then } \int_a^b f(x)\, dx \text{ converges absolutely.}$$

If there is a number μ greater than or equal to one such that

$$\lim_{x \to a + 0} (x - a)^{\mu} f(x) \text{ exists and is not zero, then } \int_a^b f(x)\, dx \text{ diverges}$$

and the same is true if

$$\lim_{x \to a + 0} (x - a)^{\mu} f(x) = \pm \infty.$$

Note. In case $f(x)$ is unbounded at $x = b$, we should find $\lim_{x \to b - 0} (b - x)^{\mu} f(x)$, other conditions remaining the same.

EXAMPLES

1. *Test the convergence of* $\displaystyle\int_0^2 \frac{\log x}{\sqrt{2 - x}}\, dx$. *(Garhwal, 2000)*

Let $f(x) = \dfrac{\log x}{\sqrt{2 - x}}$. Then $f(x)$ is unbounded both at $x = 0$ and $x = 2$.

If $0 < a < 2$, we can write

$$\int_0^2 \frac{\log x}{\sqrt{2 - x}}\, dx = \underbrace{\int_0^a \frac{\log x}{\sqrt{2 - x}}\, dx}_{(I_1)} + \underbrace{\int_a^2 \frac{\log x}{\sqrt{2 - x}}\, dx}_{(I_2)}.$$

To test the convergence of I_1, we have

$$\lim_{x \to 0} x^{\mu} f(x) = \lim_{x \to 0} \left\{ x^{\mu} \cdot \frac{\log x}{\sqrt{2 - x}} \right\} = 0, \text{ if } \mu > 0.$$

Therefore taking μ between 0 and 1, it follows by μ-test that I_1 is convergent.

To test the convergence of I_2, take $\mu = \dfrac{1}{2}$.

We have

$$\lim_{x \to 2} (2 - x)^{\mu} f(x) = \lim_{x \to 2} (2 - x)^{1/2} \cdot \frac{\log x}{\sqrt{2 - x}}$$

$$= \lim_{x \to 2} \log x = \lim_{\varepsilon \to 0} \log (2 - \varepsilon) = \log 2.$$

∴ By μ-test, I_2 is convergent because $0 < \mu < 1$.

Hence the given integral is also convergent, it being the sum of two convergent integrals.

2. *Prove that the integral* $\displaystyle\int_0^l \frac{dx}{\sqrt{x(l-x)}}$ *converges. (Garhwal, 1994)*

In the given integral the integrand $f(x) = \dfrac{1}{\sqrt{x(1-x)}}$ is unbounded both at $x = 0$ and at $x = 1$. If $0 < a < 1$, we can write

$$\int_0^1 \frac{dx}{\sqrt{x(1-x)}} = \int_0^a \frac{dx}{\sqrt{x(1-x)}} + \int_a^1 \frac{dx}{\sqrt{x(1-x)}}$$

$$= I_1 + I_2, \text{ (say)}.$$

To test the convergence of I_1, take $\mu = \dfrac{1}{2}$.

We have

$$\lim_{x \to 0} x^\mu f(x) = \lim_{x \to 0} x^{1/2} \frac{1}{\sqrt{x(1-x)}}$$

$$= \lim_{x \to 0} \frac{1}{\sqrt{1-x}} = 1, \; i.e., \text{ the limit exists.}$$

Since $0 < \mu < \dfrac{1}{2}$, therefore by μ-test, I_1 is convergent.

To test the convergence of I_2, take $\mu = \dfrac{1}{2}$.

We have

$$\lim_{x \to 1-0} (1-x)^\mu f(x) = \lim_{x \to 1-0} (1-x)^{1/2} \frac{1}{\sqrt{x(1-x)}}$$

$$= \lim_{x \to 1-0} \frac{1}{\sqrt{x}} = \lim_{\varepsilon \to 0} \frac{1}{\sqrt{1-\varepsilon}} = 1.$$

Hence by μ-test, I_2 is convergent since $0 < \mu < 1$.

Thus the given integral is the sum of two convergent integrals. Hence the given integral itself is convergent.

3. *Test the convergence of* $\displaystyle\int_0^l x^{p-1} e^{-x}\, dx.$

Let $f(x) = x^{p-1} e^{-x}$ and $I = \displaystyle\int_0^1 x^{p-1} e^{-x}\, dx.$

If $p \geq 1$, $f(x)$ is bounded throughout the interval $(0, 1)$ and so I is a proper integral and hence it is convergent if $p \geq 1$.

If $p < 1$, $f(x)$ is unbounded at $x = 0$. In this case, we have

$$\lim_{x \to 0} x^{\mu} f(x) = \lim_{x \to 0} x^{\mu} x^{p-1} e^{-x}$$

$$= \lim_{x \to 0} x^{\mu + p - 1} e^{-x} = 1, \text{ if } \mu + p - 1 = 0 \text{ i.e., } \mu = 1 - p.$$

So by μ-test when $0 < \mu < 1$, i.e., $0 < p < 1$, the given integral is convergent and when $\mu \geq 1$, i.e., $p \leq 0$, the given integral is divergent.

Hence I is convergent if $p > 0$ and is divergent if $p \leq 0$.

4. Prove that $\int_{0}^{1} (x^p + x^{-p}) \left(\dfrac{1}{x}\right) \log(1 + x)\, dx$ **converges if** $-1 < p < 1.$

Let $\quad f(x) = \left(x^p + \dfrac{1}{x^p}\right) \dfrac{\log(1 + x)}{x}$, and p be positive.

$$\lim_{x \to 0} x^p f(x) = \lim_{x \to 0} (x^{2p} + 1) \frac{\log(1 + x)}{x}.$$

Since $\quad \lim_{x \to 0} \dfrac{\log(1 + x)}{x} \to 1$ ...(i)

$\therefore \quad \lim_{x \to 0} x^p f(x) \to 1$ ...(ii)

So, by μ-test the integral converges if $p < 1$. Similarly if p is negative but > -1,

$$\lim_{x \to 0} x^{-p} f(x) \to 1.$$

So the integral converges also if $-p < 1$, i.e., $p > -1$.

Hence the given integral converges if $-1 < p < 1$.

13.84. Abel's Test. *If* $\displaystyle\int_{a}^{b} f(x)\, dx$ *converges and* $\phi(x)$ *is bounded and monotonic in* (a, b), *then* $\displaystyle\int_{a}^{b} f(x)\, \phi(x)\, dx$ *converges.*

13.85. Dirichlet's Test. *If* $\displaystyle\int_{a + \varepsilon}^{b} f(x)\, dx$ *be bounded and* $\phi(x)$ *be bounded and monotonic in* (a, b), *converging to zero as* x *tends to* a, *then* $\displaystyle\int_{a}^{b} f(x)\, \phi(x)\, dx$ *is convergent.*

EXAMPLES

1. *Test the convergence of*

$$\int_0^{\pi/2} \frac{\cos x}{x^n} \, dx.$$

When $n < 0$, the given integral is a proper integral and hence it is convergent when $n < 0$.

When $n \geq 0$, the integrand becomes unbounded at $x = 0$. Let $f(x) = \dfrac{\cos x}{x^n}$.

Then $\displaystyle \lim_{x \to 0} x^\mu f(x) = \lim_{x \to 0} x^{\mu - n} \cos x = 1$ if $\mu = n$.

Hence by μ-test, it follows that the given integral is convergent when $0 < n < 1$ and divergent when $n \geq 1$.

From the above discussion it follows that the given integral is convergent when $n < 1$ and divergent when $n \geq 1$.

2. *Show that the integral* $\displaystyle \int_0^{\pi/2} \log \sin x \, dx$ *converges.*

The only point of infinite discontinuity is $x = 0$.

Now, $\displaystyle \lim_{x \to 0} x^\mu \log \sin x$, where $\mu > 0$

$$\begin{aligned}
&= \lim_{x \to 0} \frac{\log \sin x}{x^{-\mu}} && \left[\text{Form } \frac{\infty}{\infty} \right] \\
&= \lim_{x \to 0} \frac{\cot x}{-\mu x^{-\mu - 1}} && \text{[By Hospital's rule]} \\
&= \lim_{x \to 0} -\frac{1}{\mu} \cdot \frac{x^{\mu + 1}}{\tan x} && \left[\text{Form } \frac{0}{0} \right] \\
&= \lim_{x \to 0} -\frac{1}{\mu} \cdot \frac{(\mu + 1) x^\mu}{\sec^2 x} = 0.
\end{aligned}$$

Taking μ between 0 and 1, it follows from μ-test the given integral is convergent.

3. *Discuss the convergence of the integral*

$$\int_0^1 x^{n-1} \log x \, dx. \qquad \text{(Garhwal, 1993, 95, 2000)}$$

(*i*) Since $\displaystyle \lim_{x \to 0} x^r \log x = 0$ where $r > 0$, the integral is a proper integral, when $n > 1$.

(*ii*) When $n = 1$, we have

$$\int_0^1 \log x \, dx = \lim_{\varepsilon \to 0} \int_\varepsilon^1 \log x \, dx = \lim_{\varepsilon \to 0} \left[x \log x - x \right]_\varepsilon^1$$

$$= \lim_{\varepsilon \to 0} \left[-1 - \varepsilon \log \varepsilon + \varepsilon \right] = -1.$$

∴ The integral is convergent if $n = 1$.

(*iii*) Let $n < 1$ and $f(x) = x^{n-1} \log x$.

Then $\lim_{x \to 0} x^\mu f(x) = \lim_{x \to 0} x^{\mu + n - 1} \log x = 0$, if $\mu > 1 - n$ ...(*i*)

and $\qquad\qquad\qquad\qquad = -\infty$, if $\mu \le 1 - n$ ...(*ii*)

Hence when $0 < n < 1$, we can choose μ between 0 and 1 and satisfying (*i*). The integral is therefore convergent by μ-test when $0 < n < 1$.

Again when $n < 0$, we can take $\mu = 1$ and satisfying (*ii*). Hence by μ-test the integral is divergent when $n \le 0$.

Therefore we conclude that the given integral is convergent when $n > 0$ and divergent when $n \le 0$.

4. *Discuss the convergence or divergence of the integral*

$$\int_0^\infty \frac{x^{\alpha-1}}{1+x} \, dx. \qquad\qquad (Garhwal, 1996, 2000)$$

Let $\alpha \ge 1$. In this case the integrand is bounded for all values of $x \ge 0$

and so we have to test only the integral $\int_0^\infty \dfrac{x^{\alpha-1}}{x+1} \, dx$, where $\alpha > 0$.

Now, $\qquad \lim_{x \to \infty} x^\mu \dfrac{x^{\alpha-1}}{x+1}$

$$= \lim_{x \to \infty} \frac{x^{\mu + \alpha - 1}}{x+1} = 1, \text{ if } \mu + \alpha - 1 = 1, \text{ i.e., } \mu = 2 - \alpha \le 1.$$

Hence the given integral is divergent if $\alpha \ge 1$.

Next let $\alpha < 1$. In this case the integrand becomes unbounded at $x = 0$.

$$\therefore \quad \int_0^\infty \frac{x^{\alpha-1}}{x+1} \, dx = \int_0^a \frac{x^{\alpha-1}}{x+1} \, dx + \int_a^\infty \frac{x^{\alpha-1}}{x+1} \, dx \text{ when } \alpha > 0.$$

We have $\lim_{x \to 0} x^\mu \dfrac{x^{\alpha-1}}{x+1} = 1$ if $\mu + \alpha - 1 = 0$, *i.e.*, if $\mu = 1 - \alpha$.

If we take α between 0 and 1, then μ is also between 0 and 1.

Hence by μ-test $\int\limits_{0}^{a} \dfrac{x^{\alpha-1}}{x+1}\, dx$ is convergent.

Also $\lim\limits_{x\to\infty} x^{\mu}\, \dfrac{x^{\alpha-1}}{x+1} = 1$, if $\mu = 2-\alpha > 1$ since $\alpha < 1$.

$\therefore \quad \int\limits_{0}^{\infty} \dfrac{x^{\alpha-1}}{x+1}\, dx$ is convergent by μ-test.

It follows that when $\alpha < 1$, the given integral is convergent.

5. *Test the convergence of the integral*

$$\int\limits_{0}^{\pi/4} \dfrac{dx}{\sqrt{\tan x}}.$$

(Kanpur, 2001)

The integrand is finite at $x = 0$.

Let $f(x) = \dfrac{1}{\sqrt{\tan x}}$ and $\mu = \dfrac{1}{2}$. Then

$$\lim\limits_{x\to 0} x^{\mu}\, f(x) = \lim\limits_{x\to 0} x^{1/2}\, \dfrac{1}{\sqrt{\tan x}}$$

$$= \lim\limits_{x\to 0} \sqrt{\dfrac{x}{\sin x}} \cdot \sqrt{\cos x}$$

$$= 1, \text{ since } \lim\limits_{x\to 0} \dfrac{x}{\sin x} = 1.$$

Hence by μ-test, the given integral is convergent.

6. *Let $f(x)$ be defined in the interval $0 < x \leq 1$ as follows :*

$$f(x) = 2, \ \dfrac{1}{2} < x \leq 1,$$

$$f(x) = -3, \ \dfrac{1}{3} < x \leq \dfrac{1}{2},$$

$$f(x) = 4, \ \dfrac{1}{4} < x \leq \dfrac{1}{3},$$

$$f(x) = -5, \ \dfrac{1}{5} < x \leq \dfrac{1}{4},$$

and so on, the values being alternately positive and negative. Show that

the infinite integral $\int\limits_{0}^{1} f(x)\, dx$ converges, but not absolutely.

(Garhwal, 1999)

We have

$$\int_0^1 f(x)\, dx = \int_{1/2}^1 2\, dx - \int_{1/3}^{1/2} 3\, dx + \int_{1/4}^{1/3} 4\, dx - \int_{1/5}^{1/4} 5\, dx + \dots$$

$$= 1 - \frac{1}{2} - \frac{1}{3} - \frac{1}{4} + \dots = \log 2.$$

Since the series is convergent, the given integral is also convergent.

Again

$$\int_0^1 |f(x)|\, dx = \int_{1/2}^1 |2|\, dx + \int_{1/3}^{1/2} |-3|\, dx + \int_{1/4}^{1/3} |4|\, dx + \int_{1/5}^{1/4} |-5|\, dx + \dots$$

$$= 1 + \frac{1}{2} + \frac{1}{3} + \frac{1}{4} + \dots$$

Since this series is not convergent, the given integral is not absolutely convergent.

7. *Discuss the convergence of the gamma function*

$$\Gamma_n = \int_0^\infty x^{n-1} \cdot e^{-x}\, dx.$$

(Garhwal, 1993, 97, 2000, 01; Gorakhpur, 2003)

(i) Let $n \geq 1$.

Then the integrand is bounded in $0 < x \leq a$, where a is arbitrary, and

we need only consider the convergence of $\displaystyle\int_0^\infty e^{-x} x^{n-1}\, dx$.

To test its convergence, we have

$$\lim_{x \to \infty} x^\mu f(x) = \lim_{x \to \infty} \frac{x^\mu \cdot x^{n-1}}{e^x}$$

$$= \lim_{x \to \infty} \frac{x^{\mu + n - 1}}{1 + x + \dfrac{x^2}{2!} + \dots}$$

$$= 0 \text{ for all values of } \mu \text{ and } n.$$

Taking $\mu > 1$, we see that $\displaystyle\int_0^\infty e^{-x} x^{n-1}\, dx$ is convergent for all values

of n.

(*ii*) Let $0 < n < 1$.

In this case $e^{-x} x^{n-1}$ has an infinity at $x = 0$. Here we have

$$\int_0^\infty e^{-x} x^{n-1} \, dx = \int_0^a e^{-x} x^{n-1} \, dx + \int_a^\infty e^{-x} x^{n-1} \, dx.$$

Now, $\lim_{x \to 0} x^\mu e^{-x} x^{n-1} = 1$ if $\mu + n - 1 = 0$, *i.e.*, if $\mu = 1 - n$.

Since n lies between 0 and 1, we see that μ also lies between 0 and 1.

Hence $\int_0^a e^{-x} x^{n-1} \, dx$ is convergent in this case by μ-test.

And we have seen in (*i*) that $\int_a^\infty e^{-x} x^{n-1} \, dx$ is convergent for all values of n.

Therefore the given integral is convergent when $0 < n < 1$.

(*iii*) Let $n \leq 0$.

In this case $e^{-x} x^{n-1}$ has an infinity at $x = 0$, and just as in (*ii*), it can be shown that $\int_0^a e^{-x} x^{n-1} \, dx$ is divergent.

Therefore the given integral is also divergent when $n \leq 0$.

8. *Discuss the convergence of the Beta function*

$$B(m, n) = \int_0^1 x^{m-1} (1 - x)^{n-1} \, dx.$$

(Garhwal, 1993, 96; Gorakhpur, 2002)

(*i*) When m and n both are ≥ 1, the integrand is finite for all values of x from 0 to 1. Hence it is convergent.

(*ii*) When m and n are < 1, then the integrand has infinities both at $x = 0$ and $x = 1$.

In this case, we write

$$\int_0^1 x^{m-1} (1-x)^{n-1} \, dx = \int_0^c x^{m-1} (1-x)^{n-1} \, dx + \int_c^1 x^{m-1} (1-x)^{n-1} \, dx$$

where $0 < c < 1$.

First, we consider $\int_0^c x^{m-1} (1-x)^{n-1} \, dx.$

Let $f(x) = x^{m-1} (1 - x)^{n-1}.$

Then $\quad \lim\limits_{x \to 0} x^{\mu} f(x) = \lim\limits_{x \to 0} x^{\mu + m - 1} (1 - x)^{n - 1}$

$$= 1 \text{ if } \mu + m - 1 = 0, \text{ i.e., if } \mu = 1 - m.$$

Now if $0 < m < 1$, we have $0 < \mu < 1$, and if $m \le 0$, $\mu \ge 1$.

Hence by the μ-test, $\displaystyle\int_0^c f(x)\, dx$ is convergent if $0 < m < 1$, and divergent

if $m \le 0$.

Similarly it can be proved that $\displaystyle\int_c^1 f(x)\, dx$ is convergent if $0 < n < 1$

and divergent if $n \le 0$.

Therefore from (i) and (ii) it follows that $\displaystyle\int_0^1 f(x)\, dx$ is convergent if

both m and n are greater than zero and divergent otherwise.

9. *Discuss the convergence of the integral*

$$\int_0^\infty \frac{x^a\, dx}{1 + x^b \sin^2 x}; \quad a, b > 0.$$

Let $I = \displaystyle\int_0^\infty \frac{x^a\, dx}{1 + x^b \sin^2 x}$ \qquad ...(1)

$$= \sum_{r=0}^{\infty} \int_{r\pi}^{(r+1)\pi} \frac{x^a\, dx}{1 + x^b \sin^2 x} = \sum_{r=0}^{\infty} J_r \qquad ...(2)$$

We observe that $f(x) > 0 \ \forall \ x \in [r\pi, (r + 1)\pi]$.

Therefore

$$\int_{r\pi}^{(r+1)\pi} \frac{(r\pi)^a\, dx}{1 + [(r+1)\pi]^b \sin^2 x} < \int_{r\pi}^{(r+1)\pi} \frac{x^a\, dx}{1 + x^b \sin^2 x}$$

$$< \int_{r\pi}^{(r+1)\pi} \frac{[(r+1)\pi]^a\, dx}{1 + (r\pi)^b \sin^2 x}$$

$$(r\pi)^a \int_{r\pi}^{(r+1)\pi} \frac{dx}{1 + [(r+1)\pi]^b \sin^2 x} < J_r$$

$$< [(r+1)\pi]^a \int_{r\pi}^{(r+1)\pi} \frac{dx}{1 + (r\pi)^b \sin^2 x} \qquad ...(3)$$

Now $\displaystyle\int_{r\pi}^{(r+1)\pi} \frac{dx}{1+\lambda \sin^2 x} = \int_0^\pi \frac{dt}{1+\lambda \sin^2 t} = 2\int_0^{\pi/2} \frac{dt}{1+A \sin^2 t}$

$$= \frac{\pi}{\sqrt{1+\lambda}} \qquad \qquad ...(4)$$

Using (4) in (3), we get

$$\frac{(r\pi)^a \, \pi}{\sqrt{1+[(r+1)\,\pi]^b}} < J_r < \frac{[(r+1)\,\pi]^a \, \pi}{\sqrt{1+(4\pi)^b}}$$

$$\pi^{a+1} \sum_{r=0}^\infty \frac{r^a}{\sqrt{1+(r+1)^b \, \pi^b}} < I < \pi^{a+1} \sum_{r=0}^\infty \frac{(r+1)^a}{\sqrt{1+g^b \pi^b}} \qquad ...(5)$$

But $\displaystyle\sum_{r=0}^\infty \frac{(r+1)^a}{\sqrt{1+r^b \pi^b}} \sim \sum_{r=0}^\infty \frac{1}{r^{\frac{b}{2}-a}}$, which converges if $\dfrac{b}{2} - a > 1$

and diverges if $\dfrac{b}{2} - a \leq 1$ (By Hypergeometric test). It follows by Sandwich rule that I converges if $b > 2\,(a+1)$ and diverges if $b \leq 2\,(a+1)$.

EXERCISES

Test the convergence of the following integrals :

1. $\displaystyle\int_0^2 \frac{dx}{\sqrt{x\,(1+x)}}$;

2. $\displaystyle\int_0^{\pi/2} \frac{\sin x}{x^{1+n}}\,dx$;

3. $\displaystyle\int_0^{\pi/2} \frac{\cos x}{x^2}\,dx$;

4. $\displaystyle\int_0^1 \frac{dx}{(x+1)\,\sqrt{1-x^2}}$; (Garhwal, 1999)

5. $\displaystyle\int_0^1 \frac{dx}{x^3\,(1+x^2)}$.

6. Show that $\displaystyle\int_0^1 \frac{1}{x} \sin \frac{1}{x}\,dx$, and $\displaystyle\int_0^1 \frac{1}{\sqrt{x}} \sin \frac{1}{x}\,dx$ converge, the former not absolutely and the latter absolutely.

7. Find whether the integrals

(i) $\displaystyle\int_0^\infty \frac{x\,dx}{1+x^6 \sin^2 x}$, (Garhwal, 2002)

(ii) $\displaystyle\int_0^\infty \frac{x\,dx}{1+x^4 \sin^2 x}$ converge or diverge. (Garhwal, 1997)

8. Test the convergence of the following integrals :

(i) $\displaystyle\int_0^\infty \left(\frac{1}{1+x} - e^{-x} \right) \frac{dx}{x};$ (Garhwal, 1996)

(ii) $\displaystyle\int_0^\infty \left(\frac{1}{x} - \frac{1}{\sin nx} \right) \frac{dx}{x};$ (Garhwal, 1997)

(iii) $\displaystyle\int_0^\infty \left(\frac{1}{e^x - 1} - \frac{1}{x} + \frac{1}{2} \right) \frac{e^{-\lambda x}}{x}\, dx,\ \lambda > 0;$

(iv) $\displaystyle\int_a^\infty \frac{\cos x}{\sqrt{x + x^2}}\, dx,\ a > 0;$ (Garhwal, 1998)

(v) $\displaystyle\int_0^\infty \frac{x \log x}{(1 + x^2)^2}\, dx;$

(vi) $\displaystyle\int_0^\infty \frac{\sin x^m}{x^n}\, dx\ (m - 1 < n < m + 1).$

9. Test the convergence of the following integrals :

(i) $\displaystyle\int_0^\pi \frac{\sqrt{x}}{\sin x}\, dx;$ (ii) $\displaystyle\int_1^2 \frac{\sqrt{x}}{\log x}\, dx;$

(iii) $\displaystyle\int_0^{\pi/2} x^m \operatorname{cosec}^n x\, dx;$ (Garhwal, 1996)

(iv) $\displaystyle\int_0^1 x^p \left(\log \frac{1}{x} \right)^q dx;$ (v) $\displaystyle\int_0^1 \log \sqrt{x}\, dx;$

(vi) $\displaystyle\int_0^1 x^{a-1} (1 - x)^{b-1} \log x\, dx.$

ANSWERS

1. Convergent;   2. Convergent if $n < 1$ and divergent if $n \geq 1$;

3. Divergent;   4. Convergent;

5. Divergent;   7. (i) Convergent; (ii) Divergent.

8. (i) Convergent; (ii) Convergent; (iii) Convergent; (iv) Convergent;
   (v) Convergent.

9. (i) Divergent; (ii) Divergent; (iii) Convergent is $n\ cm + 1$;
   (iv) Convergent; (v) Convergent; (vi) Convergent $a > 0,\ b > -1$.

EXERCISES ON CHAPTER 13

1. Show that the integral $\int_{0}^{1} \frac{1}{x} \sin \frac{1}{x} dx$ is convergent but it is not absolutely convergent.

2. Test the convergence of $\int_{1}^{\infty} \sin x^p \, dx$.

3. Show that $\int_{0}^{\infty} e^{-a^2 x^2} \cos bx \, dx$ is absolutely convergent.

4. Prove that

(*i*) $f(t) = \int_{0}^{\infty} e^{-tx} \frac{\sin x}{x} dx$, converges uniformly for $t \geq 0$.

(*ii*) $f(t) = \pi/2 - \tan^{-1} t$.

(*iii*) $\int_{0}^{\infty} \frac{\sin x}{x} dx = \pi/2$.

5. Examine the convergence of the integral

$$\int_{0}^{\infty} e^{-x} x^{n-1} (\log x)^m \, dx,$$

m, n positive integer.

6. Prove that if $\int_{0}^{\infty} f(x) \, dx$ converges, then $\int_{0}^{\infty} e^{-tx} f(x) \, dx$ converges uniformly for $t \geq 0$.

7. Show that $\int_{0}^{\pi/2} \frac{x^m}{\sin^n x} dx$ exists if and only if $n < (m+1)$.

8. Show that the integral $\int_{0}^{\infty} \frac{\cos x}{\sqrt{x}} dx$ diverges.

9. Examine the convergence of $\int_{a}^{\infty} \frac{\sin x}{x^n} dx, a > 0$.

10. Show that $\int_{0}^{\pi/2} \log \sin x \, dx$ converges.

OBJECTIVE QUESTIONS

To each of the following questions, four alternatives are given for the answer. Only one of them is correct. Choose the correct alternative.

1. Integral $\int_a^b f(x)\, dx$ is said to be improper if :

   (a) Both the limits are finite

   (b) $f(x)$ is bounded

   (c) One or both integration limits are infinite

   (d) None of these.

2. If one or both integration limits of the integral $\int_a^b f(x)\, dx$ are infinite then it is an improper integral of :

   (a) first kind   (b) second kind

   (c) third kind   (d) not an improper integral.

3. If in $\int_a^b f(x)\, dx$, integration limits are infinite and $f(x)$ is unbounded, then it is an improper integral of :

   (a) first kind   (b) second kind

   (c) third kind   (d) None of these.

4. $\int_0^\infty \sin x\, dx$ is an improper integral of :

   (a) first kind   (b) second kind

   (c) third kind   (d) not an improper integral.

5. $\int_0^\infty \dfrac{dx}{(1-x)^2}$ is :

   (a) an improper integral of first kind

   (b) an improper integral of second kind   (*Garhwal 2004*)

   (c) an improper integral of third kind

   (d) a proper integral.

6. Integral $\int_0^1 \dfrac{4a}{(x^2 + 4a^2)}\, dx$ is :

   (a) Convergent   (d) Divergent   (c) Oscillatory   (d) Proper.

7. Integral $\int_0^1 \dfrac{dx}{\sqrt{1-x}}$ is :

    (a) Convergent   (b) Divergent   (c) Oscillatory   (d) Proper.

8. $\int_1^\infty \dfrac{dx}{x}$ is :

    (a) Convergent   (b) Divergent

    (c) Oscillatory   (d) None of these.

9. Integral $\int_a^\infty \dfrac{dx}{x^n}$, where $a > 0$ is convergent, if :

    (a) $n = 1$ (b) $n < 1$

    (c) $n > 1$ (d) Never convergent.

10. $\int_\pi^\infty \dfrac{\sin^2 x}{x^2}\, dx$ is :

    (a) Convergent   (b) Divergent   (c) Oscillatory   (d) Proper.

11. Integral $\int_0^\infty \dfrac{x^{2n}}{1+x^{2m}}\, dx$ is convergent if :

    (a) $n < m$ (b) $n > m$

    (c) $n = m$ (d) None of these.

12. $\int_a^\infty \dfrac{\sin x}{\sqrt{x}}\, dx$, where $a > 0$ is :

    (a) Convergent   (b) Divergent   (c) Oscillatory   (d) Proper.

13. $\int_0^\infty \dfrac{\sin mx}{a^2 + x^2}\, dx$:

    (a) Converges but not absolutely

    (b) Absolutely convergent

    (c) Divergent

    (d) None of these.

14. $\int_b^\infty \dfrac{x^{3/2}\, dx}{\sqrt{x^4 - a^4}}$, where $b > a$ is :

    (a) Convergent   (b) Divergent

    (c) Absolutely convergent   (d) None of these.

15. $\displaystyle\int_a^b \frac{dx}{(x-a)^n}$ is convergent if :

    (a) $n > 1$ (b) $n = 1$ (c) $n \geq 1$ (d) $n < 1$.

16. Integral $\displaystyle\int_0^1 \frac{\sec x}{x} dx$ is :

    (a) Convergent   (b) Absolutely convergent

    (c) Divergent   (d) Proper.

17. $\displaystyle\int_0^{\pi/2} \log \sin x \, dx$ is :

    (a) Convergent

    (b) Divergent

    (c) Neither convergent nor divergent

    (d) None of these.

18. Integral $\displaystyle\int_0^{\pi/4} \frac{dx}{\sqrt{\tan x}}$ is :

    (a) Convergent but not absolutely   (Garhwal 2004)

    (b) Absolutely convergent

    (c) Divergent

    (d) Proper.

ANSWERS

1. (c)	2. (a)	3. (c)	4. (a)	5. (c)	6. (a)
7. (a)	8. (b)	9. (c)	10. (a)	11. (b)	12. (a)
13. (b)	14. (b)	15. (d)	16. (c)	17. (a)	18. (a)

14

Differentiation Under Integral Sign

14.1. Consider a continuous function $f(x, y)$ of two variables defined in a rectangle bounded by the lines

$$x = a, \; x = b; \; y = c, \; y = d$$

and the integral

$$\int_a^b f(x, y)\, dx.$$

Clearly, this integral is a function of y. We write

$$\varphi(y) = \int_a^b f(x, y)\, dx.$$

It can be shown that $\varphi(y)$ is a continuous function of y.

We further suppose that $f(x, y)$ possesses continuous first order partial derivative $f_y(x, y)$, with respect to y. *Under the supposition of the continuity of $f(x, y)$ and $f_y(x, y)$, it will be shown that*

$$\varphi'(y) = \int_a^b f_y(x, y)\, dx,$$

or in other words,

$$\frac{d}{dy} \int_a^b f(x, y)\, dx = \int_a^b \frac{\partial}{\partial y} f(x, y)\, dx,$$

i.e., the order of the two operations of differentiation and integration can be inverted.

We have,

$$\varphi(y) = \int_a^b f(x, y)\, dx.$$

Let Δy denote a change in y. We then have

$$\varphi(y + \Delta y) = \int_a^b f(x, y + \Delta y)\, dx.$$

$$\therefore \quad \varphi(y + \Delta y) - \varphi(y) = \int_a^b [f(x, y + \Delta y) - f(x, y)]\, dx.$$

Employing Lagrange's Mean value theorem of Differential Calculus, we obtain

$$\varphi(y + \Delta y) - \varphi(y) = \int_a^b \Delta y\, f_y(x, y + \theta \Delta y)\, dx, \quad 0 < \theta < 1$$

$$= \Delta y \int_a^b f_y(x, y + \theta \Delta y)\, dx$$

$$\Rightarrow \quad \frac{\varphi(y + \Delta y) - \varphi(y)}{\Delta y} = \int_a^b f_y(x, y + \theta \Delta y)\, dx$$

$$\Rightarrow \quad \frac{\varphi(y + \Delta y) - \varphi(y)}{\Delta y} = \int_a^b f_y(x, y)\, dx$$

$$+ \int_a^b [f_y(x, y + \theta \Delta y) - f_y(x, y)]\, dx.$$

Let ε, be any pre-assigned positive number. There, then exists, by virtue of continuity of $f_y(x, y)$, a positive number δ such that

$$| f_y(x, y + \theta \Delta y) - f_y(x, y) | < \varepsilon, \qquad \qquad \dots(1)$$

when $| \Delta y | < \delta$.

*It can be shown that, δ, is independent of x so that the inequality (1) holds for every value of x in $[a, b]$.

**Thus, when $| \Delta y | \le \delta$,

$$\left| \int_a^b [f_y(x, y + \theta \Delta y) - f_y(x, y)]\, dx \right| < \varepsilon (b - a),$$

i.e., $\left| \dfrac{\varphi(y + \Delta y) - \varphi(y)}{\Delta y} - \int_a^b f_y(x, y)\, dx \right| < \varepsilon (b - a)$ when $|\Delta y| \le \delta$.

---

* This is a consequence of uniform continuity. The proof is beyond the scope of this book.

** It may be easily seen from the interpretation of definite integral as an area that if

$$| f(x) | \le k,$$

then $\left| \displaystyle\int_a^b f(x)\, dx \right| \le k(b - a).$

Thus,

$$\lim_{\Delta y \to 0} \frac{\varphi(y + \Delta y) - \varphi(y)}{\Delta y} = \int_a^b f(x, y)\, dx,$$

i.e.,
$$\varphi'(y) = \int_a^b f_y(x, y)\, dx.$$

Note. The reader may be inclined to deduce the required result by taking the limit, as $\Delta y \to 0$, in (1). It should, however, be seen that in this way, apart from assuming the existence of the limit, we overlook the real point of interest and difficulty.

Thus, taking limits of (1), as $\Delta y \to 0$, we have

$$\varphi'(y) = \lim_{\Delta y \to 0} \int_a^b f_y(x, y + \theta\, \Delta y)\, dx$$

and if we now write

$$\lim_{\Delta y \to 0} \int_a^b f_y(x, y + \theta\, \Delta y)\, dx$$

$$= \int_a^b \lim_{\Delta y \to 0} f_y(x, y + \theta\, \Delta y)\, dx = \int_a^b f_y(x, y)\, dx$$

we do so on the assumption that *the limit of the integral is equal to the integral of the limit, i.e.,* the two operations of taking limit and integral are invertible. In fact the proof, as given, shows that this assumption is actually justifiable.

14.1.1. The case of variable limits of integration. Consider, now,

$$\varphi(y) = \int_{g(y)}^{h(y)} f(x, y)\, dx,$$

where the limits $g(y)$, $h(y)$ of integration are themselves functions of y. We shall assume that $g(y)$ and $h(y)$ possess continuous first order derivatives with respect to y and prove that

$$\varphi'(y) = \int_{g(y)}^{h(y)} f_y(x, y)\, dx + h'(y)\, f[h(y), y] - g'(y)\, f[g(y), y].$$

Lemma. We shall need the following result known as **Mean value theorem of the Integral Calculus.**

If $f(x)$ is continuous in an interval $[a, b]$, then there exists a number, ξ, between a and b such that

$$\int_a^b f(x)\,dx = (b-a)\,f(\xi).$$

From the interpretation of definite integral as an area or also from the integral as the limit of a sum, it follows that

$$m(b-a) \le \int_a^b f(x)\,dx \le M(b-a),$$

where m, M are the least and greatest values of $f(x)$ in $[a, b]$. Thus there exists a number, k, between m and M such that

$$\int_a^b f(x)\,dx = k(b-a).$$

As a continuous function assumes every value between its least and greatest values, it follows that there exists a number ξ such that $k = f(\xi)$. Thus,

$$\int_a^b f(x)\,dx = (b-a)\,f(\xi).$$

We now prove the theorem.

We have,

$$\varphi(y) = \int_{g(y)}^{h(y)} f(x, y)\,dx,$$

$$\varphi(y + \Delta y) = \int_{g(y+\Delta y)}^{h(y+\Delta y)} f(x, y + \Delta y)\,dx$$

$$= \int_{g(y+\Delta y)}^{g(y)} f(x, y + \Delta y)\,dx + \int_{g(y)}^{h(y)} f(x, y + \Delta y)\,dx$$

$$+ \int_{h(y)}^{h(y+\Delta y)} f(x, y + \Delta y)\,dx.$$

$$\therefore \quad \varphi(y + \Delta y) - \varphi(y) = \int_{g(y)}^{h(y)} [f(x, y + \Delta y) - f(x, y)]\,dx$$

$$+ \int_{h(y)}^{h(y+\Delta y)} f(x, y + \Delta y)\,dx - \int_{g(y)}^{g(y+\Delta y)} f(x, y + \Delta y)\,dx.$$

Now by the mean value theorem of Integral Calculus,

$$\int_{h(y)}^{h(y+\Delta y)} f(x, y + \Delta y)\, dx = [h(y+\Delta y) - h(y)]\, f(\xi, y + \Delta y)$$

and

$$\int_{g(y)}^{g(y+\Delta y)} f(x, y + \Delta y)\, dx = [g(y+\Delta y) - g(y)]\, f(\eta, y + \Delta y),$$

where ξ lies between $h(y)$ and $h(y + \Delta y)$ and η between $g(y)$ and $g(y + \Delta y)$.

$$\therefore \quad \varphi(y + \Delta y) - \varphi(y) = \int_{g(y)}^{h(y)} \Delta y\, f_y(x, y + \theta \Delta y)\, dx$$

$$+ [h(y+\Delta y) - h(y)]\, f(\xi, y + \Delta y) - [g(y+\Delta y) - g(y)]\, f(\eta, y + \Delta y),$$

$$\Rightarrow \quad \frac{\varphi(y + \Delta y) - \varphi(y)}{\Delta y} = \int_{g(y)}^{h(y)} f_y(x, y + \theta \Delta y)\, dx$$

$$+ \frac{h(y+\Delta y) - h(y)}{\Delta y} f(\xi, y + \Delta y) - \frac{g(y+\Delta y) - g(y)}{\Delta y} f(\eta, y + \Delta y) \quad ...(1)$$

As in the preceding § A.7,

$$\lim_{\Delta y \to 0} \int_{g(y)}^{h(y)} f_y(x, y + \theta \Delta y)\, dx = \int_{g(y)}^{h(y)} f_y(x, y)\, dx.$$

Thus proceeding to the limit, when $\Delta y \to 0$, we have, from (1),

$$\varphi'(y) = \int_{g(y)}^{h(y)} f_y(x, y)\, dx + h'(y)\, f[h(y), y] - g'(y)\, f[g(y), y].$$

14.2. Differentiation under Integral sign in the case of Improper Integrals. The results obtained above may not be applicable in the case of improper integrals, and the question of the validity of the results to improper integrals requires further investigation. This however, is not within the scope of this book and whenever we shall deal with any improper integral in the following, it will be assumed that the necessary conditions for validity of the results are satisfied.

EXAMPLES

1. *Evaluate*

$$\int_0^{\pi/2} \log(\alpha \cos^2 \theta + \beta \sin^2 \theta)\, d\theta. \qquad (\alpha > 0, \beta > 0)$$

Let $\varphi(\alpha, \beta) = \int\limits_0^{\pi/2} \log(\alpha \cos^2\theta + \beta \sin^2\theta)\, d\theta$.

$$\therefore \quad \varphi_\alpha(\alpha, \beta) = \int\limits_0^{\pi/2} \frac{\cos^2\theta}{\alpha\cos^2\theta + \beta\sin^2\theta}\, d\theta$$

$$= \int\limits_0^{\pi/2} \frac{d\theta}{\alpha + \beta\tan^2\theta} \qquad \qquad \dots(1)$$

$$= \int\limits_0^\infty \frac{dt}{(1+t^2)(\alpha+\beta^2 t)} \qquad \text{[Putting } \tan\theta = t]$$

$$= \frac{1}{\alpha-\beta}\int\limits_0^\infty \left(\frac{1}{1+t^2} - \frac{\beta}{\alpha+\beta t^2}\right) dt \qquad \text{[If } \alpha \neq \beta]$$

$$= \frac{1}{\alpha-\beta}\left| \tan^{-1} t - \frac{\beta}{\sqrt{\alpha\beta}}\tan^{-1}\sqrt{\beta}\, t \right|_0^\infty$$

$$= \frac{1}{\alpha-\beta}\left[\frac{\pi}{2} - \sqrt{\frac{\beta}{\alpha}}\frac{\pi}{2}\right] = \frac{\pi}{2\sqrt{\alpha}\,(\sqrt{\alpha}+\sqrt{\beta})}.$$

For $\beta = \alpha$, we have from (1),

$$\varphi_\alpha(\alpha, \beta) = \int\limits_0^{\pi/2} \frac{\cos^2\theta}{\alpha}\, d\theta = \frac{\pi}{4\alpha}.$$

This shows that we have, without exception,

$$\varphi_\alpha(\alpha, \beta) = \frac{\pi}{2\sqrt{\alpha}\,(\sqrt{\alpha}+\sqrt{\beta})}.$$

Integrating w.r.t. α, we obtain

$$\varphi(\alpha, \beta) = \pi \log(\sqrt{\alpha}+\sqrt{\beta}) + c, \qquad \dots(2)$$

where, c, is independent of α.

Also we have

$$\varphi(\alpha, \beta) = \int\limits_0^{\pi/2} \log(\alpha\cos^2\theta + \beta\sin^2\theta)\, d\theta$$

$$= \int\limits_0^{\pi/2} \log\left[\alpha\cos^2\left(\frac{\pi}{2}-\theta\right) + \beta\sin^2\left(\frac{\pi}{2}-\theta\right)\right] d\theta,$$

(§ 4.92, page 102)

$$= \int_0^{\pi/2} \log (\alpha \sin^2 \theta + \beta \cos^2 \theta) \, d\theta = \varphi (\beta, \alpha). \qquad ...(3)$$

In view of the equality $\varphi (\alpha, \beta) = \varphi (\beta, \alpha)$ we see that in (2), c, is free from β also. Thus, c, is an absolute constant.

Now, $\quad \varphi (1, 1) = \int_0^{\pi/2} \log (\cos^2 \theta + \sin^2 \theta) \, d\theta = 0.$

Putting $\alpha = 1 = \beta$ in (2), we obtain

$$\theta = \varphi (1, 1) = \pi \log 2 + c \text{ or } c = -\pi \log 2$$

$$\therefore \quad \varphi (\alpha, \beta) = \pi \log (\sqrt{\alpha} + \sqrt{\beta}) - \pi \log 2$$

$$= \pi \log \left[\frac{1}{2} (\sqrt{\alpha} + \sqrt{\beta}) \right].$$

2. Evaluate

$$\int_0^a \frac{\log (1 + ax)}{1 + x^2} \, dx$$

and show that

$$\int_0^1 \frac{\log (1 + x)}{1 + x^2} \, dx = \frac{\pi}{8} \log 2.$$

We write

$$\varphi (a) = \int_0^a \frac{\log (1 + ax)}{1 + x^2} \, dx. \qquad ...(1)$$

$$\therefore \quad \varphi' (a) = \int_0^a \frac{\partial}{\partial a} \left[\frac{\log (1 + ax)}{1 + x^2} \right] dx + 1 \cdot \frac{\log (1 + a^2)}{1 + a^2}$$

$$= \int_0^a \frac{x}{(1 + ax)(1 + x^2)} \, dx + \frac{\log (1 + a^2)}{1 + a}.$$

Throwing into partial fractions, we obtain

$$\frac{x}{(1 + ax)(1 + x^2)} = -\frac{a}{(1 + a^2)(1 + ax)} + \frac{x + a}{(1 + a^2)(1 + x^2)}.$$

$$\therefore \quad \int_0^a \frac{x}{(1 + ax)(1 + x^2)} \, dx = -\frac{1}{1 + a^2} \left| \log (1 + ax) \right|_0^a$$

$$+ \left| \frac{1}{2 (1 + a^2)} \log (1 + x^2) \right|_0^a + \left| \frac{a \tan^{-1} x}{1 + a^2} \right|_0^a$$

$$= -\frac{1}{2(1+a^2)}\log(1+a^2) + \frac{a}{1+a^2}\tan^{-1}a$$

$$\therefore \quad \varphi'(a) = \frac{1}{2(1+a^2)}\log(1+a^2) + \frac{a}{1+a^2}\tan^{-1}a.$$

Integrating, we now get

$$\varphi(a) = \frac{1}{2}\left[\int\frac{1}{1+a^2}\log(1+a^2)\,da + \int\frac{a}{1+a^2}\tan^{-1}a\,da\right]$$

$$= \frac{1}{2}\left[\tan^{-1}a\log(1+a^2) - \int\frac{2a}{1+a^2}\tan^{-1}a\,da\right]$$

$$+ \int\frac{a}{1+a^2}\tan^{-1}a\,da + c,$$

where we have applied the rule of integration by parts to the first integral on the right and, c, is any arbitrary constant. Thus,

$$\varphi(a) = \frac{1}{2}\tan^{-1}a\log(1+a^2) + c. \qquad \ldots(2)$$

From (1), we see that $\varphi(0) = 0$. Putting $a = 0$ in (2), we get $c = 0$.

$$\therefore \quad \varphi(a) = \frac{1}{2}\tan^{-1}a\log(1+a^2).$$

From this, taking $a = 1$, we get

$$\int_0^1\frac{\log(1+x)}{1+x^2}\,dx = \varphi(1) = \frac{1}{2}\tan^{-1}(1)\log 2 = \frac{\pi}{8}\log 2.$$

3. Show that

$$\int_0^\infty\frac{\tan^{-1}ax}{x(1+x^2)}\,dx = \frac{1}{2}\pi\log(1+a) \quad \textit{if } a \geq 0,$$

and find the value of the integral if $a < 0$.

We write

$$\varphi(a) = \int_0^\infty\frac{\tan^{-1}ax}{x(1+x^2)}\,dx. \qquad \ldots(1)$$

Assuming the validity of the differentiation under integral sign, we obtain

$$\varphi'(a) = \int_0^\infty\frac{1}{(1+x^2)(1+a^2x^2)}\,dx$$

$$= \int_0^\infty\frac{1}{1-a^2}\left[\frac{1}{1+x^2} - \frac{a^2}{1+a^2x^2}\right]dx$$

$$= \frac{1}{1-a^2} \left| \tan^{-1} x - a \tan^{-1} ax \right|_0^\infty$$

$$= \frac{1}{1-a^2} \left(\frac{\pi}{2} - a \frac{\pi}{2} \right) = \frac{\pi}{2(1+a)} \qquad \ldots(2)$$

Here, a, being positive we have

$$\lim_{x \to \infty} (\tan^{-1} ax) = \frac{1}{2}\pi.$$

It is easy to see that (2) is valid for $a = 0$ also.

Integrating (2) w.r.t. a, we get

$$\varphi(a) = \frac{\pi}{2} \log(1+a) + c \qquad \ldots(3)$$

where, c, is an arbitrary constant.

Also from (1)

$$\varphi(0) = 0$$

so that putting $a = 0$ in (3), we get

$$c = 0$$

$$\therefore \qquad \varphi(a) = \frac{1}{2}\pi \log(1+a).$$

Suppose now that, a is negative. We have,

$$\varphi'(a) = \frac{1}{1-a^2} \left| \tan^{-1} x - a \tan^{-1} ax \right|_0^\infty$$

$$= \frac{1}{1-a^2} \left[\frac{\pi}{2} - a \left(-\frac{\pi}{2} \right) \right] = \frac{\pi}{2(1-a)}, \qquad \ldots(4)$$

for, a, being negative,

$$\lim_{x \to \infty} (\tan^{-1} ax) = -\frac{1}{2}\pi.$$

Integrating (4), we get

$$\varphi(a) = -\frac{\pi}{2} \log(1-a) + c.$$

As before it may be shown that $c = 0$ so that we have,

$$\varphi(a) = -\frac{\pi}{2} \log(1-a).$$

4. *Evaluate*

$$\int_0^\infty e^{-\alpha x} \frac{\sin \beta x}{x} \, dx, \text{ where } \alpha \geq 0, \qquad (Kanpur, 2001)$$

and deduce that

$$\int_0^\infty \frac{\sin \beta x}{x} dx = \begin{cases} \pi/2, & \text{if } \beta > 0, \\ 0, & \text{if } \beta = 0, \\ -\pi/2, & \text{if } \beta < 0. \end{cases}$$

We write

$$\varphi(\alpha, \beta) = \int_0^\infty e^{-\alpha x} \frac{\sin \beta x}{x} dx \qquad \qquad ...(1)$$

Assuming the validity of differentiation under integral sign, we have, on differentiating w.r.t. β

$$\varphi_\beta(\alpha, \beta) = \int_0^\infty e^{-\alpha x} \cos \beta x \, dx$$

$$= \frac{\alpha}{\alpha^2 + \beta^2}, \text{ if } \alpha > 0.$$

Integrating w.r.t. β, we get

$$\varphi(\alpha, \beta) = \tan^{-1} \frac{\beta}{\alpha} + c, \qquad \qquad ...(2)$$

where, c, is a constant. From (1), we have,

$$\varphi(\alpha, 0) = 0 \qquad \qquad ...(3)$$

so that putting $\beta = 0$ in (2), we obtain $c = 0$. Thus,

$$\varphi(\alpha, \beta) = \tan^{-1} \frac{\beta}{\alpha}, \qquad \qquad ...(4)$$

where $\alpha > 0$.

Also we assume that $\varphi(\alpha, \beta)$ is a continuous function of α for $\alpha \geq 0$. We have, from (1),

$$\varphi(0, \beta) = \int_0^\infty \frac{\sin \beta x}{x} dx,$$

and from (4)

$$\lim_{\alpha \to 0} \varphi(0, \beta) = \lim_{\alpha \to 0} \left(\tan^{-1} \frac{\beta}{\alpha} \right) = \begin{cases} \pi/2, & \text{if } \beta > 0, \\ 0, & \text{if } \beta = 0, \\ -\pi/2 & \text{if } \beta < 0. \end{cases}$$

Also, because of continuity,

$$\lim_{\alpha \to 0} \varphi(\alpha, \beta) = \varphi(0, \beta).$$

$$\therefore \int_0^\infty \frac{\sin \beta x}{x} dx = \begin{cases} \pi/2, & \text{if } \beta > 0, \\ 0, & \text{if } \beta = 0, \\ -\pi/2, & \text{if } \beta < 0. \end{cases}$$

In particular, we have,

$$\int_0^\alpha \frac{\sin x}{x}\, dx = \frac{\pi}{2}.$$

5. *Assuming the validity of differentiation under integral sign, show that*

$$\int_0^\infty e^{-x^2} \cos \alpha x\, dx = \frac{1}{2}\sqrt{\pi}\, e^{-\frac{1}{4}\alpha^2}.$$

We write

$$\varphi(\alpha) = \int_0^\infty e^{-x^2} \cos \alpha x\, dx. \qquad \text{...(1)}$$

$$\therefore \quad \varphi'(\alpha) = -\int_0^\infty x e^{-x^2} \sin \alpha x\, dx.$$

Integrating by parts, we have

$$\varphi'(\alpha) = \left| \frac{1}{2} e^{-x^2} \sin \alpha x \right|_0^\infty - \frac{\alpha}{2}\int_0^\infty e^{-x^2} \cos \alpha x\, dx$$

$$= 0 - \frac{\alpha}{2}\varphi(\alpha) = \frac{-\alpha}{2}\varphi(\alpha),$$

$$\Rightarrow \quad \frac{\varphi'(\alpha)}{\varphi(\alpha)} = -\frac{\alpha}{2}.$$

Integrating, we get

$$\log \varphi(\alpha) = -\frac{1}{4}\alpha^2 + c_1 \quad \Rightarrow \quad \varphi(\alpha) = c e^{-\frac{1}{4}\alpha^2} \qquad \text{...(2)}$$

Putting $\alpha = 0$ in (1), we get

$$\varphi(0) = \int_0^\infty e^{-x^2}\, dx = \frac{\sqrt{\pi}}{2}. \quad \text{[Refer § A.6; Cor. 2, p. 327]} \qquad \text{...(3)}$$

Putting $\alpha = 0$ in (2), we get

$$\varphi(0) = c. \qquad \text{...(4)}$$

$$\therefore \quad \varphi(\alpha) = \frac{1}{2}\sqrt{\pi}\, e^{-\frac{1}{4}\alpha^2}$$

6. *Show that*

$$\int_0^\infty \frac{\tan^{-1}\alpha x \ \tan^{-1}\beta x}{x^2}\, dx = \frac{\pi}{2} \log\left[\frac{(\alpha+\beta)^{\alpha+\beta}}{\alpha^\alpha\, \beta^\beta}\right].$$

We write

$$\varphi(\alpha, \beta) = \int_0^\infty \frac{\tan^{-1} \alpha x \, \tan^{-1} \beta x}{x^2} \, dx \qquad \qquad \ldots(1)$$

Assuming the validity of differentiation under integral sign, we have

$$\varphi_\alpha(\alpha, \beta) = \int_0^\infty \frac{\tan^{-1} \beta x}{x(1 + \alpha^2 x^2)} \, dx. \qquad \qquad \ldots(2)$$

$$\varphi_{\beta\alpha}(\alpha, \beta) = \int_0^\infty \frac{1}{(1 + \beta^2 x^2)(1 + \alpha^2 x^2)} \, dx$$

$$= \frac{1}{\alpha^2 - \beta^2} \int_0^\infty \left(\frac{\alpha^2}{1 + \alpha^2 x^2} - \frac{\beta^2}{1 + \beta^2 x^2} \right) dx, \quad [\text{If } \alpha \ne \beta]$$

$$= \frac{1}{\alpha^2 - \beta^2} \left| \alpha \tan^{-1} \alpha x - \beta \tan^{-1} \beta x \right|_0^\infty$$

$$= \frac{\pi}{2(\alpha + \beta)}; \qquad \qquad \ldots(3)$$

α, β being assumed positive.

It is easy to show that (3) remains valid even for $\alpha = \beta$.

Integrating (3) w.r.t. β, we get

$$\varphi_\alpha(\alpha, \beta) = \frac{\pi}{2} \log(\alpha + \beta) + f(\alpha), \qquad \qquad \ldots(4)$$

where $f(\alpha)$ is an arbitrary function of α.

Now, from (2),

$$\varphi_\alpha(\alpha, 0) = 0. \qquad \qquad \ldots(5)$$

From (4) and (5), we have,

$$0 = \frac{\pi}{2} \log \alpha + f(\alpha),$$

$$\Rightarrow \quad f(\alpha) = -\frac{\pi}{2} \log \alpha.$$

$$\therefore \quad \varphi_\alpha(\alpha, \beta) = \frac{\pi}{2} \log(\alpha + \beta) - \frac{\pi}{2} \log \alpha \qquad \qquad \ldots(6)$$

We could similarly obtain

$$\varphi_\beta(\alpha, \beta) = \frac{\pi}{2} \log(\alpha + \beta) - \frac{\pi}{2} \log \beta \qquad \qquad \ldots(7)$$

Integrating (6), w.r.t. α, we obtain

$$\varphi(\alpha, \beta) = \frac{\pi}{2}\left[(\alpha + \beta)\log(\alpha + \beta) - (\alpha + \beta)\right]$$

$$- \frac{\pi}{2}(\alpha\log\alpha - \alpha) + g(\beta), \qquad \ldots(8)$$

$g(\beta)$ being any arbitrary function of β.

From (8), we have

$$\varphi_\beta(\alpha, \beta) = \frac{\pi}{2}\log(\alpha + \beta) + g'(\beta). \qquad \ldots(9)$$

From (7) and (9), we have

$$g'(\beta) = -\frac{\pi}{2}\log\beta$$

$$\therefore \quad g(\beta) = -\frac{\pi}{2}[\beta\log\beta - \beta] + c. \qquad \ldots(10)$$

From (8) and (1),

$$0 = \varphi(\alpha, 0) = g(0). \qquad \ldots(11)$$

From (10) and (11), we obtain $c = 0$.

$$\therefore \quad \varphi(\alpha, \beta) = \frac{\pi}{2}[(\alpha + \beta)\log(\alpha + \beta) - (\alpha + \beta)]$$

$$- \frac{\pi}{2}(\alpha\log\alpha - \alpha) - \frac{\pi}{2}(\beta\log\beta - \beta)$$

$$= \frac{\pi}{2}[(\alpha + \beta)\log(\alpha + \beta) - \alpha\log\alpha - \beta\log\beta]$$

$$= \frac{\pi}{2}\log\frac{(\alpha + \beta)^{\alpha + \beta}}{\alpha^\alpha\,\beta^\beta}.$$

EXERCISES

(For improper integrals in the following the validity of differentiation under integral sign may always be assumed.)

1. Find the value of

$$\int_0^\pi \frac{dx}{a + b\cos x}, \quad a > 0,\ |b| < a,$$

and deduce that

$$\int_0^\pi \frac{dx}{(a + b\cos x)^2} = \frac{\pi a}{(a^2 - b^2)^{3/2}}$$

and

$$\int_0^\pi \frac{\cos x\,dx}{(a + b\cos x)^2} = -\frac{\pi b}{(a^2 - b^2)^{3/2}}.$$

2. Starting from

$$\int_0^\infty e^{-ax}\, dx = \frac{1}{a},\ a > 0;$$

$$\int_0^1 x^n\, dx = \frac{1}{n+1},\ n > -1,$$

deduce that $\quad \displaystyle\int_0^\infty x^m e^{-ax}\, dx = \frac{m\,!}{a^{m+1}},$

and $\quad \displaystyle\int_0^1 x^n (\log x)^m\, dx = \frac{(-1)^m\, m\,!}{(n+1)^{m+1}},$

where, m, is any positive integer.

3. Starting from a suitable integral, show that

$$\int_0^x \frac{dx}{(x^2+a^2)^2} = \frac{1}{2a}\tan^{-1}\frac{x}{a} + \frac{x}{2a^2(x^2+a^2)}.$$

4. Differentiating under integral sign the integrals

$$\int_0^\infty e^{-ax^2}\, dx = \frac{1}{2}\sqrt{\frac{\pi}{a}},\quad \int_0^\infty \frac{dx}{x^2+a} = \frac{\pi}{2\sqrt{2}};\ a > 0,$$

show that

$$\int_0^\infty x^{2n}\, e^{-ax^2}\, dx = \frac{\sqrt{\pi}}{2}\cdot\frac{1\cdot3\,.....\,(2n-1)}{2^n\, a^{n+\frac{1}{2}}}.$$

$$\int_0^\infty \frac{dx}{(x^2+a)^{n+1}} = \frac{\pi}{2}\cdot\frac{1\cdot3\,.....\,(2n-1)}{2^n\, n!\, a^{n+\frac{1}{2}}}.$$

5. Show that for $y > 0$,

$$\int_0^\infty e^{-xy}\,\frac{\sin x}{x}\, dx = \frac{\pi}{2} - \tan^{-1} y.$$

6. If $|\,a\,| \le 1$, show that

$$\int_0^\pi \log(1 + a\cos x)\, dx = \pi \log\left[\frac{1}{2} + \frac{1}{2}\sqrt{1 - a^2}\right].$$

7. If $|a| < 1$, prove that

(i) $\displaystyle\int_0^\pi \frac{\log(1 + a \cos x)}{\cos x}\, dx = \pi \sin^{-1} a.$

(ii) $\displaystyle\int_0^{\pi/2} \frac{\log(1 + \cos \alpha \cos x)}{\cos x}\, dx = \frac{\pi^2 - 4\alpha^2}{8}.$

(*Kanpur, 2002; Gorakhpur, 2003*)

8. Show that

$$\int_0^{\pi/2} \log(1 - x^2 \cos^2 \theta)\, d\theta = \pi \log\{1 + \sqrt{1 - x^2}\} - \pi \log 2,$$

if $x^2 \cdot 1.$

9. Evaluate

$$\int_0^{\pi/2} \log\left(\frac{a + b \sin \theta}{a - b \sin \theta}\right) \operatorname{cosec} \theta\, d\theta, \quad (a > b).$$

10. Evaluate

$$I(y) = \int_0^{\pi/2} \frac{\log(1 + y \sin^2 x)}{\sin^2 x}\, dx$$

by showing that

$$I'(y) = \frac{\pi}{2\sqrt{1 + y}}.$$

11. Show that

$$y = \frac{1}{k} \int_0^x f(t) \sin k (x - t)\, dt,$$

satisfies the differential equation,

$$\frac{d^2 y}{dx^2} + k^2 y = f(x),$$

where, k, is a constant.

12. Let

$$u = \int_0^\infty e^{-x \cos \theta}\, x^{n-1} \sin(x \sin \theta)\, dx,$$

$$v = \int_0^\infty e^{-x \cos \theta}\, x^{n-1} \cos(x \sin \theta)\, dx.$$

Prove that

$$\frac{du}{d\theta} = -nv, \quad \frac{dv}{d\theta} = nu,$$

and

$$\frac{d^2u}{d\theta^2} + n^2 u = 0, \quad \frac{d^2v}{d\theta^2} + n^2 v = 0.$$

Deduce that

$$u = \Gamma(n) \cos n\theta, \quad v = \Gamma(n) \sin n\theta.$$

13. Prove that

$$\int_0^\infty e^{-ax} x^{m-1} \cos bx \, dx = \frac{\Gamma(m) \cos m\theta}{r^m},$$

where $r^2 = a^2 + b^2$ and $\theta = \tan^{-1}(a/b)$.

14. Show that

$$\int_0^\infty \frac{\cos x}{\sqrt{x}} \, dx = \sqrt{\frac{\pi}{2}} = \int_0^\infty \frac{\sin x}{\sqrt{x}} \, dx.$$

15. Prove that

$$\int_{\pi/2 - \alpha}^{\pi/2} \sin\theta \cos^{-1}(\cos\alpha \operatorname{cosec}\theta) \, d\theta = \frac{\pi}{2}(1 - \cos\alpha).$$

16. Obtain the first order differential equation satisfied by

$$\varphi(y) = \int_0^\infty e^{-x^2} \sin 2yx \, dx,$$

and hence show that

$$\varphi(y) = \int_0^y e^{x^2 - y^2} \, dx.$$

ANSWERS

9. $\pi \sin^{-1}(b/a)$.　　10. $\pi[\sqrt{1+y} - 1]$.　　16. $\dfrac{d\varphi}{dy} + 2y\varphi(y) = 1$.

MISCELLANEOUS EXERCISES

1. Compute the following indefinite integrals :

   (*i*) $\displaystyle\int \frac{\sin 2x}{1 + \sin^2 x} \, dx$　　　　　　　(*ii*) $\displaystyle\int \frac{dx}{\sqrt{3 + 2e^x}}$

   (*iii*) $\displaystyle\int \log|2 + 5x| \, dx$　　　　(*iv*) $\displaystyle\int \frac{dx}{x(1 + \log^2 |x|)}$.

2. Compute the following integrals :

   (i) $\displaystyle\int_0^{\pi/2} \sin^3 x \cos^{11} x \, dx$ (ii) $\displaystyle\int_0^{1/2} \frac{(\sin^{-1} x)^2}{\sqrt{1-x^2}} \, dx$

   (iii) $\displaystyle\int_{-\infty}^{0} \frac{x}{x^4+1} \, dx$ (iv) $\displaystyle\int_0^{\infty} e^{-x} \sin x \, dx.$

3. Trace the curve
$$x^3 - x^2 y - x - y = 0$$
and determine the area of the region between the curve and x-axis.

4. Compute the following indefinite integrals :

   (i) $\displaystyle\int \frac{e^x}{\sqrt{3 - 5e^{2x}}} \, dx$ (ii) $\displaystyle\int \log(x^2 + 1) \, dx$

   (iii) $\displaystyle\int \frac{\sin^{-1} e^x}{e^x} \, dx$ (iv) $\displaystyle\int \frac{dx}{(\sin^2 x + 3\cos^2 x)^2}$

   (v) $\displaystyle\int (\sin^{-1} x)^2 \, dx.$

5. Compute the following definite integrals :

   (i) $\displaystyle\int_0^{\pi/2} \tan x \, dx$ (ii) $\displaystyle\int_{-2}^{0} \frac{1}{(2-x)^2} \left(\frac{2-x}{2+x}\right)^{1/2} dx$

   (iii) $\displaystyle\int_0^{\pi/4} x \sec^2 x \, dx$ (iv) $\displaystyle\int_0^{\pi/2} e^{2x} \sin^2 x \, dx.$

6. Obtain a primitive of each of the following functions :

   (i) $x \rightarrow \dfrac{5\cos x + 6}{2\cos x + \sin x + 3}$

   (ii) $x \rightarrow \dfrac{\tan^{-1} x}{(1+x^2)^{3/2}}$

   (iii) $x \rightarrow (\sin^{-1} x)^2.$

7. Obtain the following definite integrals :

   (i) $\displaystyle\int_0^{1} \frac{4x^2 + 3}{8x^2 + 4x + 5} \, dx$ (ii) $\displaystyle\int_8^{15} \frac{dx}{(x-3)\sqrt{x+1}}$

   (iii) $\displaystyle\int_0^{\pi/2} \sin^3 x \cos 2x \, dx$ (iv) $\displaystyle\int_{-1}^{1} \frac{\sqrt{1-x^2}}{a-x} \, dx; \quad (a > 1).$

8. Determine the area enclosed by the curve,

$$xy^2 = (2x - 5)$$

the x-axis and the line $x = 10$. Determine also the volume of the solid obtained by revolving the curve about x-axis.

9. Trace the curve

$$x = a \cos t, \ y = a \sin t \cos t.$$

Determine the volume of the solid obtained by revolving the region bounded by the curve about x-axis.

10. Trace $y = \log (x^2 - 1)$ and determine the length of the curve between

$$\sqrt{2} \leq x \leq \sqrt{2} + 1.$$

11. Find a primitive of the function given by the following expressions :

(i) $\dfrac{(\log |x|)^2}{x^3}$

(ii) $\dfrac{(\pi - \sin^{-1} x)}{\sqrt{1 - x^2}}$

(iii) $\dfrac{1}{\sqrt{x+1} + 3\sqrt{x+1}}$

(iv) $\dfrac{1}{\sin x + \cos x}$.

12. (a) Find the following definite integrals :

(i) $\displaystyle\int_1^{10} \dfrac{dx}{x\sqrt{x^2 + x + 1}}$

(ii) $\displaystyle\int_{1/2}^1 \dfrac{2x - 3}{(3 + 4x - 4x^2)} dx$

(iii) $\displaystyle\int_0^{\pi/2} \dfrac{dx}{(2 + \sin x)^2}$.

(b) Find the result connecting

$$\int_0^{\pi/2} \sin^n x \, dx \quad \text{with} \quad \int_0^{\pi/2} \sin^{n-2} x \, dx.$$

13. Find the volume of the solid obtained by revolving the curve

$$y = e^{-x} \sqrt{\sin x}, \ 0 \leq x \leq 2\pi$$

about x-axis.

14. Find the surface area of the solid obtained by revolving

$$x^3 = y^2 (2a - x), \ 1 \leq x \leq 2$$

about x-axis.

15. Obtain a primitive of each of the following functions :

(i) $x \to \sin^3 x$

(ii) $x \to \dfrac{\sin x}{\sqrt{\cos x}}$

(iii) $x \to \dfrac{3x}{\cos^3 x^2}$

(iv) $x \to x^2 \log x$.

16. Compute the following definite integrals :

(i) $\displaystyle\int_0^{\pi/2} e^{2\cos x} \sin x \, dx$

(ii) $\displaystyle\int_{-1}^{+1} xe^x \, dx$

(iii) $\displaystyle\int_1^{-1} e^x (\log x)^2 \, dx$

(iv) $\displaystyle\int_1^3 \dfrac{dx}{x(1+\log x)^3}$.

17. (a) Consider the curves

$$y = \sin x, \ y = \cos x$$

and obtain the area of the region that contains them.

(b) Obtain the area between the curve

$$y = \tan 2x$$

and the line

$$x = \dfrac{-\pi}{6}, \ x = \dfrac{\pi}{6}.$$

18. Determine the area of the region bounded by

$$y = 4x^2 e^{-x}$$

and the lines given by

$$y = 0 \text{ and } x = a > 0.$$

What is the area of the limit where

$$a \to +\infty ?$$

19. Compute the following indefinite integrals :

(i) $\displaystyle\int \dfrac{(\sin x - \cos x)}{\sin^2 x} dx$

(ii) $\displaystyle\int \dfrac{x^{n-1}}{\sqrt{x^n + 1}} dx$.

20. Consider the curve

$$y = 2x + 1 + \dfrac{1}{n^2}$$

and find the area defined by

$$\begin{cases} 1 \le x \le 2, \\ 0 \le y \le 2x + 1 + \dfrac{1}{x^2}. \end{cases}$$

[The required area is

$$\int_1^2 \left(2x + 1 + \frac{1}{n^2}\right) dx - \int_1^2 (2x + 1)\, dx.]$$

21. Determine the volume of the solid obtained by revolving the curve

$$y = 2x + 1 + \frac{1}{x^2}, \quad 1 \le x \le 2$$

about x-axis.

22. Find the points of inflexion of the curve

$$(1 + x^2)\, y = 6x$$

and show that the points of inflexion lie on the line

$$y = 1.5x.$$

23. (a) Find the circle of curvature of the curve

$$y = \frac{x^2}{20} - a$$

at the point with abscissa $a > 0$.

(b) Find the extreme points and asymptotes of

$$y = \frac{x^3 + x}{x^4 - x^2 + 1}.$$

24. Evaluate the following definite integrals :

(i) $\displaystyle\int_0^\infty \frac{x^2}{1 + x^4}\, dx$

(ii) $\displaystyle\int_2^3 \frac{x^3\, dx}{(x-1)^2\, (x^2 + 1)}$

(iii) $\displaystyle\int_0^\pi e^{1/2x} \cos^2 x\, dx$

(iv) $\displaystyle\int_{-2}^{-1} x^2 e^{-2x}\, dx$

(v) $\displaystyle\int \sin^{-1}\left(\frac{2\sqrt{x}}{1+x}\right) dx$

(vi) $\displaystyle\frac{2 + \sin x}{\sin x\,(1 + \cos x)}\, dx.$

25. Compute the following definite integrals :

(i) $\displaystyle\int_0^1 \frac{dx}{\sqrt{4x - 4x^2}}$

(ii) $\displaystyle\int_{\pi/2}^{2\pi/3} \frac{\cos^2 x}{\sin x}\, dx$

(iii) $\displaystyle\int_{-1}^2 x\,(x^2 + 1)\, e^{x^2}\, dx$

(iv) $\displaystyle\int_0^1 x \tan^{-1} x\, dx.$

26. (a) Determine a, b, c, d of the curve
$$y = ax^3 + bx^2 + cx + d$$
(i) if it passes through the origin and touches the x-axis there;

(ii) passes through the point $\left(5, \dfrac{25}{4}\right)$ which is a stationary point on the curve.

(b) Find also the point of inflexion on the curve and the corresponding inflexional tangents.

27. Trace the curve
$$y = \frac{32x}{(x^2 + 3)^2}$$

and determine the area of the origin bounded by the curve, the x-axis and the ordinate of the point of inflexion.

28. Obtain a primitive of each of the functions given by the following expressions :

(i) $\dfrac{1}{(1 + \sin x)\tan x}$

(ii) $\dfrac{e^x}{e^{2x} - 3e^x + 2}$

(iii) $(x^3 + x)\, e^{-x^2}$

(iv) $x \tan^{-1} x$.

29. Evaluate the following definite integrals :

(i) $\displaystyle\int_0^2 (x - 2)\, e^x\, dx$

(ii) $\displaystyle\int_\pi^3 \frac{x^3 + 2x^2 + 3x - 1}{(x - 1)^2}\, dx$

(iii) $\displaystyle\int_1^6 (2x + 3\log x)\, dx$.

30. (a) How large is the area between the curve and the ordinate $x = a$? Find the limit of this area when
$$a \to +\infty.$$

(b) From the square with sides $x = 0$, $y = 0$, $x = 2$ and $y = 2$, the portion bounded by the curve, $y = e^x$ and $y = \log x$ is removed. Find the area of the remaining figure.

31. Trace the curve
$$(1 - x^2)\, y = 1 + x^2$$
and determine the area between curve and the lines
$$x = -1, x = 2, x = 3.$$

32. (a) Trace the curve

$$x^4 - 9x^2 + y^2 = 0$$

and obtain the volume obtained by revolving the curve about x-axis.

(b) The region bounded by the curve $y = 3e^{-x}(x^2 + 1)$, the co-ordinate axes and the line $x = 3$ rotates about x-axis. What is the volume of the solid generated ?

33. Determine a polynomial $f(x)$ which satisfies following conditions :

(a) $f(x) = [f'(x)]^2$ (b) $\int_0^1 f(x)\, dx = \dfrac{19}{12}$

(c) $f'(0) > 0$.

34. Compute the following integrals :

(i) $\displaystyle\int \frac{dx}{\sqrt{e^{2x} + 4e^x + 1}}$ (ii) $\displaystyle\int \left(\frac{\log x}{x}\right)^2 dx$.

35. Find a primitive of the following functions :

(i) $x \to \cos x \cos 2x \cos 3x$,

(ii) $x \to \dfrac{x}{1 + x^3}$,

(iii) $x \to e^x \log x$.

OBJECTIVE QUESTIONS

To each of the following questions, four alternatives are given for the answer. Only one of them is correct. Choose the correct alternative.

1. In definite integrals the order of integration can be changed if :

(a) limits are independent of the variables

(b) limits depend on the variables

(c) integrand is constant

(d) None of these.

2. Value of integral $\displaystyle\int_0^\infty \frac{e^{-ax} \sin mx}{x}\, dx$ is :

(a) $-\tan^{-1}\dfrac{m}{a}$ (b) $-\tan^{-1}\dfrac{a}{m}$

(c) $\tan^{-1}\dfrac{m}{a}$ (d) $\tan^{-1}\dfrac{a}{m}$.

3. Value of integral $\int\limits_{0}^{\infty} e^{-x^2}\, dx$ is :

    (a) $\dfrac{\pi}{2}$ (b) $\dfrac{\sqrt{\pi}}{2}$ (c) $\sqrt{\dfrac{\pi}{2}}$ (d) $\dfrac{\pi}{4}$.

4. If $\int\limits_{0}^{\infty} e^{-ax}\, dx = \dfrac{1}{a}$, then $\int\limits_{0}^{\infty} e^{-ax} x^n\, dx$ is equal to :

    (a) $\dfrac{n!}{a^n}$ (b) $\dfrac{n!}{a^{n+1}}$

    (c) $\dfrac{(n+1)!}{a^n}$ (d) $\dfrac{(n-1)!}{a^n}$.

5. Value of the integral $\int\limits_{0}^{\infty} \dfrac{\sin mx}{x}\, dx$ is :

    (a) $\dfrac{\pi}{2}$ (b) π (c) $\dfrac{\pi}{4}$ (d) $\dfrac{3\pi}{2}$.

ANSWERS

1. (a)   2. (c)   3. (b)   4. (b)   5. (a)

DIFFERENTIAL EQUATIONS

15

Differential Equations of First Order and First Degree

15.1. A Differential equation *is an equation that involves independent and dependent variables and the derivatives of the dependent variables.*

The following are some examples of differential equations :

(1) $(2x + 3y)\dfrac{dy}{dx} + (7x^2 + 8y) = 0.$

(2) $\dfrac{dy}{dx} + y \cos x = \sin x.$

(3) $\dfrac{d^2y}{dx^2} + a^2x = 0.$

(4) $\left[1 + \left(\dfrac{dy}{dx}\right)^2\right]^{3/2} = \dfrac{d^2y}{dx^2}.$

(5) $x^2 \left(\dfrac{d^2y}{dx^2}\right)^3 + y\left(\dfrac{dy}{dx}\right)^4 + y^4 = 0.$

(6) $x\dfrac{\partial z}{\partial x} + y\dfrac{\partial z}{\partial y} = nz.$

(7) $\dfrac{\partial^2 z}{\partial x^2} - a^2 \dfrac{\partial^2 z}{\partial y^2} = 0.$

A differential equation is said to be *Ordinary*, if the differential co-efficients have reference to a *single* independent variable only and it is said to be *Partial* if there are *two or more* independent variables.

Thus, the differential equations (1) to (5) are ordinary, but (6) and (7) are partial.

In the following, we shall be concerned with ordinary differential equations only.

The *order of a differential equation* is the order of the derivative of highest order derivative occurring in it.

The *degree of a differential equation* is the degree of the derivative of the highest order occurring in it, after it has been expressed in a form free from radicals and fractions so far as derivatives are concerned.

Thus, of the above differential equations

(1), (2) and (6) are of the first order and the first degree;

(3) and (7) are of the second order and the first degree;

(4) is of the second order and the second degree;

(5) is of the second order and the third degree.

535

A *solution or integral of a differential equation* is a relation between the variables, not involving the differential co-efficients such that this relation and the derivatives obtained from it satisfy the given differential equation. This also implies that a differential equation can be derived from its solution by the process of differentiation and other algebraic processes of elimination, etc. On this account the solution of a differential equation is also called its *primitive*.

EXAMPLES

1. *Show that*, $y = A \cos x + B \sin x$, *is a solution of the differential equation*

$$d^2y/dx^2 + y = 0.$$

We have

$$dy/dx = -A \sin x + B \cos x$$
$$d^2y/dx^2 = -A \cos x - B \sin x = -y,$$

$$\Rightarrow \quad \frac{d^2y}{dx^2} + y = 0,$$

which is the given differential equation.

2. *Show that*,

$$y = A \cos x + \sin x, \qquad\qquad ...(i)$$

is a solution of

$$\cos x \frac{dy}{dx} + y \sin x = 1. \qquad\qquad ...(ii)$$

Differentiating (*i*) w.r.t. *x*, we get

$$dy/dx = -A \sin x + \cos x \qquad\qquad ...(iii)$$

Substituting the values of y and dy/dx in the left hand side of (*ii*), we see that

$$\cos x \frac{dy}{dx} + y \sin x$$

$$= \cos x \,(-A \sin x + \cos x) + (A \cos x + \sin x) \sin x = 1,$$

so that the given differential equation is satisfied.

3. *Show that*

$$Ax^2 + By^2 = 1 \qquad\qquad ...(i)$$

is the solution of

$$x \left[y \frac{d^2y}{dx^2} + \left(\frac{dy}{dx} \right)^2 \right] - y \frac{dy}{dx} = 0. \qquad\qquad ...(ii)$$

We note that the differential equation is free of the constants A, B and is of second order.

Differentiating (*i*) twice successively, we get

$$Ax + By \frac{dy}{dx} = 0, \qquad\qquad ...(iii)$$

$$A + B\left[\left(\frac{dy}{dx}\right)^2 + y\frac{d^2y}{dx^2}\right] = 0. \qquad \qquad ...(iv)$$

On eliminating A and B from (iii) and (iv), we get

$$x\left[y\frac{d^2y}{dx^2} + \left(\frac{dy}{dx}\right)^2\right] - y\frac{dy}{dx} = 0,$$

which is the given differential equation.

4. *By the elimination of the constants h and k, find the differential equation of which* $(x - h)^2 + (y - k)^2 = a^2$, *is a solution.*

Three relations are necessary to eliminate two constants. Thus, besides the given relation, we require two more and they will be obtained by differentiating the given relation twice successively. Thus, we have

$$(x - h) + (y - k)\frac{dy}{dx} = 0, \qquad \qquad ...(i)$$

$$1 + (y - k)\frac{d^2y}{dx^2} + \left(\frac{dy}{dx}\right)^2 = 0. \qquad \qquad ...(ii)$$

From (i) and (ii), we obtain

$$y - k = -\frac{1 + (dy/dx)^2}{d^2y/dx^2},$$

$$x - h = \frac{[1 + (dy/dx)^2](dy/dx)}{d^2y/dx^2}.$$

Substituting these values in the given relation, we obtain

$$\left[1 + \left(\frac{dy}{dx}\right)^2\right]^3 = a^2\left(\frac{d^2y}{dx^2}\right)^2$$

which is the required differential equation.

5. *Find the differential equation of the system of curves*

$$y = ax^2 + b \cos nx + c,$$

where a, b and c are arbitrary constants.

We have,

$$y = ax^2 + b \cos nx + c. \qquad \qquad ...(i)$$

Differentiating, w.r.t. x, we obtain

$$\frac{dy}{dx} = 2ax - bn \sin nx \qquad \qquad ...(ii)$$

$$\frac{d^2y}{dx^2} = 2a - bn^2 \cos nx \qquad \qquad ...(iii)$$

and $\dfrac{d^3 y}{dx^3} = bn^3 \sin nx.$ ...(iv)

Eliminating a between (ii) and (iii), we get

$$x \frac{d^2 y}{dx^2} - \frac{dy}{dx} = -bn (x \cos nx - \sin nx) \qquad ...(v)$$

Eliminating b between (iv) and (v) by dividing, we get

$$\frac{\dfrac{d^3 y}{dx^3}}{x \dfrac{d^2 y}{dx^2} - \dfrac{dy}{dx}} = \frac{-x^2 \sin nx}{x \cos nx - \sin nx}.$$

This is the required differential equation. Note that here three constants have been eliminated and we have got a differential equation of third order.

EXERCISES

1. By the elimination of the constants a, b, obtain the differential equation of which $xy = ce^x + be^{-x} + x^2$ is a solution.

2. Find the equation of which $y = Ae^x + Be^{3x} + Ce^{5x}$ is a solution.

3. By the elimination of the constant, a, obtain the differential equation of which $y^2 = 4a (x + a)$ is the solution.

4. Find the differential equation of the family of curves

$$y = e^x (A \cos x + B \sin x)$$

where A and B are arbitrary constants.

ANSWERS

1. $x \dfrac{d^2 y}{dx^2} + 2 \dfrac{dy}{dx} - xy + x^2 - 2 = 0.$

2. $\dfrac{d^3 y}{dx^3} - 9 \dfrac{d^2 y}{dx^2} + 23 \dfrac{dy}{dx} - 15y = 0.$

3. $y \left[1 - \left(\dfrac{dy}{dx} \right)^2 \right] = 2x \dfrac{dy}{dx}.$

4. $\dfrac{d^2 y}{dx^2} - 2 \dfrac{dy}{dx} + 2y = 0.$

15.2. Number of arbitrary constants. In order to obtain a differential equation whose solution is

$$f (x, y, c_1, c_2, ..., c_n) = 0, \qquad ...(i)$$

where $c_1, c_2, ..., c_n$ are n arbitrary constants, we have to eliminate the n constants for which we require $(n + 1)$ equations. The given relation along with n more, obtained by successively differentiating it n times, provide us with the required $(n + 1)$ relations. The differential equation thus obtained is clearly of the nth order. The solution (i) contains n arbitrary constants, $c_1, c_2, \ldots, c_n$.

15.2.1. General and particular solutions. A solution of a differential equation which contains arbitrary constants as many as the order of the differential equation is called *General solution*. Other solutions, obtained by giving particular values to the arbitrary constants in the general solution, are called *Particular solutions*.

Also, we know that the general integral of a function contains an arbitrary constant. Therefore, the solution of a differential equation, resulting as it does from the operations of integration, must contain arbitrary constants, equal in number to the number of times the integration is involved in obtaining the solution, and this latter is equal to the order of the differential equation.

Thus, we see that *the general solution of a differential equation of the nth order must contain n and only n independent arbitrary constants.*

Note 1. We have already seen that it is not possible to obtain the integral of every function, *i.e.*, an integral which is obtained as an algebraic combination of a finite number of algebraic, trigonometric, inverse trigonometric, logarithmic and exponential functions. This possibility is still more limited in the case of differential equations. However, as in the case of integration, there exist some standard forms such that a differential equation belonging to any one of them can always be solved. A few only of these standard forms will be considered in this book.

Now in this chapter, we consider differential equations of the first order only.

Note 2. A convenient notation. The most general differential equation of the first order and first degree is

$$\frac{dy}{dx} = \frac{f(x, y)}{\varphi(x, y)}. \qquad \ldots(i)$$

It is sometimes, found convenient to write this equation in the form $\varphi(x, y)\, dy = f(x, y)\, dx.$

15.3. Equations in which the variables are separable are those equations which can be so expressed that the co-efficient of dx is only a function of x and that of dy is only a function of y.

Thus, the general form of such an equation is

$$f(x)\, dx + \varphi(y)\, dy = 0. \qquad \ldots(i)$$

To solve, it, we write

$$f(x) + \varphi(y)\frac{dy}{dx} = 0.$$

Integrating with respect to x, we get

$$\int f(x)\, dx + \int \varphi(y) \cdot \frac{dy}{dx}\, dx = c,$$

$$\Rightarrow \quad \int f(x)\, dx + \int \varphi(y)\, dy = c$$

which is the solution of (i).

Thus, the solution of (i) is obtained by adding the integrals of $f(x)$ and $\varphi(y)$ with respect to x and y respectively and equating their sum to a constant.

EXAMPLES

1. *Solve* : $y\,(1 + x)\, dx + x\,(1 + y)\, dy = 0$.

Here, we have

$$y\,(1 + x)\, dx + x\,(1 + y)\, dy = 0$$

$$\Rightarrow \quad \frac{1+x}{x}\, dx + \frac{1+y}{y}\, dy = 0$$

so that the given equation is one in which the variables are separable.

The solution, therefore, is

$$\int \frac{1+x}{x}\, dx + \int \frac{1+y}{y}\, dy = 0$$

$$\Rightarrow \quad \log x + x + \log y + y = a$$

$$\Rightarrow \quad x + y + \log xy = a$$

which is the required general solution containing the arbitrary constant 'a'.

2. *Find a curve for which the tangent at each point makes a constant angle*, α, *with the radius vector.*

If φ denotes the angle between the radius vector and the tangent at a point of the curve, we have

$$\tan \varphi = r\, \frac{d\theta}{dr}.$$

As $\varphi = \alpha$, we have

$$\tan \alpha = \frac{r\, d\theta}{dr},$$

$$\Rightarrow \quad \frac{dr}{r} = \cot \alpha\, d\theta$$

$$\Rightarrow \quad \log r = \theta \cot \alpha + c,$$

$$\Rightarrow \quad r = e^c \cdot e^{\theta \cot \alpha} = a e^{\theta \cot \alpha},$$

$$\Rightarrow \quad r = a e^{\theta \cot \alpha}$$

is the required curve; 'a' being a constant whatsoever.

3. *Solve* : $y - x\dfrac{dy}{dx} = a\left(y^2 + \dfrac{dy}{dx}\right)$.   *(Rohilkhand, 1998)*

The equation may be written as

$$(y - ay^2) = (x + a)\dfrac{dy}{dx}$$

or $$\dfrac{dy}{y(1 - ay)} = \dfrac{dx}{(x + a)}$$

or $$\left(\dfrac{1}{y} + \dfrac{a}{1 - ay}\right)dy = \dfrac{dx}{(x + a)}.$$

Integrating, we get

$$\log y - \log(1 - ay) = \log(x + a) + \log c$$

or $$\log \dfrac{y}{1 - ay} = \log c(x + a)$$

$$\therefore \quad y = c(1 - ay)(x + a).$$

4. *Solve* : $\dfrac{dy}{dx}\tan y = \sin(x + y) + \sin(x - y).$

We have,

$$\tan y \dfrac{dy}{dx} = 2\sin x \cos y\, dx$$

or $$\sec y \tan y\, dy = 2 \sin x\, dx.$$

On integration, we get

$$\sec y = -2 \cos x + c.$$

5. *Solve* : $\sqrt{1 + x^2}\ \sqrt{1 + y^2}\ dx + xy\, dy = 0.$

We can write the given differential equation as

$$\dfrac{\sqrt{1 + x^2}}{x}\, dx + \dfrac{1}{2}\cdot\dfrac{2y}{\sqrt{1 + y^2}}\, dy = 0.$$

On integration, we get

$$\int \dfrac{\sqrt{1 + x^2}}{x}\, dx + \dfrac{1}{2}\cdot 2\sqrt{1 + y^2} = c. \qquad \ldots(i)$$

Put $1 + x^2 = t^2$, $x\, dx = t\, dt$, we get

$$\int \sqrt{\dfrac{1 + x^2}{x}}\, dx = \int \dfrac{t^2}{t^2 - 1}\, dt = \int \left(1 + \dfrac{1}{t^2 - 1}\right)dt = t + \dfrac{1}{2}\log\dfrac{t - 1}{t + 1}$$

$$= \sqrt{1 + x^2} + \dfrac{1}{2}\log\left[\dfrac{\sqrt{1 + x^2} - 1}{\sqrt{1 + x^2} + 1}\right].$$

Putting this value in (*i*), we get the required solution as

$$\sqrt{1+x^2} + \frac{1}{2}\log\left[\frac{\sqrt{1+x^2}-1}{\sqrt{1+x^2}+1}\right] + \sqrt{1+y^2} = c.$$

EXERCISES

Solve the following differential equations :

1. $(xy^2 + x)\,dx + (yx^2 + y)\,dy = 0.$

2. $x\sqrt{1+x^2}\,dx + x\sqrt{1+y^2}\,dy = 0.$

3. $(x^2 - yx^2)\,dy + (y^2 + xy^2)\,y\,dx = 0.$

4. $\operatorname{cosec} x \log y\, dy + x^2 y^2\, dx = 0.$

5. $\dfrac{dy}{dx} = \dfrac{\sin x + x\cos x}{y\,(2\log y + 1)}.$

6. $x^{-1}\cos^2 y\, dy + y^{-1}\cos^2 x\, dx = 0.$

7. $x\sqrt{y}\,dx + (1+y)\sqrt{1+x}\,dy = 0.$

8. $\cos y \log(\sec x + \tan x)\,dx = \cos x \log(\sec y + \tan y)\,dx.$

9. $(3 + 2\sin x + \cos x)\,dy = (1 + 2\sin y + \cos y)\,dx.$

10. $(e^x + 1)\,y\,dy = (y + 1)\,e^x\,dx.$

11. $\dfrac{dy}{dx} = e^{x+y} + x^2 e^y.$

12. Find the equations of the curves for which the
    (*i*) cartesian sub-tangent is constant.   *(Kanpur, 2000)*
    (*ii*) cartesian sub-normal is constant.
    (*iii*) polar sub-tangent is constant.
    (*iv*) polar sub-normal is constant.

13. Find the equation of the curve for which the cartesian sub-tangent varies as the reciprocal of the square of the abscissa.

14. Find the curve which is such that the portion of the *x*-axis cuts off between the origin and the tangent at a point which is twice the abscissa and passes through the point (1, 2).

15. Find the curves for which the sum of the reciprocals of the polar sub-normal and the radius vector is constant.

16. Find the curve in which the angle between the radius vector and the tangent is *m* times the vectorial angle and which passes through the point $(a, \pi/2m)$.

ANSWERS

1. $(x^2 + 1)(y^2 + 1) = c.$

2. $\sqrt{1+x^2} + \sqrt{1+y^2} - \log\{[\sqrt{1+x^2}+1][\sqrt{1+y^2}+1]/xy\} = c.$

3. $2y^2 \log x - 2y \, (y - x)/x + 2cy^2 = 1$.

4. $(1 + \log y)/y + x^2 \cos x - 2x \sin x - 2 \cos x = c$.

5. $y^2 \log y = x \sin x + c$.

6. $(x^2 + y^2) + x \sin 2x + y \sin 2y + \dfrac{1}{2} \cos 2x + \dfrac{1}{2} \cos 2y = c$.

7. $(x - 2) \sqrt{1 + x} + (y + 3) \sqrt{y} = c$.

8. $[\log (\sec x + \tan x)]^2 - [\log (\sec y + \tan y)]^2 = c$.

9. $2 \tan^{-1}\left(1 + \tan \dfrac{1}{2} x\right) = c + \log\left(1 + 2 \tan \dfrac{1}{2} y\right)$.

10. $(1 + y) (1 + e^x) = ce^y$.

11. $e^x + e^{-y} + \dfrac{1}{3}x^3 = c$.

12. (i) $y = ke^{x/c}$.   (ii) $y^2 = 2cx + k$.

   (iii) $r \, (k - \theta) = c$.   (iv) $r = c\theta + k$.

13. $y = ce^{x^3/3k}$.   14. $xy = 2$.

15. $\theta = cr - \log r + k$.   16. $r^m = a^m \sin m\theta$.

15.4. Linear Equations. *A differential equation is said to be linear if the dependent variable and its differential co-efficients occur in the first degree only and are not multiplied together.*

Thus, the most general form of a linear equation of the first order is

$$\frac{dy}{dx} + Py = Q \qquad \qquad ...(i)$$

where, P, Q, are any functions of x.

To solve this equation, we multiply both sides by

$$e^{\int P \, dx}$$

so that we get

$$e^{\int P \, dx}\left[\frac{dy}{dx} + Py\right] = Qe^{\int P \, dx}.$$

The left hand side, now, is the differential co-efficient of

$$ye^{\int P \, dx}.$$

Thus, on integrating, we get

$$ye^{\int P \, dx} = \int Q e^{\int P \, dx} \, dx + c$$

$$\Leftrightarrow \quad y = e^{-\int P \, dx}\left[\int Q e^{\int P \, dx} \, dx + c\right]$$

as the required solution.

Note 1. The factor

$$e^{\int P\,dx}$$

on multiplying by which the left hand side of (i) becomes the differential co-efficient of a function of x and y, is called the **integrating factor** of the differential equation (i).

Note 2. It is very important to remember that on multiplying by the integrating factor, the left hand side becomes the derivative of the product of y and the integrating factor.

Note 3. It will be useful to remember that for every t

$$e^{\log t} = t.$$

15.4.1. Working Rule

(1) *Determine the integrating factor* $e^{\int P\,dx}$ *which is represented by I.F.*

(2) *Then multiply the differential equation by I.F.* $(e^{\int P\,dx})$. *Now integrate by using integration by parts methods taking* $e^{\int P\,dx}$ *as first function and y as second function. Then we get*

$$\text{Dependent variable} \times \text{I.F.} = \int \left\{ Q \cdot e^{\int P\,dx} \right\} dx + c$$

or

$$y \times \text{I.F.} = \int \left\{ Q \cdot e^{\int P\,dx} \right\} dx + c.$$

(B) *If x is independent variable then* $\text{I.F.} = e^{\int P_1\,dy}$ *and solution is*

$$x \times \text{I. F.} = \int \left\{ Q_1 e^{\int P_1\,dy} \right\} dy + c.$$

EXAMPLES

1. *Solve*

$$x^2 (x^2 - 1)\frac{dy}{dx} + x(x^2 + 1)\, y = (x^2 - 1).$$

We have,

$$\frac{dy}{dx} + \frac{x^2 + 1}{x(x^2 - 1)}\, y = \frac{1}{x^2},$$

so that it is linear.

Here, $P = \dfrac{x^2 + 1}{x(x^2 - 1)}$,

$$\therefore \quad \int P\,dx = \int \frac{x^2 + 1}{x(x^2 - 1)}\, dx$$

$$= \int \left(\frac{1}{x+1} + \frac{1}{x-1} - \frac{1}{x} \right) dx = \log \frac{x^2 - 1}{x}.$$

Thus, the integrating factor is

$$e^{\int P\,dx} = e^{\log \frac{x^2-1}{x}} = \frac{x^2-1}{x}.$$

Multiplying by $(x^2 - 1)/x$, we obtain

$$\frac{x^2-1}{x}\left[\frac{dy}{dx} + \frac{x^2+1}{x(x^2-1)}\,y\right] = \frac{1}{x^2}\cdot\frac{x^2-1}{x}.$$

Thus, the solution is

$$y\frac{x^2-1}{x} = \int \frac{x^2-1}{x^3}\,dx + c = \log x + \frac{1}{2x^2} + c.$$

2. *Solve*

$$(x + 2y^3)\frac{dy}{dx} = y. \qquad\qquad \textit{(Bilaspur, 2000)}$$

The equation which involves y^3 is not linear, if we take y as the dependent variable, but since this can be written as

$$y\frac{dx}{dy} = x + 2y^3$$

$$\Rightarrow \quad \frac{dx}{dy} - \frac{x}{y} = 2y^2,$$

we see that the equation is linear, if we take x as the dependent variable.

Integrating factor $= e^{-\int dy/y} = e^{-\log y} = y^{-1} = 1/y.$

Multiplying by this integrating factor, we obtain

$$\frac{1}{y}\left(\frac{dx}{dy} - \frac{x}{y}\right) = 2y.$$

Therefore, the solution is

$$x\frac{1}{y} = y^2 + c \text{ or } x = y\,(c + y^2).$$

3. *Solve* : $(1 + y^2) + (x - e^{\tan^{-1} y})\dfrac{dy}{dx} = 0.$

(Rohilkhand, 1994; Lucknow, 1994, 96; Ravishankar, 1999;
Sagar, 1994; Agra, 2000; Garhwal, 2003; Kumaon, 2002)

The given equation is

$$(1 + y^2)\frac{dx}{dy} + x = e^{\tan^{-1} y}$$

or $\qquad \dfrac{dx}{dy} + \dfrac{1}{1+y^2}\cdot x = \dfrac{1}{1+y^2}e^{\tan^{-1} y}.$

$$\text{I.F.} = e^{\int \frac{1}{1+y^2} dy} = e^{\tan^{-1} y} \qquad \text{(Since } x \text{ is a dependent variable.)}$$

∴ Solution of the equation will be

$$x \cdot e^{\tan^{-1} y} = \int \frac{1}{1+y^2} e^{\tan^{-1} y} \cdot e^{\tan^{-1} y} \, dy + c$$

$$= \int \frac{1}{1+y^2} e^{2 \tan^{-1} y} \, dy + c.$$

Let $\tan^{-1} y = t, \dfrac{1}{1+y^2} dy = dt.$

Then $x \cdot e^{\tan^{-1} y} = \displaystyle\int e^{2t} \, dt + c$

$$= \frac{1}{2} e^{2t} + c$$

or $\qquad x e^{\tan^{-1} y} = \dfrac{1}{2} e^{2 \tan^{-1} y} + c.$

4. Solve : $x \cos x \dfrac{dy}{dx} + y (x \sin x + \cos x) = 1.$ 　　　　　(*Indore, 1995*)

The given equation can be written as

$$\frac{dy}{dx} + y \left(\frac{x \sin x + \cos x}{x \cos x} \right) = \frac{1}{x \cos x}$$

or $\qquad \dfrac{dy}{dx} + y \left(\tan x + \dfrac{1}{x} \right) = \dfrac{1}{x \cos x}$

∴ $\quad \text{I.F.} = e^{\int \left(\tan x + \frac{1}{x} \right) dx}$

$$= e^{(\log \sec x + \log x)} = x \sec x.$$

Hence its solution is

$$x \sec x \cdot y = \int \frac{x \sec x}{x \cos x} \, dx + c$$

or $\qquad x \sec x \cdot y = \tan x + c$

or $\qquad xy \sec x = \tan x + c.$

5. Solve : $\cos x \dfrac{dy}{dx} + y \sin x = \sec^2 x.$

We have,

$$\frac{dy}{dx} + y \tan x = \sec^3 x$$

$$\text{I.F.} = e^{\int \tan x \, dx} = e^{\log \sec x} = \sec x.$$

Hence solution of the equation will be

$$\sec x \cdot y = \int \sec^4 x \, dx + c$$

or

$$y \sec x = \int (1 + \tan^2 x) \sec^2 x \, dx + c$$

$$= \int \sec^2 x \, dx + \int \tan^2 x \cdot \sec^2 x \, dx + c$$

$$= \tan x + \frac{1}{3} \tan^3 x + c.$$

6. *Solve* : $\cos^2 x \dfrac{dy}{dx} + y = \tan x.$

The given equation is

$$\frac{dy}{dx} + \frac{1}{\cos^2 x} y = \tan x \sec^2 x$$

$$\text{I.F.} = e^{\int \sec^2 x \, dx} = e^{\tan x}.$$

Hence its solution will be

$$y \cdot e^{\tan x} = \int e^{\tan x} \cdot \tan x \sec^2 x \, dx.$$

Put $\tan x = t$, $\sec^2 x \, dx = dt$,

$$\therefore \quad y e^t = \int t \cdot e^t \, dt = e^t (t - 1) + c$$

or

$$y = t - 1 + c e^{-t}$$

or

$$y = \tan x - 1 + c e^{-\tan x}.$$

7. *Solve* : $\sec x \, dy = (y + \sin x) \, dx.$

The given equation can be written as

$$\frac{dy}{dx} - y \cos x = \sin x \cos x.$$

$$\therefore \quad \text{I.F.} = e^{-\int \cos x \, dx} = e^{-\sin x}.$$

Hence the solution will be

$$y \cdot e^{-\sin x} = \int e^{-\sin x} \cdot \sin x \cos x \, dx + c.$$

Put $\sin x = t$, $\cos x \, dx = dt$,

$$= \int t e^{-t} \, dt + c$$

$$= -(t + 1) e^{-t} + c$$

$$\therefore \quad y = -(\sin x + 1) + c e^{\sin x}.$$

8. Solve : $x (1 - x^2) \, dy + (2x^2y - y - ax^3) \, dx = 0.$

(Rewa, 1999; Gorakhpur, 2000)

The given differential equation can be put in the form

$$\frac{dy}{dx} + y \cdot \frac{(2x^2 - 1)}{x (1 - x^2)} = \frac{ax^2}{(1 - x^2)}$$

$$\text{I.F.} = e^{\int \frac{(2x^2 - 1)}{x (1 - x^2)} dx} = \frac{\sqrt{1 - x^2}}{x}.$$

Hence solution will be

$$y \cdot \frac{\sqrt{1 - x^2}}{x} = \int \frac{ax^2}{1 - x^2} \cdot \frac{\sqrt{1 - x^2}}{x} \, dx + c$$

$$= \int \frac{ax}{\sqrt{1 - x^2}} \, dx$$

$$= -a \sqrt{1 - x^2} + c$$

or $$y + ax = \frac{cx}{\sqrt{1 - x^2}}.$$

9. Solve : $\sqrt{a^2 + x^2} \, \frac{dy}{dx} + y = \sqrt{a^2 + x^2} - x.$

The given equation can be put in the form

$$\frac{dy}{dx} + \frac{y}{\sqrt{a^2 + x^2}} = \frac{\sqrt{a^2 + x^2} - x}{\sqrt{a^2 + x^2}}$$

$$\therefore \quad \text{I.F.} = e^{\int \frac{1}{(a^2 + x^2)^{1/2}} dx} = e^{\log \frac{x + \sqrt{a^2 + x^2}}{a}}$$

$$= \frac{\sqrt{a^2 + x^2} + x}{a}.$$

Hence the solution of the given equation is

$$\frac{\sqrt{a^2 + x^2} + x}{a} \cdot y = \int \frac{\sqrt{a^2 + x^2} - x}{\sqrt{a^2 + x^2}} \cdot \frac{\sqrt{a^2 + x^2} + x}{a} \, dx$$

$$= \int \frac{(a^2 + x^2) - x^2}{a \sqrt{a^2 + x^2}} \, dx$$

$$= \int \frac{a}{\sqrt{a^2 + x^2}} \, dx = a \sinh^{-1} \frac{x}{a} + c.$$

EXERCISES

Solve the following equations :

1. $(x^2 - 1) \dfrac{dy}{dx} + 2xy = 1$.

2. $\sin x \dfrac{dy}{dx} + y \cos x = x \sin x$.

3. $\dfrac{dy}{dx} + 3x^2 y = x^5 \cdot e^{x^3}$.

4. $x \log x \dfrac{dy}{dx} + y = 2 \log x$.

5. $x \sin x \dfrac{dy}{dx} + (x \cos x + \sin x) y = \sin x$.

6. $\sin x \cos x \dfrac{dy}{dx} = y + \sin x$.

7. $\sin x \dfrac{dy}{dx} + 2y + \sin x (1 + \cos x) = 0$.

8. $(1 + x + xy^2) \, dy + (y + y^3) \, dx = 0$.

9. $(2x - 10y^3) \dfrac{dy}{dx} + y = 0$.   *(Kumaon, 2000)*

10. $\sqrt{x^2 + 1} \dfrac{dy}{dx} + y = \sqrt{x^2 + 1} - x$.

11. $(1 - x^2)^{3/2} \dfrac{dy}{dx} + y - 1 = 0$.

12. $x(x^2 + 1) \dfrac{dy}{dx} = y(1 - x^2) + x^3 \log x$.

13. $(x^2 - 1) \sin x \dfrac{dy}{dx} + [2x \sin x + (x^2 - 1) \cos x] y$

$$- (x^2 - 1) \cos x = 0.$$

14. $(1 + x^2) \dfrac{dy}{dx} + 2xy - 4x^2 = 0$.   *(Sagar, 1999)*

15. $\dfrac{dy}{dx} + y \sec x = \tan x$.

16. $(x + \tan y) \, dy = \sin 2y \, dx$.

17. $\dfrac{dy}{dx} + \dfrac{y}{\sqrt{(1 - x^2)^3}} = \dfrac{x + \sqrt{1 - x^2}}{(1 - x^2)^2}$.

18. $(1 + y^2) \, dx = (\tan^{-1} y - x) \, dy$.   *(Bhopal, 1997; Sagar, 1999;*
                                         Bilaspur, 1997; Jabalpur, 1998, 2000)

19. $\dfrac{dy}{dx} = y \cos x + \cos x \sin^2 x.$

20. $\dfrac{dy}{dx} - \dfrac{1 + 3x^2}{x(1 + x^2)} y = x \dfrac{1 - x^2}{1 + x^2}$ and determine the arbitrary constant

so as to make $y = 0$ when $x = 1.$

21. Find the equation of the curve which passes through the point $(2a, a)$ and for which the sum of the cartesian sub-tangent and the abscissa is equal to the constant a.

22. Find the curves for which the portion of y-axis cuts off between the origin and the tangent varies as the cube of the abscissa of the point of contact.

ANSWERS

1. $y(1 - x^2) = -x + c.$ **2.** $(y - 1) \sin x + x \cos x = c.$

3. $12y = e^{x^3}(2x^3 - 1) + ce^{-x^3}.$ **4.** $y \log x = c + (\log x)^2.$

5. $xy \sin x + \cos x = c.$ **6.** $y \cot x = c + \log \tan \dfrac{1}{2} x.$

7. $y \tan^2 \dfrac{1}{2} x = \sin x - x + c.$ **8.** $xy + \tan^{-1} y = c.$

9. $xy^2 = 2y^5 + c.$ **10.** $y[x + \sqrt{x^2 + 1}] = c + \sinh^{-1} x.$

11. $\log(y - 1) + x/\sqrt{1 - x^2} = c.$

12. $4(x^2 + 1) y + x^3(1 - 2 \log x) = cx.$

13. $y(x^2 - 1) \sin x = (x^2 - 3) \sin x + 2x \cos x + c.$

14. $y(1 + x^2) = \dfrac{4}{3} x^3 + c.$ **15.** $(y - 1)(\sec x + \tan x) + x = c.$

16. $x\sqrt{\cot y} = c + \sqrt{\tan y}.$ **17.** $y = x\sqrt{1 - x^2} + ce^{-x/\sqrt{1 - y^2}}.$

18. $x = \tan^{-1} y - 1 + ce^{\tan^{-1} y}.$

19. $y + \sin^2 x + 2 \sin x + 2 = ce^{\sin x}.$

20. $y = cx(1 + x^2) + x^2; \ c = -\dfrac{1}{2}.$

21. $(x - a) y = a^2.$ **22.** $2y + kx^3 = cx.$

15.5. Equations reducible to the linear form. The equation of the form

$$\dfrac{dy}{dx} + Py = Qy^n,$$

where P and Q are functions of x, is reducible to the linear form, as will now be seen. On dividing by y^n, we get

$$y^{-n}\frac{dy}{dx} + Py^{-n+1} = Q. \qquad \qquad ...(i)$$

Putting $y^{-n+1} = z$ so that $(-n+1)\, y^{-n}\, (dy/dx) = dz/dx$, the equation becomes

$$\frac{dz}{dx} + P(1-n)\, z = Q(1-n)$$

which is linear with, z, as dependent variable.

15.5.1. Working Rule

A. 1. *Write the equation in the form*

$$\frac{dy}{dx} + Py = Qy^n.$$

2. *Divide by y^n and bring it to the form as in § 15.5 equation (i).*

3. *Put $y^{n+1} = v$ and change the equation to the form*

$$\frac{dv}{dx} - (n-1)\, Pv = Q(1-n).$$

4. *Then apply the § 15.4.*

B. *In case of the equation*

$$\frac{dx}{dy} + P_1 x = Q_1 x^n$$

apply the similar rule, i.e., first divide by x^n, then put substitution $x^{1-n} = V$ and this brings a linear differential equation.

EXAMPLES

1. *Solve :* $(x^3 y^2 + xy)\, dx = dy.$ *(Kanpur, 2002)*

We write the equation in the form

$$\frac{dy}{dx} - xy = x^3 y^2.$$

Dividing by y^2, we get

$$\frac{1}{y^2}\frac{dy}{dx} - \frac{x}{y} = x^3.$$

On putting,

$$-\frac{1}{y} = z \implies \frac{1}{y^2}\frac{dy}{dx} = \frac{dz}{dx},$$

we obtain

$$\frac{dz}{dx} + xz = x^3,$$

which is linear. The integrating factor, now, is, $e^{\int x\, dx} = e^{\frac{1}{2}x^2}$ and, therefore, the solution is

$$ze^{\frac{1}{2}x^2} = \int x^3 e^{\frac{1}{2}x^2}\, dx + c.$$

To evaluate the integral of the right side, we put $x^2/2 = t$ and see that

$$\int x^3 e^{\frac{1}{2}x^2}\, dx = 2 \int te^t dt$$

$$= 2\,(te^t - e^t) = 2e^{\frac{1}{2}x^2}\left(\frac{1}{2}x^2 - 1\right).$$

Thus, $z = x^2 - 2 + ce^{-\frac{1}{2}x^2}$ where $z = 1/y$, is the required solution.

2. Solve : $x\dfrac{dy}{dx} + y = y^2 \log x.$ *(Gorakhpur, 1996; Bhopal, 1998;*
Ravishankar, 1998; Indore, 2000)

The given equation can be written as

$$\frac{1}{y^2}\frac{dy}{dx} + \frac{1}{x}\frac{1}{y} = \frac{1}{x}\log x.$$

Now, put $\dfrac{1}{y} = v$ $\therefore$ $-\dfrac{1}{y^2}\dfrac{dy}{dx} = \dfrac{dv}{dx}.$

Hence the equation becomes

$$-\frac{dv}{dx} + \frac{1}{x}v = \frac{1}{x}\log x$$

or $$\frac{dv}{dx} - \frac{1}{x}v = -\frac{1}{x}\log x.$$

This is linear equation in v.

$$\therefore \quad \text{I.F.} = e^{\int P\, dx} = e^{-\int \frac{1}{x}dx} = e^{-\log x} = \frac{1}{x}.$$

Hence the solution of the equation becomes

$$\frac{1}{x}\cdot v = \int -\frac{1}{x^2}\log x\, dx + c$$

$$= \frac{1}{x}\log x - \int \frac{1}{x}\cdot\frac{1}{x}dx$$

$$= \frac{1}{x}\log x + \frac{1}{x} + c$$

or $v = \log x + 1 + cx$

or $\dfrac{1}{y} = cx + \log(ex)$

or $y\,(cx + \log ex) = 1.$

3. *Solve* : $\dfrac{dy}{dx} = x^3 y^3 - xy.$ *(Rohilkhand, 1995)*

The given equation is

$$\frac{1}{y^3}\frac{dy}{dx} + \frac{x}{y^2} = x^3. \qquad \qquad ...(i)$$

Put $\dfrac{1}{y^2} = v$ $\therefore$ $-\dfrac{2}{y^3}\dfrac{dy}{dx} = \dfrac{dv}{dx}.$

Hence equation (i) becomes

$$-\frac{1}{2}\frac{dv}{dx} + vx = x^3$$

or $$\frac{dv}{dx} - 2x \cdot v = -2x^3$$

I.F. $= e^{-\int 2x\, dx} = e^{-x^2}.$

$\therefore$ Solution of the equation will be

$$e^{-x^2} \cdot v = \int -2x^3 \cdot e^{-x^2}\, dx + c.$$

Put $-x^2 = t,\ -2x\, dx = dt$

$$= -\int te^t\, dt + c$$

$$= -(t-1)e^t + c$$

or $$e^{-x^2}\frac{1}{y^2} = -(-x^2-1)e^{-x^2} + c$$

or $$\frac{1}{y^2} = (x^2+1)ce^{x^2}.$$

4. *Solve* : $\dfrac{dy}{dx} - \dfrac{\tan y}{1+x} = (1+x)\, e^x \sec y.$

(Gorakhpur, 2002; Kanpur, 2003)

The given equation is

$$\cos y \frac{dy}{dx} - \frac{\sin y}{1+x} = (1+x)\, e^x. \qquad \qquad ...(i)$$

Let $\sin y = v,\ \cos y \dfrac{dy}{dx} = \dfrac{dv}{dx}.$

Hence (i) becomes $\dfrac{dv}{dx} - \dfrac{v}{1+x} = (1+x)\, e^x$

I.F. $= e^{\int -\frac{1}{1+x}dx} = e^{-\log(1+x)} = \dfrac{1}{1+x}.$

Hence the solution is

$$\frac{1}{1+x} \cdot v = \int e^x \, dx + c$$

$$= e^x + c$$

or $\quad \sin y = (1 + x)(e^x + c)$.

5. *Solve* : $\cos x \, dy = y(\sin x - y)\, dx$. (*Kanpur, 1995*)

The given equation is

$$\cos x \frac{dy}{dx} - y \sin x = -y^2$$

or $\quad \dfrac{dy}{dx} - y \tan x = -y^2 \sec x$

or $\quad -\dfrac{1}{y^2}\dfrac{dy}{dx} + \dfrac{1}{y}\tan x = \sec x.$

Putting $\dfrac{1}{y} = v$ so that $-\dfrac{1}{y^2}\dfrac{dy}{dx} = \dfrac{dv}{dx}$,

we get, $\quad \dfrac{dv}{dx} + v \tan x = \sec x$

I.F. $= e^{\int \tan x \, dx} = \sec x.$

Hence the solution is

$$v \sec x = \int \sec^2 x \, dx + c$$

or $\quad \dfrac{1}{y}\sec x = \tan x + c$

or $\quad \sec x = y(\tan x + c).$

6. *Solve* : $y - x\dfrac{dy}{dx} = a\left(y^2 + \dfrac{dy}{dx}\right).$

(*Rohilkhand, 2000; Sagar, 2000*)

The equation can be written as

$$(x + a)\frac{dy}{dx} - y = -ay^2$$

or $\quad -\dfrac{1}{y^2}\dfrac{dy}{dx} + \dfrac{1}{y}\cdot\dfrac{1}{x+a} = \dfrac{a}{x+a}$ [By dividing with $-y^2(x+a)$]

Put $\dfrac{1}{y} = v$ so that $-\dfrac{1}{y^2}\dfrac{dy}{dx} = \dfrac{dv}{dx}$ $\therefore$ $\dfrac{dv}{dx} + \dfrac{1}{x+a}v = \dfrac{a}{x+a}$

I.F. $= e^{\int \frac{1}{x+a} dx} = (x + a).$

Hence the solution of the equation is

$$v(x+a) = \int \frac{a}{x+a} \cdot (x+a)\,dx + c$$

$$= ax + c$$

or $\quad \dfrac{1}{y}(x+a) = ax + c$

or $\quad (x+a) = y\,(ax+c).$

7. *Solve* : $\dfrac{dz}{dx} + \dfrac{z}{x}\log z = \dfrac{z}{x^2}(\log z)^2.$

The given equation is

$$\frac{1}{z(\log z)^2}\frac{dz}{dx} + \frac{1}{x}\cdot\frac{1}{\log z} = \frac{1}{x^2} \qquad \qquad \ldots(i)$$

Put $\quad -\dfrac{1}{\log z} = v \quad \therefore \quad \dfrac{1}{(\log z)^2}\cdot\dfrac{1}{z}\dfrac{dz}{dx} = \dfrac{dv}{dx}.$

Hence equation (i) becomes

$$\frac{dv}{dx} - \frac{1}{x}v = \frac{1}{x^2}.$$

This is a linear equation where

$$\text{I.F.} = e^{-\int \frac{1}{x}dx} = \frac{1}{x}.$$

Hence the solution is

$$\frac{1}{x}\cdot v = \int \frac{1}{x^3}\,dx + c$$

or $\quad \dfrac{1}{x}\left(-\dfrac{1}{\log z}\right) = -\dfrac{1}{2x^2} + c$

or $\quad \dfrac{1}{x\log z} = \dfrac{1}{2x^2} - c.$

8. *Solve* : $\dfrac{dy}{dx} + y\cos x = y^n\sin 2x.$

The given equation may be written as

$$\frac{1}{y^n}\frac{dy}{dx} + \frac{1}{y^{n-1}}\cos x = 2\sin x\cos x.$$

Put $\quad \dfrac{1}{y^{n-1}} = v \quad \therefore \quad (1-n)\cdot\dfrac{1}{y^n}\dfrac{dy}{dx} = \dfrac{dv}{dx}$

$\therefore \quad \dfrac{1}{1-n}\dfrac{dv}{dx} + v\cos x = 2\sin x\cos x$

or $\dfrac{dv}{dx} + v(1-n)\cos x = 2(1-n)\sin x \cos x.$

This is a linear equation whose

I.F. $= e^{\int (1-n)\cos x\, dx} = e^{(1-n)\sin x}.$

Hence, solution of equation becomes

$e^{(1-n)\sin x} \cdot v = \displaystyle\int 2(1-n)\sin x \cos x \cdot e^{(1-n)\sin x}\, dx + c.$

Put $(1-n)\sin x = t$ $\therefore$ $(1-n)\cos x\, dx = dt$

$\therefore$ $ve^{t} = \displaystyle\int 2\,\dfrac{t}{1-n}\, e^{t}\, dt + c$

$= \dfrac{2}{1-n}\, e^{t}(t-1) + c$

or $v = \dfrac{2}{(1-n)}(t-1) + ce^{-t}$

or $\dfrac{1}{y^{n-1}} = \dfrac{2}{(1-n)}(\sin x - 1) + c\cdot e^{-(1-n)\sin x}.$

9. Solve : $\dfrac{dy}{dx} = e^{x-y}(e^{x} - e^{y}).$

(*Lucknow, 1997; Rewa, 2000; Avadh, 2000*)

The given equation is

$\dfrac{dy}{dx} = \dfrac{e^{x}}{e^{y}}(e^{x} - e^{y})$

or $e^{y}\,\dfrac{dy}{dx} + e^{x}\cdot e^{y} = e^{x}\cdot e^{x}.$

Put $e^{y} = v$ $\therefore$ $e^{y}\cdot\dfrac{dy}{dx} = \dfrac{dv}{dx}.$

Hence equation becomes

$\dfrac{dv}{dx} + ve^{x} = e^{x}\cdot e^{x},$

which is linear and its I.F. $= e^{e^{x}}.$

Hence solution of equation is

$e^{e^{x}}\cdot v = \displaystyle\int e^{x}\cdot e^{x}\cdot e^{e^{x}}\, dx + c.$

Put $e^{x} = t$ $\therefore$ $e^{x}\, dx = dt$, we get

$e^{t}\cdot v = \displaystyle\int te^{t}\, dt + c$

$= e^{t}(t-1) + c$

$\therefore$ $e^{y} = (e^{x} - 1) + ce^{-e^{x}}.$

10. *Solve* : $\dfrac{dy}{dx} + (2x \tan^{-1} y - x^3)(1 + y^2) = 0.$

The given equation can be written as

$$\frac{1}{1+y^2}\frac{dy}{dx} + 2x \tan^{-1} y = x^3.$$

Put $\tan^{-1} y = v$ $\therefore$ $\dfrac{1}{1+y^2}\dfrac{dy}{dx} = \dfrac{dv}{dx}$

$\therefore$ $\dfrac{dv}{dx} + 2xv = x^3.$

This is a linear equation whose I.F. $= e^{x^2}$.

Hence the solution of equation is

$$ve^{x^2} = \int x^3 e^{x^2}\, dx + c$$

$$= \frac{1}{2}e^{x^2}(x^2 - 1) + c$$

or $\qquad 2\tan^{-1} y = x^2 - 1 + 2ce^{-x^2}.$

EXERCISES

Solve the following equations :

1. $\dfrac{dy}{dx} + \dfrac{y}{x} = y^2 x$

2. $x\dfrac{dy}{dx} + y = y^2 \log x$

3. $x\dfrac{dy}{dx} + y = y^2 x^3 \cos x$

4. $x^3 \dfrac{dy}{dx} - x^2 y + y^4 \cos x = 0$

(Jiwaji, 2000)

5. $\dfrac{dy}{dx} = y \tan x - y^2 \sec x$

6. $x\dfrac{dy}{dx} + y = x^3 y^4$

7. $\dfrac{1}{y}\dfrac{dy}{dx} + \dfrac{x}{1-x^2} = xy^{-1/2}$

8. $(xy - x^2)\dfrac{dy}{dx} = y^2$

9. $\dfrac{dy}{dx} + \dfrac{y}{x-1} = xy^{1/3}$

10. $\dfrac{dy}{dx} + xy = y^2 e^{\frac{1}{2}x^2} \log x$

11. $y(x^2 y + e^x)\, dx - e^x\, dy = 0$

12. $3\dfrac{dy}{dx} + \dfrac{2}{x+1}y = \dfrac{x^3}{y^2}$

(Gorakhpur, 2003)

13. $\dfrac{dy}{dx} + y \cot x = y^2 \sin^2 x$

14. $\dfrac{dy}{dx}(x^2 y^3 + xy) = 1$

(Ajmer, 1998)

15. $\dfrac{dy}{dx} + yx = y^2 e^{x^2/2} \sin x$ *(Garhwal, 1996)*

16. $y\,(2xy + e^x)\,dx - e^x\,dy = 0$ *(Vikram, 1998)*

17. $\dfrac{dy}{dx} + \dfrac{1}{x} \tan y = \dfrac{1}{x^2} \tan y \sin y$

18. $\dfrac{dy}{dx} + x \sin 2y = x^3 \cos^2 y$

(Lucknow, 1993, 96; Bilaspur, 1995, 99)

19. $xy - \dfrac{dy}{dx} = y^3 e^{-x^2}$ **20.** $2\dfrac{dy}{dx} - y \sec x = y^3 \tan x$

(Ravishankar, 2000)

ANSWERS

1. $1 + x^2 y + cxy = 0.$ **2.** $y\,(1 + cx + \log x) = 1.$

3. $xy\,(x \sin x + \cos x + c) + 1 = 1.$ **4.** $x^3 = (c + 3 \sin x)\,y^3.$

5. $\sec x = (c + \tan x)\,y.$ **6.** $(-3 \log x + c)\,x^3 y^3 = 1.$

7. $\sqrt{y} = \dfrac{1}{3}(x^2 - 1) + c\sqrt[4]{1 - x^2}.$ **8.** $y = (\log y + c)\,x.$

9. $y^{2/3} = c\,(x-1)^{-2/3} + \dfrac{1}{4}(x-1)^2 + \dfrac{2}{5}(x-1).$

10. $ye^{\frac{1}{2}x^2}(c + x - x \log x) = 1.$ **11.** $x^3 y + 3e^x = cy.$

12. $y^2\,(x+1)^2 = \dfrac{1}{6}x^6 + \dfrac{2}{5}x^5 + \dfrac{1}{4}x^4 + c.$

13. $\dfrac{1}{y}\operatorname{cosec} x = \cos x - c.$ **14.** $-\dfrac{1}{x} = y^2 - 2 + ce^{-y^2/2}.$

15. $ye^{x^2/2}(x \log x - x + c) + 1 = 0.$ **16.** $y\,(x^2 + c) + e^x = 0.$

17. $2x = \sin y\,(1 - 2cx^2).$

18. $\tan y = \dfrac{1}{2}(x^2 - 1) + ce^{-x^2}.$ **19.** $e^{x^2} = y^2\,(2x + c).$

20. $-\dfrac{1}{y^2}(\sec x + \tan x) = \sec x + \tan x - x + c.$

15.6. Change of Variables

Sometimes a substitution or the change of variables reduces a given differential equation to the form in which the variables are separable. The following examples will make the students familiar with the process.

EXAMPLES

1. *Solve* : $(x + y)^2 \dfrac{dy}{dx} = a^2$. (*Lucknow, 1995*)

Put $x + y = v$, then $1 + \dfrac{dy}{dx} = \dfrac{dv}{dx}$

or $\qquad \dfrac{dy}{dx} = \dfrac{dv}{dx} - 1$.

Putting the values in given equation, we have

$$v^2 \left(\dfrac{dv}{dx} - 1 \right) = a^2$$

or $\qquad v^2 \dfrac{dv}{dx} = (v^2 + a^2)$

or $\qquad dx = \dfrac{v^2}{v^2 + a^2}\, dv = \dfrac{v^2 + a^2 - a^2}{v^2 + a^2}\, dv$

$$= \left(1 - \dfrac{a^2}{v^2 + a^2} \right) dv.$$

Integrating, we get

$$x = v - a \tan^{-1} \dfrac{v}{a} + c$$

or $\qquad x = x + y - a \tan^{-1} \dfrac{x + y}{a} + c$

or $\qquad a \tan \left(\dfrac{y - c}{a} \right) = x + y$.

2. *Solve* : $\cos (x + y)\, dy = dx$.

  (*Poorvanchal, 1994; Rohilkhand, 1999*)

We have,

$$\cos (x + y) \dfrac{dy}{dx} = 1.$$

Put $x + y = v$ $\therefore$ $1 + \dfrac{dy}{dx} = \dfrac{dv}{dx}$, we get

$$\cos v \left(\dfrac{dv}{dx} - 1 \right) = 1$$

or $\qquad dx = \dfrac{\cos v}{1 + \cos v}\, dv = \left(1 - \dfrac{1}{1 + \cos v} \right) dv$

or $\qquad dx = \left(1 - \dfrac{1}{2} \sec^2 \dfrac{v}{2} \right) dv$.

Integrating the above equation, we get

$$x + c = v - \tan \frac{v}{2}.$$

Now, replacing v by $(x + y)$; we get

$$y - c = \tan\left(\frac{x+y}{2}\right).$$

3. *Solve* : $\dfrac{dy}{dx} = (4x + y + 1)^2$.   (*Bilaspur, 2000*)

Put $4x + y + 1 = v$,

$$\therefore \quad \frac{dy}{dx} = \frac{dv}{dx} - 4.$$

Hence the given equation becomes

$$\frac{dv}{dx} - 4 = v^2$$

or $$\frac{dv}{v^2 + 4} = dx.$$

Integrating it, we get

$$\frac{1}{2} \tan^{-1} \frac{v}{2} = x + c$$

or $4x + y + 1 = 2 \tan (2x + c)$.

4. *Solve* : $x\, dy - y\, dx = (x^2 \pm y^2)^{1/2}\, dx$.

Divide both sides by x^2

$$\frac{x\, dy - y\, dx}{x^2} = \frac{1}{2} \sqrt{1 \pm \left(\frac{y^2}{x^2}\right)}\, dx.$$

Put $\dfrac{y}{x} = t \quad \therefore \quad \dfrac{x\, dy - y\, dx}{x^2} = dt$

$$\therefore \quad dt = \frac{1}{x} \sqrt{1 \pm t^2}\, dx$$

or $$\frac{dt}{\sqrt{1 \pm t^2}} = \frac{dx}{x}.$$

On integration, we get

$$\sin^{-1} t = \log x + c \text{ or } \sinh^{-1} t = \log x + c$$

or $\dfrac{y}{x} = \sin \log (kx)$ or $\dfrac{y}{x} = \sinh (\log kx)$

or $y = x \sin (\log kx)$

or $y = x \sinh (\log kx)$.

5. Solve : $\dfrac{x\,dx + y\,dy}{x\,dy - y\,dx} = \sqrt{\dfrac{a^2 - x^2 - y^2}{x^2 + y^2}}.$

(Rohilkhand, 2002; Jabalpur, 2000;
Agra, 1994; Garhwal, 2000; Kumaon, 2002)

Let

$$x = r \cos\theta; \quad \therefore \quad \frac{dx}{d\theta} = \frac{dr}{d\theta}\cos\theta - r\sin\theta$$

$$y = r \sin\theta; \quad \therefore \quad \frac{dy}{d\theta} = \frac{dr}{d\theta}\sin\theta + r\cos\theta$$

$$\frac{dy}{dx} = \frac{dy/d\theta}{dx/d\theta}. \text{ Also } x^2 + y^2 = r^2.$$

By these substitutions the given equation reduces to

$$\frac{r\cos\theta\left(\dfrac{dr}{d\theta}\cos\theta - r\sin\theta\right) + r\sin\theta\left(\dfrac{dr}{d\theta}\sin\theta + r\cos\theta\right)}{r\cos\theta\left(\dfrac{dr}{d\theta}\sin\theta + r\cos\theta\right) - r\sin\theta\left(\dfrac{dr}{d\theta}\cos\theta - r\sin\theta\right)} = \sqrt{\frac{a^2 - r^2}{r^2}}$$

or $\qquad \dfrac{r\dfrac{dr}{d\theta}(\cos^2\theta + \sin^2\theta)}{r^2(\cos^2\theta + \sin^2\theta)} = \dfrac{(a^2 - r^2)^{1/2}}{r}$

or $\qquad \dfrac{dr}{d\theta} = (a^2 - r^2)^{1/2}$

or $\qquad \dfrac{dr}{(a^2 - r^2)^{1/2}} = d\theta$ or $\sin^{-1}\dfrac{r}{a} = \theta + c$

$\therefore \quad r = a\sin(\theta + c).$

By putting the values of r and θ, we get

$$(x^2 + y^2)^{1/2} = a\sin\left\{\tan^{-1}\left(\frac{y}{x}\right) + c\right\}.$$

EXERCISES

Solve the following differential equations :

1. $(x - y)^2 \dfrac{dy}{dx} = a^2$
    2. $\dfrac{dy}{dx} = \sin(x + y) + \cos(x + y)$

(Garhwal, 2001)

3. $\sin^{-1}\left(\dfrac{dy}{dx}\right) = x + y$
    4. $\dfrac{dy}{dx} = (x + y)^2$ (Rohilkhand, 2003)

5. $x\,dy - y\,dx = (x^2 + y^2)\,dx$

6. $\dfrac{dy}{dx} - x \tan(y - x) = 1$ 7. $\left(\dfrac{x+y-a}{x+y-b}\right)\dfrac{dy}{dx} = \dfrac{x+y+a}{x+y+b}$

8. $\sin y \dfrac{dy}{dx} = \cos y \,(1 - x \cos y)$ *(Rohilkhand, 1999)*

9. $\sec^2 y \dfrac{dy}{dx} + 2x \tan y = x^3$

10. $\dfrac{dy}{dx} = e^{x-y} \,(e^x - e^y)$ *(Rohilkhand, 1996)*

ANSWERS

1. $2y + c = a \log \dfrac{x - y - a}{x - y + a}$.

2. $\log\left(1 + \tan \dfrac{x+y}{2}\right) = x + c$.

3. $(x + c)\left\{1 + \tan\left(\dfrac{x+y}{2}\right)\right\} + 2 = 0$.

4. $x + y = \tan(x + c)$.

5. $y = x \tan(c - ay)$.

6. $\sin(y - x) = ce^{1/2x^2}$.

7. $(b - a) \log \{(x + y)^2 - ab\} = 2\,(x - y) + c$.

8. $\sec y = (x + 1) + ce^x$.

9. $\tan y = ce^{-x^2} + \dfrac{1}{2}(x^2 - 1)$.

10. $e^y = ce^{-e^x} + e^x - 1$.

15.7. Homogeneous Equations. A differential equation of the form

$$\frac{dy}{dx} = \frac{f(x, y)}{\varphi(x, y)},$$

where $f(x, y)$ and $\varphi(x, y)$ are homogeneous functions of x, y and of the same degree, is said to be *homogeneous*. Such equations can be solved by putting

$$y = vx,$$

so that the dependent variable y is changed to another variable v.

Since $f(x, y)$ and $\varphi(x, y)$ are homogeneous functions of the same degree say, n, they can be written as

$$f(x, y) = x^n f_1\left(\frac{y}{x}\right) \text{ and } \varphi(x, y) = x^n \varphi_1\left(\frac{y}{x}\right).$$

As $y = vx$, we have

$$\frac{dy}{dx} = v + x\frac{dv}{dx}.$$

The given differential equation, therefore, becomes

$$v + x\frac{dv}{dx} = \frac{f_1(v)}{\varphi_1(v)}$$

$$\Rightarrow \quad \frac{\varphi_1(v)\,dv}{f_1(v) - v\,\varphi_1(v)} = \frac{dx}{x},$$

so that the variables v and x are now separable.

15.7.1. Working Rule

1. *Put $y = vx$ (or $x = vy$).*
2. *Transform the given equation in terms of v and x (or v and y).*
3. *Apply the method of separation of variables.*
4. *In the end, after integration replace v by y/x (or x/y).*

EXAMPLES

1. *Solve :* $x^2\,dy + y(x + y)\,dx = 0$.

Here, we have

$$\frac{dy}{dx} + \frac{y(x + y)}{x^2} = 0,$$

so that the equation is homogeneous. Putting $y = vx$, we get

$$v + \frac{x\,dv}{dx} + v(1 + v) = 0$$

$$\Rightarrow \quad \frac{dv}{v^2 + 2v} = -\frac{dx}{x},$$

$$\Rightarrow \quad \frac{1}{2}\left(\frac{1}{v} - \frac{1}{v + 2}\right)dv = -\frac{dx}{x}.$$

Thus, the solution is

$$\frac{1}{2}\log\frac{v}{v + 2} = -\log x + c,$$

$$\Rightarrow \quad \log\sqrt{\frac{y}{y + 2x}} + \log x = c,$$

$$\Rightarrow \quad \log\left(x\sqrt{\frac{x}{y + 2x}}\right) = c,$$

$$\Rightarrow \quad x\sqrt{\frac{x}{y + 2x}} = e^c = a,$$

where, a, is a constant,

$$\Rightarrow \quad x^2 y = a^2(y + 2x).$$

2. *Solve* : $(x^2 + y^2)\dfrac{dy}{dx} = xy.$

The given equation can be written as

$$\frac{dy}{dx} = \frac{xy}{x^2 + y^2},$$

which is homogeneous. To solve it, put $y = vx$

$$\therefore \quad \frac{dy}{dx} = v + x\frac{dv}{dx}.$$

By substituting these values, the given equation becomes

$$v + x\frac{dv}{dx} = \frac{x \cdot vx}{x^2 + v^2 x^2} = \frac{v}{1 + v^2}$$

or $\qquad x\dfrac{dv}{dx} = \dfrac{v}{1 + v^2} - v$

or $\qquad x\dfrac{dv}{dx} = \dfrac{v - v - v^3}{1 + v^2} = -\dfrac{v^2}{1 + v^2}$

or $\qquad \left(-\dfrac{1 + v^2}{v^3}\right) dv = \dfrac{dx}{x}$

or $\qquad \left(-\dfrac{1}{v^3} - \dfrac{1}{v}\right) dv = \dfrac{dx}{x}.$

Integrating both sides of above equation, we get

$$\frac{1}{2v^2} - \log v = \log x + \log c$$

or $\qquad \dfrac{1}{2v^2} = \log vxc$

or $\qquad \dfrac{1}{2}\dfrac{x^2}{y^2} = \log \dfrac{y}{x} \cdot x \cdot c = \log cy$

or $\qquad cy = e^{x^2/2y^2}.$

3. *Solve* : $x^2 y\, dx - (x^3 + y^3)\, dy = 0.$

The given equation is

$$\frac{dy}{dx} = \frac{x^2 y}{x^3 + y^3}.$$

This is a homogeneous differential equation. To solve it, we put

$$y = vx \quad \therefore \quad \frac{dy}{dx} = v + x\frac{dv}{dx}.$$

Then given equation becomes

$$v + x \frac{dv}{dx} = \frac{x^2 \cdot vx}{x^3 + v^3 \cdot x^3} = \frac{v}{1 + v^3}$$

$$\therefore \quad x \frac{dv}{dx} = \frac{v}{1 + v^3} - v = \frac{-v^4}{1 + v^3}$$

or $$\left(-\frac{1}{v^4} - \frac{1}{v} \right) dv = \frac{dx}{x}.$$

Integrating it, we get

$$\frac{1}{3v^3} - \log v = \log x + \log c$$

$$\therefore \quad \log cxv = \frac{1}{3v^2}$$

or $$cy = e^{x^3/3y^3}.$$

4. Solve : $x \dfrac{dy}{dx} + \dfrac{y^2}{x} = y.$

We have,

$$\frac{dy}{dx} = \frac{xy - y^2}{x^2}.$$

Put $y = vx$ $\therefore$ $\dfrac{dy}{dx} = v + x \dfrac{dv}{dx},$

we get, $$v + x \frac{dv}{dx} = \frac{x \cdot vx - v^2 x^2}{x^2} = v - v^2$$

or $$x \frac{dv}{dx} = -v^2$$

or $$\frac{dv}{-v^2} = \frac{dx}{x}.$$

On integrating, we get

$$\frac{1}{v} = \log x + \log c$$

or $$\frac{x}{y} = \log cx$$

or $$cx = e^{x/y}.$$

5. Solve : $y - x \dfrac{dy}{dx} = x + y \dfrac{dy}{dx}$ or $(x + y)\, dy + (x - y)\, dx = 0.$

The given equation can be written as

$$\frac{dy}{dx} = \frac{y - x}{y + x}.$$

Put $y = vx$, $\dfrac{dy}{dx} = v + x\dfrac{dv}{dx}$, we get

$$v + x\frac{dv}{dx} = \frac{vx - x}{vx + x} = \frac{v - 1}{v + 1}$$

or $\quad x\dfrac{dv}{dx} = \dfrac{v - 1}{v + 1} - v = -\dfrac{1 + v^2}{v + 1}$

$\therefore \quad \dfrac{v + 1}{1 + v^2}\, dv = -\dfrac{dx}{x}$.

Integrating it, we get

$$\frac{1}{2}\log(1 + v^2) + \tan^{-1} v = -\log x + \log c$$

or $\quad \dfrac{1}{2}\log\dfrac{(1 + v^2)\, x^2}{c^2} = -\tan^{-1} v$

or $\quad \log\dfrac{x^2 + y^2}{c^2} = -2\tan^{-1}(y/x)$

or $\quad x^2 + y^2 = c^2 e^{-2\tan^{-1}(y/x)}$.

6. *Solve* : $x\cos\dfrac{y}{x}(y\, dx + x\, dy) = y\sin\dfrac{y}{x}(x\, dy - y\, dx)$.

(Agra, 2000; Kumaon, 2003)

The given equation can be written as

$$x\cos\frac{y}{x}\left(y + x\frac{dy}{dx}\right) = y\sin\frac{y}{x}\left(x\frac{dy}{dx} - y\right)$$

or $\quad \dfrac{dy}{dx}\left(x\cos\dfrac{y}{x} - y\sin\dfrac{y}{x}\right) = -y\left(y\sin\dfrac{y}{x} + x\cos\dfrac{y}{x}\right)$

or $\quad \dfrac{dy}{dx} = \dfrac{y}{x}\cdot\dfrac{y\sin(y/x) + x\cos(y/x)}{y\sin(y/x) - x\cos(y/x)}$.

Put $y = vx$ $\therefore$ $\dfrac{dy}{dx} = v + x\dfrac{dv}{dx}$, we get

$$v + x\frac{dv}{dx} = \frac{v(v\sin v + \cos v)}{(v\sin v - \cos v)}$$

or $\quad x\dfrac{dv}{dx} = \dfrac{v(v\sin v + \cos v)}{v\sin v - \cos v} - v$

$$= v\left(\frac{v\sin v + \cos v - v\sin v + \cos v}{v\sin v - \cos v}\right)$$

or $\qquad x\dfrac{dv}{dx} = \dfrac{2v\cos v}{v\sin v - \cos v}$

or $\qquad \left(\dfrac{v\sin v - \cos v}{v\cos v}\right)dv = 2\dfrac{dx}{x}$

or $\qquad \left(\tan v - \dfrac{1}{v}\right)dv = 2\dfrac{dx}{x}.$

Integrating it, we get

$\qquad \log \sec v - \log v = 2\log x + \log c$

or $\qquad \log \dfrac{\sec v}{v} = \log cx^2$

or $\qquad \sec(y/x) = cxy.$

7. Solve : $x\dfrac{dy}{dx} - y = x\sqrt{x^2 + y^2}.$ $\qquad$ *(Avadh, 2002)*

The given equation is

$$\dfrac{dy}{dx} = \dfrac{y + x\sqrt{x^2 + y^2}}{x}.$$

Put $y = vx$ so that $\dfrac{dy}{dx} = v + x\dfrac{dv}{dx}$, we get

$$v + x\dfrac{dv}{dx} = \dfrac{vx + x\sqrt{x^2 + v^2 x^2}}{x}$$

$$= v + x\sqrt{1 + v^2}$$

or $\qquad \dfrac{dv}{\sqrt{1 + v^2}} = dx.$

Integrating the above equation, we get

$\qquad \sinh^{-1} v = x + c$

or $\qquad v = \sinh(x + c)$

or $\qquad y = x\sinh(x + c).$

EXERCISES

Solve the following differential equations :

1. $(x + y)\,dy + (x - y)\,dx = 0$ $\qquad$ **2.** $\dfrac{2\,dy}{dx} = \dfrac{y}{x} + \dfrac{y^2}{x^2}$

3. $(x^3 + y^3)\,dx = (x^2 y + xy^2)\,dy$ $\qquad$ **4.** $(x^2 - y^2)\,dx + 2xy\,dy = 0$

5. $\dfrac{dy}{dx} + \dfrac{x - 2y}{2x - y} = 0$ $\qquad$ **6.** $x(x - y)\,dy = y(x + y)\,dx$

7. $(x^2 + xy) \, dy = (x^2 + y^2) \, dx$ *(Garhwal, 2001)*

8. $x^2 y \, dy + (x^3 + x^2 y - 2xy^2 - y^3) \, dx = 0$

9. $[2\sqrt{xy} - x] \, dy + \cdot dx = 0$ **10.** $x^2 \dfrac{dy}{dx} = \dfrac{y(x+y)}{2}$

11. $\dfrac{dy}{dx} + \dfrac{x^2 + 3y^2}{3x^2 + y^2} = 0$

12. $x \sin \dfrac{y}{x} \, dy = \left(y \sin \dfrac{y}{x} - x \right) dx$ *(Gorakhpur, 2000)*

13. $(6x^2 + 2y^2) \, dx - (x^2 + 4xy) \, dy = 0$

14. $\dfrac{dy}{dx} = \dfrac{y}{x} + \tan \dfrac{y}{x}$

15. $(1 + e^{x/y}) \, dx + e^{x/y} \left(1 - \dfrac{x}{y} \right) dy = 0$

16. $\{ x \sqrt{x^2 + y^2} - y^2 \} \, dx + xy \, dy = 0$

17. $(2x - y) \, dx + (x - 2y) \, dy = 0$

18. $x \dfrac{dy}{dx} = y (\log y - \log x + 1)$

ANSWERS

1. $\dfrac{1}{2} \log (x^2 + y^2) + \tan^{-1}(y/x) = c.$ **2.** $y - x = c\sqrt{xy}.$

3. $y + x \log [c(x - y)] = 0.$ **4.** $x^2 + y^2 = cx.$

5. $(x + y)^3 = c(y - x).$ **6.** $cxy = e^{-x/y}.$

7. $(x - y)^2 = cxe^{-y/x}.$

8. $\log \dfrac{c(y - x)}{x^4 (y + x)} = \dfrac{2x}{x + y}.$ **9.** $\log y + \sqrt{x/y} = c.$

10. $(y - x)^2 = cy^2 x.$

11. $\log (x + y) + 2xy (x + y)^{-2} = c.$ **12.** $\log x = \cos(y/x) + c.$

13. $(2x + y)(2y - 3x) = cx.$ **14.** $\sin(y/x) = cx.$

15. $x + ye^{x/y} = c.$

16. $\sqrt{x^2 + y^2} = x \log(c/x).$ **17.** $(x + y)^3 (x - y) = c.$

18. $y = xe^{cx}.$

15.8. Equations reducible to the homogeneous form. The equations of the form

$$\frac{dy}{dx} = \frac{ax + by + c}{Ax + By + C}$$

can be reduced to a homogeneous form by changing the variables x, y to X, Y related by the equations

$$x = X + h, \; y = Y + k,$$

where h, k are the constants to be chosen so as to make the given equation homogeneous. We have,

$$\frac{dy}{dx} = \frac{d(Y+k)}{dx} = \frac{dY}{dx} = \frac{dY}{dX} \cdot \frac{dX}{dx} = \frac{dY}{dX} \qquad \qquad ...(1)$$

∴ The equation becomes

$$\frac{dY}{dX} = \frac{aX + bY + (ah + bk + c)}{AX + BY + (Ah + Bk + C)}. \qquad \qquad ...(2)$$

Let h and k be chosen so as to satisfy the equations

$$ah + bk + c = 0, \; Ah + Bk + C = 0.$$

These give

$$h = \frac{bC - Bc}{aB - Ab}, \quad k = \frac{Ac - aC}{aB - Ab},$$

which are meaningful except when $aB - Ab = 0$, *i.e.*, when $a/A = b/B$.

The homogeneous equation

$$\frac{dY}{dX} = \frac{aX + bY}{AX + BY}$$

can now be solved by means of the substitution

$$Y = vX.$$

Exceptional case. Let

$$\frac{a}{A} = \frac{b}{B} = r, \text{ say}$$

∴ $a = Ar, \; b = Br$.

The equation now becomes

$$\frac{dy}{dx} = \frac{r(Ax + By) + c}{Ax + By + C}.$$

We put, $Ax + By = z$ so that $A + B\dfrac{dy}{dx} = \dfrac{dz}{dx}$ and obtain

$$\frac{dz}{dx} = B\frac{rz + c}{z + C} + A,$$

so that we obtain a differential equation with variables separable.

15.8.1. Working Rule

1. *Put $x = X + h$, $y = Y + k$ in the given differential equation.*

2. *Equate the constant terms in the numerator and denominator to zero.*

3. *Solve these resulting equations of h and k obtained in (2) for h and k.*

4. *Solve the resulting homogeneous equations in X and Y by method of § 15.7.*

5. *Replace X by $x - h$ and Y by $y - k$.*

6. *Substitute the values of h and k.*

Case (B). When $\dfrac{a}{A} = \dfrac{b}{B}$

1. *Put $ax + by = v$.*

2. *Solve the resulting equation by using § 15.3 (variables separable method).*

EXAMPLES

1. *Solve* :

$$\frac{dy}{dx} = \frac{x + 2y + 3}{2x + 3y + 4}.$$

Putting $x = X + h$, $y = Y + k$, the above equation becomes

$$\frac{dY}{dX} = \frac{X + 2Y + (h + 2k + 3)}{2X + 3Y + (2h + 3k + 4)}.$$

To determine h and k, we have

$$h + 2k + 3 = 0, \quad 2h + 3k + 4 = 0.$$

$$\Rightarrow \quad h = 1, \, k = -2$$

$$\therefore \quad \frac{dY}{dX} = \frac{X + 2Y}{2X + 3Y}.$$

Putting $Y = vX$, we get

$$v + X\frac{dv}{dx} = \frac{1 + 2v}{2 + 3v}$$

$$\Rightarrow \quad \frac{2 + 3v}{3v^2 - 1}\, dv = -\frac{dX}{X}$$

$$\Rightarrow \quad \left[\frac{2 + \sqrt{3}}{2(\sqrt{3}\, v - 1)} - \frac{2 - \sqrt{3}}{2(\sqrt{3}\, v + 1)} \right] dv = -\frac{dX}{X}$$

$$\Rightarrow \quad \frac{2 + \sqrt{3}}{2} \log(\sqrt{3}\, v - 1) - \frac{(2 - \sqrt{3})}{2} \log(\sqrt{3}\, v + 1)$$

$$= [-\log X + c]\sqrt{3}$$

$$\Rightarrow \frac{2+\sqrt{3}}{2} \log(\sqrt{3}\,Y - X) - \frac{2-\sqrt{3}}{2} \log(\sqrt{3}\,Y + X) = \sqrt{3}\,c = a.$$

This is the required solution where $X = x - 1$, $Y = y + 2$.

2. *Solve* : $(2x + y + 3)\, dx = (2y + x + 1)\, dy.$

The given equation is

$$\frac{dy}{dx} = \frac{2x + y + 3}{2y + x + 1}.$$

Here $\dfrac{a}{A} = \dfrac{2}{1} = 2$, $\dfrac{b}{B} = \dfrac{1}{2} \Rightarrow \dfrac{a}{A} \neq \dfrac{b}{B}$ (Case A above).

This is the equation reducible to homogeneous form. To solve it, put $x = X + h$ and $y = Y + k$, we get

$$\frac{dY}{dX} = \frac{2X + Y + (2h + k + 3)}{2Y + X + (h + 2k + 1)}.$$

Putting $2h + k + 3 = 0$, $h + 2k + 1 = 0$, *i.e.*, $h = -\dfrac{5}{3}$, $k = \dfrac{1}{3}$.

Hence $x = X - \dfrac{5}{3}$ and $y = Y + \dfrac{1}{3} \Rightarrow X = x + \dfrac{5}{3}$ and $Y = y - \dfrac{1}{3}$,

we get, $\dfrac{dY}{dX} = \dfrac{2X + Y}{2Y + X}.$

Put $Y = vX$ so that $\dfrac{dY}{dX} = v + X\dfrac{dv}{dx}$,

$$\therefore \quad v + X\frac{dv}{dx} = \frac{2 + v}{2v + 1}$$

or $\quad X\dfrac{dv}{dx} = \dfrac{2 + v}{2v + 1} - v = \dfrac{2(1 - v^2)}{2v + 1}$

or $\quad \dfrac{2v + 1}{(1 - v)(1 + v)}\, dv = 2\dfrac{dX}{X}$

or $\quad \left[\dfrac{3}{2}\cdot\dfrac{1}{1 - v} - \dfrac{1}{2(1 + v)}\right] dv = 2\dfrac{dX}{X}.$

Integrating the above equation, we get

$$-3 \log(1 - v) - \log(1 + v) = 4 \log X - \log c$$

or $\quad \log X^4 (1 + v)(1 - v)^3 = \log c$

or $\quad X^4\left(1 + \dfrac{Y}{X}\right)\left(1 - \dfrac{Y}{X}\right)^3 = c$

or $\quad (X + Y)(X - Y)^3 = c.$

Putting the values of X, Y and h, k, we get

$$\left(x + y + \frac{4}{3}\right)(x - y + 2)^3 = c.$$

3. Solve : $\dfrac{dy}{dx} + \dfrac{x - y - 2}{x - 2y - 3} = 0.$ (*Avadh, 2000*)

The given equation is reducible to homogeneous equation. To solve it, put $x = X + h$, $y = Y + k$, we have

$$\frac{dY}{dX} + \frac{X - Y + (h - k - 2)}{(X - 2Y) + (h - 2k - 3)} = 0.$$

Choose $h - k - 2 = 0$ and $h - 2k - 3 = 0$

$\therefore \quad h = 1$, $k = -1$

$\therefore \quad \dfrac{dY}{dX} + \dfrac{X - Y}{X - 2Y} = 0.$

Put $Y = vX$ so that $\dfrac{dY}{dX} = v + X\dfrac{dv}{dx}$, we get

$$v + X\frac{dv}{dX} + \frac{1 - v}{1 - 2v} = 0$$

or $$X\frac{dv}{dX} + \frac{1 - 2v^2}{1 - 2v} = 0$$

or $$\frac{(2 - 4v)\,dv}{(1 - 2v^2)} + \frac{2\,dX}{X} = 0$$

or $$\left[2\cdot\frac{1}{2\left(\frac{1}{2} - v^2\right)} + \frac{-4v}{(1 - 2v^2)}\right]dv + \frac{2\,dX}{X} = 0$$

or $$\frac{1}{2\cdot\frac{1}{\sqrt{2}}}\log\left(\frac{\frac{1}{\sqrt{2}} + v}{\frac{1}{\sqrt{2}} - v}\right) + \log(1 - 2v^2) + \log X^2 = \log c$$

or $$\frac{1}{\sqrt{2}}\log\left(\frac{1 + \sqrt{2}\,v}{1 - \sqrt{2}\,v}\right) + \log(1 - 2v^2)X^2 = \log c$$

or $$\log\left(\frac{1 + \sqrt{2}\,v}{1 - \sqrt{2}\,v}\right)^{1/\sqrt{2}} + \log(X^2 - 2Y^2) = \log c$$

or $\log \left(\dfrac{X + \sqrt{2}\,Y}{X - \sqrt{2}\,Y} \right)^{1/\sqrt{2}} + \log\,(X^2 - 2Y^2) = \log c$

where $X = x - 1$ and $Y = y + 1$.

4. *Solve* : $\dfrac{dy}{dx} = \dfrac{x + 2y - 3}{2x + y - 3}$.   *(Avadh, 2002; Lucknow, 1993)*

Put $x = X + h$ and $y = Y + k$, we get

$$\frac{dY}{dX} = \frac{X + 2Y + (h + 2k - 3)}{2X + Y + (2h + k - 3)}.$$

Choose h and k such that $h + 2k - 3 = 0$ and $2h + k - 3 = 0$.

$\therefore \quad h = 1, \ k = 1$.

Then $\dfrac{dY}{dX} = \dfrac{X + 2Y}{2X + Y}$.

Putting $Y = vX$ $\therefore \ \dfrac{dY}{dX} = v + X\dfrac{dv}{dX}$, we get

$$v + X\frac{dv}{dX} = \frac{1 + 2v}{2 + v}$$

or $X\dfrac{dv}{dX} = \dfrac{1 + 2v}{2 + v} - v = \dfrac{1 - v^2}{2 + v}$

or $\dfrac{2 + v}{(1 - v)\,(1 + v)}\,dv = \dfrac{dX}{X}$

or $\left[\dfrac{3}{2\,(1 - v)} + \dfrac{1}{2\,(1 + v)} \right] dv = \dfrac{dX}{X}$.

On integration, we get

$- 3 \log (1 - v) + \log (1 + v) = 2 \log X + \log c$

or $\dfrac{1 + v}{(1 - v)^3} = cX^2$

or $\left(1 + \dfrac{Y}{X} \right) = cX^2 \left(1 - \dfrac{Y}{X} \right)^3$

or $(X + Y) = c\,(X - Y)^3$

or $(x + y - 2) = c\,(x - y)^3$.

5. *Solve* : $\dfrac{dy}{dx} = \dfrac{x - y + 3}{2x - 2y + 5}$.   *(Garhwal, 2002)*

The given equation can be put as

$$\frac{dy}{dx} = \frac{x - y + 3}{2\,(x - y) + 5}.$$

Put $x - y = v$ $\therefore$ $1 - \dfrac{dy}{dx} = \dfrac{dv}{dx}$

$\therefore$ $1 - \dfrac{dv}{dx} = \dfrac{v+3}{2v+5}$

or $\dfrac{dv}{dx} = 1 - \dfrac{v+3}{2v+5} = \dfrac{v+2}{2v+5}$

$\therefore$ $\dfrac{2v+5}{v+2}\,dv = dx$

or $\left(2 + \dfrac{1}{v+2}\right)dv = dx.$

On integrating it, we get

$2v + \log(v+2) = x + c$

or $2(x-y) + \log(x-y+2) = x + c$

or $x - 2y + \log(x-y+2) = c.$

6. *Solve* : $(x+y)(dx - dy) = dx + dy.$

The given equation can be put in the form

$(x+y+1)\,dy = (x+y-1)\,dx$

or $\dfrac{dy}{dx} = \dfrac{x+y-1}{x+y+1}.$

Put $x+y = v$ so that $1 + \dfrac{dy}{dx} = \dfrac{dv}{dx}$

$\therefore$ $\dfrac{dv}{dx} - 1 = \dfrac{v-1}{v+1}$

or $\dfrac{dv}{dx} = \dfrac{v-1}{v+1} + 1 = \dfrac{2v}{v+1}$

or $\dfrac{v+1}{v}\,dv = 2\,dx$

or $\left(1 + \dfrac{1}{v}\right)dv = 2\,dx.$

On integrating the above equation, we get

$v + \log v = 2x + c$

or $x + y + \log(x+y) = 2x + c$

or $\log(x+y) = x - y + c.$

EXERCISES

Solve the following differential equations :

1. $\dfrac{dy}{dx} = \dfrac{x - 2y + 5}{2x + y - 1}$

2. $(3y - 7x - 3)\, dx + (7y - 3x - 7)\, dy = 0$

3. $(4x + 6y + 5)\, dx = (2x + 3y + 4)\, dy$

4. $\dfrac{dy}{dx} = \dfrac{ax + by - a}{bx + ay - b}$

5. $(2x + y + 1)\, dx + (4x + 2y - 1)\, dy = 0$

6. $(2x + 3y - 6)\, dy = (6x - 2y - 7)\, dx$

7. $(2x + 3y - 8)\, dx = (x + y - 3)\, dy$

8. $(6x - 5y + 4)\, dy + (y - 2x - 1)\, dx = 0$

9. $(2x + 3y - 5)\dfrac{dy}{dx} + (3x + 2y - 5) = 0$ *(Kanpur, 2000)*

10. $\dfrac{dy}{dx} = \dfrac{2x + 9y - 20}{6x + 2y - 10}$

11. $(y + x + 5)\, dy = (y - x + 1)\, dx$ *(Garhwal, 1996)*

12. $(2x - y + 1)\, dx + (2y - x - 1) = 0$

13. $\dfrac{dy}{dx} = \dfrac{2y + x - 1}{2x + 4y + 3}$ *(Gorakhpur, 2002)*

14. $\dfrac{dy}{dx} = \dfrac{4x + 6y + 5}{3y + 2x + 4}$

15. $(2x + 3y - 5)\dfrac{dy}{dx} + (2x + 3y + 1) = 0$

16. $(x + y - 1)\, dy = (x + y)\, dx$

ANSWERS

1. $x^2 - y^2 - 4xy + 10x + 2y = c.$

2. $c\,(y - x - 1)^2\,(y + x - 1)^5 = 1.$

3. $\dfrac{1}{8}(2x + y^3) + \dfrac{9}{64}\log(16x + 24y + 23) = x + c.$

4. $(y - x + 1)^{a+b}\,(y + x - 1)^{a-b} = c.$

5. $\log(2x + y - 1) + x + 2y = c.$

6. $3x^2 - \dfrac{3}{2}y^2 - 2xy - 7x + 6y = c.$

7. $\sqrt{3}\log(Y^2 - 2XY - 2X^2)$
$+ 2\log[\{Y - (1 + \sqrt{3})X\} / \{Y - (1 - \sqrt{3})X\}] = c;$
where $X = x - 1,\ Y = y - 2.$

8. $\log c \left(x + \dfrac{1}{4} \right)^{-2} = \left[\log (5v - 2)(v - 1) - \dfrac{5}{3} \log \dfrac{5(v-1)}{(5v-2)} \right]$,

where $v = \dfrac{y - 1/2}{x + 1/4}$.

9. $3(x^2 + y^2) + 4xy - 10(x + y) = c$.

10. $(y - 2x)^2 = c(2y + x - 5)$.

11. $\log (x^2 + y^2 + 4x + 6y + 13) + 2 \tan^{-1} \dfrac{y+3}{x+2} = c$.

12. $x^2 + y^2 - xy + x - y = c$.

13. $2y - x + \dfrac{1}{4} \log (8y + 4x + 5) = c$.

14. $y - 2x + \dfrac{3}{8} \log (24y + 16x + 23) = c$.

15. $x + y - 6 \log (2x + 3y + 13) = c$.

16. $2(y - x) - \log (2x + 2y - 1) = c$.

15.9. Exact Differential Equations. A differential equation is said to be exact if it can be derived from its primitive by direct differentiation without any further transformation such as elimination, etc.

Illustration. The differential equation

$$(x^2 - ay) \, dx + (y^2 - ax) \, dy = 0$$

is exact in as much as it can be derived from its primitive

$$x^3 - 3axy + y^3 = c$$

by direct differentiation.

Theorem. *The necessary and sufficient condition for the differential equation*

$$M + N \dfrac{dy}{dx} = 0 \;\Rightarrow\; M \, dx + N \, dy = 0 \qquad \ldots(1)$$

be exact is that

$$\dfrac{\partial M}{\partial y} = \dfrac{\partial N}{\partial x}. \qquad \textit{(Ravishankar, 1995)}$$

The proof for sufficiency being beyond the scope of this book, we will only prove that the condition is necessary.

Let $\qquad\qquad f(x, y) = c \qquad\qquad\qquad \ldots(2)$

be the primitive where, c, is an arbitrary constant.

Differentiating (2) with respect to x, we have

$$\dfrac{\partial f}{\partial x} + \dfrac{\partial f}{\partial y} \dfrac{dy}{dx} = 0. \qquad \ldots(3)$$

As the equation (1) is exact, the equation (3) must be identical with (1), so that, we have

$$\frac{\partial f}{\partial x} = M. \qquad ...(4)$$

$$\frac{\partial f}{\partial y} = N. \qquad ...(5)$$

Differentiating (4) and (5) partially with respect to y and x respectively, we obtain,

$$\frac{\partial^2 f}{\partial y \partial x} = \frac{\partial M}{\partial y}, \; \frac{\partial^2 f}{\partial x \partial y} = \frac{\partial N}{\partial x}.$$

Since

$$\frac{\partial^2 f}{\partial y \partial x} = \frac{\partial^2 f}{\partial x \partial y},$$

we obtain

$$\frac{\partial M}{\partial y} = \frac{\partial N}{\partial x}.$$

If the equation $M \, dx + N \, dy = 0$, is exact, then it can be integrated as follows :

Firstly, integrate M with respect to x regarding y as a constant. Then integrate with respect to y those of the terms in N which do not involve x. The sum of the two expressions thus obtained equated to a constant is the required solution.

EXAMPLES

1. *Show that the equation*

$$(x^4 - 2xy^2 + y^4) \, dx - (2x^2y - 4xy^3 + \sin y) \, dy = 0$$

is exact and also solve it.

Here $M = x^4 - 2xy^2 + y^4$,

$N = - (2x^2y - 4xy^3 + \sin y)$

$$\left. \begin{array}{l} \dfrac{\partial M}{\partial y} = -4xy + 4y^3 \\[2mm] \dfrac{\partial N}{\partial x} = -4xy + 4y^3 \end{array} \right\} \Rightarrow \frac{\partial M}{\partial y} = \frac{\partial N}{\partial x}.$$

Thus, the given equation is exact.

Integrating M with respect to x regarding y as constant, we obtain

$$\frac{1}{5}x^5 - x^2y^2 + xy^4. \qquad ...(1)$$

Now the only term in N which does not involve x is $-\sin y$. Its integral is

$$\int - \sin y \, dy = \cos y \qquad ...(2)$$

The primitive, therefore, is

$$\frac{1}{5}x^5 - x^2 y^2 + xy^4 + \cos y = c.$$

2. *Solve* : $x\,dx + y\,dy + \dfrac{x\,dy - y\,dx}{x^2 + y^2} = 0.$

(Indore, 1997; Agra, 2001; Kanpur, 2002)

The given equation is

$$\left\{ x - \frac{y}{(x^2 + y^2)} \right\} dx + \left\{ y + \frac{x}{(x^2 + y^2)} \right\} dy = 0.$$

Comparing it with equation M dx + N dy = 0, we get

$$M = x - \frac{y}{(x^2 + y^2)}, \quad N = y + \frac{x}{(x^2 + y^2)}.$$

Now, $\dfrac{\partial M}{\partial y} = -\dfrac{x^2 + y^2 - y \cdot 2y}{(x^2 + y^2)^2} = -\dfrac{x^2 - y^2}{(x^2 + y^2)^2} = \dfrac{y^2 - x^2}{(x^2 + y^2)^2}$

$$\frac{\partial N}{\partial x} = \frac{x^2 + y^2 - x \cdot 2x}{(x^2 + y^2)^2} = \frac{y^2 - x^2}{(x^2 + y^2)^2}.$$

Hence $\dfrac{\partial M}{\partial y} = \dfrac{\partial N}{\partial x}.$

Therefore, the given equation is exact. Its solution will be

$$\int M\,dx \qquad + \int N\,dy = c$$

(y constant)   (leaving the terms containing x)

or $\qquad \displaystyle\int \left(x - \frac{y}{x^2 + y^2} \right) dx + \int y\,dx = c$

(y constant)

or $\qquad \dfrac{x^2}{2} - y \cdot \dfrac{1}{y} \tan^{-1} \dfrac{x}{y} + \dfrac{y^2}{2} = c$

or $\qquad x^2 + y^2 - 2 \tan^{-1} \dfrac{x}{y} = 2c = k.$

3. *Solve* : $\cos x\,(\cos x - \sin a \sin y)\,dy$

$$+ \cos y\,(\cos y - \sin a \sin x)\,dy = 0.$$

Comparing the given equation with M dx + N dy = 0, we get

$$M = \cos^2 x - \sin a \cos x \sin y$$

$$N = \cos^2 y - \sin a \sin x \cos y.$$

$\therefore \quad \dfrac{\partial M}{\partial y} = -\cos x \sin a \cos y$ and $\dfrac{\partial N}{\partial x} = -\cos x \sin a \cos y,$

i.e., $\dfrac{\partial M}{\partial y} = \dfrac{\partial N}{\partial x}$.

Hence the equation is exact and its solution is

$$\int (\cos^2 x - \sin a \sin y \cos x)\, dx + \int \cos^2 y\, dy = c$$

$$(y \text{ constant})$$

or $$\int \left\{ \frac{1}{2}(1 + \cos 2x) - \sin a \sin y \cos x \right\} dx$$

$$+ \int \frac{1}{2}(1 + \cos 2y)\, dy = c$$

or $$\frac{1}{2}\left(x + \frac{\sin 2x}{2} \right) - \sin a \sin y \sin x + \frac{1}{2}\left(y + \frac{\sin 2y}{2} \right) = c$$

or $2\,(x + y) + \sin 2x + \sin 2y - 4 \sin a \sin y \sin x = 4c = k$.

4. *Solve* : $(1 + e^{x/y})\, dx + e^{x/y}\,(1 - x/y)\, dy = 0$.

(Bilaspur, 1998; Jabalpur, 1999)

Comparing the given equation with M dx + N dy = 0, we get

$$M = 1 + e^{x/y}, \ N = e^{x/y}\left(1 - \frac{x}{y} \right)$$

$$\therefore \quad \frac{\partial M}{\partial y} = e^{x/y}\left(-\frac{x}{y^2} \right)$$

$$\frac{\partial N}{\partial x} = e^{x/y}\frac{1}{y}\left(1 - \frac{x}{y} \right) + e^{x/y}\left(-\frac{1}{y} \right)$$

$$= e^{x/y}\left(-\frac{x}{y^2} \right).$$

Hence $\dfrac{\partial M}{\partial y} = \dfrac{\partial N}{\partial x}$ and the equation is exact. Its solution is

$$\int (1 + e^{x/y})\, dx + \int 0 \cdot dy = 0$$

$$(y \text{ constant})$$

or $x + ye^{x/y} = c$.

EXERCISES

Solve :

1. $(ax + hy + g)\, dx + (hx + by + f)\, dy = 0$ *(Vikram, 1995)*

2. $x\, dy + (x + y)\, dx = 0$

3. $(e^y + 1)\cos x\, dx + e^y \sin x\, dy = 0$

4. $x\,(y^2 - x^2 - a^2x)\, dx + y\,(y^2 + x^2 - b^2y)\, dy = 0$

5. $[y (1 + x^{-1}) + \sin y] \, dx + (x + \log x + x \cos y) \, dy = 0$

6. $(x^2 - ay) \, dx + (y^2 - ax) \, dy = 0$

7. $x \, dx + y \, dy = \dfrac{a^2 (x \, dy - y \, dx)}{x^2 + y^2}$

                                   (Ajmer, 1995, 98; Rohilkhand, 2000, 02)

8. $(x^2 - 2xy - y^2) \, dx - (x + y)^2 \, dy = 0$

                                   (Ajmer, 1996; Rohilkhand, 1997)

9. $(a^2 - 2xy - y^2) \, dx - (x + y)^2 \, dy = 0$ *(Bhopal, 2000)*

10. $(y^2 e^{xy^2} + 4x^3) \, dx + (2xy e^{xy^2} - 3y^2) \, dy = 0$

11. $(\cos y + y \cos x) \, dx + (\sin x - x \sin y) \, dy = 0$

12. $(2xy + y - \tan y) \, dx + (x^2 - x \tan^2 y + \sec^2 y) \, dy = 0$

ANSWERS

1. $ax^2 + 2hxy + by^2 + 2gx + 2fy + c = 0.$

2. $xy + \dfrac{1}{2} x^2 = c.$ **3.** $(e^y + 1) \sin x = c.$

4. $6x^2 y^2 - 3x^4 + 3y^4 - 4a^2 x^3 - 4b^2 y^3 = c.$

5. $xy + y \log x + x \sin y = c.$ **6.** $x^3 + y^3 - 3axy = c.$

7. $x^2 + y^2 + 2a^2 \tan^{-1} \dfrac{x}{y} = c.$ **8.** $x^3 - y^3 = 3xy (x + y) + c.$

9. $a^2 x - x^2 y - xy^2 - \dfrac{1}{3} y^3 = c.$ **10.** $e^{xy^2} + x^4 - y^3 = c.$

11. $x \cos y + y \sin x = c.$ **12.** $x^2 y + xy - x \tan y + \tan y = c.$

15.10. Integrating Factors. Sometimes an equation which is not exact may become so on multiplication by some suitable function known as an *Integrating factor.*

The equation

$$x \, dy - y \, dx = 0$$

which is not exact becomes so on multiplication by $1/y^2$, for we then obtain

$$\frac{x}{y^2} \, dy - \frac{1}{y} \, dx = 0,$$

which is easily seen to be exact.

For the linear equation

$$\frac{dy}{dx} + Py + Q = 0$$

the function $e^{\int P \, dx}$ is an integrating factor.

Hence some equations which are not exact can be made exact by multiplication with the integrating factor and then we can solve it either by re-arranging the terms and making them exact differential or by the method of exact equations.

15.1.1. Integrating Factors found by Inspection

The following exact differentials may be committed to memory :

1. $d\left(\dfrac{x}{y}\right) = \dfrac{y\,dx - x\,dy}{y^2}$

2. $d\left(\dfrac{y}{x}\right) = \dfrac{x\,dy - y\,dx}{x^2}$

3. $d\left(\tan^{-1}\dfrac{x}{y}\right) = \dfrac{y\,dx - x\,dy}{x^2 + y^2}$

4. $d\left(\tan^{-1}\dfrac{y}{x}\right) = \dfrac{x\,dy - y\,dx}{x^2 + y^2}$

5. $d\left(\log\dfrac{x}{y}\right) = \dfrac{y\,dx - x\,dy}{xy}$

6. $d\left(\log\dfrac{y}{x}\right) = \dfrac{x\,dy - y\,dx}{xy}$

7. $d\,(xy) = x\,dy + y\,dx$

8. $d\left(\dfrac{1}{xy}\right) = -\dfrac{x\,dy + y\,dx}{x^2 y^2}$

9. $d\left(\dfrac{x^2}{y}\right) = \dfrac{2xy\,dx - x^2\,dy}{y^2}$

10. $d\left(\dfrac{y^2}{x}\right) = \dfrac{2xy\,dy - y^2\,dx}{x^2}$

11. $d\left(\dfrac{y^2}{x^2}\right) = \dfrac{2x^2 y\,dy - 2y^2 x\,dx}{x^4}$

12. $d\left(\dfrac{x^2}{y^2}\right) = \dfrac{2xy^2\,dx - 2yx^2\,dy}{y^4}$

13. $d\left(\dfrac{e^x}{y}\right) = \dfrac{ye^x\,dx - e^x\,dy}{y^2}$

14. $d\,[\log(x^2 + y^2)] = \dfrac{2x\,dx + 2y\,dy}{x^2 + y^2}$.

EXAMPLES

1. Solve : $(y^2 e^x + 2xy)\,dx - x^2\,dy = 0$.

In this equation

$$M = y^2 e^x + 2xy, \quad N = -x^2$$

$$\frac{\partial M}{\partial y} = 2ye^x + 2x, \quad \frac{\partial N}{\partial x} = -2x.$$

Clearly, $\dfrac{\partial M}{\partial y} \neq \dfrac{\partial N}{\partial x}$.

Hence the equation is not exact.

Now, if in the solution e^x is multiplied by some other function, then it must occur twice in the differential equation. But since it is occurring only once, therefore, we should divide by y^2.

$$\therefore \quad e^x\, dx + \frac{2xy\, dx - x^2\, dy}{y^2} = 0$$

or

$$\left(e^x + \frac{2x}{y}\right) dx + \left(-\frac{x^2}{y^2}\right) dy = 0.$$

Now, $\quad M = e^x + \dfrac{2x}{y}, \quad N = -\dfrac{x^2}{y^2}$

$$\frac{\partial M}{\partial y} = -\frac{2x}{y^2}, \quad \frac{\partial N}{\partial x} = -\frac{2x}{y^2}.$$

Now, the equation is exact and its solution is

$$\int \left(e^x + \frac{2x}{y}\right) dx = c$$

(y constant)

or

$$e^x + \frac{x^2}{y} = c.$$

2. *Solve* : $(x^2 + y^2 + x)\, dx - (2x^2 + 2y^2 - y)\, dy = 0.$

(Lucknow, 1997; Bhopal, 1996)

The given equation is not exact. This equation can be written as

$$(x^2 + y^2)(dx - 2\, dy) + x\, dx + y\, dy = 0$$

or

$$dx - 2\, dy + \frac{x\, dx + y\, dy}{(x^2 + y^2)} = 0.$$

We know that $\quad d\{\log(x^2 + y^2)\} = \dfrac{2x\, dx + 2y\, dy}{x^2 + y^2}.$

Hence, we can write given equation as

$$2\, dx - 4\, dy + \frac{2x\, dx + 2y\, dy}{(x^2 + y^2)} = 0$$

or

$$d(2x - 4y) + d\{\log(x^2 + y^2)\} = 0.$$

On integration, this gives

$$2x - 4y + \log(x^2 + y^2) = c.$$

3. *Solve* : $y\, dx - x\, dy + (1 + x^2)\, dx + x^2 \sin y\, dy = 0.$ *(Garhwal, 2000)*

The given equation is not exact. Since there is no trigonometrical function except $x^2 \sin y$, therefore we must divide by x^2.

$$\therefore \quad \frac{y\, dx - x\, dy}{x^2} + \left(\frac{1}{x^2} + 1\right) dx + \sin y\, dy = 0$$

or

$$-\frac{x\, dy - y\, dx}{x^2} + d\left(-\frac{1}{x} + x\right) + d(-\cos y) = 0$$

or $\qquad -d\left(\dfrac{y}{x}\right)+d\left(-\dfrac{1}{x}+x\right)+d\left(-\cos y\right)=0.$

Integrating, we get

$$-\dfrac{y}{x}-\dfrac{1}{x}+x-\cos y = c$$

or $\qquad x^2 - y - 1 - x \cos y = cx.$

4. *Solve* : $(1+xy)\, y\, dx + (1-xy)\, x\, dy = 0.$

(Ravishankar, 1996; Vikram, 1997, 2000; Jiwaji, 1998)

We know that $y\, dx + x\, dy = d\,(xy)$ and hence we write the given equation as under :

$$y\, dx + x\, dy + xy^2\, dx - yx^2\, dy = 0$$

or $\qquad d\,(xy) + xy^2\, dx - yx^2\, dy = 0.$

Divide it by $x^2 y^2$, we have

$$\dfrac{d\,(xy)}{x^2 y^2}+\dfrac{dx}{x}-\dfrac{dy}{y}=0.$$

Integrating the above equation, we get

$$-\dfrac{1}{xy}+\log x - \log y = \log c$$

or $\qquad -\dfrac{1}{xy}+\log\dfrac{x}{y}=\log c$

or $\qquad \log\dfrac{x}{cy}=\dfrac{1}{xy}$

or $\qquad \dfrac{x}{cy}=e^{1/xy}$ or $x = cye^{1/xy}.$

5. *Solve* : $y\,(2x^2y + e^x)\, dx - (e^x + y^3)\, dy = 0.$ $\qquad$ *(Avadh, 2000)*

The equation can be written as $(\,ye^x\, dx - e^x\, dy\,) + 2x^2 y^2\, dx - y^3\, dy = 0.$ Since e^x occurs twice, it must have been obtained by differentiation of e^x multiplied by some other function.

Hence dividing by $\dfrac{1}{y^2}$, we get

$$\dfrac{ye^x\, dx - e^x\, dy}{y^2} + 2x^2\, dx - y\, dy = 0$$

or $\qquad d\left(\dfrac{e^x}{y}\right)+d\left(\dfrac{2x^3}{3}\right)-d\left(\dfrac{y^2}{2}\right)=0.$

On integration, we get

$$\dfrac{e^x}{y}+\dfrac{2x^3}{3}-\dfrac{y^2}{2}=c.$$

EXERCISES

Solve following differential equations :

1. $x\,dy - y\,dx + 2x^3\,dx = 0$

2. $x\,dy - (y - x)\,dx = 0$

3. $y\,(axy + e^x)\,dx - e^x\,dy = 0$ (*Kanpur, 2001*)

4. $e^y\,dx + (xe^y + 2y)\,dy = 0$

5. $a\,(x\,dy + 2y\,dx) = xy\,dy$

6. $(x^3 e^x - my^2)\,dx + mxy = 0$ (*Ravishankar, 1999*)

7. $x\,dx + y\,dy + (x^2 + y^2)\,dy = 0$

8. $(x^2 + y^2 - a^2)\,x\,dx + (x^2 - y^2 - b^2)\,y\,dy = 0$

9. $y\,dy\,(x^2 + y^2 + a^2) + x\,dx\,(x^2 + y^2 - a^2) = 0$ (*Gorakhpur, 2001*)

ANSWERS

1. $y + x^3 = cx.$ **2.** $\dfrac{y}{x} + \log x = c.$

3. $\dfrac{ax^2}{2} + \dfrac{e^x}{y} = c.$ **4.** $xe^y + y^2 = c.$

5. $a \log y + 2a \log x - y = c.$ **6.** $e^x + \dfrac{1}{2}\,m\,\dfrac{y^2}{x^2} = c.$

7. $x^2 + y^2 = ce^{-2y}.$

8. $(x^2 - a^2)^2 - (y^2 + b^2)^2 + 2x^2 y^2 = c.$

9. $\dfrac{1}{2}(x^2 + y^2)^2 + a^2\,(y^2 - x^2) = c.$

15.1.2. Some Rules for finding Integrating Factors of differential equation

$$M\,dx + N\,dy = 0$$

to make it exact.

We have already done some questions in which I.F. was found by inspection. Below we shall give some rules for finding I.F.

Rule 1. *If $Mx + Ny \neq 0$ and the equation is homogeneous, then*
$$\frac{1}{Mx + Ny} \text{ is an I.F. of } M\,dx + N\,dy = 0.$$

Rule 2. *If the equation $M\,dx + N\,dy = 0$ is not exact but is of the form*
$$f_1\,(xy)\,y\,dx + f_2\,(xy)\,x\,dy = 0, \text{ then } \frac{1}{Mx - Ny} \text{ is an integrating}$$
factor provided $Mx - Ny \neq 0$.

EXAMPLES

1. *Solve* : $(x^2y - 2xy^2)\, dx - (x^3 - 3x^2y)\, dy = 0.$ *(Bilaspur, 1994)*

In this equation

$$M = x^2y - 2xy^2, \ N = 3x^2y - x^3.$$

$$\frac{\partial M}{\partial y} = x^2 - 4xy, \ \frac{\partial N}{\partial x} = 6xy - 3x^2.$$

Clearly, $\dfrac{\partial M}{\partial y} \neq \dfrac{\partial N}{\partial x}$, hence the given equation is not exact.

In this equation M and N are homogeneous functions of x and y and

$$\frac{1}{Mx + Ny} = \frac{1}{x^2 y^2} \neq 0.$$

Hence $\text{I.F.} = \dfrac{1}{x^2 y^2}.$

Multiplying the given equation by I.F., we get

$$\left(\frac{1}{y} - \frac{2}{x}\right) dx + \left(\frac{3}{y} - \frac{x}{y^2}\right) dy = 0$$

in this equation

$$M = \frac{1}{y} - \frac{2}{x}, \ N = \frac{3}{y} - \frac{x}{y^2}$$

$$\frac{\partial M}{\partial y} = -\frac{1}{y^2}, \ \frac{\partial N}{\partial x} = -\frac{1}{y^2}.$$

Hence this equation is exact and its solution is

$$\frac{x}{y} + \log \frac{y^3}{x^2} = c.$$

2. *Solve* : $(x^2y^2 + xy + 1)\, y\, dx + (x^2y^2 - xy + 1)\, x\, dy = 0.$

The given equation is not exact. M and N are of the form $y f_1(xy)$ and $x f_2(xy)$ respectively.

Now, $Mx - Ny = x^3y^3 + x^2y^2 + xy - x^3y^3 + x^2y^2 - xy = 2x^2y^2 \neq 0.$

Hence $\text{I.F.} = \dfrac{1}{2x^2 y^2}.$

Multiplying the given equation by I.F., we get

$$\frac{1}{2}\left(y + \frac{1}{x} + \frac{1}{x^2 y}\right) dx + \frac{1}{2}\left(x - \frac{1}{y} + \frac{1}{xy^2}\right) dy = 0$$

which can be shown to be exact and whose solution as usual is

$$xy - \frac{1}{xy} + \log \frac{x}{y} = c.$$

3. *Solve* : $(x^3y^3 + x^2y^2 + xy + 1) \, y \, dx + (x^3y^3 - x^2y^2 - xy + 1) \, x \, dy = 0.$

The given equation is not exact. Also, we have

$$Mx = xy \, (x^3y^3 + x^2y^2 + xy + 1)$$
$$Ny = xy \, (x^3y^3 - x^2y^2 - xy + 1)$$

$\therefore$ $Mx - Ny = xy \, (2x^2y^2 + 2xy) = 2x^2y^2 \, (xy + 1) \neq 0.$

$\therefore$ I.F. $= \dfrac{1}{2x^2y^2 \, (xy + 1)}.$

Multiplying the given equation by I.F., we get

$$\frac{(xy + 1) \, (x^2y^2 + 1)}{2x^2y^2 \, (xy + 1)} \, y \, dx + \frac{(xy + 1) \, (x^2y^2 - 2xy + 1)}{2x^2y^2 \, (xy + 1)} \, x \, dy = 0$$

or $$\frac{1}{2}\left(\frac{x^2y^2 + 1}{x^2y^2} \right) y \, dx + \frac{1}{2}\left(\frac{x^2y^2 - 2xy + 1}{x^2y^2} \right) x \, dy = 0$$

or $$\frac{1}{2}\left(y + \frac{1}{x^2y} \right) dx + \frac{1}{2}\left(x - \frac{2}{y} + \frac{1}{xy^2} \right) dy = 0.$$

Now, $M = \dfrac{1}{2}\left(y + \dfrac{1}{x^2y} \right)$, $N = \dfrac{1}{2}\left(x - \dfrac{2}{y} + \dfrac{1}{xy^2} \right)$

$$\frac{\partial M}{\partial y} = \frac{1}{2}\left(1 - \frac{1}{x^2y^2} \right), \quad \frac{\partial N}{\partial x} = \frac{1}{2}\left(1 - \frac{1}{x^2y^2} \right).$$

Now, $\dfrac{\partial M}{\partial y} = \dfrac{\partial N}{\partial x}$, hence the equation is exact and its solution is

$$\int \frac{1}{2}\left(y + \frac{1}{x^2y} \right) dx + \frac{1}{2}\int \frac{-2}{y} \, dy = c$$

(y constant)

or $$\frac{1}{2}\left(xy - \frac{1}{xy} - 2 \log y \right) = c$$

or $$xy - \frac{1}{xy} - \log y^2 = 2c = k.$$

EXERCISES

Solve the following differential equations :

1. $x^2y \, dx - (x^3 + y^3) \, dy = 0$ *(Sagar, 1997)*

2. $y \, (xy + 2x^2y^2) \, dx + x \, (xy - x^2y^2) \, dy = 0$ *(Ravishankar, 1997)*

3. $(xy \sin xy + \cos xy) \, y \, dx + (xy \sin xy - \cos xy) \, x \, dy = 0$

(Lucknow, 1993, 97; Jabalpur, 1997; Jiwaji, 1999; Vikram, 1999)

4. $(x^4y^4 + x^2y^2 + xy) \, y \, dx + (x^4y^4 - x^2y^2 + xy) \, x \, dy = 0$

(Ravishankar, 1996; Vikram, 1997, 2000)

ANSWERS

1. $y = ce^{x^3/3y^3}$.

2. $\log \dfrac{x^2}{y} - \dfrac{1}{xy} = c$.

3. $x = cy \cos xy$.

4. $\dfrac{1}{2} x^2 y^2 - \dfrac{1}{xy} + \log \dfrac{x}{y} = c$.

15.1.3. Rule 3. When $\dfrac{\dfrac{\partial M}{\partial y} - \dfrac{\partial N}{\partial x}}{N}$ is a function of x alone, say $f(x)$, then

$I.F. = e^{\int f(x)\,dx}$.

Rule 4. When $\dfrac{\dfrac{\partial M}{\partial x} - \dfrac{\partial M}{\partial y}}{M}$ is a function of y alone, say $f(y)$, then

$I.F. = e^{\int f(y)\,dy}$.

EXAMPLES

1. Solve : $(x^2 + y^2 + 2x)\,dx + 2y\,dy = 0$.

(*Vikram, 2000; Bilaspur, 1996*)

We have,

$$M = x^2 + y^2 + 2x; \ N = 2y$$

$$\frac{\partial M}{\partial y} = 2y; \ \frac{\partial N}{\partial x} = 0$$

But $\dfrac{\dfrac{\partial M}{\partial y} - \dfrac{\partial N}{\partial x}}{N} = \dfrac{2y - 0}{2y} = 1$

which may be regarded as function of x.

$\therefore$ I.F. $= e^{\int 1\,dx} = e^x$.

Multiplying the given equation by e^x, we get

$$e^x (x^2 + y^2 + 2x)\,dx + 2ye^x\,dy = 0.$$

Now, $M = e^x (x^2 + y^2 + 2x), \ N = 2ye^x$

$\therefore \ \dfrac{\partial M}{\partial y} = 2ye^x, \ \dfrac{\partial N}{\partial x} = 2ye^x$.

Hence this equation is exact and its solution as usual shall be

$$e^x (x^2 + y^2) = c.$$

2. Solve : $\left(y + \dfrac{1}{3} y^3 + \dfrac{1}{2} x^2 \right) dx + \dfrac{1}{4} (x + xy^2)\,dy = 0$.

In this equation, we have

$$M = y + \frac{1}{3} y^3 + \frac{1}{x^2}, \ N = \frac{1}{4} (x + xy^2)$$

$$\frac{\partial M}{\partial y} = 1 + y^2, \quad \frac{\partial N}{\partial x} = \frac{1}{4}(1 + y^2).$$

Hence, the equation is not exact, but

$$\frac{1}{N}\left(\frac{\partial M}{\partial y} - \frac{\partial N}{\partial x}\right) = \frac{3}{x},$$

which is a function of x. Hence

$$\text{I.F.} = e^{\int \frac{3}{x} dx} = x^3.$$

Multiplying by I.F., the given equation becomes

$$\left(x^3 y + \frac{1}{3}x^3 y^3 + \frac{1}{2}x^5\right) + \frac{1}{4}x^4 (1 + y^2)\, dy = 0$$

which can be shown to be exact, whose solution as usual is

$$x^4 y\,(3 + y^2) + x^6 = c.$$

3. *Solve* : $(3x^2 y^4 + 2xy)\, dx + (2x^3 y^3 - x^2)\, dy = 0.$ *(Gorakhpur, 1992)*

In the given equation, we have

$$M = 3x^2 y^4 + 2xy, \quad N = 2x^3 y^3 - x^2$$

$$\frac{\partial M}{\partial y} = 12x^2 y^3 + 2x, \quad \frac{\partial N}{\partial x} = 6x^2 y^3 - 2x.$$

Hence the equation is not exact, but

$$\frac{\dfrac{\partial N}{\partial x} - \dfrac{\partial M}{\partial y}}{M} = \frac{6x^2 y^3 - 2x - 12x^2 y^3 - 2x}{xy\,(3xy^3 + 2)}$$

$$= -\frac{2x\,(3xy^3 + 2)}{xy\,(3xy^2 + 2)} = -\frac{2}{y},$$

which is a function of y alone.

$$\therefore \quad \text{I.F.} = e^{\int -\frac{2}{y} dy} = \frac{1}{y^2}.$$

Multiplying the given equation by $\dfrac{1}{y^2}$, we get

$$\left(3x^2 y^2 + \frac{2x}{y}\right) dx + \left(2x^3 y - \frac{x^2}{y^2}\right) dy = 0$$

which can be shown to be exact.

$\therefore$ Solution is

$$\int \left(3x^2y^2 + \frac{2x}{y} \right) dx = c$$

(y constant)

as there being no term in N free from x.

$$x^2y^2 + \frac{x^2}{y} = c$$

or $x^2y^3 + x^2 = cy.$

EXERCISES

Solve the following differential equations :

1. $(x^3 + xy^4)\, dx + 2y^3\, dy = 0$ *(Gorakhpur, 2003)*
2. $(x^2 + y^2)\, dx - 2xy\, dy = 0$
3. $(x^2 + y^2 + 1)\, dx - 2xy\, dy = 0$
4. $(xy^3 + y)\, dx + 2\,(xy^2 + x + y^4)\, dy = 0$ *(Gorakhpur, 1994)*
5. $(y^4 + 2y)\, dx + (xy^3 + 2y^4 - 4x)\, dy = 0$
6. $(xy^2 - x^2)\, dx + (3x^2y^2 + x^2y - 2x^3 + y^2)\, dy$ *(Lucknow, 1996)*
7. $(20x^2 + 8xy + 4y^2 + 3y^3)\, y\, dx + 4\,(x^2 + xy + y^2 + y^3)\, x\, dy = 0$

ANSWERS

1. $e^{x^2}\,(x^2 - 1 + y^4) = c.$ 2. $x^2 - y^2 = cx.$

3. $x^2 - y^2 - 1 = cx.$ 4. $3x^2y^4 + 6xy^3 + 2y^6 = c.$

5. $xy + y^2 + \dfrac{2x}{y^2} = c.$ 6. $4x^5y + 2x^4y^2 + \dfrac{4}{3}x^3y^3 + y^4x^3 = c.$

15.1.4. Rule 5. If an equation is of the form

$$x^a y^b\,(my\, dx + nx\, dy) + x^r y^s\,(py\, dx + qx\, dy) = 0$$

where a, b, m, n, p, q, r and s are all constants having any value, then the integrating factor will be $x^h y^k$ where h and k are such that after multiplying by the integrating factor the condition of exactness is satisfied.

EXAMPLES

1. *Solve* : $(2x^2y - 3y^4)\, dx + (3x^3 + 2xy^3)\, dy = 0.$

The given equation can be put in the form

$$x^2\,(2y\, dx + 3x\, dy) + y^3\,(-3y\, dx + 2x\, dy) = 0,$$

which is of the above form, where

$$a = 2,\, b = 0,\, m = 2,\, n = 3,\, p = -3,\, q = 2,\, r = 0,\, s = 3.$$

Hence the integrating factor must be $x^h y^k$.

Multiplying the original equation by the I.F., we get

$(2x^{h+2}y^{k+3} - 3x^hy^{k+4}) dx + (3x^{h+3}y^k + 2x^{h+1}y^{k+3}) dy = 0.$

Hence

$M = 2x^{h+2}y^{k+3} - 3x^hy^{k+4}, \quad N = 3x^{h+3}y^k + 2x^{h+1}y^{k+3}.$

Then

$$\frac{\partial M}{\partial y} = 2(k+1) x^{h+2}y^k - 3(k+4) x^hy^{k+3}$$

$$\frac{\partial N}{\partial x} = 3(h+3) x^{h+2}y^k + 2(h+1) x^hy^{k+3}.$$

Both these must be equal for exactness.

$\therefore$ By comparing, we get

$2(k+1) = 3(h+3)$

and $\quad -3(k+4) = 2(h+1).$

Solving it, we get $h = -\dfrac{49}{13}, k = -\dfrac{23}{13}.$

$\therefore \quad x^{-49/13}y^{-23/13}$ is the required I.F.

Multiplying by the I.F., the given equation must become exact

$(2x^{-23/13}y^{-15/13} - 3x^{-49/13}y^{29/13}) dx$

$\qquad + (3x^{10/13}y^{-28/13} + 2x^{-36/13}y^{11/13}) dy = 0.$

Its solution will be

$$\int (2x^{-23/13}y^{-15/13} - x^{-49/13}y^{29/13}) dx = c$$

(y constant)

or $\quad -\dfrac{13}{10} 2x^{-10/13}y^{-15/13} + 3 \cdot \dfrac{13}{36} x^{-36/13}y^{29/13} = c$

or $\quad 5x^{-36/13}y^{29/13} - 12x^{-10/13}y^{-15/13} = c.$

2. *Solve* : $(y^2 + 2x^2y) dx + (2x^3 - xy) dy = 0.$

(*Rohilkhand, 2001; Bhoj, 1999; Garhwal, 2003*)

The given equation is not exact. It can be put in the form

$$y(y\,dx - x\,dy) + x^2(2y\,dx + 2x\,dy) = 0.$$

Let x^hy^k is an I.F. Multiplying the original equation by it, we get

$(x^hy^{k+2} + 2x^{h+2}y^{k+1}) dx + (2x^{h+3}y^k - x^{h+1}y^{k+1}) dy = 0.$

Here, $M = x^hy^{k+2} + 2x^{h+2}y^{k+1}, \quad N = 2x^{h+3}y^k - x^{h+1}y^{k+1}$

$\therefore \quad \dfrac{\partial M}{\partial y} = (k+2) x^hy^{k+1} + 2(k+1) x^{h+2}y^k$

and $\quad \dfrac{\partial N}{\partial x} = -(h+1) x^hy^{k+1} + 2(h+3) x^{h+2}y^k.$

These two must be equal for exactness and hence comparing, we get

$$k + 2 = -(h + 1)$$

and $\quad 2(k + 1) = 2(h + 3).$

Solving these two equations, we get $h = -\dfrac{5}{2}$ and $k = -\dfrac{1}{2}.$

$\therefore \ x^{-5/2}y^{-1/2}$ is the integrating factor.

Multiplying, we get

$$(x^{-5/2}y^{3/2} + 2x^{-1/2}y^{1/2})\,dx + (2x^{1/2}y^{-1/2} - x^{3/2}y^{1/2})\,dy = 0.$$

Which is now exact and its solution as usual is

$$\int (x^{-5/2}y^{3/2} + 2x^{-1/2}y^{1/2})\,dx = c$$

(y constant)

there being no term in N free from x.

$$4x^{1/2}y^{1/3} + \frac{2}{3}x^{-3/2}y^{3/2} = c.$$

EXERCISES

Solve the following differential equations :

1. $(2y\,dx + 3x\,dy) + 2xy\,(3y\,dx + 4x\,dy) = 0$

(*Jabalpur, 1996, 99*, 2000)

2. $(3x + 2y^2)\,y\,dx + 2x\,(2x + 3y^2)\,dy = 0$

3. $x\,(3y\,dx + 2x\,dy) + 8y^4\,(y\,dx + 3x\,dy) = 0$

4. $(20x^2 + 8xy + 4y^2 + 3y^3)\,y\,dx + 4\,(x^2 + xy + y^2 + y^3)\,x\,dy = 0$

ANSWERS

1. $x^2y^3 + 2x^2y^4 = c.$ $\qquad$ 2. $x^2y^4\,(x + y^2) = c.$

3. $x^2y^2\,(x + 4y^4) = c.$ $\qquad$ 4. $\left(4x^4 + 2x^4y - \dfrac{4}{3}x^3y^2 + x^3y^3\right)y = c.$

EXERCISES ON CHAPTER 15

Solve the following differential equations :

1. $x^2\dfrac{dy}{dx} = \dfrac{y(x + y)}{2}$ $\qquad$ 2. $\cos^3 x\,\dfrac{dy}{dx} + y\cos x = \sin x$

3. $\dfrac{dy}{dx} + y\sec x = \tan x$ $\qquad$ 4. $\dfrac{dy}{dx} = \dfrac{x + 2y - 3}{2x + y - 3}$

5. $\dfrac{dy}{dx} + y\cot x = 2\cos x$ $\qquad$ 6. $(x^2 + y^2)\dfrac{dy}{dx} = xy$

7. $\sec^2 x\tan y\,dx + \sec^2 y\tan x\,dy = 0$

8. $2(1-xy)\dfrac{dy}{dx} = y^2$

9. $\dfrac{dy}{dx} - 2y\tan x = y^2 \tan^2 x$

10. $(x^2+y^2)\,dx - 2xy\,dy = 0$

11. $\dfrac{1}{2x}\dfrac{dy}{dx} + \dfrac{x+y}{x^2+y^2} = 0$

12. $\dfrac{dy}{dx} + \dfrac{y}{\sqrt{x^2+a^2}} - 3x$ such that $y = a^2$ when $x = 0$

13. $x\,dy - y\,dx = \sqrt{x^2+y^2}\,dx$

14. $(x+y)\,dx + (y-x)\,dy = 0$

15. $y^2(y\,dx + 2x\,dy) - x^2(2y\,dx + x\,dy) = 0$

16. $(1+x^2)\dfrac{dy}{dx} + y = \tan^{-1} x$

17. $\dfrac{dy}{dx} + \dfrac{x}{1-x^2}y = x\sqrt{y}$

18. $\dfrac{dy}{dx} + y\cos x = \sin 2x$

19. $\cos^2 x\dfrac{dy}{dx} + y = \tan x$

20. $\dfrac{dy}{dx} + \dfrac{y}{x} = \dfrac{y^2}{x^2}$

21. $(xy^2 - e^{1/x^3})\,dx - x^2 y\,dy = 0$

22. $(2x - y + 1)\,dx + (2y - x - 1)\,dy = 0$

23. $xy^2(xy_1 + y) = a^2$

24. $(y^3 - 2yx^2)\,dx + (2xy^2 - x^3)\,dy = 0$

25. $\sec^2 y\dfrac{dy}{dx} + 2x\tan y = x^3$

26. $(x+y+1)\dfrac{dy}{dx} = 1$

27. $(x^2 + 2xy - y^2)\,dx + (y^2 + 2xy - x^2)\,dy = 0$

28. Obtain the differential equation of all circles in a plane in the form
$$y_3(1 + y_1^2) - 3y_1 y_2^2 = 0.$$

29. Find the differential equation of all conics whose axes coincide with the axes of co-ordinates.

30. Show that the equation
$$(4x + 3y + 1)\,dx + (3x + 2y + 1)\,dy = 0$$
represents a family of hyperbolas having as asymptotes the lines $x + y = 0$, $2x + y + 1 = 0$.

31. Solve :
$$\left\{ x\cos\frac{y}{x} + y\sin\frac{y}{x} \right\} y = \left\{ y\sin\frac{y}{x} + x\cos\frac{y}{x} \right\} x\frac{dy}{dx}.$$

ANSWERS

1. $(y - x)^2 = cxy^2$.

2. $1 + y = \tan x + ce^{-\tan x}$.

3. $(y - 1)(1 + \sin x) = (c - x) \cos x$.

4. $c(x - y)^3 = x + y - 2$.

5. $2y \sin x + \cos 2x + c = 0$.

6. $cy = e^{x^2/2y^2}$.

7. $c \cot x \cot y = 1$.

8. $xy^2 = 2y + c$.

9. $y(\sin^3 x + c \cos^3 x) + 3 \cos x = 0$.

10. $c(x^2 - y^2) = x$.

11. $y^3 + 3yx^2 + 2x^3 = c$.

12. $y(x + \sqrt{a^2 + x^2}) = x^3 + (a^2 + x^2)^{3/2}$.

13. $c(\sqrt{x^2 + y^2} - y) = 1$.

14. $c\sqrt{x^2 + y^2} = e^{\tan^{-1}(y/x)}$.

15. $xy\sqrt{x^2 - y^2} = c$.

16. $y + 1 = \tan^{-1} x + ce^{-\tan^{-1} x}$.

17. $3\sqrt{y} + 1 - x^2 = c(1 - x^2)^{1/4}$.

18. $y + 2 = 2 \sin x + ce^{-\sin x}$.

19. $y + 1 = \tan x + ce^{-\tan x}$.

20. $y - 2x = cx^2y$.

21. $x^{-2}y^2 = \dfrac{2}{3}e^{1/x^3} + c$.

22. $x^2 - xy + x + y^2 - y = c$.

23. $2x^3y^3 = 3a^2x^2 + c$.

24. $xy\sqrt{y^2 - x^2} = c$.

25. $2 \tan y = x^2 - 1 + ce^{-x^2}$.

26. $x + y + 2 = ce^y$.

27. $c(x^2 + y^2) = x + y$.

29. $xyy_2 + xy_1^2 = yy_1$.

30. $xy \cos \dfrac{y}{x} = c$.

OBJECTIVE QUESTIONS

For each of the following questions, four alternatives are given for the answer. Only one of them is correct. Choose the correct alternative.

1. The differential equation of the family of curves $y^2 = 4a(x + a)$, where a is an arbitrary constant is :

(a) $y\left[1 + \left(\dfrac{dy}{dx}\right)^2\right] = 2x \dfrac{dy}{dx}$

(b) $y\left[1 - \left(\dfrac{dy}{dx}\right)^2\right] = 2x \dfrac{dy}{dx}$

(c) $\dfrac{d^2y}{dx^2} + 2\dfrac{dy}{dx} = 0$

(d) $\left(\dfrac{dy}{dx}\right)^3 + 3\dfrac{dy}{dx} + y = 0$.

2. The differential equation of the family of curves $y = e^x$ (A cos x + B sin x), where A and B are arbitrary constants, is :

(a) $\dfrac{d^2y}{dx^2} - \dfrac{2\,dy}{dx} + 2y = 0$ (b) $\dfrac{d^2y}{dx^2} + \dfrac{2\,dy}{dx} - 2y = 0$

(c) $\dfrac{d^2y}{dx^2} + \left(\dfrac{dy}{dx}\right)^2 + y = 0$ (d) $\dfrac{d^2y}{dx^2} - 7\dfrac{dy}{dx} + 2y = 0.$

3. Differential equation of the family of curves $y = a\cos \mu x + b\sin \mu x$, where a, b are arbitrary constants, is given by :

(a) $\dfrac{d^2y}{dx^2} + \mu y = 0$ (b) $\dfrac{d^2y}{dx^2} + \mu^2 y = 0$

(c) $\dfrac{d^2y}{dx^2} - \mu^2 y = 0$ (d) None of these.

4. The order and degree of the differential equation

$$\dfrac{d^2y}{dx^2} + \sqrt{x + \left(\dfrac{dy}{dx}\right)^3} = 0 \text{ is :}$$

(a) (2, 2)   (b) (3, 2)   (c) (2, 3)   (d) (1, 3).

5. The degree of differential equation

$$\dfrac{d^2y}{dx^2} + 3\left(\dfrac{dy}{dx}\right)^2 = x^2 \log\left(\dfrac{d^2y}{dx^2}\right) \text{ is :}$$

(a) 1   (b) 2

(c) 3   (d) None of these.

6. The degree of differential equation satisfying $y_2^{3/2} - y_1^{1/2} - 4 = 0$ is :

(a) 6   (b) 3   (c) 2   (d) 4.

7. The differential equation $\left(\dfrac{d^2y}{dx^2}\right)^2 - \dfrac{dy}{dx} = y^3$ has degree :

(a) $\dfrac{1}{2}$ (b) 2   (c) 3   (d) 4.

8. The degree of the differential equation

$$\left[5 + \left(\dfrac{dy}{dx}\right)^2\right]^{5/3} = x^5 \left(\dfrac{d^2y}{dx^2}\right) \text{ is :}$$

(a) 4   (b) 2   (c) 5   (d) 3.

9. Which of the following differential equations is linear :

(Garhwal, 2002)

(a) $\dfrac{dy}{dx} + x^2 y = \sin y$ (b) $\dfrac{dy}{dx} - x^2 y = \sin x$

(c) $(1+y)\dfrac{dy}{dx} + \sin x = 0$ (d) $\dfrac{dy}{dx} + y(y+x) = x^2.$

10. The solution of the variable separable equation

$$(x^2 + 1)(y^2 - 1)\, dx + xy\, dy = 0 .$$

is :

(a) $y^2 - 1 = x^2 + 1 + c$ (b) $\log(y^2 - 1) = c \log(x^2 + 1)$

(c) $y^2 = 1 + (c/x)\, e^{-x^2}$ (d) None of these.

11. Which of the following differential equations is homogeneous :

(a) $2r\, dr = (\tan\theta - r^2 \sec\theta)\, d\theta$

(b) $(x + y)\, dx + (3x + 3y - 4)\, dy = 0$

(c) $(x^2 + y)\, dx - x\, dy = 0$

(d) None of these.

12. To solve the equation $(x - y - 2)\, dx - (2x - 2y - 3)\, dy = 0$, we shall put :

(a) $y = vx$ (b) $x - y = v$

(c) $x = X + h, y = Y + k$ (d) None of these.

13. The homogeneous differential equation $M\, dx + N\, dy = 0$ can be reduced to a differential equation in which variables are separable, by the substitution :

(a) $y = vx$ (b) $xy = v$

(c) $x + y = v$ (d) $x - y = v.$

14. If P, Q are functions of x, then the solution of the differential equation $\dfrac{dy}{dx} + Py = Q$ is :

(a) $y e^{\int P\, dx} = \int Q e^{\int P\, dx}\, dx + C$ (b) $y = e^{\int P\, dx} \int Q e^{\int P\, dx}\, dx + C$

(c) $y^P = \int Q e^{\int P\, dx}\, dx + C$ (d) None of these.

15. The integrating factor of the differential equation

$$(1 + x^2)\dfrac{dy}{dx} + y = \tan^{-1} x$$

is :   (Avadh, 2002; Garhwal, 2001)

(a) $e^{\tan x}$ (b) $e^{\tan^{-1} x}$ (c) $e^{-\tan x}$ (d) $\tan x.$

16. The differential equation of the form $\dfrac{dy}{dx} + P(x)\, y = Q(x)\, y^n$ is called :

   (a) auxiliary equation   (b) linear equation
   (c) Euler's equation   (d) Bernoulli's equation.

17. Which of the following differential equations is exact :

   (a) $(x^2 + y)\, dx - x\, dy = 0$
   (b) $(x + y - 3)\, dy + (x + 2y - 3)\, dx = 0$
   (c) $x\, dx + y\, dy + \dfrac{x\, dy - y\, dx}{x^2 + y^2} = 0$
   (d) None of these.

18. The differential equation $M\, dx + N\, dy = 0$ is exact if and only if :
   (*Kanpur, 2001; Avadh, 2001, 02; Rohilkhand, 2002, 03*)

   (a) $\dfrac{\partial M}{\partial x} = \dfrac{\partial M}{\partial y}$ (b) $\dfrac{\partial^2 M}{\partial y^2} = \dfrac{\partial^2 N}{\partial x^2}$

   (c) $\dfrac{\partial M}{\partial y} = \dfrac{\partial N}{\partial x}$ (d) $\dfrac{\partial^2 M}{\partial x^2} = \dfrac{\partial^2 N}{\partial y^2}$.

19. The integrating factor to make the differential equation
   $$x^2 y\, dx - (x^3 + y^3)\, dy = 0$$
   exact is :

   (a) $-y^{-4}$ (b) y^4 (c) $x^2 y^2$ (d) x^4.

20. If $\dfrac{1}{M}\left(\dfrac{\partial N}{\partial x} - \dfrac{\partial M}{\partial y} \right) = f(y)$, then the integrating factor of $M\, dx + N\, dy = 0$ is :

   (a) $e^{-\int f(y)\, dy}$ (b) $e^{\int f(y)\, dy}$
   (c) $f(y)\, e^{\int f(y)\, dy}$ (d) $\int e^{f(y)}\, f(y)\, dy$.

21. The solution of the differential equation $(1 + x) + (x + y)\dfrac{dy}{dx} = 0$
   is :   (*Garhwal, 2001*)

   (a) $x^2 + y^2 + 2x + 2y = A$
   (b) $x^2 - y^2 + 2x + 2y = A$
   (c) $x^2 + y^2 + 2xy + 2x + 2y = A$
   (d) $x^2 + y^2 - 2xy + 2x + 2y = A$.

22. The solution of the differential equation $\dfrac{dy}{dx} = \dfrac{1 + y^2}{1 + x^2}$ is :

   (a) $\tan^{-1} y - \tan^{-1} x = 0$ (b) $\tan^{-1} y + \tan^{-1} x = 0$
   (c) $y - x = c(1 + yx)$ (d) None of these.

23. To solve $\cos (x + y)\, dy = dx$, we will put :

(a) $y = vx$ (b) $x + y = v$

(c) $x = vy$ (d) None of these.

24. Integrating factor of the equation $(1 + x^2)\dfrac{dy}{dx} + 2xy = \cos x$ is :

(a) $\tan^{-1} x$ (b) $\dfrac{1}{1 + x^2}$

(c) $1 + x^2$ (d) $\tan^{-1}\dfrac{1}{x}$.

25. Integrating factor of the differential equation $\cos^2 x \dfrac{dy}{dx} + y = \tan x$ is :

(a) $e^{\cos x}$ (b) $e^{\tan x}$ (c) $\tan x$ (d) $\cos x$.

ANSWERS

1. (b)	**2.** (a)	**3.** (b)	**4.** (a)	**5.** (d)
6. (a)	**7.** (b)	**8.** (d)	**9.** (b)	**10.** (c)
11. (d)	**12.** (b)	**13.** (a)	**14.** (a)	**15.** (b)
16. (d)	**17.** (c)	**18.** (c)	**19.** (a)	**20.** (b)
21. (a)	**22.** (c)	**23.** (b)	**24.** (c)	**25.** (b)

16

Equations of the First Order but not of the First Degree

16.1. In the discussion of equations of the first order which are not of the first degree, it is usual to denote dy/dx by p. The following types of equations, now, present themselves for discussion :

1. *Equations solvable for p.*
2. *Equations solvable for y.*
3. *Equations solvable for x.*

These will be considered in the following sections :

16.2. **Equations solvable for p.** The following examples will make the procedure clear.

EXAMPLES

1. *Solve* : $p^2 + 2py \cot x = y^2$.

(Vikram, 1999; Bhopal, 1999; Agra, 2000)

Solving for p, we obtain

$$p = \frac{-2y \cot x \pm \sqrt{4y^2 \cot^2 x + 4y^2}}{2}$$

$$= -y \cot x \pm y \operatorname{cosec} x$$

$$= y(-\cot x \pm \operatorname{cosec} x).$$

Thus we have

$$\frac{dy}{dx} = y(-\cot x + \operatorname{cosec} x), \qquad \qquad ...(1)$$

and $\quad \dfrac{dy}{dx} = -y(\cot x + \operatorname{cosec} x).$ $\qquad \qquad ...(2)$

In (1) and (2), the variables are separable.

(1) gives

$$\frac{dy}{y} = (-\cot x + \operatorname{cosec} x)\, dx.$$

$$\Rightarrow \quad \log y = -\log \sin x + \log \tan \frac{x}{2} + \log c = \log \frac{c \tan \dfrac{x}{2}}{\sin x}$$

$$\Rightarrow \quad y = \frac{c \tan \dfrac{x}{2}}{\sin x} = \frac{c}{2 \cos^2 \dfrac{x}{2}} = \frac{c}{1 + \cos x} \qquad \ldots(3)$$

Again (2) gives

$$\frac{dy}{y} = -(\cot x + \operatorname{cosec} x)\, dx$$

$$\Rightarrow \quad \log y = -\left(\log \sin x + \log \tan \frac{x}{2}\right) + \log c$$

$$= \log \frac{c}{\sin x \tan \dfrac{x}{2}}.$$

$$\Rightarrow \quad y = \frac{c}{\sin x \tan \dfrac{x}{2}} = \frac{c}{2 \sin^2 \dfrac{x}{2}} = \frac{c}{1 - \cos x} \qquad \ldots(4)$$

Thus the solutions of (1) and (2) are

$$y - \frac{c}{1 + \cos x} = 0, \quad y - \frac{c}{1 - \cos x} = 0.$$

The composite solution of the given differential equation, therefore, is

$$\left(y - \frac{c}{1 + \cos x}\right)\left(y - \frac{c}{1 - \cos x}\right) = 0.$$

2. *Solve* : $3p^2y^2 - 2xyp + 4y^2 - x^2 = 0$.

Multiplying throughout by 3, we get

$$9p^2y^2 - 6xyp + 12y^2 - 3x^2 = 0$$

or $\quad (3yp - x)^2 - 4(x^2 - 3y^2) = 0.$ $\qquad \ldots(i)$

Put $x^2 - 3y^2 = v^2$

$$\therefore \quad 2x - 6y\frac{dy}{dx} = 2v\frac{dv}{dx}$$

or $\quad (x - 3py) = v\dfrac{dv}{dx}.$

Putting in (i), we get

$$v^2\left(\frac{dv}{dx}\right)^2 - 4v^2 = 0$$

$$\therefore \quad \frac{dv}{dx} = \pm 2.$$

or $\quad v = c \pm 2x \quad$ or $\quad v^2 = (c \pm 2x)^2$

or $\quad x^2 - 3y^2 = (c \pm 2x)^2.$

3. Solve : $\left(1 - y^2 + \dfrac{y^4}{x^2}\right) p^2 - 2\dfrac{y}{x} p + \dfrac{y^2}{x^2} = 0.$

The given equation can be written as

$$p^2 - \dfrac{2y}{x} p + \dfrac{y^2}{x^2} = p^2 y^2 \left(1 - \dfrac{y^2}{x^2}\right)$$

or $(px - y)^2 = p^2 y^2 (x^2 - y^2)$

or $px - y = \pm\, py \sqrt{x^2 - y^2}$

$\therefore$ $p\left[x \mp y \sqrt{x^2 - y^2}\right] = y$

or $\dfrac{dx}{dy} = \dfrac{x \mp y \sqrt{x^2 - y^2}}{y}.$

Put $x = vy, \dfrac{dx}{dy} = v + y \cdot \dfrac{dv}{dx}$

$\therefore$ $v + \dfrac{dv}{dy} = \dfrac{vy \mp y^2 \sqrt{v^2 - 1}}{y}$

$$= v \mp y \sqrt{v^2 - 1}$$

or $\dfrac{dv}{dy} = \mp \sqrt{v^2 - 1}$

or $\dfrac{dv}{\sqrt{v^2 - 1}} = \mp\, dy$

$\therefore$ $\cosh^{-1} v = (c \mp y)$

or $\log\left[v + \sqrt{v^2 - 1}\right] = c \mp y$

$\therefore$ $\log \dfrac{x + \sqrt{x^2 - y^2}}{y} = c \mp y.$

EXERCISES

Solve the following differential equations :

1. $x\left(\dfrac{dy}{dx}\right)^2 + (y - x)\dfrac{dy}{dx} - y = 0.$ *(Bilaspur, 2000)*

2. $y^2 + xyp - x^2 p^2 = 0.$

3. $xyp^2 - (x^2 + y^2) p + xy = 0.$

4. $x^2\left(\dfrac{dy}{dx}\right)^2 + xy\dfrac{dy}{dx} - 6y^2 = 0.$

5. $p^2y + (x - y)\, p - x = 0.$

6. $xp^2 + (y - x)\, p - y = 0.$

7. $xy\,(p^2 + 1) = (x^2 + y^2)\, p.$

8. $4y^2p^2 + 2pxy\,(3x + 1) + 3x^3 = 0.$

9. $x^2 \left(\dfrac{dy}{dx}\right)^2 - 2xy\,\dfrac{dy}{dx} + 2y^2 - x^2 = 0.$

(Bilaspur, 1998; Jabalpur, 1996, 97; Rewa, 1997)

10. $p^2 - 2p \cosh x + 1 = 0.$ *(Sagar, 2000)*

11. $(x - y)^2\, p^2 - 3y\,(x - y)\, p + 2y^2 + xy - x^2 = 0.$ *(Jiwaji, 2000)*

ANSWERS

1. $(y - c - x)\,(xy - c) = 0.$

2. $(y^2 - cx^{1 + \sqrt{5}})(y^2 - cx^{1 - \sqrt{5}}) = 0.$

3. $(y - cx)\,(x^2 - y^2 - c) = 0.$

4. $(y - cx^2)\,(x^3y - c) = 0.$

5. $(x^2 + y^2 - c)\,(y - x - c) = 0.$

6. $(y - x - c)\,(xy - c) = 0.$

7. $(y^2 - x^2 - c)\,(y - cx) = 0.$

8. $x^2 + 2y^2 = c,\ x^3 + y^2 = c.$

9. $\sin^{-1}(y/x) = \pm \log cx.$

10. $(y - e^x + c)\,(y + e^{-x} + c) = 0.$

11. $\left[e^{2\tan^{-1}(y/x)} - c\,(x^2 + y^2)\right]\left[\left\{\dfrac{2y + (1 - \sqrt{5})\,x}{2y + (1 + \sqrt{5})\,x}\right\}^{3/55}\right.$

$$\left. - c\,(y^2 + yx - x^2)\right] = 0.$$

16.3. Equations solvable for y. Suppose that the given differential equation, on solving for y, gives

$$y = f(x, p). \qquad ...(1)$$

Differentiating with respect to x, we obtain

$$p = \frac{dy}{dx} = \varphi\left(x, p, \frac{dp}{dx}\right)$$

so that we obtain a new differential equation with variables x and p.

Suppose that it is possible to solve this equation.

Let the solution be

$$F(x, p, c) = 0, \qquad ...(2)$$

where, c, is the arbitrary constant.

The solution of (1) may be exhibited in either of the *two* forms. We may either eliminate p between (1) and (2) and obtain $\psi(x, y, c)$ as the required solution or we may solve (1) and (2) for x, y and obtain

$$x = f_1(p, c), \quad y = f_2(p, c)$$

as the required solution, where, p, is the parameter.

EXAMPLES

1. *Solve* : $y + px = p^2 x^4$.

                    (*Vikram, 1995, 97; Rohilkhand, 2000; Kumaon, 2002*)

Differentiating with respect to x, we have

$$\frac{dy}{dx} + p + x\frac{dp}{dx} = 4x^3 p^2 + 2x^4 p \frac{dp}{dx}$$

$$\Rightarrow \quad 2p - 4x^3 p^2 - 2x^4 p\frac{dp}{dx} + x\frac{dp}{dx} = 0$$

$$\Rightarrow \quad 2p(1 - 2x^3 p) + x(1 - 2x^3 p)\frac{dp}{dx} = 0$$

$$\Rightarrow \quad 2p + x\frac{dp}{dx} = 0$$

$$\Rightarrow \quad \frac{dp}{p} + \frac{2\,dx}{x} = 0$$

$$\Rightarrow \quad \log p + 2\log x = \text{constant} = \log c, \text{ say}$$

$$\Rightarrow \quad px^2 = c \quad \Leftrightarrow \quad p = c/x^2.$$

Substituting this value of, p, in the given differential equation so as to eliminate, p, we obtain

$$y = -c/x + c^2 \quad \Rightarrow \quad xy = c^2 x - c$$

as the required solution.

2. *Solve* : $y - 2px = f(xp^2)$.

The given equation is

$$y = 2px + f(xp^2) \qquad \qquad ...(i)$$

Differentiating with respect to x, we get

$$p = 2p + 2x\frac{dp}{dx} + f'(xp^2) \cdot \left\{ p^2 + x \cdot 2p\frac{dp}{dx} \right\}$$

or $\quad 0 = \left(p + 2x\frac{dp}{dx} \right) + p f'(xp^2)\left\{ p + 2x\frac{dp}{dx} \right\}$

or $\quad 0 = \{1 + p f'(xp^2)\}\left\{ p + 2x\frac{dp}{dx} \right\} = 0$

$\therefore \quad p + 2x\frac{dp}{dx} = 0 \quad \text{or} \quad \frac{dx}{x} + \frac{2}{p}\,dp = 0$

or $\qquad \log x + \log p^2 = \log c$

or $\qquad p^2 x = c \quad \therefore \quad p = \dfrac{c}{\sqrt{x}}.$

Putting the value of p in (i), we get

$$y = 2x \frac{c}{\sqrt{x}} + f\left(x \cdot \frac{c^2}{x}\right)$$

or $\qquad y = 2c\sqrt{x} + f(c^2).$

3. *Solve* : $xp^2 - 2yp + x = 0.$

The given equation is

$$2yp = x(p^2 + 1)$$

or $\qquad 2y = x\left(p + \dfrac{1}{p}\right)$ $\qquad\qquad\qquad$ ...(i)

Differentiating with respect to x, we get

$$2p = \left(p + \frac{1}{p}\right) \cdot 1 + x\left(1 - \frac{1}{p^2}\right) \cdot \frac{dp}{dx}$$

or $\qquad \left(p - \dfrac{1}{p}\right) = x\left(1 - \dfrac{1}{p^2}\right)\dfrac{dp}{dx}$

or $\qquad p = x\dfrac{dp}{dx}$

$\therefore \qquad \dfrac{dp}{p} = \dfrac{dx}{x} \quad$ or $\quad \log p = \log x + \log c$

or $\qquad p = cx.$

Putting for p in the given equation, we get

$$2y \cdot cx = x(c^2 x^2 + 1)$$

or $\qquad 2cy = c^2 x^2 + 1.$

4. *Solve* : $y = 2px + p^n.$ $\qquad\qquad$ (*Jabalpur, 1994; Vikram, 1998*)

Differentiating the given differential equation w.r.t. x, we get

$$\frac{dy}{dx} = 2p + 2x\frac{dp}{dx} + np^{n-1}\frac{dp}{dx}$$

$$\Rightarrow \quad -p = (2x + np^{n-1})\frac{dp}{dx}$$

$$\Rightarrow \quad p(dx/dp) + 2x + np^{n-1} = 0$$

$$\Rightarrow \quad \frac{dx}{dp} + \left(\frac{2}{p}\right)x = -np^{n-2}.$$

This is a linear differential equation in x and its

$$\text{I.F.} = e^{\int (2/p)\,dt} = e^{2 \log p} = p^2.$$

$\therefore$ Its solution is

$$x \cdot p^2 = c - \int np^{n-2} \cdot p^2 \, dp = c - \frac{np^{n+1}}{(n+1)}$$

$$\Rightarrow \qquad x = \frac{c}{p^2} - \frac{np^{n-1}}{(n+1)} \qquad \qquad \text{...(1)}$$

By putting this value of x in the given differential equation, we get

$$y = \frac{2c}{p} - \frac{2n}{(n+1)} p^n + p^n = \frac{2c}{p} - \frac{n-1}{n+1} p^n \qquad \text{...(2)}$$

Equations (1) and (2) give required solution where p is a parameter.

5. *Solve* : $y = \sin p - p \cos p$.   *(Bilaspur, 1994, 97; Vikram, 1996)*

The equation is already solved for y, hence, differentiating it w.r.t. x, we get,

$$p = (\cos p - \cos p + p \sin p) \frac{dp}{dx}$$

or $\qquad\qquad 1 = \sin p \dfrac{dp}{dx} \qquad\qquad\qquad\qquad\qquad$ ...(i)

which is in variables separable for hence, integrating it, we get,

$$x + c_1 = \int \sin p \, dp$$

or $\qquad x + c_1 = - \cos p$

or $\qquad \cos p = c - x. \qquad\qquad\qquad\qquad\qquad\qquad$ ...(ii)

Eliminating p from (ii) and the given differential equation, we get,

$$y = \sqrt{1 - (c - x)^2} - (c - x) \cdot \cos^{-1} (c - x)$$

or $\quad \cos\left[\left(\sqrt{1 - c^2 + 2cx - x^2} - y \right)(c - x) \right] = c - x$

which is the general solution of the given differential equation.

6. *Solve* : $x^2 + p^2 x - yp = 0$.   *(Bhopal, 2000)*

Solving the given differential equation for y, we get,

$$y = px + \frac{x^2}{p} \qquad\qquad\qquad\qquad\qquad\qquad \text{...(i)}$$

Differentiating (i) with respect to x, we get,

$$p = p + \frac{dp}{dx} + \frac{2xp - x^2 \dfrac{dp}{dx}}{p^2}$$

or $\qquad (p^2 - x) \dfrac{dp}{dx} + 2p = 0$

or $\qquad \dfrac{dx}{dp} - \dfrac{x}{2p} = -\dfrac{1}{2} p$ ...(ii)

which is a linear differential equation of first order and of first degree in x and p, hence,

$$\text{I.F.} = e^{-\frac{1}{2}\int \frac{1}{p} dp} = e^{-\frac{1}{2}\log p} = \dfrac{1}{\sqrt{p}}.$$

Therefore, solution of (ii) is

$$x \cdot \dfrac{1}{\sqrt{p}} = c - \dfrac{1}{2} \int p \cdot \dfrac{1}{\sqrt{p}} \, dp$$

$$= c - \dfrac{1}{2} \dfrac{p^{3/2}}{3/2}$$

or $\qquad\qquad x = c\sqrt{p} - \dfrac{1}{3} p^2$ ...(iii)

Equation (iii) with original equation gives the general solution of the given differential equation.

Note. Putting the value of x from (iii) in (i), we get,

$$y = p\left(c\sqrt{p} - \dfrac{1}{3} p^2 \right) + \dfrac{1}{p}\left(c\sqrt{p} - \dfrac{1}{3} p^2 \right)^2 \quad ...(iv)$$

then, (iii) and (iv) give the general solution of the differential equation in parametric form having p as parameter.

EXERCISES

Solve the following differential equations :

1. $x^3 p^3 + x^2 py + a^3 = 0$.

2. $y = 2px + p^4 x^3$.

3. $\dfrac{x}{p} = ap$. (*Vikram, 1993*)

4. $y = 2px - p^2$.

5. $y = 2px + p^2$.

6. $x - yp = ap^2$.

7. $y - x = x\dfrac{dy}{dx} + \left(\dfrac{dy}{dx} \right)^2$.

8. $x + yp = ap^2$.

9. $y = 3x + a \log p$. (*Jiwaji, 1993*)

10. $p^3 + mp^2 = a\,(y + mx)$.

11. $4p^3 + 3px = y$.

12. $y = xp^2 + p$.

             (*Indore, 1993*)

13. $y = \dfrac{1}{\sqrt{1 + p^2}} + b$.

14. $y = p^2 x + p^4$.

15. $y = 3x + a \log \log p$.

             (*Vikram, 1998*)

16. $y = p \tan p + \log \cos p$.

17. $p^3 - 4xyp + 8y^2 = 0$.

         (*Garhwal, 2000; Avadh, 2001*)

ANSWERS

1. $c^2 + cxy + a^3x = 0$.

2. $(y - c^2)^2 = 4cx$.

3. $x = \dfrac{p}{\sqrt{1-p^2}} (c + a \sin^{-1} p), \; y = -ap + \dfrac{1}{\sqrt{1-p^2}} (c + a \sin^{-1} p)$.

4. $x = cp^{-2} + \dfrac{2}{3} p, \; y = 2cp^{-1} + \dfrac{1}{3} p^2$.

5. $4(y^2 - 3cx)(x^2 + y) = (xy + 3c)^2$.

6. $y = \dfrac{1}{\sqrt{1-p^2}} (c + a \sin^{-1} p) - ap, \; x = \dfrac{p}{\sqrt{1-p^2}} (c + a \sin^{-1} p)$.

7. $y - x = xp + p^2, \; x = ce^{-p} - 2(p - 1)$.

8. $x = \dfrac{\sqrt{p^2 + 1}}{p} = (a \sinh^{-1} p + c), \; y = -\dfrac{x}{p} + \dfrac{a}{p}$.

9. $y = 3x + a \log \dfrac{3}{1 - ce^{3x/a}}$.

10. $ax = c + \dfrac{3p^2}{2} - mp + m^2 \log(p + m)$,

$ay = -m \left[c + \dfrac{3}{2} p^2 - mp + m^2 \log(p + m) \right] + mp^2 + p^3$.

11. $y = -\dfrac{8}{7} p^3 + cp^{-1/2}, \; x = -\dfrac{12}{7} p^3 + \dfrac{c}{3} p^{-3/2}$.

12. $x(p - 1)^2 = c - p + \log p$ and given equation.

13. $(x + c)^2 (y - b)^2 = 1$.

14. $x = \dfrac{1}{(1 - p)^2} \left(\dfrac{4}{3} p^3 - p^4 + c \right), \; y = p^2 x + p^4$.

16. $x = \tan p + c, \; y = p \tan p + \log \cos p$.

17. $y = c(x - c)^2$.

16.4. Equations solvable for x. Suppose that the given differential equation, on solving for x, gives

$$x = f(y, p). \qquad \qquad ...(1)$$

Differentiating with respect to y, we obtain

$$\frac{1}{p} = \frac{dx}{dy} = \varphi(y, p, dp/dy), \text{ say}$$

so that we obtain a new differential equation in variables y and p. *Suppose that it is possible to solve this equation.*

Let the solution be

$$F(p, y, c) = 0. \qquad ...(2)$$

As in the preceding article, the elimination of p between (1) and (2) will give the solution, or (1) and (2) may be solved to express x and y in terms of p and c where p is to be regarded as a parameter.

EXAMPLES

1. *Solve* : $y = 2px + y^2 p^3$. *(Indore, 1994, 97, 2000; Jabalpur, 1995)*
Solving it for x, we obtain

$$x = \frac{y - y^2 p^3}{2p} = \frac{y}{2p} - \frac{y^2 p^2}{2}.$$

Differentiating with respect to y, we obtain

$$\frac{1}{p} = \frac{dx}{dy} = \frac{1}{2p} - \frac{y}{2p^2}\frac{dp}{dy} - yp^2 - py^2\frac{dp}{dy}$$

$$\Rightarrow \quad \frac{1}{2p} + p^2 y + \left(\frac{y}{2p^2} + py^2\right)\frac{dp}{dy} = 0$$

$$\Rightarrow \quad \frac{1 + 2p^3 y}{2p} + \frac{y(1 + 2p^3 y)}{2p^2}\cdot\frac{dp}{dy} = 0$$

$$\Rightarrow \quad 1 + \frac{y}{p}\frac{dp}{dy} = 0$$

$$\Rightarrow \quad \frac{dy}{y} + \frac{dp}{p} = 0$$

$$\Rightarrow \quad \log y + \log p = \text{constant} = \log c, \text{ say}$$

$$\Rightarrow \quad py = c \quad \Leftrightarrow \quad p = c/y.$$

Substituting this value of, p, in the given equation, we obtain

$$y = \frac{2cx}{y} + y^2 \cdot \frac{c^3}{y^3} \quad \Rightarrow \quad y^2 = 2cx + c^3,$$

which is the required solution.

2. *Solve* : $x = y + p^2$.
Differentiating given equation with respect to y, we get

$$\frac{dx}{dy} = \frac{1}{p} = 1 + 2p\frac{dp}{dy}$$

or

$$dy = \frac{2p^2}{1-p}dp = -2\left(p + 1 + \frac{1}{p-1}\right)dp.$$

Integration gives

$$y = -2\left[\frac{1}{2}p^2 + p + \log(p-1)\right] + c$$

or $$y = c - [p^2 + 2p + 2 \log (p - 1)] \qquad ...(i)$$

Substituting this in the given equation, we obtain

$$x = c - [2p + 2 \log (p - 1)] \qquad ...(ii)$$

Relations (i) and (ii) together give the required solution.

3. *Solve* : $y^2 \log y = xyp + p^2.$ (*Avadh, 1999*)

The given equation is

$$x = \frac{y \log y}{p} - \frac{p}{y} \qquad ...(i)$$

Differentiating with respect to y, we get

$$\frac{dx}{dy} = \frac{1}{p} \cdot \frac{p(1 + \log y) - y \log y \cdot \dfrac{dp}{dy}}{p^2} - \frac{y \cdot \dfrac{dp}{dy} - p}{y^2}$$

or $$\frac{1}{p} = \frac{1}{p} + \frac{1}{p} \log y - \frac{y}{p^2} \log y \frac{dp}{dy} - \frac{1}{y} \cdot \frac{dp}{dy} + \frac{p}{y^2}$$

or $$\frac{1}{y} \frac{dp}{dy} \left(1 + \frac{y^2}{p^2} \log y \right) = \frac{p}{y^2} \left(1 + \frac{y^2}{p^2} \log y \right)$$

or $$\frac{dp}{dy} = \frac{p}{y},$$

on cancelling the common factor on either side.

$$\therefore \quad \frac{dp}{p} = \frac{dy}{y} \quad \therefore \quad \log p - \log y = \log c$$

or $$\frac{p}{y} = c \quad \text{or} \quad p = cy.$$

Substituting the value of p in the given equation, we get

$$\log y = cx + x^2.$$

4. *Solve* : $ayp^2 + (2x - b) p - y = 0.$ (*Avadh, 2000*)

The given equation can be written as

$$2x = \frac{y}{p} + b - \frac{a}{y}.$$

Differentiating with respect to y, we get

$$2 \cdot \frac{1}{p} = \frac{1}{p} - \frac{1}{p^2} y \frac{dp}{dy} - a \left(p + y \frac{dp}{dy} \right)$$

or $$\frac{1}{p^2} \left(p + y \frac{dp}{dy} \right) + a \left(p + y \frac{dp}{dy} \right) = 0$$

or $$\left(\frac{1}{p^2} + a \right) \left(p + y \frac{dp}{dy} \right) = 0$$

$$\therefore \quad \frac{y}{p}\frac{dp}{dy} + 1 = 0 \quad \text{or} \quad \frac{dp}{p} + \frac{dy}{y} = 0$$

or
$$\log p + \log y = \log c \quad \text{or} \quad py = c \quad \text{or} \quad p = \frac{c}{y}.$$

On putting the value of p in given equation, we get

$$2x = \frac{y^2}{c} + b - ac$$

or
$$2xc = y^2 + bc - ac^2$$
$$ac^2 + (2x - b)\,c - y^2 = 0.$$

EXERCISES

Solve the following differential equations :

1. $p^2 y + 2px - y = 0.$

2. $ap^2 + py - x = 0.$

3. $\left(\dfrac{dy}{dx}\right)^3 - 4xy\dfrac{dy}{dx} + 8y^2 = 0.$

4. $\left(\dfrac{dy}{dx}\right)^3 y^2 - 2x\dfrac{dy}{dx} + y = 0.$

5. $4p^3 + 3xp = y.$

6. $yp^2 - 2xp + y = 0.$

7. $p^3 - 4xyp + 8y^2 = 0.$

(Vikram, 1998; Ravishankar, 2000)

8. $p = \tan\left(x - \dfrac{p}{1 + p^2}\right).$

(Vikram, 2000)

9. $x + \dfrac{p}{\sqrt{1 + p^2}} = a.$

10. $x = y + a\log p.$

ANSWERS

1. $x = \dfrac{c(1 - p^2)}{p^2},\ y = \dfrac{2c}{p}.$

2. $x = \dfrac{(c - a\cosh^{-1} p)}{\sqrt{p^2 - 1}}\,p,\ y = \dfrac{c - a\cosh^{-1} p}{\sqrt{p^2 - 1}} - ap.$

3. $64y = c\,(4x - c)^2.$

4. $2cx = c^3 + y^2.$

5. $y = -\dfrac{8}{7}p^3 + cp^{-1/2},\ x = -\dfrac{12}{7}p^2 + \dfrac{c}{3}p^{-3/2}.$

6. $y^2 = 2cx - c^2.$

7. $y = c\,(c - x)^2.$

8. $y = c - \dfrac{1}{1 + p^2},\ x = \tan^{-1} p + \dfrac{p}{1 + p^2}.$

9. $(y + c)^2 + (x - a)^2 = 1.$

10. $y = c - a\log(p - 1),\ x = c + a\log\dfrac{p}{p - 1}.$

16.5. Clairut's Equation. The equation

$$y = px + f(p),\qquad \text{...(1)}$$

is known as Clairut's equation. Here $f(p)$ is a function of p. To solve (1), we differentiate with respect to x and obtain

$$p = p + x\frac{dp}{dx} + f'(p)\frac{dp}{dx},$$

$$\Rightarrow \ [x + f'(p)]\frac{dp}{dx} = 0.$$

$$\Rightarrow \ \begin{cases} \dfrac{dp}{dx} = 0 & \text{...(2)} \\[2mm] x + f'(p) = 0. & \text{...(3)} \end{cases}$$

Now, (2) gives

$$p = \text{constant} = c, \text{ say.} \qquad \text{...(4)}$$

Eliminating p between (1) and (4), we obtain

$$y = cx + f(c) \qquad \text{...(5)}$$

as a solution of (1).

If we eliminate p between (1) and (3), we will obtain another solution not contained in the general solution (5). This solution is known as the *singular solution*. (Refer § 16.7)

Note. Sometimes, change of variables transforms a given equation to Clairut's equation.

EXAMPLES

1. *Solve* : $y = px + \log p$.

The solution of this equation which is Clairut's form, is

$$\mathbf{y} = cx + \log c,$$

obtained on changing, p, to the arbitrary constant c.

2. *Solve* : $x^2(y - px) = p^2 y$.   (*Lucknow, 1995*; *Kumaon, 2003*)

We put

$$x^2 = u, \ y^2 = v.$$

$$\Rightarrow \ 2x\,dx = du \text{ and } 2y\,dy = dv.$$

$$\Rightarrow \ \frac{y\,dy}{x\,dx} = \frac{dv}{du} \ \Rightarrow \ p = \frac{dy}{dx} = \frac{x}{y}\cdot\frac{dv}{du}.$$

Substituting this value of p in the given differential equation, we obtain

$$x^2\left(y - \frac{x^2}{y}\cdot\frac{dv}{du}\right) = \frac{x^2}{y}\left(\frac{dv}{du}\right)^2,$$

$$\Rightarrow \ \left(y^2 - x^2\frac{dv}{du}\right) = \left(\frac{dv}{du}\right)^2,$$

$$\Rightarrow \quad \left(v - u\frac{dv}{du}\right) = \left(\frac{dv}{du}\right)^2,$$

$$\Rightarrow \quad v = u\frac{dv}{du} + \left(\frac{dv}{du}\right)^2,$$

which is Clairut's form. The solution, therefore, is

$$v = cu + c^2 \quad \Rightarrow \quad y^2 = cx^2 + c^2.$$

3. *Solve* : $y = x f_1(p) + f_2(p)$.

While this equation is *not* Clairut's it will be seen that the method adopted for solving Clairut's equations will deliver the goods.

Differentiating with respect to x, we obtain

$$p = f_1(p) + x f_1'(p)\frac{dp}{dx} + f_2'(p)\frac{dp}{dx}$$

$$\Rightarrow \quad \frac{dx}{dp} = \frac{f_1'(p)}{p - f_1(p)}x + \frac{f_2'(p)}{p - f_1(p)},$$

which is linear with, p, as independent and, x, as dependent variable. Suppose that on solving this linear equation, we obtain

$$\varphi(x, p, c) = 0.$$

Then, eliminating p between this solution and the given equation, we obtain the required solution.

4. *Solve* : $(x^2 + y^2)(1 + p)^2 - 2(x + y)(1 + p)(x + yp) + (x + yp)^2 = 0.$

The given equation can be written as

$$x^2 + y^2 - 2(x + y)\frac{(x + yp)}{(1 + p)} + \left(\frac{x + yp}{1 + p}\right)^2 = 0.$$

Put $x^2 + y^2 = v$ $\therefore$ $2x + 2yp = \dfrac{dv}{dx}$

and $x + y = u$ $\therefore$ $1 + p = \dfrac{du}{dx}.$

$\therefore \quad \dfrac{x + yp}{1 + p} = \dfrac{1}{2}\dfrac{dv}{du}.$

Making the above substitutions, we get

$$v - 2u \cdot \frac{1}{2}\frac{dv}{du} + \frac{1}{4}\left(\frac{dv}{du}\right)^2 = 0$$

or $v = u\dfrac{dv}{du} - \dfrac{1}{4}\cdot\left(\dfrac{dv}{du}\right)^2.$

Putting $\dfrac{dv}{du} = P$, we get

$$v = uP - \frac{1}{4}P^2,$$

which is Clairut's form and hence its solution is

$$v = u \cdot c - \frac{1}{4}c^2$$

or $\quad x^2 + y^2 = c(x+y) - \dfrac{1}{4}c^2.$

5. *Reduce* $x^2\left(\dfrac{dy}{dx}\right)^2 + y(2x+y)\dfrac{dy}{dx} + y^2 = 0$ *to Clairut's form by using the substitution* $y = u$ *and* $xy = v$.

Clearly, $x = \dfrac{v}{u}$,

$\therefore \quad dx = \dfrac{u\,dv - v\,du}{u^2}$ and $dy = du$

$\therefore \quad \dfrac{dy}{dx} = \dfrac{u^2\,du}{u\,dv - v\,du} = \dfrac{u}{\dfrac{dv}{du} - \dfrac{v}{u}}.$

Putting the values of x, y and $\dfrac{dy}{dx}$ in the given equation, we get

$$\frac{v^2}{u^2} \cdot \frac{u^2}{\left(\dfrac{dv}{du} - \dfrac{v}{u}\right)^2} + u\left(2\frac{v}{u} + u\right)\frac{u}{\left(\dfrac{dv}{du} - \dfrac{v}{u}\right)} + u^2 = 0$$

or $\quad \dfrac{v^2}{u^2} + \left(\dfrac{2v}{u} + u\right)\left(\dfrac{dv}{du} - \dfrac{v}{u}\right) + \left(\dfrac{dv}{du} - \dfrac{v}{u}\right)^2 = 0$

or $\quad \dfrac{v^2}{u^2} + \dfrac{2v}{u}\dfrac{dv}{du} + u\dfrac{dv}{du} - \dfrac{2v^2}{u^2} - v + \left(\dfrac{dv}{du}\right)^2 - 2\dfrac{v}{u}\dfrac{dv}{du} + \dfrac{v^2}{u^2} = 0$

or $\quad v = u\dfrac{dv}{du} + \left(\dfrac{dv}{du}\right)^2.$

If we put $\dfrac{dv}{du} = P$, we get

$$v = uP + P^2.$$

This is clearly of Clairut's form. Hence the solution is

$v = uc + c^2$

or $\quad xy = cy + c^2.$

EXERCISES

Solve

1. $(y - px)(p - 1) = p$.   *(Jabalpur, 1997; Agra, 2001)*

2. $y = x\dfrac{dy}{dx} + \left(\dfrac{dy}{dx}\right)^2$.

3. $y = x\dfrac{dy}{dx} + e^{dy/dx}$.

4. $(px - y)(py + x) = a^2 p$.   [Put $x^2 = u,\ y^2 = v$]

           (Poorvanchal, 1995; Sagar, 1996; Indore, 1995;
                   Ravishankar, 1995, 96, 99S; Bilaspur, 1998)

5. $y + xp \log p = (2 + 3 \log p) p^3$.

6. $y = 2px - p^2$.

7. $p = \log(px - y)$.   *(Sagar, 1995; Kumaon, 2002)*

8. $y = px + \sqrt{a^2 p^2 + b^2}$.   *(Vikram, 1996; Bilaspur, 1996; Rewa, 2000)*

9. $\sin px \cos y = \cos px \sin y + p$.

10. $p^2(x^2 - a^2) - 2xyp + y^2 - b^2 = 0$.

11. $y = 2px + y^2 p^3$.   *(Jabalpur, 1995)*

12. $e^{3x}(p - 1) + p^3 e^{2y} = 0$.   *(Vikram, 1995)*

ANSWERS

1. $(y - cx)(c - 1) = c$.   2. $y = cx + c^2$.

3. $y = cx + e^c$.   4. $y^2 = cx^2 - a^2 c/(1 + c)$.

5. $x = 3p^2 + cp^{-1}, y = 2p^3 - c \log p$.

6. $x = \dfrac{2}{3} p + cp^{-2},\ y = \dfrac{1}{3} p^2 + 2cp^{-1}$.

7. $y = cx - e^c$.   8. $y = cx + \sqrt{a^2 c^2 + b^2}$.

9. $y = cx - \sin^{-1} c$.   10. $c^2(x^2 - a^2) - 2xyc + y^2 - b^2 = 0$.

11. $y^2 = cx + \dfrac{c^3}{8}$.   12. $e^y = ce^x + c^3$.

16.6. Geometrical meaning of a differential equation of the first order.

Consider a differential equation

$$\varphi(x, y, dy/dx) = 0 \qquad \ldots(1)$$

and let

$$f(x, y, c) = 0 \qquad \ldots(2)$$

be its general solution; c, being the arbitrary constant.

For each value of the arbitrary constant c, the equation (2) represents a curve so that the equation (2) represents a family of curves; c being the parameter for the family. We thus say that *Every differential equation of the first order represents a family of curves.*

Now take a point in the plane and substitute its coordinates (x, y) in (1) and (2) and solve the resulting equations in dy/dx and c. Then the values of c, so obtained, are the values of the parameter for the particular curves of the family through (x, y) and the values of dy/dx are the slopes of the tangents to these curves at the point. Thus, in general, we expect that the degree of, c in (2) must be equal to that of dy/dx in (1) which is known as the degree of the differential equation.

16.7. Singular Solutions. In addition to the *General solution* and the *particular solutions*, obtained by giving particular values to the arbitrary constants in the general solution, a differential equation may also possess other solutions. The solutions of differential equations, other than the general and particular, are known as *Singular solutions*. In this connection, we have the following result.

Whenever the family of curves
$$f(x, y, c) = 0 \qquad \qquad ...(1)$$
represented by the differential equation
$$\varphi\,(x, y, dy/dx) = 0 \qquad \qquad ...(2)$$
possesses an envelope, the equation of the envelope is the singular solution of the differential equation (2).

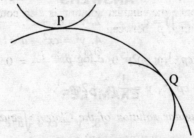

Suppose that the family of curves possesses an envelope. Take any point P (x, y) on the envelope. There exists a curve of the family, say,
$$f(x, y, c_1) = 0,$$
which touches the envelope at (x, y). The values of $x, y, dy/dx$ for the curve at P satisfy the given differential equation. Also the values of $x, y, dy/dx$ at P for the envelope are the same as for the curve. Thus we see that the values of $x, y, dy/dx$ at every point of the envelope satisfy the given differential equation. Hence the equation of the envelope is a solution of the differential equation.

This solution does not contain an arbitrary constant and, in general, cannot be obtained from the general solution by giving particular values to the arbitrary constants.

16.71. Determination of Singular Solutions. Let

$$\varphi\,(x,\,y,\,dy\,/\,dx) = 0$$

be a given differential equation and let $f(x, y, c) = 0$ be its general solution. Now it is known that the envelope of any family of curves

$$f(x,\,y,\,c) = 0 \qquad\qquad ...(1)$$

is *contained* in the locus obtained on eliminating c, between (1) and

$$\frac{\partial f(x,\,y,\,c)}{\partial c} = 0. \qquad\qquad ...(2)$$

Let this eliminant be

$$\psi\,(x,\,y) = 0. \qquad\qquad ...(3)$$

As the eliminant given by (3) may represent loci other than the envelope; it is necessary to verify if any part of the locus represented by (3) is or is not a solution of the given differential equation.

Another Method. From the Theory of Equations, it is known that the equation (3) represents the locus of points (x, y) such that at least two or the corresponding values of, c, are equal, *i.e.*, such that at least two of the curves of the family through (x, y) coincide. As the equation $\varphi\,(x, y, dy\,/\,dx)$ $= 0$, *i.e.*, $\varphi\,(x, y, p) = 0$ determines the slopes of the tangents to the curves of the family through (x, y) we see that for a point (x, y) satisfying (3) at least two of the corresponding values of p must coincide. Hence we see that the envelope and hence the singular solution is also contained in the locus obtained on eliminating, p, between

$$\varphi\,(x,\,y,\,p) = 0, \quad \frac{\partial \varphi\,(x,\,y,\,p)}{\partial p} = 0.$$

EXAMPLES

1. *Find the singular solution of the Clairut's equation*

$$y = px + f\,(p). \qquad\qquad ...(1)$$

The general solution is

$$y = cx + f\,(c) \qquad\qquad ...(2)$$

so that the singular solution is obtained on eliminating, c between (2) and

$$0 = x + f'\,(c) \qquad\qquad ...(3)$$

which is obtained on differentiating (2) partially w.r.t. c.

Differentiating (1) partially w.r.t. p, we obtain

$$0 = x + f'\,(p) \qquad\qquad ...(4)$$

so that the singular solution is also obtained on eliminating, p, between (1) and (4). Clearly the c-eliminant and the p-eliminant are the same.

2. *Solve the equation*

$$x^2p^2 + yp(2x + y) + y^2 = 0,$$

using the substitutions $y = u$, $xy = v$ *and find its singular solution.*

We have

$$y = u, \qquad x = v/u$$

$$\Rightarrow \qquad \frac{dy}{du} = 1, \qquad \frac{dx}{du} = \frac{u\dfrac{dv}{du} - v}{u^2}.$$

These give

$$p = \frac{dy}{dx} = \frac{u^2}{u\dfrac{dv}{du} - v}.$$

Making substitutions in the given differential equation, we shall obtain

$$\left(u\frac{dv}{du} - v\right)^2 + (u^2 + 2v)\left(u\frac{dv}{du} - v\right) + v^2 = 0,$$

$$\Rightarrow \quad v = u\frac{dv}{du} + \left(\frac{dv}{du}\right)^2.$$

This is Clairut's equation. Its general solution is

$$v = cu + c^2$$

$$\Rightarrow \quad xy = cy + c^2. \qquad\qquad\qquad ...(1)$$

To obtain the singular solution, we differentiate (1) partially w.r.t. c, and obtain

$$0 = y + 2c. \qquad\qquad\qquad ...(2)$$

Eliminating, c, between (1) and (2), we obtain

$$y(y + 4x) = 0.$$

Consider $y = 0$. Differentiating this we obtain $p = 0$. Substituting $y = 0$, $p = 0$, we see that the given differential equation is satisfied.

Consider now, $y + 4x = 0$. This gives $p = -4$. Substituting $y = -4x$ and $p = -4$ in the given differential equation, we see that it is again satisfied. Thus $y = 0$, $y + 4x = 0$ are both singular solutions.

3. *Find the general and singular solution of*

$$9p^2(2 - y)^2 = 4(3 - y).$$

(Jabalpur, 1995; Rewa, 1998; Indore, 1999;
Ravishankar, 2001; Rohilkhand, 2002; Gorakhpur, 2003)

The given equation is $\left(\text{as } p = \dfrac{dy}{dx}\right)$,

$$3p = 3\frac{dy}{dx} = \pm\frac{2\sqrt{3 - y}}{2 - y}.$$

Separating the variables, we get

$$dx = \pm \frac{3}{2} \frac{2-y}{\sqrt{3-y}} \, dy.$$

Substituting $3 - y = t^2$, and integrating, we get

$$x + c = \pm \frac{3}{2} \int \frac{(t^2 - 1)(-2t \, dt)}{t}$$

$$= \pm t \, (t^2 - 3)$$

i.e., $(x + c)^2 = y^2 \, (3 - y).$ ...(i)

This is the *general solution*. The singular solution can be found by any of the following two methods :

First method. The general solution can be written as

$$c^2 + 2xc + x^2 - y^2 \, (3 - y) = 0 \qquad ...(ii)$$

This is a quadratic equation in the parameter c, and so its envelope is

$$4x^2 - 4 \{x^2 - y^2 \, (3 - y)\} = 0$$

i.e., $y^2 \, (3 - y) = 0$ ...(iii)

so that either $y = 0$ or $3 - y = 0$.

Now, $y = 0$ gives $p = 0$. These values of y and p do not satisfy the original differential equation. Hence $y = 0$ is not a solution.

Again, $3 - y = 0$ gives $p = 0$. Substitution shows that these values of y and p satisfy the given differential equation. Hence $3 - y = 0$ or $y = 3$ is the required singular solution.

Second method. The original equation is a quadratic equation in the parameter p. Since the singular solution is included in the envelope of this equation, which is given by $(B^2 - 4AC = 0)$

$$0 + 4 \cdot 9 \, (2 - y)^2 \cdot 4 \, (3 - y) = 0$$

i.e., $(2 - y)^2 \, (3 - y) = 0$ ...(iv)

Therefore, either $2 - y = 0$ or $3 - y = 0$.

From $2 - y = 0$, $p = 0$. These values of y and p do not satisfy the given differential equation so that $2 - y = 0$ is not a singular solution.

Also $3 - y = 0$ gives $p = 0$. These values of y and p clearly satisfy the original differential equation. Hence the singular solution is $3 - y = 0$ or $y = 3$.

Note : The singular solution is the part which is common to the result (*iii*) and (*iv*).

4. *Find general and singular solution of the differential equation* $y = px - p^2$.   (*Rewa, 1996*)

This equation is of Clairut's form. Hence its general solution will be

$$y = cx - c^2 \text{ or } c^2 - cx + y = 0 \qquad ...(1)$$

Again, since $f(x, y, c) = 0$ is a quadratic equation in c, hence c-discriminant will be

$$B^2 - 4AC = 0 \implies x^2 - 4y = 0 \qquad \qquad ...(2)$$

Again $f(x, y, p) = 0$ is $p^2 - px + y = 0$.

Hence p-discriminant will be

$$x^2 - 4y = 0 \qquad \qquad ...(3)$$

As $x^2 - 4y' = 0$ is common in both c- and p-discriminants hence this is the singular solution.

Again, $x^2 - 4y = 0$, $2x - 4 (dy / dx) = 0 \implies p = x / 2$.

By putting it in the differential equation,

$$y = (x / 2) \cdot x - (x^2 / 4) = x^2 / 4 \implies x^2 = 4y, \text{ which is true.}$$

5. *Solve and examine for singular solution*

$$(8p^3 - 27) x = 12p^2 y. \qquad \qquad (Bhopal, 2000)$$

The given differential equation is

$$(8p^3 - 27) x = 12p^2 y \qquad \qquad ...(i)$$

Solving the above differential equation for y, we get,

$$y = \frac{8p^3 x - 27x}{12p^2}$$

or $\qquad y = \frac{2}{3} px - \frac{9}{4} \frac{x}{p^2} \qquad \qquad ...(ii)$

Differentiating (ii) with respect to x, we get,

$$p = \frac{2}{3} p + \frac{2}{3} x \frac{dp}{dx} - \frac{9}{4} \left(\frac{p^2 - x \cdot 2p \dfrac{dp}{dx}}{p^4} \right)$$

or $\qquad \left(\dfrac{4p^3 + 27}{12p^2} \right) = \left(\dfrac{4p^3 + 27}{6p^3} \right) x \dfrac{dp}{dx}$

which gives $\quad 4p^3 + 27 = 0 \qquad \qquad ...(iii)$

and $\qquad \dfrac{1}{2} = \dfrac{x}{p} \dfrac{dp}{dx} \qquad \qquad ...(iv)$

Solving (iv), we get,

$$p^2 = c_1 x \qquad \qquad ...(v)$$

Eliminating p from (i) and (v), we get, general solution of (i) as

$$[8 (c_1 x)^{3/2} - 27] x = 12 c_1 xy$$

or $\qquad [8 (c_1 x)^{3/2} - 27 - 12 c_1 y] x = 0$

giving, $\quad x = 0$

and $\qquad 8 (c_1 x)^{3/2} - 27 - 12 c_1 y = 0$

or $\qquad 8 (c_1 x)^{3/2} = 27 + 12 c_1 y$

or $64c_1{}^3x^3 = (12c_1y + 27)^2$

or $x^3 = \dfrac{144c_1{}^2}{64c_1{}^3}\left(y + \dfrac{27}{12c_1}\right)^2 = \dfrac{9}{4c_1}\left(y + \dfrac{9}{4c_1}\right)^2.$

Replacing $\dfrac{9}{4c_1}$ by c, we get,

$$x^3 = c\,(y + c)^2.$$

Hence, the general solution of (i) is given by

$$x\,[x^2 - c\,(y + c)^2] = 0.$$

6. *Find general and singular solutions of the differential equation*
$xp^2 - 2yp + 4x = 0.$ *(Bhoj, 1999)*

Solving the given differential equation for p, we get

$$p = \frac{2y \pm 2\sqrt{y^2 - 4x^2}}{2x} \quad \text{or} \quad p = \frac{y \pm \sqrt{y^2 - 4x^2}}{x} \qquad \text{...(1)}$$

By putting $y = vx$ in (1), we get

$$v + x\frac{dv}{dx} = \frac{vx \pm \sqrt{v^2x^2 - 4x^2}}{x}$$

$$\Rightarrow \quad x\frac{dv}{dx} = \pm\sqrt{v^2 - 4} \quad \Rightarrow \quad \frac{dx}{x} = \pm\frac{dv}{\sqrt{v^2 - 4}}.$$

On integration, we get

$$\log x = \log c_1 \pm \log[v + \sqrt{v^2 - 4}]$$

i.e., $\log x = \log\,[c_1 \cdot \{v + \sqrt{v^2 - 4}\}],\ \log x = \log\left[\dfrac{c_1}{v + \sqrt{v^2 - 4}}\right]$

i.e., $x = c_1\,[v + \sqrt{v^2 - 4}],\ x = \dfrac{c_1}{[v + \sqrt{v^2 - 4}]}$

i.e., $x^2 = c_1\,[y + \sqrt{y^2 - 4x^2}\,],\ y + \sqrt{y^2 - 4x^2} = c_1$

i.e., $(x^2 - c_1y)^2 = c_1\,(y^2 - 4x^2),\ (y - c_1)^2 = y^2 - 4x^2$

i.e., $x^4 - 2cx^2y + 4c_1{}^2x^2 = 0,\ 4x^2 - 2c_1y + c_1{}^2 = 0$

i.e., $c^2x^2 - 2cy + 4 = 0,$ where $1\,/\,c_1 = c$

or $c^2x^2 - 2cy + 4 = 0,$ where $c_1\,/\,4 = c.$

Hence, required general solution is

$$c^2x^2 - 2cy + 4 = 0.$$

Singular Solution : p-discriminant is $4y^2 - 16x^2 = 0$ [from $B^2 - 4AC = 0$]

or $\qquad\qquad\qquad y^2 = 4x^2,\ i.e.,\ y = \pm 2x.$

Again, c-discriminant is

$$4y^2 - 16x^2 = 0 \text{ or } y^2 = 4x^2,\ y = \pm 2x.$$

This is the required singular solution.

EXERCISES

1. Find the general and singular solution of

$$y^2 - 2pxy + p^2 (x^2 - 1) = m^2.$$

2. Prove that, for the equation

$$y = px - (1 + p^3)^{1/2}$$

the envelope has the equation

$$(x^3 + y^3)^2 - 2 (x^3 - y^3) + 1 = 0.$$

3. Find the general and singular solution of

$$9p^2 (1 - y)^2 = 4 (2 - y).$$

4. Show that the equation

$$x^2 (y - px) = p^2 y$$

has *no* singular solution.   *(Gorakhpur, 2001)*

5. Solve and examine for singular solution the differential equation

$$x^3 p^2 + x^2 yp + a^3 = 0. \qquad\qquad (Gorakhpur,\ 2002)$$

6. Solve

$$y = 2x \frac{dy}{dx} + y^2 \left(\frac{dy}{dx}\right)^3,$$

and find the singular solution also.

7. Show that the singular solution of

$$px + y = p^2 x^4$$

is $\qquad\qquad\qquad\qquad 4x^2 y + 1 = 0.$

8. Find the general and singular solutions of

$$(y - px)^2 + a^2 p = 0. \qquad (Jiwaji,\ 1999;\ Indore,\ 1996)$$

9. Find the general and singular solutions of

$$(xp - y)^2 = p^2 - 1.$$

(Bilaspur, 1999; Rewa, 1997; Vikram, 1998; Agra, 2001)

10. Solve and examine for singular solution of the differential equation

$$(px - y) (x - py) = 2p. \qquad (Kumaon,\ 2001;\ Rewa,\ 1999)$$

11. Find the complete primitive and singular solution of

$$y = px + \sqrt{b^2 + a^2 p^2}.$$

Interpret your result geometrically.

(Vikram, 1996; Bilaspur, 1996; Rewa, 2000)

12. Reduce the equation
$$xp^2 - 2yp + x + 2y = 0$$
to Clairut's form by putting $y - x = v$ and $x^2 = u$. Hence obtain and interpret the primitive and singular solution of the equation. Show that the given equation represents a family of parabolas touching a pair of straight lines.

ANSWERS

1. $(y - cx)^2 = m^2 + c^2$, $y^2 + m^2x^2 = m^2$.

3. $(x + c)^2 = (y + 1)^2 (2 - y)$, $y = 2$.

5. $c^2x - cxy + a^3 = 0$, $xy^2 = 4a^3$.

6. $y^2 = 2cx + c^3$, $27y^4 + 32x^3 = 0$.

8. $(y - cx)^2 + a^2c = 0$; $4xy = a^2$.

9. $(cx - y)^2 = c^2 - 1$; $x^2 - y^2 = 1$.

10. $x^2 + y^2 - c(x^2 - y^2) - 1 + c^2 = 0$;
$x^4 - 2x^2y^2 + y^4 - x(x^2 + y^2) + 4 = 0$.

11. $y = cx + \sqrt{b^2 + a^2c^2}$; $\dfrac{x^2}{a^2} + \dfrac{y^2}{b^2} = 1$. The complete primitive is a

system of straight lines, each member touching the ellipse $\dfrac{x^2}{a^2} + \dfrac{y^2}{b^2} = 1$.

12. $2c^2x^2 - 2c(y - x) + 1 = 0$; $y - x = \pm\sqrt{2}\,x$. The complete primitive represents a family of parabolas, each member touching the line $y - x = \pm\sqrt{2}\,x$.

EXERCISES ON CHAPTER 16

1. $p^2 + py = x(x + y)$.   **2.** $p = \sin(x - y)$.

3. $p(p - y) = x(x + y)$.   **4.** $p^2xy + p(4x^2 - 3y^2) - 12xy = 0$.

5. $(1 + p^2)y = 2px$.   **6.** $p^2x^2 - 2pxy + y^2 + 4p = 0$.

7. $p^2(p + m) = a(y + mx)$.   **8.** $y = 2px + f(p^2x)$.

10. Solve and examine for singular solution the equation
$$xp^2 - (x - a)^2 = 0.$$

11. A curve satisfies the differential equation
$$y = p^2(x - p);$$
and also that $p = 0$ when $x = 1/2$; determine its equation.

12. Integrate
$$xp^2 - py - y = 0,$$
and examine the relationship of the lines
$$y^2 + 4xy = 0,$$
to the integral curves of the differential equation.

13. Solve the following
$$e^{3x} (p - 1) + p^3 e^{2y} = 0.$$

14. Show that all integral curves of the equation
$$y + \frac{dy}{dx} = 1 + \frac{dx}{dy} + x \frac{dy}{dx},$$
   are either parabolas or straight lines.

15. Solve and determine singular solutions :
   (i) $(px^2 + y^2) (px + y) = (p + 1)^2.$
   $$[\text{Use the substitution} : u = xy, v = x + y]$$
   (ii) $4p^2x (x - 1) (x - 2) = (3x^2 - 6x + 2)^2.$

16. Solve completely
$$y^2 (y - px) = x^4 p^2.$$
   $$[\text{Use the substitution} : u = 1 / x, v = 1 / y]$$

ANSWERS

1. $(2y - x^2 - c) (x + y - 1 - ce^{-x}) = 0.$

2. $x + c = \cot \left[\dfrac{1}{4} \pi - \dfrac{1}{2} (x - y) \right].$

3. $(y + x - 1 - ce^x) (x^2 + 2y - c) = 0.$

4. $(y - cx^3) (y^2 + 4x^2 + c) = 0.$

5. $x = c (1 + p^2) / p^2, y = 2c / p.$

6. $c^2x^2 - 2cxy + 4c + y^2 = 0.$

7. $x = \dfrac{1}{a} \left\{ \dfrac{3}{2} p^2 - mp + m^2 \log (p + m) \right\} + c;$

   $y = \dfrac{1}{a} \left[p^2 \left(p - \dfrac{1}{2} m \right) + m^2 p - m^3 \log (p + m) \right] - mc.$

8. $y = 2c \sqrt{x} + f (c^2).$

9. $v^2 = 2cx + c^n.$

10. $9 (y + c)^2 = 4x (x - 3a)^2, x = 0.$

11. $(2x - 1)^2 = 8y.$

12. $x = c (1 + p) e^p, y = cp^2 e^p.$

13. $e^y = ce^x + c^3.$

15. (i) $x + y = cxy + c^2, x^2y^2 + 4 (x + y) = 0.$
   (ii) $(y + c)^2 = x (x - 1) (x - 2); x = 0, x = 1, x = 2.$

16. $x = c + c^2xy; y + 4x^2 = 0.$

OBJECTIVE QUESTIONS

To each of the following questions, four alternatives are given for the answer. Only one of them is correct. Choose the correct alternative.

1. For a differential equation $f(x, y, p) = 0$, then p-discriminant satisfies :

   (a) $f(x, y, p) = 0$

   (b) $\dfrac{\partial f(x, y, p)}{\partial p} = 0$

   (c) $f(x, y, p) = 0$ and $\dfrac{\partial f(x, y, p)}{\partial p} = 0$

   (d) $f(x, y, p) = 0$ or $\dfrac{\partial f(x, y, p)}{\partial p} = 0$.

2. Number of arbitrary constants in singular solution of an equation of degree n are :

   (a) n (b) $n - 1$ (c) 0   (d) 1.

3. Singular solution of $y = xp + a\sqrt{1 + p^2}$ is :

   (a) $x^2 + y^2 = a^2$ (b) $x^2 - y^2 = a^2$

   (c) $xy = a^2$ (d) None of these.

4. Singular solution of $p^2 + px - y = 0$ is :

   (a) $x^2 = 4y$ (b) $y^2 = 4x$

   (c) $x^2 + 4y = 0$ (d) $y^2 + 4x = 0$.

5. Singular solution of $p^2 + y^2 = 1$, is :

   (a) $x^2 + y^2 = a^2$ (b) $xy = a^2$

   (c) $y^2 = ax$ (d) No singular solution.

6. Singular solution of $3xy = 2px^2 - 2p^2$ is :

   (a) $y = x^3$ (b) $x^3 = y$

   (c) $6y = x^3$ (d) $6x = y^3$.

7. Solution of the equation $p^2 - 5p + 6 = 0$ is :

   (a) $y = 2x + c$

   (b) $y = 3x + c$

   (c) $(y - 2x - c)(y - 3x - c) = 0$

   (d) None of these.   *(Rohilkhand, 2001)*

8. Solution of the equation $p^2 - 7p + 12 = 0$ is :

   (a) $(y - 4x + c)(y - 3x + c) = 0$

   (b) $(y + 4x + c)(y + 3x + c) = 0$

   (c) $(4y - x + c)(3y - x + c) = 0$

   (d) $(4y + x + c)(3y + x + c) = 0$.

9. The equation $y = px + f(p)$ is known as :
   (a) Bernoulli's equation
   (b) Clairut's equation
   (c) Exact equation
   (d) Linear equation.

   (Avadh, 2001)

10. Solution of the equation $y = px + a/p$ is :
    (a) $y = cx$
    (b) $y = cx + a/c$
    (c) $y + cx = a$
    (d) $cy = x + a$.

    (Rohilkhand, 2002)

11. Solution of the differential equation $y = x \dfrac{dy}{dx} + \left(\dfrac{dy}{dx}\right)^2$ is :

    (a) $y = cx$
    (b) $y = cx + c$
    (c) $y = cx + \dfrac{1}{c}$
    (d) $y = cx + c^2$.

ANSWERS

1. (c)   2. (c)   3. (a)   4. (c)   5. (d)   6. (c)
7. (c)   8. (a)   9. (b)   10. (b)   11. (d)

17

Trajectories of a Family of Curves

17.1. Def. *A curve which cuts every member of a given family of curves according to a given law is called a Trajectory of the given family.*

We shall consider only the case when each trajectory cuts every member of a given family at a *constant* angle. The trajectory will be called *Orthogonal*, if the constant angle is a right angle. For example, every line through the origin of coordinates is an orthogonal trajectory of the family of concentric circles with centre at the origin.

17.2. Cartesian Coordinates. *To find the trajectories which cut every member of the family $f(x, y, c) = 0$, at a constant angle; (c parameter).*

Differentiating

$$f(x, y, c) = 0 \qquad \qquad ...(1)$$

with respect to x and eliminating, c, between (1) and the derived result, we will obtain the differential equation of the given family. Let it be

$$\varphi\left(x, y, \frac{dy}{dx}\right) = 0. \qquad ...(2)$$

Let (X, Y) be the current coordinates of any point on a trajectory so that dY / dX is the slope of the tangent at the point (X, Y) thereof.

At a point of intersection of any member of (2), with the trajectory, we have

$$x = X, \qquad \qquad ...(3)$$

$$y = Y, \qquad \qquad ...(4)$$

$$\tan z = \frac{\dfrac{dy}{dx} - \dfrac{dY}{dX}}{1 + \dfrac{dY}{dX}\dfrac{dy}{dx}} \qquad ...(5)$$

Now, (5) gives

$$\frac{dy}{dx} = \frac{\dfrac{dY}{dX} + \tan \alpha}{1 - \dfrac{dY}{dX} \tan \alpha} \qquad ...(6)$$

625

From (2), (3), (4) and (6), we have, on eliminating x, y and dy/dx,

$$\varphi\left(X, Y, \frac{\dfrac{dY}{dX} + \tan\alpha}{1 - \dfrac{dY}{dX}\tan\alpha}\right) = 0, \qquad\qquad ...(7)$$

as the differential equation of the required family of trajectories. Solving (7), we shall obtain the cartesian equation of the family of trajectories.

Cor. *Orthogonal trajectories.* For orthogonal trajectories, we have to replace the relation (5) by

$$\frac{dy}{dx}\cdot\frac{dY}{dX} = -1 \iff \frac{dy}{dx} = -\frac{dX}{dY}.$$

Thus the differential equation of the family of orthogonal trajectories is

$$\varphi\left(X, Y, -\frac{dX}{dY}\right) = 0.$$

In the usual notation, we see that the differential equation of the family of orthogonal trajectories of the family of curves given by

$$\varphi\,(x, y, dy/dx) = 0,$$

is

$$\varphi\,(x, y, -dx/dy) = 0,$$

so that it is obtained on replacing, dy/dx, by $-dx/dy$.

17.3. Polar Coordinates. Orthogonal Trajectories. *To find the orthogonal trajectories of the family of curves*

$$f\,(r, \theta, c) = 0;\ c\ being\ a\ parameter.$$

Differentiating

$$f\,(r, \theta, c) = 0$$

with respect to θ, and eliminating c between (1) and the derived result, we shall obtain the differential equation of the given family.

Let the eliminant be

$$\psi\,(r, \theta, dr/d\theta) = 0.$$

Let r', θ' be the current coordinates of any point on a trajectory. At a point of intersection of any number of (2) with the trajectory, let φ, φ' be the angles which the tangents to the two curves make with the common radius vector. We have

$$\tan\varphi = r\frac{d\theta}{dr}, \quad \tan\varphi' = r'\frac{d\theta'}{dr'}.$$

Also

$$\varphi - \varphi' = \frac{\pi}{2}.$$

$\Rightarrow \quad \varphi = \varphi' + \dfrac{\pi}{2}$

$\Rightarrow \quad \tan \varphi = - \cot \varphi'$

$\Rightarrow \quad \tan \varphi \tan \varphi' = - 1,$

$\Rightarrow \quad rr' \dfrac{d\theta}{dr} \dfrac{d\theta'}{dr'} = - 1.$ ...(3)

Also

$$r = r' \quad \Rightarrow \quad \theta = \theta'.$$ ...(4)

We re-write (3) as

$$\dfrac{dr}{d\theta} = - rr' \dfrac{d\theta'}{dr'}.$$ ...(5)

From (2), (3), (4) and (5), on eliminating

$$r, \theta, dr / d\theta$$

we obtain

$$\psi \left(r', \theta', - r'^2 \dfrac{d\theta'}{dr'} \right) = 0,$$ ...(6)

as the differential equation of the required family of trajectories.

In the usual notation, we re-write (7) as

$$\psi \left(r, \theta, - r^2 \dfrac{d\theta}{dr} \right) = 0,$$

which may be obtained from the differential equation (1) of the given family on changing

$$r, \theta, dr / d\theta \text{ to } r, \theta, - r^2 d\theta / dr$$

respectively.

17.31. Working Rule

(1) *Form the differential equation of the family of curves.*

(2) *Write* $- \dfrac{1}{dy / dx}$ *for* $\dfrac{dy}{dx}$ *or* $- r^2 \dfrac{d\theta}{dr}$ *for* $\dfrac{dr}{d\theta}$.

(3) *Solve this new differential equation to get the equation of orthogonal trajectory.*

17.4. Self Orthogonal Families   (*Ravishankar, 1999S*)

If every member of a family of curves cuts all other members of the family at right angle, then the family is the system of orthogonal trajectories of itself and hence it is called self-orthogonal family.

Thus, if the differential equation of the family is identical with the differential equation to its orthogonal trajectory then the family is self-orthogonal.

EXAMPLES

1. *Find the orthogonal trajectories of the curves*

$$\frac{x^2}{a^2+\lambda} + \frac{y^2}{b^2+\lambda} = 1, \qquad \text{...(1)}$$

λ *being the parameter of the family.*

(Ravishankar, 1995; Indore, 1998; Vikram, 1998, 2000)

Differentiating (1) with respect to x, we have

$$\frac{x}{a^2+\lambda} + \frac{y}{b^2+\lambda}\frac{dy}{dx} = 0. \qquad \text{...(2)}$$

From (1) and (2), we have to eliminate λ.

Now, (2) gives

$$\lambda = -\frac{b^2 x + a^2 y\dfrac{dy}{dx}}{x + y\dfrac{dy}{dx}}$$

$$\Rightarrow \qquad a^2 + \lambda = \frac{(a^2 - b^2)\,x}{x + y\,(dy/dx)}, \quad b^2 + \lambda = \frac{(a^2 - b^2)\,y\,(dy/dx)}{x + y\,(dy/dx)}.$$

Substituting these values in (1), we get

$$\left(x - y\frac{dx}{dy}\right)\left(x + y\frac{dy}{dx}\right) = a^2 - b^2, \qquad \text{...(3)}$$

as the differential equation of the given family.

Changing dy/dx to $-dx/dy$ in (3), we obtain

$$\left(x + y\frac{dy}{dx}\right)\left(x - y\frac{dx}{dy}\right) = a^2 - b^2, \qquad \text{...(4)}$$

which is the same as (3). Thus we see that the family (1) is self-orthogonal, *i.e.*, every member of the family (1) cuts every other member of the same family orthogonally.

2. *Find the orthogonal trajectories of the family of co-axial circles*

$$x^2 + y^2 + 2gx + c = 0 \qquad \text{...(1)}$$

where, g, is the parameter.   *(Rewa, 1999; Sagar, 2000)*

Differentiating (1), we have

$$x + y\frac{dy}{dx} + g = 0. \qquad \text{...(2)}$$

Eliminating, g, from (1) and (2) we have

$$x^2 + y^2 - 2x\left(x + y\frac{dy}{dx}\right) + c = 0,$$

$$\Rightarrow \quad y^2 - x^2 - 2xy\frac{dy}{dx} + c = 0.$$

Changing dy / dx to $- dx / dy$ we see that the differential equation of the required family of orthogonal trajectories is

$$y^2 - x^2 + 2xy\frac{dx}{dy} + c = 0,$$

$$\Rightarrow \quad 2xy\frac{dx}{dy} - x^2 = -c - y^2.$$

Putting $x^2 = t$, we will obtain a linear equation with, t, as dependent variable.

The solution can now easily be seen to be

$$x^2 + y^2 + 2fy - c = 0,$$

which represents a co-axial system of circles orthogonal to the given system with, f, as parameter.

3. *Find the orthogonal trajectory of the family of cardioides*

$$r = a\ (1 + \cos\theta);$$

a being the parameter.   *(Indore, 1994)*

Differentiating

$$r = a\ (1 + \cos\theta),\qquad\qquad\qquad ...(1)$$

with respect to θ, we obtain

$$\frac{dr}{d\theta} = -a\sin\theta.\qquad\qquad\qquad ...(2)$$

Eliminating, a, between (1) and (2), we obtain

$$\frac{r}{dr / d\theta} = -\frac{1 + \cos\theta}{\sin\theta}$$

which is the differential equation of the given family. Changing $dr / d\theta$ to $-r^2\ d\theta / dr$, we obtain

$$\frac{r}{-r^2\ d\theta / dr} = -\frac{1 + \cos\theta}{\sin\theta} \quad\Rightarrow\quad \frac{1}{r}\frac{dr}{d\theta} = \frac{1 + \cos\theta}{\sin\theta} \qquad ...(3)$$

as the differential equation of the family of orthogonal trajectories. To solve (3), we re-write the same as

$$\frac{dr}{r} = \frac{1 + \cos\theta}{\sin\theta}d\theta = (\text{cosec}\ \theta + \cot\theta)\ d\theta.$$

$$\Rightarrow \quad \log r = \log\tan\frac{\theta}{2} + \log\sin\theta + \log c$$

$$= \log\left(c\sin\theta\tan\frac{\theta}{2}\right)$$

$$\Rightarrow \quad r = c \sin \theta \tan \frac{\theta}{2}$$

$$= 2c \sin \frac{\theta}{2} \cos \frac{\theta}{2} \tan \frac{\theta}{2}$$

$$= 2c \sin^2 \frac{\theta}{2} = c\,(1 - \cos \theta).$$

Thus the orthogonal trajectories of the family

$$r = a\,(1 + \cos \theta)$$

of cardioides is the family of cardioides

$$r = c\,(1 - \cos \theta).$$

The integration could also be completed by writing

$$\frac{1 + \cos \theta}{\sin \theta} = \cot \frac{\theta}{2}.$$

4. *Prove that the orthogonal trajectories of the curves* $A = r^2 \cos \theta$ *are the curves* $B = r \sin^2 \theta$.   *(Ravishankar, 1999)*

Equation of the given family of curves is

$$A = r^2 \cos \theta \qquad \qquad ...(i)$$

A being the parameter.

Differentiating (*i*) with respect to θ, we get,

$$0 = 2r \frac{dr}{d\theta} \cdot \cos \theta + r^2 \cdot (- \sin \theta) \qquad \qquad ...(ii)$$

as differential equation of the family. Replacing $\dfrac{dr}{d\theta}$ by $-r^2 \dfrac{d\theta}{dr}$, we get the differential equation of the system of orthogonal trajectories of the family (*i*) as

$$0 = 2r \left(-r^2 \frac{d\theta}{dr} \right) \cos \theta - r^2 \sin \theta$$

or $$2r \cos \theta \frac{d\theta}{dr} = - \sin \theta \qquad \qquad ...(iii)$$

Integrating this equation by separating the variables, we get,

$$\int \frac{1}{r}\,dr - \log c_1 = -2 \int \frac{\cos \theta}{\sin \theta}\,d\theta$$

or $$\log r = \log c_1 - \log \sin^2 \theta.$$

5. *Find the orthogonal trajectories of the system of circles touching a given straight line at a given point.*   *(Gorakhpur, 2001)*

Let the circle touch the x-axis at the point $(0, 0)$ so that its centre is $(0, a)$ on y-axis, where a is the radius. Hence its equation is $x^2 + (y - a)^2 = a^2$ or $x^2 + y^2 - 2ay = 0$, where a is the parameter.

Differentiating, we get

$$2x + (2y - 2a)\frac{dy}{dx} = 0$$

or $\quad x + \left(y - \dfrac{x^2 + y^2}{2y}\right)\dfrac{dy}{dx} = 0.$

or $\quad 2xy + (y^2 - x^2)\dfrac{dy}{dx} = 0.$

This is the differential equation of the family of circles. Its orthogonal trajectory is obtained on replacing $\dfrac{dy}{dx}$ by $-\dfrac{1}{dy/dx}$ whose equation becomes,

$$2xy - (y^2 - x^2)\frac{dx}{dy} = 0$$

or $\quad 2xy\dfrac{dy}{dx} - (y^2 - x^2) = 0$

or $\quad 2y\dfrac{dy}{dx} - \dfrac{y^2}{x} = -x.$

Put $y^2 = v$

$\therefore \quad 2y\dfrac{dy}{dx} = \dfrac{dv}{dx}.$

Hence the equation becomes

$$\frac{dv}{dx} - \frac{1}{x}v = -x.$$

This is linear equation whose I.F. $= e^{-\int \frac{1}{x}dx} = e^{-\log x} = \dfrac{1}{x}.$

Thus the solution of the equation will be

$$v\frac{1}{x} = \int \frac{1}{x}(-x)\, dx + c$$

or $\quad y^2 \cdot \dfrac{1}{x} = -x + c$

or $\quad y^2 + x^2 = cx$

or $\quad x^2 + y^2 - 2bx = 0$

where $\quad c = 2b$

or $\quad (x - b)^2 + y^2 = b^2.$

This represents a family of circles touching y-axis at $(0, 0)$ and whose radius is b so that its centre is $(b, 0)$.

6. *Find the differential equation satisfied by the system of parabolas* $y^2 = 4a\,(x + a)$, *and show that orthogonal trajectories of the system belong to the system itself.*

(Bilaspur, 1999; Indore, 1996; Rewa, 1997; Sagar, 1995; Vikram, 1994; Kumaon, 2000; Gorakhpur, 2000; Ravishankar, 2001)

Equation of the family of parabolas is

$$y^2 = 4a\,(x + a) \qquad \qquad ...(i)$$

a being the parameter.

Differentiating (i) with respect to x, we get,

$$2y\frac{dy}{dx} = 4a$$

or

$$y\frac{dy}{dx} = 2a \qquad \qquad ...(ii)$$

Eliminating a from (i) and (ii), we get the differential equation of the system given by (i) as

$$y^2 = 2y\frac{dy}{dx}\left(x + \frac{1}{2}\,y\frac{dy}{dx}\right)$$

or

$$y^2 = 2xy\frac{dy}{dx} + y^2\left(\frac{dy}{dx}\right)^2 \qquad \qquad ...(iii)$$

Replacing $\dfrac{dy}{dx}$ by $-\dfrac{dx}{dy}$ from (iii), we get the differential equation of the system of orthogonal trajectories of (i) as

$$y^2 = 2xy\left(-\frac{dx}{dy}\right) + y^2\left(-\frac{dx}{dy}\right)^2 .$$

Multiplying above by $\left(\dfrac{dy}{dx}\right)^2$, we get,

$$y^2\left(\frac{dy}{dx}\right)^2 = -2xy\frac{dy}{dx} + y^2$$

or

$$y^2 = 2xy\frac{dy}{dx} + y^2\left(\frac{dy}{dx}\right)^2 \qquad \qquad ...(iv)$$

Comparing (iii) and (iv) we conclude that both being identical, the family (i) is self-orthogonal.

EXERCISES

1. Find the orthogonal trajectories of the family of semicubical parabolas $ay^2 = x^3$ where, a, is a variable parameter.

2. Find the orthogonal trajectories of the family of parabolas

$$y = ax^2.$$

(Jiwaji, 1996; Sagar, 1999; Bilaspur, 2000)

3. Find the orthogonal trajectories of

$$\frac{x^2}{a^2} + \frac{y^2}{a^2 + \lambda} = 1,$$

where λ is an arbitrary parameter. (*Ravishankar, 1997; Gorakhpur, 2002*)

4. Find the equation of the system of orthogonal trajectories of a series of confocal and co-axial parabolas

$$r = 2a / (1 + \cos \theta). \qquad (Vikram, 1999; Kumaon, 2003)$$

5. Find the orthogonal trajectories of a system of equal circle with collinear centres. Sketch a typical curve of the family which is the required family of trajectories.

6. Find the orthogonal trajectories of

(*i*) $r\theta = a$,

(*ii*) $r = a\theta$,

(*iii*) $r^n = a^n \cos n\theta$,

              (*Jiwaji, 2000; Indore, 1998; Ravishankar, 1997, 98*)

(*iv*) $r^n \cos n\theta = a^n$,

(*v*) $r = a (1 - \cos \theta)$, (*Jiwaji, 1995, 99; Jabalpur, 1998, 2000;*

                                  Rewa, 1998; Bilaspur, 1996)

(*vi*) $r = c \sin^2 \theta$.

7. Find the orthogonal trajectories of the following families of curves :

(*i*) $x^{2/3} + y^{2/3} = \lambda^{2/3}$, (*Garhwal, 1999*)   (*ii*) $r \sin 2\theta = \lambda$,

(*iii*) $r = \tan (\theta + \alpha)$,   (*iv*) $x^2 + y^2 = r^2$.

8. Show that the orthogonal trajectories of the family of conics $y^2 - x^2 + 4xy - 2cx = 0$ consists a family of cubics, with the common asymptote $x + y = 0$.

9. Find the orthogonal trajectories of $r^n \sin n\theta = a^n$. (*Indore, 1995*)

10. Find the orthogonal trajectories of the curve $y = \dfrac{x^3 - a^3}{3x}$, a being the parameter. (*Indore, 1997, 2000; Ravishankar, 2000*)

11. Prove that the orthogonal trajectories of the rectangular hyperbola $xy = a^2$ is $x^2 - y^2 = c^2$. (*Vikram, 1995; Kumaon, 1999*)

12. Find the orthogonal trajectory of $r = e^{a\theta}$.

ANSWERS

1. $3y^2 + 2x^2 = c^2$.   **2.** $x^2 + 2y^2 = c^2$.

3. $x^2 + y^2 + c = 2a^2 \log x$.   **4.** $r = 2b / (1 - \cos \theta)$.

5. $x = r (\tanh t - t) + c$, $y = r \operatorname{sech} t$; the given family of the circles being $x^2 + y^2 - 2gx + g^2 = r^2$.

6. (i) $r^2 = ce^{\theta^2}$.   (ii) $r = ce^{-\theta^2/2}$.

   (iii) $r^n = c^n \sin n\theta$.   (iv) $r^n \sin n\theta = c^n$.

   (v) $r = c (1 + \cos \theta)$.   (vi) $r^2 = c \cos \theta$.

7. (i) $y^{4/3} - x^{4/3} = c^{4/3}$.   (ii) $r^4 \cos 2\theta = c^4$.

   (iii) $\theta + r = c + r^{-1}$.   (iv) $y = mx$.

9. $r^n \cos n\theta = c^n$.   10. $x^2 = y - \dfrac{1}{2} + ke^{-2y}$.

12. $(\log r)^2 + \theta^2 = c^2$.

OBJECTIVE QUESTIONS

To each of the following questions, four alternatives are given for the answer. Only one of them is correct. Choose the correct alternative.

1. Differential equation of the orthogonal trajectory of the family of curves $f\left(r, \theta, \dfrac{dr}{d\theta}\right) = 0$ is :   (*Garhwal, 2002*)

   (a) $f\left(r, \theta, r\dfrac{d\theta}{dr}\right) = 0$ (b) $f\left(r, \theta, -r\dfrac{d\theta}{dr}\right) = 0$

   (c) $f\left(r, \theta, r^2\dfrac{d\theta}{dr}\right) = 0$ (d) $f\left(r, \theta, -r^2\dfrac{d\theta}{dr}\right) = 0$.

2. Differential equation of the orthogonal trajectory of the family of curves $f\left(x, y, \dfrac{dy}{dx}\right) = 0$ is :

   (a) $f\left(x, y, -\dfrac{dy}{dx}\right)$ (b) $f\left(x, y, -\dfrac{dx}{dy}\right) = 0$

   (c) $f\left(x, y, \dfrac{dx}{dy}\right) = 0$ (d) None of these.

3. Orthogonal trajectory of the family of parabolas $y = ax^2$ is :
   (a) $x^2 + 2y^2 = c^2$ (b) $x^2 - 2y^2 = c^2$
   (c) $x^2 + y^2 = c^2$ (d) $x^2 - y^2 = c^2$.

4. Orthogonal trajectory of the family of curves $y = ax^3$ is :
   (a) $x^2 + 2y^2 = c^2$ (b) $x^2 - 2y^2 = c^2$
   (c) $x^2 + 3y^2 = c^2$ (d) $x^2 - 3y^2 = c^2$.

ANSWERS

     1. (*d*)   2. (*b*)   3. (*a*)   4. (*c*)

18

Linear Equations

18.1. Linear Differential Equations *are the equations in which the dependent variable and its derivatives appear only in the first degree and are not multiplied together.* Thus the general linear differential equation of the nth order is

$$\frac{d^n y}{dx^n} + P_1 \frac{d^{n-1} y}{dx^{n-1}} + P_2 \frac{d^{n-2} y}{dx^{n-2}} + \ldots + P_n y = X,$$

where P_1, P_2, ..., P_n, and X are functions of x only.

The discussion of the general equation is beyond the scope of this book and only linear differential equations with constant coefficients and homogeneous linear equations will be considered in this book.

18.2. Linear Differential Equations with constant coefficients. *To solve the differential equation*

$$\frac{d^n y}{dx^n} + a_1 \frac{d^{n-1} y}{dx^{n-1}} + a_2 \frac{d^{n-2} y}{dx^{n-2}} + \ldots + a_n y = X, \qquad \ldots(A)$$

where a_1, a_2, ..., a_n are constants and X is a function of x.

Consider the differential equation

$$\frac{d^n y}{dx^n} + a_1 \frac{d^{n-1} y}{dx^{n-1}} + a_2 \frac{d^{n-2} y}{dx^{n-2}} + \ldots + a_n y = 0, \qquad \ldots(B)$$

obtained on equating to zero the left hand expression of (A).

We will, now, show that *y_1, y_2 are any two solutions of* (B), *then, $c_1 y_1 + c_2 y_2$ is also a solution of* (B); *c_1, c_2 being arbitrary constants.*

Since y_1, y_2 are solutions of (B), we have

$$\frac{d^n y_1}{dx^n} + a_1 \frac{d^{n-1} y_1}{dx^{n-1}} + a_2 \frac{d^{n-2} y_1}{dx^{n-2}} + \ldots + a_n y_1 = 0, \qquad \ldots(i)$$

$$\frac{d^n y_2}{dx^n} + a_1 \frac{d^{n-1} y_2}{dx^{n-1}} + a_2 \frac{d^{n-2} y_2}{dx^{n-2}} + \ldots + a_n y_2 = 0. \qquad \ldots(ii)$$

If c_1, c_2 are any two arbitrary constants, we have

$$\frac{d^n(c_1 y_1 + c_2 y_2)}{dx^n} + a_1 \frac{d^{n-1}(c_1 y_1 + c_2 y_2)}{dx^{n-1}}$$

$$+ a_2 \frac{d^{n-2}(c_1 y_1 + c_2 y_2)}{dx^{n-2}} + ...$$

$$= c_1 \left(\frac{d^n y_1}{dx^n} + a_1 \frac{d^{n-1}y_1}{dx^{n-1}} + a_2 \frac{d^{n-2}y_1}{dx^{n-2}} + ... \right)$$

$$+ c_2 \left(\frac{d^n y_2}{dx^n} + a_1 \frac{d^{n-1}y_2}{dx^{n-1}} + a_2 \frac{d^{n-2}y_2}{dx^{n-2}} + ... \right)$$

$$= c_1 \cdot 0 + c_2 \cdot 0 = 0. \qquad\qquad \text{[By } (i) \text{ and } (ii)\text{]}$$

This proves the statement made above.

Since the general solution of a differential equation of the nth order contains, n arbitrary constants, we deduce from above that if y_1, y_2, ..., y_n be any n *independent* solutions of (B), then

$$c_1 y_1 + c_2 y_2 + ... + c_n y_n = u, \text{ say}$$

is the *general* solution of (B); c_1, c_2, ..., c_n being n arbitrary constants.

Again, let v be any *particular* solution of (A), so that we have

$$\frac{d^n v}{dx^n} + a_1 \frac{d^{n-1}v}{dx^{n-1}} + a_2 \frac{d^{n-2}v}{dx^{n-2}} + ... = X.$$

It will be shown that

$$c_1 y_1 + c_2 y_2 + ... + c_n y_n + v = u + v,$$

is the *general* solution of (A), containing, as it does, n arbitrary constants.

Now we have

$$\frac{d^n(u+v)}{dx^n} + a_1 \frac{d^{n-1}(u+v)}{dx^{n-1}} + a_2 \frac{d^{n-2}(u+v)}{dx^{n-2}} + ...$$

$$= \frac{d^n u}{dx^n} + a_1 \frac{d^{n-1}u}{dx^{n-1}} + a_2 \frac{d^{n-2}u}{dx^{n-2}} + ...$$

$$+ \frac{d^n v}{dx^n} + a_1 \frac{d^{n-1}v}{dx^{n-1}} + a_2 \frac{d^{n-2}v}{dx^{n-2}} + ...$$

$$= 0 + X = X,$$

for, u, is a solution of (B).

Thus we see that $u + v$, is the general solution of (A). It follows that in order to be able to solve the differential equation (A), where a_1, a_2, etc., are constants and X is a function of x, *we have first to obtain n independent solutions* y_1, y_2, ..., y_n, *of the auxiliary equation* (B), *and any solution, v, not involving any arbitrary constant of* (A) *and then*

$$y = c_1 y_1 + c_2 y_2 + ... + c_n y_n + v,$$

is the general solution of (A).

The part, $c_1 y_1 + c_2 y_2 + \ldots + c_n y_n$ is called the **Complementary Function** (C.F.) and v the **Particular Integral** (P.I.).

Thus it appears that in order to be able to solve the differential equation (A), we have first to learn to solve the equation (B). This is done in § 18.5. As a preparation for this, we introduce the notion of operators in the next section.

The method of finding a particular integral of the equation (A) is given in § 18.7.

Note. It is easy to see that the conclusions arrived at above hold good for general linear differential equations also, *i.e.*, even when the coefficients are functions of x.

18.3. Operators. The part, d / dx of the symbol dy / dx, can be thought of as an *operator* such that, when it operates on y, the result is the derivative of y.

From this point of view, the symbol d / dx is called an *operator* and the function y is called *operand*. We can similarly think of d^2 / dx^2, d^3 / dx^3, etc., as operators. For the sake of convenience, the operators, d / dx, d^2 / dx^2, d^3 / dx^3, etc., are denoted by D, D^2, D^3, etc. The index of D indicates the number of times the operation of differentiation is to be carried out. Extending these ideas, we write

$$\frac{d^n y}{dx^n} + a_1 \frac{d^{n-1} y}{dx^{n-1}} + a_2 \frac{d^{n-2} y}{dx^{n-2}} + \ldots + a_{n-1} \frac{dy}{dx} + a_n y$$

$$= (D^n + a_1 D^{n-1} + a_2 D^{n-2} + \ldots + a_{n-1} D + a_n) \, y = f(D) \, y$$

$$\Rightarrow \quad D^n + a_1 D^{n-1} + a_2 D^{n-2} + \ldots + a_{n-1} D + a_n = f(D).$$

18.3.1. Product of operators. If $f(D)$ and $\varphi(D)$ be two operators, then $f(D) \, \varphi(D)$ is also an operator which indicates that the *operator $f(D)$ is to operate on the function obtained as a result of the operation of $\varphi(D)$ on a given function.*

For example, we calculate

$$(2D - 3) (D^2 - 4D + 5) \sin x.$$

Now, $(D^2 - 4D + 5) \sin x$

$$= \frac{d^2 \sin x}{dx^2} - 4 \frac{d \sin x}{dx} + 5 \sin x$$

$$= 4 \sin x - 4 \cos x.$$

Again, $(2D - 3) (4 \sin x - 4 \cos x)$

$$= 2 \frac{d}{dx} (4 \sin x - 4 \cos x) - 3 (4 \sin x - 4 \cos x)$$

$$= 20 \cos x - 4 \sin x.$$

18.4. *To prove that*

$$(D - \alpha)(D - \beta) y \equiv (D - \beta)(D - \alpha) y,$$

α, β *being any constants whatsoever.*

$$(D - \beta) y = \frac{dy}{dx} - \beta y.$$

$$\Rightarrow \quad (D - \alpha)(D - \beta) y = (D - \alpha)\left(\frac{dy}{dx} - \beta y\right)$$

$$= \frac{d}{dx}\left(\frac{dy}{dx} - \beta y\right) - \alpha\left(\frac{dy}{dx} - \beta y\right)$$

$$= \frac{d^2 y}{dx^2} - \beta \frac{dy}{dx} - \left(\alpha \frac{dy}{dx} - \alpha\beta y\right)$$

$$= \frac{d^2 y}{dx^2} - (\beta + \alpha)\frac{dy}{dx} + \alpha\beta y$$

$$= [D^2 - (\alpha + \beta) D + \alpha\beta] y.$$

We can similarly show that

$$(D - \beta)(D - \alpha) y = [D^2 - (\alpha + \beta) D + \alpha\beta] y.$$

$$\therefore \quad (D - \alpha)(D - \beta) y = (D - \beta)(D - \alpha) y,$$

so that the *order* of the operational factors is immaterial.

Cor. We have seen that

$$(D - \alpha)(D - \beta) y = [D^2 - (\alpha + \beta) D + \alpha\beta] y$$

so that the operators

$$(D - \alpha)(D - \beta) \text{ and } D^2 - (\alpha + \beta) D + \alpha\beta$$

are the same.

If D were a number, then by the ordinary laws of multiplication of numbers, we see that

$$(D - \alpha)(D - \beta) = D^2 - (\beta + \alpha) D + \alpha\beta.$$

In general, let

$$f(D) = D^n + a_1 D^{n-1} + a_2 D^{n-2} + \ldots + a_{n-1} D + a_n.$$

Regarding D as a number we may factorize $f(D)$ so that, from this point of view, we may have

$$f(D) \equiv (D - m_1)(D - m_2) \ldots (D - m_n) \qquad \ldots(1)$$

The result above now shows that the equality (1) remains valid when D is given its operational character and also that, while carrying out the operations on the R.H.S. of (1), we may interchange the order of the factors at will.

18.5. *To solve the differential equation*

$$\frac{d^n y}{dx^n} + a_1 \frac{d^{n-1}}{dx^{n-1}} + a_2 \frac{d^{n-2} y}{dx^{n-2}} + \dots + a_{n-1} \frac{dy}{dx} + a_n y = 0.$$

Writing the equation in the symbolic form, we have

$$f(D) y = (D^n + a_1 D^{n-1} + a_2 D^{n-2} + \dots + a_{n-1} D + a_n) y = 0.$$

Suppose α_1 is a *non-repeated* root of the equation

$$f(D) \equiv D^n + a_1 D^{n-1} + a_2 D^{n-2} + \dots + a_{n-1} D + a_n = 0. \quad \dots(1)$$

Regarding D as a number, we may write

$$f(D) = \varphi(D) (D - \alpha_1),$$

where $\varphi(D)$ is a polynomial in D. We have

$$0 = f(D) y = \varphi(D) (D - \alpha_1) y \qquad \dots(2)$$

The solution of the equation

$$(D - \alpha_1) y = 0 \qquad \dots(3)$$

will clearly be a solution of the given equation (2). Now, (3), gives

$$\frac{dy}{dx} - \alpha_1 y = 0 \implies \frac{dy}{y} - \alpha_1 \, dx = 0$$

$$\implies \log y = \alpha_1 x \implies y = e^{\alpha_1 x}$$

where we have omitted the arbitrary constant.

Thus $e^{\alpha_1 x}$, is a solution of the given differential equation (2).

Now if $\alpha_1, \alpha_2, \alpha_3, \dots, \alpha_n$ are different roots of (1), then, as proved above,

$$e^{\alpha_1 x}, \, e^{\alpha_2 x}, \, e^{\alpha_3 x}, \dots, e^{\alpha_n x}$$

will be, n, different independent solutions of the given equation.

Thus, as shown in § 18.2,

$$c_1 e^{\alpha_1 x} + c_2 e^{\alpha_2 x} + \dots + c_n e^{\alpha_n x}$$

is the general solution of the given equation; $c_1, c_2, \dots, c_n$ being n arbitrary constants.

Case of repeated roots. In case some roots are equal, then, proceeding as above, we will obtain less than, n, independent solutions and the solution obtained above will not be general. In this case, we proceed as follows :

Firstly, we suppose that α is a root repeated twice only so that we may write

$$f(D) = \psi(D) (D - \alpha)^2$$

$$\implies \quad 0 = f(D) y = \psi(D) (D - \alpha)^2 y.$$

The solution of

$$(D - \alpha)^2 y = 0 \qquad \dots(i)$$

will clearly be a solution of

$$f(D) y = 0.$$

We have

$$(D - \alpha)(D - \alpha) y = 0.$$

Let

$$(D - \alpha) y = z \qquad \qquad \qquad ...(ii)$$

so that

$$(D - \alpha) z = 0.$$

$$\Rightarrow \quad \frac{dz}{dx} - \alpha z = 0.$$

$$\Rightarrow \quad \frac{dz}{z} - \alpha \, dx = 0 \quad \Rightarrow \quad z = c_1 e^{\alpha x}$$

taking the general solution with, c_1 as an arbitrary constant. Substituting this value of z in (i), we obtain

$$(D - \alpha) y = c_1 e^{\alpha x} \quad \Rightarrow \quad \frac{dy}{dx} - \alpha y = c_1 e^{\alpha x}.$$

Multiplying this linear equation with the integrating factor $e^{-\alpha x}$, and integrating we get

$$ye^{-\alpha x} = c_1 \int e^{-\alpha x} e^{\alpha x} \, dx + c_2 = c_1 x + c_2$$

$$\Rightarrow \quad y = (c_1 x + c_2) e^{\alpha x},$$

which is the general solution of (i) in this case; c_1, c_2 being two arbitrary constants.

Thus we get a solution containing two arbitrary constants corresponding to a root repeated twice.

In general, we may similarly show that corresponding to a root, α, repeated r times, the solution is

$$(c_1 x^{r-1} + c_2 x^{r-2} + \,.....\, + c_{r-1} x + c_r) \, e^{\alpha x}$$

containing r, arbitrary constants.

Note. If the coefficients in $f(D)$ be real then the roots of the equation $f(D) = 0$ will be either real or conjugate imaginary in pairs. In case the roots are imaginary; the solution of the equation

$$f(D) = 0,$$

be real, then the roots will be either real or conjugate imaginary in pairs. In case the roots are imaginary, the solution of the equation

$$f(D) y = 0,$$

can be exhibited in a form free from imaginaries by making use of Euler's Theorem which states that

$$e^{i\theta} = \cos \theta + i \sin \theta.$$

Let $\alpha + i\beta$, $\alpha - i\beta$ be two conjugate imaginary roots of $f(D) = 0$. Then the corresponding part of the solution is

$$c_1 e^{(\alpha + i\beta)\,x} + c_2 e^{(\alpha - i\beta)\,x}$$

$$= e^{\alpha x}\,(c_1 e^{i\beta x} + c_2 e^{-i\beta x})$$

$$= e^{\alpha x}\,[c_1\,(\cos\beta x + i\sin\beta x) + c_2\,(\cos\beta x - i\sin\beta x)]$$

$$= e^{\alpha x}\,[(c_1 + c_2)\cos\beta x + i\,(c_1 - c_2)\sin\beta x]$$

$$= e^{\alpha x}\,(p_1\cos\beta x + p_1\sin\beta x),$$

where we have written

$$c_1 + c_2 = p_1,\ i\,(c_1 - c_2) = p_2.$$

It can similarly be shown that if $\alpha + i\beta$, $\alpha - i\beta$ are conjugate imaginary roots, each repeated, r times, then the corresponding part of the solution is

$$e^{\alpha x}\,[(p_1 + p_2 x + \ldots + p_{r-1}x^{r-1})\cos\beta x$$
$$+ (q_1 + q_2 x + \ldots + q_{r-1}x^{r-1})\sin\beta x].$$

EXAMPLES

1. *Solve*

(i) $\dfrac{d^2 y}{dx^2} - 5\dfrac{dy}{dx} + 6y = 0,$ (ii) $4\dfrac{d^2 y}{dx^2} + 4\dfrac{dy}{dx} + y = 0,$

(iii) $2\dfrac{d^2 y}{dx^2} + 3\dfrac{dy}{dx} + 4y = 0.$

(i) We have $(D^2 - 5D + 6)\,y = 0$.

Since the roots of $D^2 - 5D + 6 = 0$ are 2 and 3, the general solution is

$$y = c_1 e^{2x} + c_2 e^{3x}.$$

(ii) We have $(4D^2 + 4D + 1)\,y = 0$.

Since both the roots of $4D^2 + 4D + 1 = 0$ are equal to $-1/2$, the general solution is

$$y = (c_1 x + c_2)\,e^{-x/2}.$$

(iii) We have $(2D^2 + 3D + 4)\,y = 0$.

Since the two roots of $2D^2 + 3D + 4 = 0$ are $\dfrac{1}{4}[-3 \pm i\sqrt{23}]$

i.e.,

$$-\frac{3}{4} \pm i\,\frac{\sqrt{23}}{4},$$

therefore, the general solution is

$$e^{-3x/4}\left[c_1\cos\frac{\sqrt{23}}{4}x + c_2\sin\frac{\sqrt{23}}{4}x\right],$$

where c_1, c_2 are arbitrary constants.

2. *Solve the differential equation*

$$\frac{d^4y}{dx^4} - 2\frac{d^3y}{dx^3} + 5\frac{d^2y}{dx^2} - 8\frac{dy}{dx} + 4y = 0.$$

We have

$$(D^4 - 2D^3 + 5D^2 - 8D + 4)\, y = 0.$$

Now

$$D^4 - 2D^3 + 5D^2 - 8D + 4 = (D - 1)^2 \, (D^2 + 4),$$

so that the roots of

$$D^4 - 2D^3 + 5D^2 - 8D + 4 = 0,$$

are

$$1, 1, 2i, -2i;$$

the root, 1, being repeated twice. Therefore,

$$y = (c_1 + c_2 x)\, e^x + (c_3 \cos 2x + c_4 \sin 2x)$$

is the solution.

3. *Solve $(D^3 + 1)\, y = 0.$*

We have

$$D^3 + 1 = (D + 1)\, (D^2 - D + 1).$$

Now roots of $D^3 + 1 = 0$ are

$$-1, \frac{1}{2} \pm \frac{\sqrt{3}\, i}{2}.$$

$$\therefore \quad y = ce^{-x} + e^{x/2}\left(c_1 \cos \frac{\sqrt{3}}{2} x + c_2 \sin \frac{\sqrt{3}}{2} x\right)$$

is the required solution.

4. *Solve $\dfrac{d^4y}{dx^4} + m^4 y = 0.$*

(Rohilkhand, 1996; Jiwaji, 1995; Rewa, 1997; Garhwal, 2002)

The given equation is

$$(D^4 + m^4)\, y = 0.$$

The auxiliary equation is

$$\lambda^4 + m^4 = 0.$$

Making it a perfect square,

$$(\lambda^4 + 2\lambda^2 m^2 + m^4) - 2\lambda^2 m^2 = 0$$

or

$$(\lambda^2 + m^2)^2 - (\sqrt{2}\, \lambda m)^2 = 0$$

or

$$(\lambda^2 + \sqrt{2}\, \lambda m + m^2)(\lambda^2 - \sqrt{2}\, \lambda m + m^2) = 0$$

$$\therefore \quad \lambda = -\frac{m}{\sqrt{2}} \pm i\frac{m}{\sqrt{2}} \text{ and } \frac{m}{\sqrt{2}} \pm i\frac{m}{\sqrt{2}}.$$

Hence general solution of the equation will be

$$y = e^{(-m/\sqrt{2})x}\left[c_1 \cos\frac{m}{\sqrt{2}}x + c_2 \sin\frac{m}{\sqrt{2}}x\right]$$

$$+ e^{(m/\sqrt{2})x}\left[c_3 \cos\frac{m}{\sqrt{2}}x + c_4 \sin\frac{m}{\sqrt{2}}x\right].$$

5. *Solve* : $\dfrac{d^4 y}{dx^4} - 4\dfrac{d^3 y}{dx^3} + 8\dfrac{d^2 y}{dx^2} - 8\dfrac{dy}{dx} + 4y = 0.$

(Rohilkhand, 1995; Garhwal, 2003)

The given equation is

$$(D^4 - 4D^3 + 8D^2 - 8D + 4)\,y = 0.$$

Auxiliary equation is

$$m^4 - 4m^3 + 8m^2 - 8m + 4 = 0$$

or $(m^2 - 2m + 2)^2 = 0$

$\therefore \quad m = 1 \pm i,\ 1 \pm i.$

Hence solution of the equation is

$$y = e^x \{(c_1 + c_2 x)\cos x + (c_3 + c_4 x)\sin x\}.$$

EXERCISES

Solve the following differential equations :

1. $\dfrac{d^2 y}{dx^2} - 3\dfrac{dy}{dx} + 2y = 0.$ **2.** $(D^2 + D + 1)\,y = 0.$

3. $(9D^2 + 12D + 4)\,y = 0.$ **4.** $(D^2 + 7D + 10)\,y = 0.$

5. $\dfrac{d^2 y}{dx^2} + a^2 y = 0.$ **6.** $\dfrac{d^2 y}{dx^2} + 4\dfrac{dy}{dx} + 13y = 0.$

7. $(8D^2 - 6D - 5)\,y = 0.$ **8.** $16\dfrac{d^2 y}{dx^2} + 24\dfrac{dy}{dx} + 9y = 0.$

9. $\dfrac{d^4 y}{dx^4} - y = 0.$ **10.** $(D^3 + 3D^2 + 3D + 1)\,y = 0.$

11. $\dfrac{d^4 y}{dx^4} + 4y = 0.$ *(Ravishankar, 2001)*

12. $(D^2 + 1)^2 (D - 1)^2\,y = 0.$ **13.** $(D^2 + D + 1)^2 (D - 2)\,y = 0.$

14. $(D^4 - 2D^3 + 5D^2 - 8D + 4)\,y = 0.$

15. Find the value of y which satisfies the equation

$$\frac{d^2 y}{dx^2} + 4\frac{dy}{dx} - 12y = 0,$$

given that $y = 0$ and $dy / dx = 1$, when $x = 0$.

16. Solve

$$\frac{d^2y}{dx^2} - 4\frac{dy}{dx} + 5y = 0,$$

given that $y = 1$ and $dy / dx = 2$, when $x = 0$.

17. Solve

$$\frac{d^2x}{dt^2} + \mu x = 0, \ \mu > 0,$$

given that $x = a$ and $dx / dt = 0$, when $t = \pi / \sqrt{\mu}$.

ANSWERS

1. $y = ae^x + be^{2x}$.

2. $y = e^{-\frac{1}{2}x}\left(a\cos\frac{\sqrt{3}}{2}x + b\sin\frac{\sqrt{3}}{2}x\right)$.

3. $y = (a + bx)\, e^{-2x/3}$.   4. $y = ae^{-5x} + be^{-2x}$.

5. $y = c_1\cos ax + c_2\sin ax$.   6. $y = (a\cos 3x + b\sin 3x)\, e^{-2x}$.

7. $y = ae^{-(1/2)x} + be^{3x/4}$.   8. $y = (a + bx)\, e^{-3x/4}$.

9. $y = ae^x + be^{-x} + c\cos x + d\sin x$.

10. $y = (a + bx + cx^2)\, e^{-x}$.

11. $y = e^{-x}(c_1\cos x + c_2\sin x) + e^x(c_3\cos x + c_4\sin x)$.

12. $y = (c_1 + c_2x)\sin x + (c_3 + c_4x)\cos x + (c_5 + c_6x)\, e^x$.

13. $y = e^{-x/2}\left\{(c_1 + c_2x)\cos\left(\frac{1}{2}x\sqrt{3}\right) + (c_3 + c_4x)\sin\left(\frac{1}{2}x\sqrt{3}\right)\right\}$

$$+ c_5 e^{2x}.$$

14. $y = (c_1 + c_2x)\, e^x + c_3\cos 2x + c_4\sin 2x$.

15. $y = -\frac{1}{8}e^{-6x} + \frac{1}{8}e^{2x}$.   16. $y = e^{2x}\cos x$.

17. $x = -a\cos\sqrt{\mu}\, t$.

18.6. Inverse operators. The operator

$$\frac{1}{D - \alpha}; \ \alpha \text{ being a constant.}$$

Def. *If X is a function of x, then*

$$\frac{1}{D - \alpha}X$$

stands for the function such that when $(D - \alpha)$ operates on it the result is the function X.

Thus, $\dfrac{1}{D} X$ stands for the integral of X.

To evaluate

$$\frac{1}{D-\alpha} X,$$

we write

$$y = \frac{1}{D-\alpha} X.$$

By definition, y is a function such that when $(D - \alpha)$ operates on it, the result is X, *i.e.*,

$$(D - \alpha) y = X \iff \frac{dy}{dx} - \alpha y = X$$

which is a linear differential equation.

Multiplying by the integrating factor, $e^{-\alpha x}$ we see that the solution is

$$ye^{-\alpha x} = \int X e^{-\alpha x} \, dx + c,$$

so that

$$y = e^{\alpha x} \left\{ \int X e^{-\alpha x} \, dx + c \right\}$$

$$\therefore \quad y = \frac{1}{D-\alpha} X = e^{\alpha x} \left\{ \int X e^{-\alpha x} \, dx + c \right\}.$$

If any *one* value of $\dfrac{1}{D-\alpha} X$ be required, we omit the constant c, and write

$$\frac{1}{D-\alpha} X = e^{\alpha x} \int X e^{-\alpha x} \, dx.$$

The symbol, $\dfrac{1}{(D-\beta)(D-\alpha)} X$, *means that* $\dfrac{1}{D-\beta}$ *is to operate on* $\dfrac{1}{(D-\alpha)} X$.

Let $y = \dfrac{1}{(D-\beta)(D-\alpha)} X$.

Then, by definition,

$$(D - \beta) y = \frac{1}{D-\alpha} X.$$

Again, by definition

$$(D - \alpha)(D - \beta) y = X.$$

Thus the symbol, $\dfrac{1}{(D-\beta)(D-\alpha)}$ X, denotes the function y which satisfies the differential equation

$$(D-\alpha)(D-\beta)\, y = X.$$

EXAMPLES

Evaluate the following, obtaining only particular values :

(i) $\dfrac{1}{D} x^3.$ (ii) $\dfrac{1}{D^2} x^4.$

(iii) $\dfrac{1}{D-2} \sin x.$ (iv) $\dfrac{1}{(D-2)(D-3)} e^{2x}.$

(i) $\dfrac{1}{D} x^3 = \displaystyle\int x^3\, dx = \dfrac{x^4}{4}.$

(ii) $\dfrac{1}{D^2} x^4 = \dfrac{1}{D}\cdot\dfrac{1}{D} x^4 = \displaystyle\int\left[\int x^4\, dx\right] dx = \int \dfrac{x^5}{5}\, dx = \dfrac{x^6}{30}.$

(iii) $\dfrac{1}{D-2} \sin x = e^{2x} \displaystyle\int e^{-2x} \sin x\, dx$

$$= e^{2x}\, \frac{e^{-2x}}{\sqrt{5}} \sin\left(x + \tan^{-1}\frac{1}{2}\right)$$

$$= \frac{1}{\sqrt{5}} \sin\left(x + \tan^{-1}\frac{1}{2}\right).$$

(iv) $\dfrac{1}{D-3} e^{2x} = e^{3x} \displaystyle\int e^{-3x}\cdot e^{2x}\, dx = -e^{2x}.$

$$\frac{1}{D-2}\cdot\left(\frac{1}{D-3} e^{2x}\right) = \frac{1}{D-2}(-e^{2x})$$

$$= e^{2x}\int e^{-2x}(-e^{2x})\, dx = e^{2x}\int -1\cdot dx = -xe^{2x}.$$

$$\frac{1}{(D-2)(D-3)} e^{2x} = -xe^{2x}.$$

EXERCISES

Evaluate the following obtaining only particular values :

(i) $\dfrac{1}{D^2} e^{-x},$ (ii) $\dfrac{1}{(D+1)(D-1)} \cos x,$

(iii) $\dfrac{1}{D+2} (x + e^x),$ (iv) $\dfrac{1}{(D+1)(D-1)} e^x,$

(v) $\dfrac{1}{D+2} x^2,$ (vi) $\dfrac{1}{(D+3)(D-3)} (\sin 2x + 2e^{3x}).$

ANSWERS

(i) e^{-x}.　　(ii) $-\dfrac{1}{2}\cos x$.　　(iii) $-\dfrac{1}{4}x-\dfrac{1}{16}-\dfrac{1}{3}e^x$.

(iv) $\dfrac{1}{2}x^2 e^x$.　(v) $\dfrac{1}{2}x^2-\dfrac{1}{2}x+\dfrac{1}{4}$.　(vi) $-\dfrac{1}{18}\sin 2x+\dfrac{1}{3}xe^x$.

18.7. To determine the particular integral of

$$f(\mathrm{D})\,y = \mathrm{X}. \qquad \ldots(1)$$

By definition

$$\frac{1}{f(\mathrm{D})}\,\mathrm{X} \qquad \ldots(2)$$

means a function such that when $f(\mathrm{D})$ operates on it, the result is the function X, so that the symbol (2) stands for a solution of the differential equation (1).

Let $f(\mathrm{D}) = (\mathrm{D}-m_1)(\mathrm{D}-m_2)\ldots(\mathrm{D}-m_n)$.

$$\therefore\quad \mathrm{P.I.} = \frac{1}{f(\mathrm{D})}\,\mathrm{X} = \frac{1}{(\mathrm{D}-m_1)(\mathrm{D}-m_2)\ldots(\mathrm{D}-m_n)}\,\mathrm{X}$$

$$= \frac{1}{(\mathrm{D}-m_1)(\mathrm{D}-m_2)\ldots(\mathrm{D}-m_{n-1})}\,e^{m_n x}\int \mathrm{X}e^{-m_n x}\,dx.$$

We write

$$\mathrm{X}' = e^{m_n x}\int \mathrm{X}e^{-m_n x}\,dx.$$

$$\therefore\quad \mathrm{P.I.} = \frac{1}{(\mathrm{D}-m_1)(\mathrm{D}-m_2)\ldots(\mathrm{D}-m_{n-1})}\,\mathrm{X}'$$

$$= \frac{1}{(\mathrm{D}-m_1)(\mathrm{D}-m_2)\ldots(\mathrm{D}-m_{n-1})}\,e^{m_{n-1} x}\int \mathrm{X}'e^{-m_{n-1}\cdot x}\,dx.$$

Proceeding in this manner we will, after a finite number of steps, obtain the particular integral as required.

Another method. We have, resolving into partial fractions,

$$\frac{1}{f(\mathrm{D})} = \frac{1}{(\mathrm{D}-m_1)(\mathrm{D}-m_2)\ldots(\mathrm{D}-m_n)}$$

$$= \frac{\mathrm{A}_1}{\mathrm{D}-m_1}+\frac{\mathrm{A}_2}{\mathrm{D}-m_2}+\ldots+\frac{\mathrm{A}_n}{\mathrm{D}-m_n}$$

$$\therefore\quad \mathrm{P.I.} = \frac{1}{f(\mathrm{D})}\,\mathrm{X} = \left[\frac{\mathrm{A}_1}{\mathrm{D}-m_1}+\frac{\mathrm{A}_2}{\mathrm{D}-m_2}+\ldots+\frac{\mathrm{A}_n}{\mathrm{D}-m_n}\right]\mathrm{X}$$

$$= \mathrm{A}_1 e^{m_1 x}\int \mathrm{X}e^{-m_1 x}\,dx + \mathrm{A}_2 e^{m_2 x}\int \mathrm{X}e^{-m_2 x}\,dx + \ldots$$

$$\ldots + \mathrm{A}_n e^{-m_n x}\int \mathrm{X}e^{-m_n x}\,dx.$$

Note 1. The method given here is a general one which can be employed to obtain a particular integral in any given case. Shorter methods depending upon the form of the function X will be given in the following sections.

Note 2. As we require only a *particular integral*, we may not introduce any arbitrary constant in carrying out the integrations in the method explained above.

EXAMPLES

1. *Solve*

$$\frac{d^2y}{dx^2} + 3\frac{dy}{dx} + 2y = e^{2x}.$$

The equation may be re-written as
$$(D^2 - 3D + 2)\, y = e^{2x}.$$

Since, the roots of, $D^2 - 3D + 2 = 0$, are 1, 2, the complementary function, (C.F.), is $c_1 e^x + c_2 e^{2x}$.

To find the particular integral, (P.I.), we have to evaluate

$$\frac{1}{(D-2)(D-1)} e^{2x}.$$

Now $\quad \dfrac{1}{(D-1)} e^{2x} = e^x \int e^{-x} \cdot e^{2x}\, dx = e^{2x}.$

Again $\quad \dfrac{1}{D-2}\dfrac{1}{D-1} e^{2x} = \dfrac{1}{D-2} e^{2x}$

$$= e^{2x}\int e^{-2x} \cdot e^{2x}\, dx = xe^{2x}.$$

$\therefore \qquad y = c_1 e^x + c_2 e^{2x} + xe^{2x},$

is the general solution.

2. *Solve the differential equation*

$$\frac{d^2y}{dx^2} + 9y = \sec 3x.$$

We have the equation
$$(D^2 + 9)\, y = \sec 3x.$$

Since the roots of $D^2 + 9 = 0$, are $\pm 3i$, we have

C.F. $= a_1 \cos 3x + a_2 \sin 3x.$

Again P.I. $= \dfrac{1}{D^2 + 9} \sec 3x$

$$= \frac{1}{(D+3i)(D-3i)} \sec 3x,$$

$$= \frac{1}{6i}\left(\frac{1}{D-3i} - \frac{1}{D+3i}\right)\sec 3x$$

$$= \frac{1}{6i}\left[\frac{1}{D-3i}\sec 3x - \frac{1}{D+3i}\sec 3x\right]$$

$$= \frac{1}{6i}\left[e^{3ix}\int e^{-3ix}\sec 3x\, dx - e^{-3ix}\int e^{3ix}\sec 3x\, dx\right].$$

Now $\displaystyle\int e^{-3ix}\sec 3x\, dx = \int (\cos 3x - i\sin 3x)\sec 3x\, dx$

$$= \int (1 - i\tan 3x)\, dx = x + \frac{i}{3}\log\cos 3x.$$

Also $\displaystyle\int e^{3ix}\sec 3x\, dx = \int (\cos 3x + i\sin 3x)\sec 3x\, dx$

$$= \int (1 + i\tan 3x)\, dx = x - \frac{i}{3}\log\cos 3x.$$

$\therefore$ P.I. $= \dfrac{1}{6i}\left[e^{3ix}\left(x + \dfrac{i}{3}\log\cos 3x\right) - e^{-3ix}\left(x - \dfrac{i}{3}\log\cos 3x\right)\right]$

$$= \frac{1}{6i}\left[(\cos 3x + i\sin 3x)\left(x + \frac{i}{3}\log\cos 3x\right)\right.$$
$$\left. - (\cos 3x - i\sin 3x)\left(x - \frac{i}{3}\log\cos 3x\right)\right]$$

$$= \frac{1}{6i}\left[2ix\sin 3x + \frac{2i}{3}\cos 3x\log\cos 3x\right]$$

$$= \frac{x}{3}\sin 3x + \frac{\cos 3x}{9}\log\cos 3x$$

$\therefore \qquad y = a_1\cos 3x + a_2\sin 3x + \dfrac{x}{3}\sin 3x + \dfrac{\cos 3x}{9}\log\cos 3x.$

EXERCISES

Solve the following equations :

1. $9\dfrac{d^2 y}{dx^2} - y = e^{-x}.$

2. $\dfrac{d^2 y}{dx^2} + \dfrac{dy}{dx} - 2y = 2x.$

3. $(D^2 - 2D + 1)y = x^2 - 1.$

4. $(6D^2 - D - 2)y = xe^{-x}.$

5. $(D^2 + 4)y = \tan 2x.$

(Ravishankar, 1996)

6. $\dfrac{d^2 y}{dx^2} + a^2 y = \sec ax.$ *(Ravishankar, 1999; Indore, 1997, 2000; Jabalpur, 2000; Bhopal, 1997; Sagar, 2000; Gorakhpur, 2001, 03; Vikram, 1995; Avadh, 2000; Garhwal, 2000, 02, 03)*

7. $\dfrac{d^2y}{dx^2} + y = \operatorname{cosec} x.$ (*Sagar, 2000; Rewa, 1997; Jabalpur, 1997*)

8. $\dfrac{d^2y}{dx^2} + y = \sec x.$ (*Bilaspur, 2000*)

ANSWERS

1. $y = ae^{-x/3} + be^{x/3} + \dfrac{1}{8} e^{-x}.$ 2. $y = ae^{-2x} + be^x - \left(x + \dfrac{1}{2}\right).$

3. $y = (a + bx) e^x + (x^2 + 4x + 5).$

4. $y = ae^{2x/3} + be^{-x/2} + \dfrac{1}{5} (12/5 + x) e^{-x}.$

5. $y = a \cos 2x + b \sin 2x - \dfrac{1}{4} \cos 2x \log \tan \left(x + \dfrac{1}{4} \pi\right).$

6. $y = a_1 \cos ax + a_2 \sin ax + \dfrac{1}{a} x \sin ax + \dfrac{1}{a^2} \cos ax \log \cos ax.$

7. $y = c_1 \cos x + c_2 \sin x - x \cos x + \log (\sin x) \sin x.$

8. $y = c_1 \cos x + c_2 \sin x + \cos x \log (\cos x) + x \sin x.$

18.81. Rule for finding the particular integral when X is of the form e^{mx}.

We have to find a particular value of y which satisfies the differential equation

$$f(D) y = e^{mx},$$

i.e., we have to evaluate the symbol

$$\dfrac{1}{f(D)} e^{mx},$$

where

$$f(D) \equiv D^n + a_1 D^{n-1} + a_2 D^{n-2} + \ldots + a_{n-1} D + a_n.$$

We know that

$$D^r e^{mx} = m^r e^{mx}.$$

$$f(D) e^{mx} = (D^n + a_1 D^{n-1} + a_2 D^{n-2} + \ldots + a_{n-1} D + a_n) e^{mx}$$

$$= D^n e^{mx} + a_1 D^{n-1} e^{mx} + a_2 D^{n-2} e^{mx}$$

$$\qquad\qquad\qquad\qquad + \ldots + a_{n-1} D e^{mx} + a_n e^{mx}$$

$$= m^n e^{mx} + a_1 m^{n-1} e^{mx} + a_2 m^{n-2} e^{mx}$$

$$\qquad\qquad\qquad\qquad + \ldots + a_{n-1} m e^{mx} + a_n e^{mx}$$

$$= (m^n + a_1 m^{n-1} + a_2 m^{n-2} + \ldots + a_{n-1} m + a_n) e^{mx}$$

$$= f(m) e^{mx}.$$

Thus we see that

$$f(D) e^{mx} = f(m) e^{mx}.$$

Let

$$f(m) \neq 0.$$

Operating on both sides with $1/f(D)$, we have

$$e^{mx} = \frac{1}{f(D)} f(m) e^{mx} = f(m) \frac{1}{f(D)} e^{mx}.$$

Dividing by $f(m) \neq 0$, we obtain

$$\frac{1}{f(m)} e^{mx} = \frac{1}{f(D)} e^{mx}.$$

Let $f(m) = 0$, so that m is a root of the equation $f(D) = 0$.

Suppose that m is a root repeated r-times so that $(D - m)^r$ is a factor of $f(D)$.

Let

$$f(D) = (D - m)^r \varphi(D),$$

where

$$\varphi(m) \neq 0.$$

We have

$$\frac{1}{f(D)} e^{mx} = \frac{1}{(D - m)^r \varphi(D)} e^{mx} = \frac{1}{(D - m)^r} \cdot \frac{1}{\varphi(D)} e^{mx}.$$

As proved in the first part, we have

$$\frac{1}{\varphi(D)} e^{mx} = \frac{1}{\varphi(m)} e^{mx}, \text{ for } \varphi(m) \neq 0.$$

$$\therefore \quad \frac{1}{f(D)} e^{mx} = \frac{1}{(D - m)^r} \frac{1}{\varphi(m)} e^{mx} = \frac{1}{\varphi(m)} \frac{1}{(D - m)^r} e^{mx}.$$

Now

$$\frac{1}{D - m} e^{mx} = e^{mx} \int e^{-mx} \cdot e^{mx} \, dx = xe^{mx}$$

$$\frac{1}{(D - m)^2} e^{mx} = \frac{1}{D - m} \frac{1}{D - m} e^{mx} = \frac{1}{D - m} xe^{mx}$$

$$= e^{mx} \int e^{-mx} xe^{mx} \, dx = \frac{x^2}{2} e^{mx}.$$

$$\frac{1}{(D - m)^3} e^{mx} = \frac{1}{D - m} \frac{1}{(D - m)^2} e^{mx}$$

$$= \frac{1}{D - m} \frac{x^2}{2} e^{mx}$$

$$= e^{mx} \int e^{-mx} \cdot \frac{x^2}{2} \, dx = \frac{x^3}{3!} e^{mx}.$$

Continuing in this manner, we may show that

$$\frac{1}{(D-m)^r}e^{mx} = \frac{x^r}{r!}e^{mx}.$$

$$\therefore \quad \frac{1}{f(D)}e^{mx} = \frac{1}{\varphi(m)}\frac{x^r}{r!}e^{mx},$$

where $$f(D) = (D-m)^r\,\varphi(D),$$

and m is *not* a root of $\varphi(D) = 0$.

EXAMPLES

Solve :

1. $4\dfrac{d^2y}{dx^2} + 4\dfrac{dy}{dx} - 3y = e^{2x}.$

2. $\dfrac{d^2y}{dx^2} + 4\dfrac{dy}{dx} + 3y = e^{-3x}.$

(*Bhoj, 1999*)

3. $\dfrac{d^2y}{dx^2} + 6\dfrac{dy}{dx} + 9y = 2e^{-3x}.$

4. $\dfrac{d^2y}{dx^2} - 2k\dfrac{dy}{dx} + k^2y = e^x.$

(*Jabalpur, 1995, 97*)

1. We have

$$(4D^2 + 4D - 3)\,y = e^{2x}.$$

The roots of $4D^2 + 4D - 3 = 0$ are $1/2$ and $-3/2$.

$\therefore$ C.F. $= c_1e^{x/2} + c_2e^{-3x/2}.$

$$\text{P.I.} = \frac{1}{4D^2 + 4D - 3}e^{2x} = \frac{1}{4(2)^2 + 4(2) - 3}e^{2x} = \frac{e^{2x}}{21}.$$

$\therefore$ The solution is

$$y = c_1e^{x/2} + c_2e^{-3x/2} + \frac{1}{21}e^{2x}.$$

2. We have

$$(D^2 + 4D + 3)\,y = e^{-3x}.$$

The roots of $D^2 + 4D + 3 = 0$ are -1 and -3.

$\therefore$ C.F. $= c_1e^{-x} + c_2e^{-3x}$

$$\text{P.I.} = \frac{1}{D^2 + 4D + 3}e^{-3x}.$$

Now $D^2 + 4D + 3$ becomes 0 for $D = -3$. Therefore, we write

$$\text{P.I.} = \frac{1}{(D+3)(D+1)}e^{-3x} = \frac{1}{D+3}\cdot\frac{1}{(-3+1)}e^{-3x}$$

$$= \frac{1}{D+3}\cdot\frac{1}{-2}e^{-3x} = -\frac{x}{2}e^{-3x}.$$

$$\therefore \quad y = c_1 e^{-x} + c_2 e^{-3x} - \frac{1}{2} xe^{-3x},$$

is the general solution.

3. We have

$$(D^2 + 6D + 9) y = 2e^{-3x}.$$

The roots of $D^2 + 6D + 9 = 0$ are both equal to -3.

$$\therefore \quad \text{C.F.} = (c_1 x + c_2) e^{-3x}$$

$$\text{P.I.} = \frac{1}{D^2 + 6D + 9} \cdot 2e^{-3x}$$

$$= \frac{1}{(D+3)^2} 2e^{-3x}$$

$$= 2 \cdot \frac{1}{(D+3)^2} e^{-3x} = 2 \cdot \frac{1}{2} x^2 e^{-3x} = x^2 e^{-3x}.$$

$$\therefore \quad y = (c_1 x + c_2) e^{-3x} + x^2 e^{-3x},$$

is the general solution.

4. Solve $\dfrac{d^2 y}{dx^2} - 2k \dfrac{dy}{dx} + k^2 y = e^x$ *(Jabalpur 1995, 97)*

Re-writing the given differential equation we have,

$$(D^2 - 2kD + k^2) y = e^x \qquad \qquad \dots(i)$$

Auxiliary equation is

$$m^2 - 2km + k^2 = 0$$

or $(m - k)^2 = 0.$

Hence $m = k, k.$

Therefore $\text{C.F.} = (c_1 + c_2 x) e^{kx}$

and $\text{P.I.} = \dfrac{1}{(D-k)^2} e^x = \dfrac{1}{(1-k)^2} e^x.$

Hence, general solution of the given differential equation is

$$y = \text{C.F.} + \text{P.I.}$$

or $y = (c_1 + c_2 x) e^{kx} + \dfrac{1}{(1-k)^2} e^x.$

EXERCISES

Solve the following differential equations :

1. $6\dfrac{d^2 y}{dx^2} + 17\dfrac{dy}{dx} + 12y = e^{-x}.$ 2. $\dfrac{d^2 y}{dx^2} - \dfrac{dy}{dx} + y = e^{2x} + e^x.$

3. $3\dfrac{d^2 y}{dx^2} + 2\dfrac{dy}{dx} - y = e^{x/2} + 2e^{3x}.$ 4. $(D^2 - 4) y = 3e^{2x} - 4e^{-2x}.$

5. $\dfrac{d^2 y}{dx^2} - (a + b)\dfrac{dy}{dx} + aby = e^{ax} + e^{bx}.$

6. $\dfrac{d^2 y}{dx^2} - 5 \dfrac{dy}{dx} + 6y = e^{4x}.$

(*Kumaon, 2003; Vikram, 1995; Rohilkhand, 2001*)

7. $\dfrac{d^2 y}{dx^2} + 2 \dfrac{dy}{dx} + y = e^{x/2} + e^{-x/2}.$

8. $9 \dfrac{d^2 y}{dx^2} + 12 \dfrac{dy}{dx} + 4y = e^{-2x/3}.$

9. $\dfrac{d^2 y}{dx^2} + 31 \dfrac{dy}{dx} + 240y = 272 e^{-x}.$ (*Jiwaji, 2000*)

10. $\dfrac{d^3 y}{dx^3} - \dfrac{d^2 y}{dx^2} - 4 \dfrac{dy}{dx} + 4y = e^{2x}.$

11. $(3D^2 - 4D + 5) y = e^x - 2e^{2x} + 3e^{3x}.$

12. $(D - 3)^2 y = 2e^{3x} + e^{-x}.$ **13.** $(D^2 - 2D + 1) y = (1 + e^{-x})^2.$

14. Solve $(D^2 + 5D + 6) y = e^{2x}$, given that $y = 0$, $dy/dx = 0$, when $x = 0$.

15. Solve $(D^2 - 7D + 6) y = 2e^{3x}$, given that $y = 1$, $dy/dx = 0$, when $x = 0$.

ANSWERS

1. $y = ae^{-3x/2} + be^{-4x/3} + e^{-x}.$

2. $y = \left(a \cos \dfrac{\sqrt{3}}{2} x + b \sin \dfrac{\sqrt{3}}{2} x \right) e^{x/2} + e^x + \dfrac{e^{3x}}{4}.$

3. $y = ae^{x/3} + be^{-x} + \dfrac{4}{3} e^{x/2} + \dfrac{1}{16} e^{3x}.$

4. $y = ae^{2x} + be^{-2x} + \dfrac{3}{4} xe^{2x} + xe^{-2x}.$

5. $y = c_1 e^{ax} + c_2 e^{ax} + \dfrac{x}{a-b} (e^{ax} - e^{bx}).$

6. $y = c_1 e^{2x} + c_2 e^{3x} + \dfrac{1}{2} e^{4x}.$

7. $y = (a + bx) e^{-x} + e^{x/2} + 4e^{-x/2}.$

8. $y = (a + bx) e^{-2x/3} + \dfrac{1}{8} x^2 e^{-2x/3}.$

9. $y = c_1 e^{-15x} + c_2 e^{-16x} + \dfrac{136}{105} e^{-x}.$

10. $y = ae^x + be^{2x} + ce^{-2x} + \dfrac{1}{4} xe^{3x}.$

11. $y = e^{2x/3} \left(a \cos \dfrac{\sqrt{11}}{3} x + b \sin \dfrac{\sqrt{11}}{3} x \right) + \dfrac{1}{4} e^x - \dfrac{2}{9} e^{2x} - \dfrac{3}{20} e^{3x}.$

12. $y = (a + bx) e^{3x} + \dfrac{1}{16} e^{-x} + x^2 e^{3x}.$

13. $y = (a + bx) e^x + 1 + \dfrac{1}{9} e^{-2x} + \dfrac{1}{2} e^{-x}.$

14. $y = \dfrac{1}{5} e^{-3x} - \dfrac{1}{4} e^{-2x} + \dfrac{1}{10} e^{2x}.$

15. $y = \dfrac{1}{5} e^x - \dfrac{1}{15} e^{6x} - \dfrac{1}{3} e^{3x}.$

18.82. To determine the particular integral, when X is of the form sin mx or cos mx.

Here we have to find a particular value of, y, which satisfies the differential equation

$$f(D) y = \sin mx,$$

so that we have to evaluate the symbol

$$\frac{1}{f(D)} \sin mx.$$

First we consider the case when $f(D)$ contains even powers of D only so that it is a function of D^2. Let

$$f(D) = \varphi(D^2)$$
$$= (D^2)^n + a_1 (D^2)^{n-1} + a_2 (D^2)^{n-2} + \ldots + a_{n-1} D^2 + a_n.$$

We have
$$D \sin mx = m \cos mx,$$
$$D^2 \sin mx = (-m^2) \sin mx,$$
$$D^4 \sin mx = (-m^2)^2 \sin mx,$$
$$D^6 \sin mx = (-m^2)^3 \sin mx, \text{ etc.}$$

With the help of these results, we may easily see that

$$\varphi(D^2) \sin mx = \varphi(-m^2) \sin mx.$$

Let $\varphi(-m^2) \neq 0$. Operating on both sides with $1 / \varphi(D^2)$, we have

$$\sin mx = \frac{1}{\varphi(D^2)} \varphi(-m^2) \sin mx,$$

$$= \varphi(-m^2) \frac{1}{\varphi(D^2)} \sin mx.$$

Dividing by $\varphi(-m^2) \neq 0$, we obtain

$$\frac{1}{\varphi(-m^2)} \sin mx = \frac{1}{\varphi(D^2)} \sin mx.$$

Similarly we may show that

$$\frac{1}{\varphi(D^2)}\cos mx = \frac{1}{\varphi(-m^2)}\cos mx, \text{ if } \varphi(-m^2) \neq 0.$$

The method of procedure for the case of failure which arises when $\varphi(-m^2) = 0$ is indicated in the Example ??? on page ???.

Suppose now, that $f(D)$ contains odd powers of D also. In this case, breaking up $f(D)$ into its even and odd parts, we may write

$$f(D) = \varphi_1(D^2) + D\varphi_2(D^2).$$

We have

$$\frac{1}{f(D)}\sin mx$$

$$= \frac{1}{\varphi_1(D^2) + D\varphi_2(D^2)}\sin mx$$

$$= [\varphi_1(D^2) - D\varphi_2(D^2)]\frac{1}{[\varphi_1(D^2) + D\varphi_2(D^2)][\varphi_1(D^2) - D\varphi_2(D^2)]}\sin mx$$

$$= [\varphi_1(D^2) - D\varphi_2(D^2)]\frac{1}{[\varphi_1(D^2)]^2 - D^2[\varphi_2(D^2)]^2}\sin mx$$

$$= [\varphi_1(D^2) - D\varphi_2(D^2)]\frac{1}{[\varphi_1(-m^2)]^2 - (-m^2)[\varphi_2(-m^2)]^2}\sin mx.$$

We write

$$[\varphi_1(-m^2)] = p, [\varphi_2(-m^2)] = q.$$

$$\therefore \quad \frac{1}{f(D)}\sin mx = \frac{1}{p^2 + m^2 q^2}[\varphi_1(D^2) - D\varphi_2(D^2)]\sin mx$$

$$= \frac{1}{p^2 + m^2 q^2}[\varphi_1(-m^2) - D\varphi_2(-m^2)]\sin mx$$

$$= \frac{1}{p^2 + m^2 q^2}[\varphi_1(-m^2)\sin mx - m\varphi_2(-m^2)\cos mx]$$

$$= \frac{p\sin mx - mq\cos mx}{p^2 + m^2 q^2}.$$

The following *shorter* procedure has its justification in the result obtained above.

We write

$$\frac{1}{f(D)}\sin mx = \frac{1}{\varphi_1(D^2) + D\varphi_2(D^2)}\sin mx$$

$$= \frac{1}{\varphi_1(-m^2) + D\varphi_2(-m^2)} \sin mx$$

$$= \frac{1}{p + Dq} \sin mx$$

$$= (p - Dq) \frac{1}{(p + Dq)(p - Dq)} \sin mx$$

$$= (p - Dq) \frac{1}{p^2 - D^2 q^2} \sin mx$$

$$= (p - Dq) \frac{1}{p^2 + m^2 q^2} \sin mx$$

$$= \frac{1}{p^2 + m^2 q^2} (p - Dq) \sin mx$$

$$= \frac{1}{p^2 + m^2 q^2} (p \sin mx - mq \cos mx),$$

which is the same as obtained before.

The case of, cos mx, can be similarly treated.

EXAMPLES

1. *Solve* $\dfrac{d^2 y}{dx^2} - 5\dfrac{dy}{dx} + 6y = \sin 3x.$ *(Avadh, 2003; Kanpur, 2003)*

We have

$$(D^2 - 5D + 6)\, y = \sin 3x.$$

The roots of $D^2 - 5D + 6 = 0$ are 2, 3 so that, the complementary function is

$$c_1 e^{2x} + c_2 e^{3x}.$$

Also

$$\text{P.I.} = \frac{1}{D^2 - 5D + 6} \sin 3x.$$

Replacing D^2 by $(-3^2) = -9$, we obtain

$$\text{P.I.} = \frac{1}{-9 - 5D + 6} \sin 3x$$

$$= \frac{1}{-3 - 5D} \sin 3x$$

$$= -(3 - 5D) \frac{1}{(3 - 5D)(3 + 5D)} \sin 3x$$

$$= -(3 - 5D) \frac{1}{9 - 25D^2} \sin 3x$$

$$= -(3 - 5D)\frac{1}{9 - 25(-9)}\sin 3x$$

$$= -\frac{1}{234}(3 - 5D)\sin 3x$$

$$= -\frac{1}{234}(3\sin 3x - 15\cos 3x)$$

$$= -\frac{1}{78}(\sin 3x - 5\cos 3x).$$

Thus the required solution is

$$y = c_1 e^{2x} + c_2 e^{3x} - \frac{1}{78}(\sin 3x - 5\cos 3x).$$

2. *Solve* $(D^2 + 4)\, y = cos\ 2x.$

The roots of $D^2 + 4 = 0$ are $2i, -2i$ and therefore

$$\text{C.F.} = c_1 \cos 2x + c_2 \sin 2x.$$

Also $\quad \text{P.I.} = \dfrac{1}{D^2 + 4}\cos 2x.$

Since $D^2 + 4$ becomes zero on replacing D^2 by $-2^2 = -4$, we have here a case of failure of the procedure outlined in § ???.

The procedure, now is as follows :

The P.I. is the real part of

$$\frac{1}{D^2 + 4}e^{2ix}.$$

Now, $D^2 + 4$ vanishes for $D = 2i$. Therefore, we write

$$D^2 + 4 = (D - 2i)(D + 2i)$$

$$\therefore \quad \frac{1}{D^2 + 4}e^{2ix} = \frac{1}{(D - 2i)(D + 2i)}e^{2ix}$$

$$= \frac{1}{4i} \cdot \frac{1}{D - 2i}e^{2ix}$$

$$= \frac{1}{4i}xe^{2ix}$$

$$= -\frac{1}{4}ix(\cos 2x + i\sin 2x)$$

$$= \frac{1}{4}x\sin 2x - i\frac{1}{4}x\cos 2x$$

$$\therefore \quad y = c_1 \cos 2x + c_2 \sin 2x + \frac{1}{4}x\sin 2x.$$

3. *Solve* $(D^3 + 1)\, y = \cos 2x$.   *(Jabalpur, 1995; Bilaspur, 1997;*

                                              Bhopal, 1999; Vikram, 2000)

It can easily be shown that

$$\text{C.F.} = c_1 e^{-x} + e^{x/2}\left(c_2 \cos\frac{\sqrt{3}\,x}{2} + c_3 \sin\frac{\sqrt{3}\,x}{2}\right).$$

Also $\text{P.I.} = \dfrac{1}{D^3 + 1}\cos 2x$

$$= \frac{1}{D \cdot D^2 + 1}\cos 2x$$

$$= \frac{1}{D(-2^2) + 1}\cos 2x$$

$$= \frac{1}{1 - 4D}\cos 2x$$

$$= (1 + 4D)\frac{1}{(1 + 4D)(1 - 4D)}\cos 2x$$

$$= (1 + 4D)\frac{1}{1 - 16D^2}\cos 2x$$

$$= (1 + 4D)\frac{1}{1 - 16(-4)}\cos 2x$$

$$= \frac{1}{65}(1 + 4D)\cos 2x = \frac{1}{65}(\cos 2x - 8\sin 2x).$$

$\therefore \quad y = c_1 e^{-x} + e^{x/2}\left(c_2 \cos\frac{\sqrt{3}\,x}{2} + c_3 \sin\frac{\sqrt{3}\,x}{2}\right)$

$$+ \frac{1}{65}(\cos 2x - 8\sin 2x).$$

4. *Solve* $(D^2 + D + 1)\, y = \sin 2x$.

                 (Indore, 1996; Sagar, 1998; Gorakhpur, 2000)

Here $\text{C.F.} = e^{-x/2}\left(c_1 \cos\frac{\sqrt{3}}{2}x + c_2 \sin\frac{\sqrt{3}}{2}x\right).$

$$\text{P.I.} = \frac{1}{D^2 + D + 1}\sin 2x$$

$$= \frac{1}{-(2)^2 + D + 1}\sin 2x$$

$$= \frac{1}{D - 3}\sin 2x$$

$$= \frac{D+3}{D^2-9} \sin 2x$$

$$= \frac{D(\sin 2x) + 3 \sin 2x}{-4-9}$$

$$= -\frac{1}{13}(2 \cos 2x + 3 \sin 2x).$$

∴   General solution of the equation is

$$y = \text{C.F.} + \text{P.I.}$$

or $$y = e^{-x/2}\left(c_1 \cos \frac{\sqrt{3}}{2}x + c_2 \sin \frac{\sqrt{3}}{2}x\right) - \frac{1}{13}(2 \cos 2x + 3 \sin 2x).$$

5. *Solve* $\dfrac{d^2 y}{dx^2} - 8\dfrac{dy}{dx} + 9y = 40 \sin 5x.$

(Rewa, 2000; Bilaspur, 1998; Jabalpur, 1996)

Re-writing the differential equation we have,

$$(D^2 - 8D + 9)\, y = 40 \sin 5x \qquad\qquad ...(i)$$

Auxiliary equation is $m^2 - 8m + 9 = 0$, giving $m = 4 \pm \sqrt{7}.$

Hence,   C.F. $= c_1 e^{4x} \cosh(\sqrt{7}\, x + c_2)$

and   P.I. $= \dfrac{1}{D^2 - 8D + 9}\, 40 \sin 5x$

$$= 40\,\frac{1}{D^2 - 8D + 9}\sin 5x$$

[Since 40 is constant hence is taken out of operator.]

$$= 40\,\frac{1}{-5^2 - 8D + 9}\sin 5x$$

$$= 40\,\frac{1}{-8D - 16}\sin 5x = -5\cdot\frac{1}{D+2}\sin 5x$$

$$= -5\cdot\frac{D-2}{D^2 - 4}\sin 5x = -5\,(D-2)\frac{1}{-5^2 - 4}\sin 5x$$

$$= \frac{5}{29}(D \sin 5x - 2 \sin 5x) = \frac{5}{29}(5 \cos 5x - 2 \sin 5x)$$

$$= \frac{25}{29}\cos 5x - \frac{10}{29}\sin 5x.$$

Hence, the complete solution is given as

$$y = \text{C.F.} + \text{P.I.}$$

i.e., $$y = c_1 e^{4x} \cosh(\sqrt{7}\, x + c_2) + \frac{25}{29}\cos 5x - \frac{10}{29}\sin 5x.$$

EXERCISES

Solve the following differential equations :

1. $\dfrac{d^2 y}{dx^2} - 3\dfrac{dy}{dx} + 2y = \cos 2x.$ **2.** $(D^2 + 4D - 3)\, y = 2 \sin 3x.$

3. $\dfrac{d^2 y}{dx^2} + a^2 y = \sin ax.$ **4.** $\dfrac{d^2 y}{dx^2} + 4y = \cos 3x + \sin 3x.$

5. $\dfrac{d^2 y}{dx^2} + 9y = e^x - \cos 2x.$ **6.** $\dfrac{d^2 y}{dx^2} - 3\dfrac{dy}{dx} + y = 2 \sin 3x.$

7. $2\dfrac{d^2 y}{dx^2} - 3\dfrac{dy}{dx} + 4y = 3 \cos \dfrac{x}{2}.$ **8.** $(D^2 - 8D + 9)\, y = 40 \sin 5x.$

9. $(4D^2 + 16D - 9)\, y = 4e^{x/2} + 3 \sin \dfrac{1}{4}x.$

10. $(D^4 + 2D^3 - 3D^2)\, y = 3e^{2x} + 4 \sin x.$

11. $\dfrac{d^2 y}{dx^2} - 4y = \cos^2 x.$ *(Jabalpur, 1999)*

12. $(D^2 + D + 1)\, y = (1 + \sin x)^2.$ **13.** $(D^4 - 2D^2 + 1)\, y = \cos x.$

14. $(D^3 + D^2 + D + 1)\, y = \sin 2x.$ **15.** $(D^2 + 1)\, y = \sin x \sin 2x.$

16. Solve $\dfrac{d^2 y}{dx^2} + 2\dfrac{dy}{dx} + 10y + 37 \sin 3x = 0$ and find the value of y

when $x = \pi/2$, if it is given that $y = 3$ and $dy/dx = 0$, when $x = 0$.

ANSWERS

1. $y = ae^{2x} + be^x - \dfrac{1}{20}\cos 2x - \dfrac{3}{20}\sin 2x.$

2. $y = ae^{(-2+\sqrt{7})x} + be^{(-2-\sqrt{7})x} - \dfrac{1}{12}(\cos 3x + \sin 3x).$

3. $y = c_1 \cos ax + c_2 \sin ax - \dfrac{x \cos ax}{2a}.$

4. $y = a \cos 2x + b \sin 2x - \dfrac{1}{5}(\cos 3x + \sin 3x).$

5. $y = a \cos 3x + b \sin 3x + \dfrac{1}{10}e^x - \dfrac{1}{5}\cos 2x.$

6. $y = ae^{\frac{3+\sqrt{5}}{2}x} + be^{\frac{3-\sqrt{5}}{2}x} + \dfrac{18}{145}\cos 3x - \dfrac{16}{145}\sin 3x.$

7. $y = \left(a \cos \dfrac{\sqrt{23}}{4}x + b \sin \dfrac{\sqrt{23}}{4}x\right)e^{\frac{3}{4}x} + \dfrac{3}{29}\left(7 \cos \dfrac{x}{2} - 3 \sin \dfrac{x}{2}\right).$

8. $y = ae^{(4+\sqrt{7})x} + be^{(4-\sqrt{7})x} + \dfrac{5}{29}(5\cos 5x - 2\sin 5x)$.

9. $y = ae^{x/2} + be^{-9x/2} + \dfrac{1}{5}xe^{x/2} - \dfrac{48}{1625}\left(4\cos\dfrac{x}{4} + \dfrac{37}{4}\sin\dfrac{x}{4}\right)$.

10. $y = (c_1 + c_2 x) + c_3 e^x + c_4 e^{-3x} + \dfrac{2}{5}(2\sin x + \cos x)$.

11. $y = ae^{2x} + be^{-2x} - \dfrac{1}{8}\left(1 + \dfrac{1}{2}\cos 2x\right)$.

12. $y = \left(a\cos\dfrac{\sqrt{3}}{2}x + b\sin\dfrac{\sqrt{3}}{2}x\right)e^{-x/2} + \dfrac{3}{2}$

$$+ \dfrac{1}{26}(3\cos 2x - 2\sin 2x) - 2\cos x.$$

13. $y = (a + bx)e^x + (c + dx)e^{-x} + \dfrac{1}{4}\cos x$.

14. $y = a\cos x + b\sin x + ce^{-x} + \dfrac{1}{15}(2\cos 2x - \sin 2x)$.

15. $y = (c_1\cos x + c_2\sin x) + \dfrac{x}{4}\sin x + \dfrac{1}{16}\cos 3x$.

16. $y = e^{-x}(a\cos 3x + b\sin 3x) = 6\cos 3x - \sin 3x;\ y = 1$.

14.83. *To find particular integral when X is of the form x^m, m being a positive integer.*

Here we have to evaluate

$$\dfrac{1}{f(D)}x^m.$$

The general method is to expand $1/f(D)$ in ascending integral powers of D, regarding D as a number, and to let each term of the expression operate on x^m. Then the sum of the results of these operations is the required value. Since $(m+1)$th and higher derivatives of x^m are zero, it is enough to expand $1/f(D)$ in ascending powers of, D, up to mth power only.

The justification for this expansion will become clear by the following discussion.

As in § 18.7, we decompose $1/f(D)$ into partial fractions and obtain

$$\dfrac{1}{f(D)} = \dfrac{A_1}{D - \alpha_1} + \dfrac{A_2}{D - \alpha_2} + \ldots + \dfrac{A_n}{D - \alpha_n}.$$

We expand $1/(D - \alpha_1)$, regarding D as a number and obtain

$$\frac{1}{D - \alpha_1} = -\frac{1}{\alpha_1}\left(1 - \frac{D}{\alpha_1}\right)^{-1}$$

$$= -\frac{1}{\alpha_1}\left(1 + \frac{D}{\alpha_1} + \frac{D^2}{\alpha_1^2} + \frac{D^3}{\alpha_1^3} + \ldots\right).$$

The above equality has now to be justified when D is given its operational character, *i.e.*, we have to prove that

$$\frac{1}{D - \alpha_1}X = -\frac{1}{\alpha_1}\left(1 + \frac{D}{\alpha_1} + \frac{D^2}{\alpha_1^2} + \frac{D^3}{\alpha_1^3} + \ldots\right)X,$$

where X is any function of x. By the definition of inverse operations, this will be so if

$$(D - \alpha_1)\left[-\frac{1}{\alpha_1}\left(1 + \frac{D}{\alpha_1} + \frac{D^2}{\alpha_1^2} + \ldots\right)X\right] = X,$$

which is easily seen to be a fact.

Thus we have seen that the partial fractions of $1/f(D)$ can, with justification, be expanded in ascending integral powers of D. Also we know that the direct expansion of $1/f(D)$ in ascending integral powers of D will be same as the sum of the expansions of its partial fractions.

EXAMPLES

1. *Solve* $(D^3 + 2D^2 + 4D + 8)y = x^2$.

We have

$$D^3 + 2D^2 + 4D + 8 = D^2(D + 2) + 4(D + 2) = (D + 2)(D^2 + 4),$$

so that the roots of $D^3 + 2D^2 + 4D + 8 = 0$ are $-2, 2i, -2i$.

$$\therefore \quad \text{C.F.} = c_1 e^{-2x} + c_2 \cos 2x + c_3 \sin 2x.$$

Again $\text{P.I.} = \dfrac{1}{D^3 + 2D^2 + 4D + 8}x^2$

$$= \frac{1}{8}\left[1 + \frac{4D + 2D^2 + D^3}{8}\right]^{-1} x^2$$

$$= \frac{1}{8}\left[1 - \frac{4D + 2D^2 + D^3}{8} + \left(\frac{4D + 2D^2 + D^3}{8}\right)^2 + \ldots\right]x^2$$

$$= \frac{1}{8}\left[1 - \frac{1}{2}D + 0D^2 + \ldots\right]x^2 = \frac{1}{8}(x^2 - x).$$

$$\therefore \quad y = c_1 e^{-2x} + c_2 \cos 2x + c_3 \sin 2x + \frac{1}{8}(x^2 - x).$$

2. *Solve the equation* $\dfrac{d^2y}{dx^2} = a + bx + cx^2$, *given that* $\dfrac{dy}{dx} = 0$ *when* $x = 0$ *and* $y = d$ *when* $x = 0$.

Auxiliary equation is $m^2 = 0$ $\quad\therefore\quad m = 0, 0.$

$\therefore$ C.F. $= (c_1 + c_2 x)\, e^{0\cdot x} = (c_1 + c_2 x).$

$$\text{P.I.} = \frac{1}{D^2}(a + bx + cx^2)$$

$$= \frac{1}{D}\left(ax + x\,\frac{b}{2}\,x^2 + \frac{c}{3}\,x^3\right)$$

$$= \left(\frac{ax^2}{2} + \frac{b}{6}\,x^3 + \frac{c}{12}\,x^4\right).$$

$\therefore\quad y = c_1 + c_2 x + \dfrac{1}{2}\,ax^2 + \dfrac{1}{6}\,bx^3 + \dfrac{1}{12}\,cx^4$ ...(i)

$\dfrac{dy}{dx} = c_2 + ax + \dfrac{1}{2}\,bx^2 + \dfrac{1}{3}\,cx^3$ ...(ii)

Putting $x = 0$, $y = d$ and $\dfrac{dy}{dx} = 0$ in (i) and (ii), we get

$$c_2 = 0 \text{ and } c_1 = d.$$

$\therefore\quad y = d + \dfrac{1}{2}\,ax^2 + \dfrac{1}{6}\,bx^3 + \dfrac{1}{12}\,cx^4.$

3. *Solve* : $(D^4 - a^4)\, y = x^4 + \sin bx.$

Here, we have

$$\text{C.F.} = c_1 e^{ax} + c_2 e^{-ax} + (c_3 \cos ax + c_4 \sin ax).$$

$$\text{P.I. of } x^4 = \frac{x^4}{D^4 - a^4} = -\frac{1}{a^4}\left(1 - \frac{D^4}{a^4}\right)^{-1} x^4$$

$$= -\frac{1}{a^4}\left(1 + \frac{D^4}{a^4} + \ldots\right) x^4$$

$$= -\frac{1}{a^4}\left[x^4 + \frac{1}{a^4}\cdot(4\,!)\right]$$

$$= -\frac{1}{a^4}\left(x^4 + \frac{24}{a^4}\right).$$

$$\text{P.I. of } \sin bx = \frac{\sin bx}{D^4 - a^4}$$

Put $D^2 = -b^2$ $\quad\therefore\quad D^4 = b^4$

$$= \frac{\sin bx}{b^4 - a^4}.$$

Hence general solution will be

$$y = c_1 e^{ax} + c_2 e^{-ax} + c_3 \cos ax + c_4 \sin ax$$

$$-\frac{1}{a^4}\left(x^4 + \frac{24}{a^4}\right) + \frac{1}{(b^4 - a^4)} \sin bx.$$

4. *If* $\dfrac{d^2x}{dt^2} + \dfrac{g}{b}(x - a) = 0$, *(a, b and g being positive numbers) and*

$x = a'$ *and* $\dfrac{dx}{dt} = 0$ *when* $t = 0$, *show that*

$$x = a + (a' - a)\cos\left(\sqrt{g/b}\ t\right). \qquad (Jiwaji, 1997)$$

The given equation can be written as

$$\left(D^2 + \frac{g}{b}\right)x = \frac{ga}{b}, \text{ where } D = \frac{d}{dt}.$$

$\therefore$ The auxiliary equation is $m^2 + (g/b) = 0$ or $m = \pm i\sqrt{g/b}$.

$\therefore$ C.F. $= C_1 \cos\sqrt{g/b}\ t + C_2 \sin\sqrt{g/b}\ t$

where C_1 and C_2 are arbitrary constants and

$$P.I. = \frac{1}{(D^2 + g/b)}\frac{ga}{b} = \frac{1}{(g/b)\{1 + (b/g)D^2\}}\frac{ga}{b}$$

$$= \frac{b}{g}\left(1 + \frac{b}{g}D^2\right)^{-1}\frac{ga}{b} = \frac{b}{g}\left(1 - \frac{b}{g}D^2 + \dots\right)\frac{ga}{b}$$

$$= (b/g)(ga/b) = a.$$

$\therefore$ The complete solution of the given equations is

$$x = \text{C.F.} + \text{P.I.}$$

or $x = C_1 \cos\left(\sqrt{g/b}\ t\right) + C_2 \sin\left(\sqrt{g/b}\ t\right) + a.$ ...(i)

Differentiating (i) with respect to t, we have

$$\frac{dx}{dt} = -C_1\sqrt{g/b}\sin\left(\sqrt{g/b}\ t\right) + C_2\sqrt{g/b}\cos\left(\sqrt{g/b}\ t\right) \qquad ...(ii)$$

Now it is given that $x = a'$ when $t = 0$.

$\therefore$ From (i), $a' = C_1 + a$ or $C_1 = a' - a$.

Also $dx/dt = 0$ when $t = 0$.

$\therefore$ From (ii), $0 = C_2\sqrt{g/b}$ or $C_2 = 0$.

Substituting these values of C_1 and C_2 in (i), we have the required solution as

$$x = (a' - a)\cos\left(\sqrt{g/b}\ t\right) + a.$$

EXERCISES

Solve

1. $\dfrac{d^2y}{dx^2} + 2\dfrac{dy}{dx} + y = 2x + x^2$.

2. $\dfrac{d^3y}{dx^3} - \dfrac{d^2y}{dx^2} - 6\dfrac{dy}{dx} = 1 + x^2$.

(Bhopal, 1997, 98; Kanpur, 2000; Gorakhpur, 2002)

3. $\dfrac{d^2y}{dx^2} - 4y = x^2$.   4. $(D^4 + D^3 + D^2 - D - 2) = x^2$.

5. $(D^3 + 3D^2 + 2D)\, y = x^2$.

6. $\dfrac{d^2y}{dx^2} - 5\dfrac{dy}{dx} + 6y = x$.

(Kumaon, 1999; Vikram, 1996; Bilaspur, 2000)

7. $(D^3 - D^2 - 6D)\, y = x^2 + 1$.

8. $(D^3 + 2D^2 + D)\, y = e^{2x} + x^2 + x$.

(Vikram, 1998; Agra, 2000; Bilaspur, 1993)

9. $\dfrac{d^2y}{dx^2} - 4\dfrac{dy}{dx} + y = 73\sin 2x + x + 13e^{-x/2}$.

10. $\dfrac{d^2y}{dx^2} - 4y = e^x + \sin 2x + \cos^2 x$.

11. $\dfrac{d^2y}{dx^2} + 2\dfrac{dy}{dx} + y = 2x + x^2$.

12. $(D^2 + 5D + 4)\, y = 3 - 2x$.   *(Vikram, 1999)*

ANSWERS

1. $y = (a + bx)\, e^{-x} + x^2 - 2x + 2$.

2. $y = a + be^{3x} + ce^{-2x} - \dfrac{1}{6}\left(\dfrac{25}{18}x + \dfrac{1}{6}x^2 + \dfrac{1}{3}x^3\right)$.

3. $y = ae^{2x} + be^{-2x} - \dfrac{1}{4}\left(x^2 + \dfrac{1}{2}\right)$.

4. $y = ae^{-x} + be^x + e^{-\frac{1}{2}x}\left(c\cos\dfrac{\sqrt{7}}{2}x + d\sin\dfrac{\sqrt{7}}{2}x\right)$

$-\left(x^2 - x + \dfrac{1}{2}\right)$.

5. $y = a + be^{-2x} + ce^{-x} + \dfrac{1}{12}x\,(2x^2 - 9x + 21)$.

6. $y = ae^{2x} + be^{3x} + \dfrac{1}{6}x + \dfrac{5}{36}.$

7. $y = a + be^{3x} + ce^{-2x} - \left(\dfrac{25}{108}\right)x - \dfrac{1}{18}x^3 + \dfrac{1}{36}x^2.$

8. $y = a + (b + cx)e^{-x} + \dfrac{1}{6}x\left(2x^2 - 9x + 24 + \dfrac{1}{18}e^{2x}\right).$

9. $y = ae^{(2+\sqrt{3})x} + be^{(2-\sqrt{3})x} + 8\cos 2x - 3\sin 2x$
$$+ x + 4 + 4e^{-x/2}.$$

10. $y = ae^{2x} + be^{-2x} - \dfrac{1}{3}e^x - \dfrac{1}{8}\sin 2x - \dfrac{1}{16}\cos 2x - \dfrac{1}{8}.$

11. $y = (a + bx)e^{-x} + x - 2x + 2.$

12. $y = ae^{-x} + be^{-4x} + \dfrac{1}{4}\left(\dfrac{11}{2} - 2x\right).$

18.9. The following two sections will give us formulae which will be helpful in finding particular integrals of the differential equations of the form
$$f(D)\,y = e^{ax}\,V, \quad f(D)\,y = xV,$$
where V is a function of x.

18.91. *To show that*
$$\frac{1}{f(D)}e^{ax}\,V = e^{ax}\,\frac{1}{f(D+a)}V,$$

where V is a function of x.

We consider any function V_1 of x to be later on determined in terms of the given function V.

We have
$$D(e^{ax}\,V_1) = e^{ax}\,DV_1 + ae^{ax}\,V_1 = e^{ax}(D+a)\,V_1.$$
In general, by the Leibnitz's Theorem of Differential Calculus,
$$D'(e^{ax}\,V_1) = e^{ax}\,D^r V_1 + {}^rC_1\,ae^{ax}\,D^{r-1}V_1 + {}^rC_2\,a^2 e^{ax}\,D^{r-2}V_2$$
$$+ \ldots + \ldots + a^r e^{ax}\,V_1$$
$$= e^{ax}(D^r + {}^rC_1\,aD^{r-1} + {}^rC_2\,a^2 D^{r-2} + \ldots + a^r)\,V_1$$
$$= e^{ax}(D+a)^r\,V_1$$
$$\therefore\quad f(D)\,e^{ax}\,V_1 = (D^n + a_1 D^{n-1} + a_2 D^{n-2} + a_3 D^{n-3}$$
$$+ \ldots + a_r D^{n-r} + \ldots + a_{n-1}D + a_n)\,e^{ax}\,V_1$$
$$= e^{ax}[(D+a)^n + a_1(D+a)^{n-1} + \ldots$$
$$+ a_r(D+a)^{n-r} + \ldots + a_n]\,V_1$$
$$= e^{ax}\,f(D+a)\,V_1.$$

$$\therefore \quad f(D)\, e^{ax}\, V_1 = e^{ax}\, f(D+a)\, V_1. \qquad \ldots(1)$$

Suppose, now that V_1 is given by

$$f(D+a)\, V_1 = V \implies V_1 = \frac{1}{f(D+a)}\, V. \qquad \ldots(2)$$

From (1) and (2),

$$f(D)\, e^{ax}\, \frac{1}{f(D+a)}\, V = e^{ax}\, V.$$

Operating by $\dfrac{1}{f(D)}$ on both sides, we obtain

$$e^{ax}\, \frac{1}{f(D+a)}\, V = \frac{1}{f(D)}\, e^{ax}\, V.$$

Thus we have the given result.

EXAMPLES

1. *Solve* $\dfrac{d^2 y}{dx^2} - 2\dfrac{dy}{dx} + 4y = e^x \cos x.$

(*Jabalpur, 1998; Bhopal, 1995; Rohilkhand, 2002*)

We have

$$(D^2 - 2D + 4)\, y = e^x \cos x.$$

Now the roots of $D^2 - 2D + 4 = 0$ are $1 \pm \sqrt{3}\, i$, so that

$$\text{C.F.} = e^x\, (c_1 \cos \sqrt{3}\, x + c_2 \sin \sqrt{3}\, x).$$

Again $\text{P.I.} = \dfrac{1}{D^2 - 2D + 4}\, e^x \cos x$

$$= e^x\, \frac{1}{(D+1)^2 - 2(D+1) + 4}\, \cos x$$

$$= e^x\, \frac{1}{D^2 + 3}\, \cos x = e^x\, \frac{1}{(-1^2) + 3}\, \cos x$$

$$= \frac{1}{2}\, e^x \cos x.$$

$$\therefore \qquad y = e^x\, (c_1 \cos \sqrt{3}\, x + c_2 \sin \sqrt{3}\, x) + \frac{1}{2}\, e^x \cos x.$$

2. *Solve* : $\dfrac{d^2 y}{dx^2} - 2\dfrac{dy}{dx} + y = x^2 e^{3x}.$

(*Rohilkhand, 1997; Indore, 1996, 2000; Jiwaji, 1995;
Vikram, 1995; Bilaspur, 1999; Sagar, 1999*)

Here $C.F. = (c_1 + c_2 x) e^x.$

Now, $P.I. = \dfrac{1}{(D-1)^2} x^2 e^{3x}$

$= e^{3x} \dfrac{1}{(D+3-1)^2} x^2$

$= e^{3x} \cdot \dfrac{1}{(D+2)^2} x^2$

$= \dfrac{e^{3x}}{4} \left\{ \left(1 + \dfrac{D}{2}\right)^{-2} \right\} x^2$

$= \dfrac{e^{3x}}{4} \left\{ 1 - 2\left(\dfrac{D}{2}\right) + 3\left(\dfrac{D^2}{4}\right) - ..... \right\} x^2$

$= \dfrac{e^{3x}}{4} \left(1 - D + \dfrac{3}{4} D^2 - ..... \right) x^2$

$= \dfrac{e^{3x}}{4} \left(x^2 - 2x + \dfrac{3}{4} \cdot 2 \right)$

$= \dfrac{1}{8} e^{3x} (2x^2 - 4x + 3).$

Hence general solution is

$$y = (c_1 + c_2 x) e^x + \dfrac{1}{8} e^{3x} (2x^2 - 4x + 3).$$

3. Solve : $(D^4 + D^2 + 1) y = e^{-x/2} \cos \dfrac{\sqrt{3}}{2} x.$

Auxiliary equation is

$m^4 + m^2 + 1 = 0$

or $(m^2 + m + 1)(m^2 - m + 1) = 0$

$\therefore \quad m = -\dfrac{1}{2} \pm i \dfrac{\sqrt{3}}{2}; \dfrac{1}{2} \pm i \dfrac{\sqrt{3}}{2}.$

$\therefore \quad C.F. = e^{x/2} \left(c_1 \cos \dfrac{\sqrt{3}}{2} x + c_2 \sin \dfrac{\sqrt{3}}{2} x \right)$

$$+ e^{-x/2} \left(c_3 \cos \dfrac{\sqrt{3}}{2} x + c_4 \sin \dfrac{\sqrt{3}}{2} x \right).$$

$P.I. = \dfrac{1}{D^4 + D^2 + 1} \cdot e^{-x/2} \cos \dfrac{\sqrt{3}}{2} x$

$$= e^{-x/2} \left[\cfrac{1}{\left(D - \cfrac{1}{2} \right)^4 + \left(D - \cfrac{1}{2} \right)^2 + 1} \right] \cos \frac{\sqrt{3}}{2} x$$

$$= e^{-x/2} \left[\cfrac{1}{D^4 - 4D^3 \cdot \cfrac{1}{2} + 6D^2 \cdot \cfrac{1}{4} - 4D \cdot \cfrac{1}{8} + \cfrac{1}{16} + D^2 - D + \cfrac{1}{4} + 1} \right]$$
$$\times \cos \frac{\sqrt{3}}{2} x$$

$$= e^{-x/2} \left[\cfrac{1}{D^4 - 2D^3 + \cfrac{5}{2} D^2 - \cfrac{3}{2} D + \cfrac{21}{16}} \right] \cos \frac{\sqrt{3}}{2} x.$$

Putting $D^2 = -3/4$ the denominator vanishes, and as such we write it as $(D^2 + 3/4)(D^2 - 2D + 7/4)$ in which we shall put $D^2 = -3/4$ in the second bracket which becomes $(1 - 2D)$ (Method in next article).

$$\text{P.I.} = e^{-x/2} \left[\cfrac{1}{(D^2 + 3/4)(1 - 2D)} \right] \cos \frac{\sqrt{3}}{2} x$$

$$= e^{-x/2} \left[\cfrac{1 + 2D}{(D^2 + 3/4)(1 - 4D^2)} \right] \cos \frac{\sqrt{3}}{2} x$$

$$= e^{-x/2} \left[\cfrac{\cos \cfrac{\sqrt{3}}{2} x - 2 \cdot \cfrac{\sqrt{3}}{2} \sin \cfrac{\sqrt{3}}{2} x}{(D^2 + 3/4)(1 + 3)} \right]$$

$$= \frac{1}{4} e^{-x/2} \left[\cfrac{\cos \cfrac{\sqrt{3}}{2} x - \sqrt{3} \sin \cfrac{\sqrt{3}}{2} x}{(D^2 + 3/4)} \right]$$

$$= \frac{1}{4} e^{-x/2} \left[\frac{x}{2} \int \cos \frac{\sqrt{3}}{2} x \, dx - \sqrt{3} \cdot \frac{x}{2} \int \sin \frac{\sqrt{3}}{2} x \, dx \right]$$

$$= \frac{1}{8} x e^{-x/2} \left[\frac{2}{\sqrt{3}} \sin \frac{\sqrt{3}}{2} x + \sqrt{3} \cdot \frac{2}{\sqrt{3}} \cos \frac{\sqrt{3}}{2} x \right]$$

$$= \frac{1}{4\sqrt{3}} x e^{-x/2} \left[\sin \frac{\sqrt{3}}{2} x + \sqrt{3} \cos \frac{\sqrt{3}}{2} x \right].$$

Hence general solution is

$$y = e^{x/2} \left(c_1 \cos \frac{\sqrt{3}}{2} x + c_2 \sin \frac{\sqrt{3}}{2} x \right)$$

$$+ e^{-x/2} \left(c_3 \cos \frac{\sqrt{3}}{2} x + c_4 \sin \frac{\sqrt{3}}{2} x \right)$$

$$+ \frac{1}{4\sqrt{3}} x e^{-x/2} \left(\sin \frac{\sqrt{3}}{2} x + \sqrt{3} \cos \frac{\sqrt{3}}{2} x \right).$$

4. *Solve* $(D^2 - 1) y = \cosh x \cos x.$ *(Ravishankar, 1995, 97S)*

Here   C.F. $= C_1 e^x + C_2 e^{-x}$

and   P.I. $= \dfrac{1}{D^2 - 1} (\cosh x \cos x)$

$$= \frac{1}{D^2 - 1} \left[\frac{e^x + e^{-x}}{2} \cos x \right]$$

$$= \frac{1}{2} \frac{1}{D^2 - 1} e^x \cos x + \frac{1}{2} \frac{1}{D^2 - 1} e^{-x} \cos x \qquad ...(i)$$

Now $\dfrac{1}{D^2 - 1} e^x \cos x = e^x \dfrac{1}{(D+1)^2 - 1} \cos x$

$$= e^x \cdot \frac{1}{(D^2 + 2D)} \cos x + e^x \cdot \frac{1}{-1 + 2D} \cos x$$

$$\text{[Putting } D^2 = -1.]$$

$$= e^x \cdot \frac{1}{4D^2 - 1} (2D + 1) \cos x$$

$$= e^x \cdot \frac{1}{\{4(-1) - 1\}} (-2 \sin x + \cos x)$$

$$\text{[Putting } D^2 = -1.]$$

$$= \frac{1}{5} e^x (-2 \sin x + \cos x)$$

$$= (2 \sin x - \cos x) \frac{1}{5} e^x.$$

Similarly we can prove that

$$\frac{1}{D^2 - 1} e^{-x} \cos x = -\frac{e^{-x}}{5} (2 \sin x + \cos x).$$

$\therefore$ From (i)

$$P.I. = \frac{1}{2}(2\sin x + \cos x)\frac{1}{5}e^x - \frac{1}{2}\cdot\frac{1}{5}e^{-x}(2\sin x + \cos x)$$

$$= \frac{1}{5}(e^x - e^{-x})\sin x - \frac{1}{5}\left(\frac{e^x + e^{-x}}{2}\right)\cos x$$

$$= \frac{2}{5}\sinh x \sin x - \frac{1}{5}\cosh x \cos x.$$

Hence the required solution is $y = $ C.F. + P.I.

or $y = C_1 e^x + C_2 e^{-x} + \dfrac{2}{5}\sinh x \sin x - \dfrac{1}{5}\cosh x \cos x.$

5. *Solve* $(D + 1)^3 y = x^2 e^{-x}.$ (*Vikram, 1994; Bhopal, 1999*)

Here the auxiliary equation is $(m + 1)^3 = 0$ or $m = -1$ thrice.

$\therefore$ C.F. $= (C_1 x^2 + C_2 x + C_3)\, e^{-x}$, where C_1, C_2 and C_3 are arbitrary constants

and $P.I. = \dfrac{1}{(D+1)^3} x^2 e^{-x} = e^{-x} \dfrac{1}{(D-1+1)^3} x^2 = e^{-x}\dfrac{1}{D^3}x^2$

$$= e^{-x}\frac{1}{D^2}\int x^2\, dx = e^{-x}\frac{1}{D^2}\left(\frac{1}{3}x^3\right) = \frac{1}{3}e^{-x}\frac{1}{D}\int x^3\, dx$$

$$= \frac{1}{3}e^{-x}\frac{1}{D}\left(\frac{1}{4}x^4\right) = \frac{1}{12}e^{-x}\int x^4\, dx = \frac{1}{60}e^{-x}x^5.$$

$\therefore$ The required solution is $y = $ C.F. + P.I.

or $y = (C_1 x^2 + C_2 x + C_3)\, e^{-x} + \dfrac{1}{60}x^5 e^{-x}.$

6. *Solve* $(D^4 + D^2 + 1) y = ax^2 + be^{-x}\sin 2x.$

(*Ravishankar, 1994; Jiwaji, 1996*)

$$C.F. = e^{-x/2}\left(C_1 \cos\frac{1}{2}x\sqrt{3} + C_2 \sin\frac{1}{2}x\sqrt{3}\right)$$

$$+ e^{x/2}\left(C_3 \cos\frac{1}{2}x\sqrt{3} + C_4 \sin\frac{1}{2}x\sqrt{3}\right)$$

and $P.I. = \dfrac{1}{D^4 + D^2 + 1}(ax^2 + be^{-x}\sin 2x)$

$$= a\cdot\frac{1}{D^4 + D^2 + 1}x^2 + b\cdot\frac{1}{D^4 + D^2 + 1}e^{-x}\sin 2x \qquad ...(i)$$

Now $\dfrac{1}{D^4 + D^2 + 1}x^2 = (1 + D^2 + D^4)^{-1} x^2$

$$= (1 - D^2 + ...) x^2 = x^2 - 2$$

and $\dfrac{1}{D^4 + D^2 + 1} e^{-x} \sin 2x$

$$= e^{-x} \dfrac{1}{\{(D-1)^4 + (D-1)^2 + 1\}} \sin 2x$$

$$= e^{-x} \cdot \dfrac{1}{D^4 - 4D^3 + 7D^2 - 6D + 3} \sin 2x$$

$$= e^{-x} \cdot \dfrac{1}{(-4)^2 - 4(-4)D + 7(-4) - 6D + 3} \sin 2x,$$

Putting $D^2 = -4$

$$= e^{-x} \cdot \dfrac{1}{10D - 9} \sin 2x = e^{-x} \dfrac{1}{(100D^2 - 81)} (10D + 9) \sin 2x$$

$$= -e^x (1/481)(20 \cos 2x + 9 \sin 2x), \qquad [\text{Putting } D^2 = -4.]$$

$\therefore$ The required solution is $y = $ C.F. $+$ P.I.

EXERCISES

Solve

1. $(D^2 + 3D + 2) y = e^{2x} \sin x.$ *(Agra, 2001)*

2. $\dfrac{d^2 y}{dx^2} + 2y = x^2 e^{3x} + e^x \cos 2x.$

3. $(D^3 - D^2 + 3D + 5) = e^x \cos 2x.$

4. $(D^3 - 7D - 6) y = e^{2x} (1 + x).$

5. $(D^2 - 4D + 3) y = e^{2x} \sin 3x.$

6. $(D^2 - D - 6) y = e^{2x} (x - 1).$ *(Indore, 2000)*

7. $(D^2 + 1) y = e^{-x} + \cos x + x^3 + e^x \cos x.$

8. $(D^2 + 1) y = e^{-x} + \cos x + x^3 + e^x \sin x.$

                                      (Bhopal, 1995; Jiwaji, 1995)

9. $(D^3 + 1) y = e^{2x} \sin x + e^{x/2} \sin\left(\dfrac{\sqrt{3}}{2} x\right).$

10. $(D^3 - D^2 + 3D + 5) y = x^2 + e^x \cos 2x.$

ANSWERS

1. $y = ae^{-2x} + be^{-x} + \dfrac{1}{170} (11 \sin x - 7 \cos x) e^{2x}.$

2. $y = a \cos \sqrt{2} \, x + b \sin \sqrt{2} \, x - \dfrac{1}{17} (\cos 2x - 4 \sin 2x) e^x$

$$+ \dfrac{1}{11} (x^2 - 12x/11 + 50/121) e^{3x}.$$

3. $y = ae^{-x} + (b\cos 2x + c\sin 2x)\,e^x - \dfrac{1}{16}\,xe^x\,(\cos 2x - \sin 2x).$

4. $y = ae^{-x} + be^{3x} + ce^{-2x} - \dfrac{1}{12}\,(17/12 + x)\,e^{2x}.$

5. $y = ae^x + be^{3x} - \dfrac{1}{10}\,e^{2x}\sin 3x.$

6. $y = ae^{2x} + e^{-x}\,(b\cos x\sqrt{2} + c\sin x\sqrt{2})$
$$+ \dfrac{1}{121}\,e^{2x}\left(\dfrac{11}{2}x^2 - 17x\right).$$

7. $y = a\cos x + b\sin x + \dfrac{1}{2}e^{-x} + \dfrac{1}{2}x\sin x + x^3 - 6x$
$$+ \dfrac{1}{5}e^x\,(2\sin x + \cos x).$$

8. $y = a\cos x + b\sin x + \dfrac{1}{2}e^{-x} + \dfrac{1}{2}x\sin x + x^3 - 6x$
$$- \dfrac{1}{5}e^x\,(2\cos x - \sin x).$$

9. $y = ae^{-x} + e^{x/2}\left(b\cos\dfrac{\sqrt{3}}{2}x + c\sin\dfrac{\sqrt{3}}{2}x\right)$
$$- \dfrac{1}{6}\,xe^{x/2}\left(\sin\dfrac{\sqrt{3}}{2}x + \sqrt{3}\cos\dfrac{\sqrt{3}}{2}x\right).$$

10. $y = ae^{-x} + e^x\,(b\cos 2x + c\sin 2x) + \dfrac{1}{16}\,xe^x\,(\sin 2x - \cos 2x).$

18.92. Two special cases :

To evaluate $\dfrac{1}{f(D)}e^{ax}$, when $f(D) = 0$ and $\dfrac{1}{f(D^2)}\sin ax$ or $\cos ax$, when $f(-a^2) = 0$, then methods of § 18.81 and § 1882 do not apply. To find the values of P.I., we will follow the following method :

(i) **To evaluate** $\dfrac{1}{f(D)}e^{ax}$, **when** $f(D) = 0.$

In this case, if we calculate P.I. by previous method, then
$$\text{P.I.} = \dfrac{1}{f(D)}e^{ax} = \dfrac{1}{f(a)}e^{ax} = \dfrac{e^{ax}}{0},$$
hence this method fails.

Now, since a is a root of $f(D)$, $(D - a)$ must be a factor of $f(D)$ which can be written in the form $(D - a)\,\phi(D).$

$$\therefore \quad \text{P.I.} = \frac{1}{(D-a)\,\phi\,(D)}\,e^{ax}$$

$$= \frac{1}{(D-a)\,\phi\,(a)}\,e^{ax} \text{ where } \phi\,(a) \text{ is now a constant only.}$$

$$= \frac{1}{\phi\,(a)} \cdot \frac{e^{ax}\cdot 1}{(D-a)} = \frac{1}{\phi\,(a)}\,e^{ax} \cdot \frac{1}{(D+a-a)}\cdot 1$$

$$= \frac{1}{\phi\,(a)}\,e^{ax}\left(\frac{1}{D}\right)\cdot 1 = \frac{1}{\phi\,(a)}\,e^{ax}\cdot x.$$

Similarly, if $f\,(D) = (D-a)^p\,\phi\,(D)$ then P.I. of e^{ax} is

$$\frac{e^{ax}}{f\,(D)} = \frac{e^{ax}}{(D-a)^p\,\phi\,(D)} = \frac{e^{ax}\cdot 1}{\phi\,(a)\,(D-a)^p}$$

$$= \frac{e^{ax}}{\phi\,(a)}\cdot\left[\frac{1}{(D+a-a)^p}\right]\cdot 1$$

$$= \frac{e^{ax}}{\phi\,(a)}\left(\frac{1}{D^p}\right)\cdot 1 = \frac{e^{ax}}{\phi\,(a)}\cdot\frac{x^p}{p\,!}.$$

Rule : *Put $D = a$ in those factors of $f\,(D)$ which do not vanish for $D = a$ and then make the question as P.I. of a product of e^{ax} and 1 which is calculated by § 18.91 and reduces to the calculation of $\frac{1}{D}\cdot 1$ or $\frac{1}{D^2}\cdot 1$ or $\frac{1}{D^3}\cdot 1$ and so on which are $x, \frac{x^2}{2\,!}, \frac{x^3}{3\,!}$ respectively.*

EXAMPLES

1. *Solve $\dfrac{d^2 y}{dx^2} + 4\dfrac{dy}{dx} + 4y = 2\sinh 2x.$*

Auxiliary equation is

$$m^2 + 4m + 4 = 0, \text{ i.e., } (m+2)^2 = 0, m = -2, -2.$$

$$\therefore \quad \text{C.F.} = (c_1 + c_2 x)\,e^{-2x}$$

$$\text{P.I.} = \frac{1}{(D+2)^2}\,e^{2x} - e^{-2x} = \frac{1}{(D+2)^2}\,e^{2x} - \frac{1}{(D+2)^2}\,e^{-2x}$$

$$= \frac{1}{(2+2)^2}\,e^{2x} - e^{-2x}\frac{1}{(D-2+2)^2}\cdot 1$$

$$= \frac{1}{16}\,e^{2x} - e^{-2x}\cdot\frac{1}{D^2}\cdot 1 = \frac{1}{16}\,e^{2x} - e^{-2x}\cdot\frac{x^2}{2\,!}$$

$$= \frac{1}{16}\,e^{2x} - \frac{1}{2}\,e^{-2x}x^2.$$

$\therefore$ General solution of the equation is

$$y = (c_1 + c_2 x)\, e^{-2x} + \frac{1}{16} e^{2x} - \frac{1}{2} x^2 e^{-2x}.$$

2. *Solve* $(D^3 + 3D^2 + 3D + 1)\, y = e^{-x}$.   (*Bilaspur, 1997*)

Auxiliary equation is

$$(m + 1)^3 = 0 \quad \text{or} \quad m = -1, -1, -1.$$

$\therefore$ C.F. $= (c_1 + c_2 x + c_3 x^2)\, e^{-x}$.

$$\text{P.I.} = \frac{1}{(D+1)^3} e^{-x} = e^{-x} \cdot \frac{1}{(D-1+1)^3} \cdot 1$$

$$= e^{-x} \cdot \frac{1}{D^3} \cdot 1 = e^{-x} \cdot \frac{x^3}{3!}.$$

$\therefore$ General solution is

$$y = (c_1 + c_2 x + c_3 x^2)\, e^{-x} - \frac{1}{6} x^3 e^{-x}.$$

3. $(D^2 - 3D + 2)\, y = \cosh x$.

Here the auxiliary equation is $m^2 - 3m + 2 = 0$.

$\therefore$ C.F. $= C_1 e^x + C_2 e^{2x}$, where C_1 and C_2 are arbitrary constants

and $$\text{P.I.} = \frac{1}{D^2 - 3D + 2} \cosh x = \frac{1}{D^2 - 3D + 2} \left(\frac{e^x + e^{-x}}{2} \right)$$

$$= \frac{1}{2} \cdot \frac{1}{D^2 - 3D + 2} e^x + \frac{1}{2} \cdot \frac{1}{D^2 - 3D + 2} e^{-x}$$

$$= \frac{1}{2} e^x \frac{1}{(D+1)^2 - 3(D+1) + 2} 1$$

$$+ \frac{1}{2} \frac{1}{(-1)^2 - 3(-1) + 2} e^{-x}$$

$$= \frac{1}{2} e^x \frac{1}{D^2 - D} 1 + \frac{1}{12} e^{-x}$$

$$= -\frac{1}{2} e^x \frac{1}{D} (1 - D)^{-1} 1 + \frac{1}{12} e^{-x}$$

$$= -\frac{1}{2} e^x \frac{1}{D} (1 + D + \ldots) 1 + \frac{1}{12} e^{-x}$$

$$= -\frac{1}{2} e^x \frac{1}{D} (1) + \frac{1}{12} e^{-x} = -\frac{1}{2} e^x x + \frac{1}{12} e^{-x}.$$

$\therefore$ The required solution is $y = $ C.F. + P.I.

or $$y = c_1 e^x + c_2 e^{2x} - \frac{1}{2} x e^x + \frac{1}{12} e^{-x}.$$

4. *Solve* $(D^3 - 3D^2 + 4D - 2) y = e^x + \cos x$.

Its auxiliary equation is $m^3 - 3m^2 + 4m - 2 = 0$

or $(m - 1) (m^2 - 2m + 2) = 0$ or $m = 1, 1 \pm i$.

$\therefore$ C.F. $= C_1 e^x + e^x (C_2 \cos x + C_3 \sin x)$, where C_1, C_2 and C_3 are arbitrary constants,

and   P.I. $= \dfrac{1}{D^3 - 3D^2 + 4D - 2} (e^x + \cos x)$

$= \dfrac{1}{D^3 - 3D^2 + 4D - 2} e^x + \dfrac{1}{D^3 - 3D^2 + 4D - 2} \cos x$

$= e^x \dfrac{1}{(D+1)^3 - 3(D+1)^2 + 4(D+1) - 2} 1$

$\qquad - \dfrac{1}{D(-1^2) - 3(-1^2) + 4D - 2} \cos x$

$= e^x \dfrac{1}{D^3 + D} 1 + \dfrac{1}{3D + 1} \cos x$

$= e^x \dfrac{1}{D} (1 + D^2)^{-1} 1 + \dfrac{(3D - 1)}{9D^2 - 1} \cos x$

$= e^x \dfrac{1}{D} (1 - D^2 + ...) 1 + \dfrac{(3D - 1)}{-9 - 1} \cos x$

$= e^x \displaystyle\int dx - (1/10) (3D - 1) \cos x$

$= e^x x + (1/10) (3 \sin x + \cos x)$.

$\therefore$ Required solution is

$y = C_1 e^x + e^x (C_2 \cos x + C_3 \sin x) + xe^x$

$\qquad\qquad\qquad\qquad\qquad + (1/10) (3 \sin x + \cos x)$.

(ii) To evaluate $\dfrac{1}{f(D^2)}$ **sin** ax **or cos** ax, **when** $f(-a^2) = 0$.

In such cases instead of calculating P.I. for $\sin ax$ or $\cos ax$ we shall calculate P.I. for e^{iax}

$\qquad\qquad e^{iax} = \cos ax + i \sin ax$

Thus   P.I. for e^{iax} = P.I. for $(\cos ax + i \sin ax)$.

$\therefore$ **Real part of P.I. for** e^{iax} = **P.I. for cos** ax

and   **Imaginary part of P.I. for** e^{iax} = **P.I. for sin** ax.

$\therefore$ $\dfrac{\cos ax}{D^2 + a^2}$ **and** $\dfrac{\sin ax}{D^2 + a^2}$ are respectively real and imaginary parts

of $\dfrac{e^{iax}}{D^2 + a^2}$

$$= \frac{e^{iax}}{(D + ai)(D - ai)} = \frac{e^{aix}}{(ai + ai)(D - ai)}$$

$$= \frac{e^{iax}}{2ai} \left(\frac{1}{D + ai - ai} \right) \cdot 1$$

$$= \frac{e^{iax}}{2ai} \cdot \frac{1}{D} \cdot 1 = \frac{x}{2ai} (e^{aix})$$

$$= -\frac{ix (\cos ax + i \sin ax)}{2a}$$

$$= -\frac{ix}{2a} \cos ax + \frac{x}{2a} \sin ax.$$

$\therefore$ **Real part** $= \dfrac{x}{2a} \sin ax = \dfrac{\cos ax}{D^2 + a^2}$ (*Jiwaji, 1996, 98*)

Imaginary part $= \dfrac{x}{2a} \cos ax = \dfrac{\sin ax}{D^2 + a^2}.$

EXAMPLES

1. *Solve* : $(D^2 + 4) y = \cos 2x + \sin 2x.$ (*Kumaon, 2001*)

C.F. $= c_1 \cos 2x + c_2 \sin 2x.$

P.I. $= \dfrac{1}{D^2 + 4} \cos 2x + \sin 2x.$

To determine it let us find the P.I. of e^{2ix}, *i.e.*,

$$\frac{1}{D^2 + 4} e^{2ix}$$

$$= \frac{1}{(D + 2i)(D - 2i)} e^{2ix}$$

$$= \frac{1}{4i} e^{2ix} \cdot \frac{1}{D + 2i - 2i} \cdot 1$$

$$= \frac{1}{4i} e^{2ix} \frac{1}{D} \cdot 1$$

$$= \frac{xe^{2ix}}{4i} = -\frac{ix}{4} e^{2ix} = -\frac{ix}{4} (\cos 2x + i \sin 2x)$$

$$= -\frac{ix}{4} \cos 2x + \frac{x}{4} \sin 2x \qquad \qquad \dots(i)$$

Hence P.I. for $\cos 2x$ is the real part of $(i) = \dfrac{x}{4} \sin 2x$ and P.I. for $\sin 2x$

is the imaginary part of $(i) = -\dfrac{1}{4} x \cos 2x.$

Hence   P.I. $= \dfrac{1}{4}\, x \sin 2x - \dfrac{1}{4}\, x \cos 2x$

$\qquad\qquad = \dfrac{1}{4}\, x\,(\sin 2x - \cos 2x)$.

The general solution is

$$y = c_1 \cos 2x + c_2 \sin 2x + \dfrac{1}{4}\, x\,(\sin 2x - \cos 2x).$$

2. *Solve* : $(D^3 + a^2 D)\, y = \sin ax$.   (*Jabalpur, 1994; Rewa, 1993*)

Auxiliary equation is $m^3 + a^2 m = 0$ or $m = 0, \pm\, ai$.

$\therefore$ C.F. $= c_1 + c_2 \cos ax + c_3 \sin ax$

$$\text{P.I.} = \dfrac{1}{D\,(D^2 + a^2)} \sin ax = \dfrac{1}{(D^2 + a^2)} \int \sin ax\; dx$$

$$= -\,\dfrac{1}{a}\, \dfrac{1}{(D^2 + a^2)} \cos ax\; dx = -\,\dfrac{1}{a}\cdot \dfrac{x}{2} \int \cos ax\; dx$$

$$= -\,\dfrac{x}{2a^2} \sin ax.$$

Hence general solution is

$$c_1 + c_2 \cos ax + c_3 \sin ax - \dfrac{x}{2a^2} \sin ax.$$

EXERCISES

Solve the following differential equations :

1. $\dfrac{d^2 y}{dx^2} - 3\dfrac{dy}{dx} + 2y = e^x$.   (*Sagar, 1996; Vikram, 1998*)

2. $(D^3 - 3D^2 + 3D - 1)\, y = xe^x + e^x$.

3. $(D^2 - 3D + 2)\, y = 6e^{2x} + \sin 2x$. (*Bhopal, 1995, 97; Jabalpur, 1999*)

4. $(D^2 - 1)\, y = \cosh x$.

5. $(D - 1)^2 (D^2 + 1)^2\, y = e^x$.

6. $(D^2 - a^2)\, y = \cosh ax$.

7. $(D^2 + 4)\, y = e^x + \sin 2x$.

8. $(D^2 + 4)\, y = \sin^2 x$.   (*Ravishankar, 1999; Jiwaji, 1999*)

9. $\dfrac{d^2 y}{dx^2} + a^2 y = \cos ax$.   (*Vikram, 1999*)

10. $\dfrac{d^2 y}{dx^2} + a^2 y = \sin ax$.   (*Bhopal, 1997; Vikram, 1998;*
                                        Ravishankar, 1999; Jiwaji, 2000)

ANSWERS

1. $y = a e^x + b e^{2x} - x e^x$.

2. $y = (ax^2 + bx + c) e^x + \dfrac{1}{24} (x^4 + 4x^3) e^x$.

3. $y = a e^x + b e^{2x} + \dfrac{1}{20} (3 \cos 2x - \sin 2x)$.

4. $y = a e^x + b e^{-x} + \dfrac{1}{2} x \sinh x$.

5. $y = (a + bx) e^x + (c + dx) \cos x + (e + fx) \sin x + \dfrac{1}{8} x^2 e^x$.

6. $y = a e^{ax} + b e^{-ax} + \left(\dfrac{x}{2a} \right) \sinh ax$.

7. $y = (a \cos 2x + b \sin 2x) + \dfrac{1}{5} e^x - \dfrac{1}{4} x \cos 2x$.

8. $y = a \cos 2x + b \sin 2x + \dfrac{1}{8} - \dfrac{1}{8} x \sin 2x$.

9. $y = c_1 \sin ax + c_2 \cos ax + \dfrac{x}{2a} \sin ax$.

10. $y = c_1 \sin ax + c_2 \cos ax - \dfrac{x}{2a} \cos ax$.

18.93. *To show that*

$$\frac{1}{f(D)} xV = \left[x - \frac{1}{f(D)} f'(D) \right] \frac{1}{f(D)} V.$$

Here also we start with a function V_1 of x to be determined later on in terms of V.

We have

$$D(xV_1) = xDV_1 + V_1 = xDV_1 + (D)' V_1,$$

$$D^2(xV_1) = xD^2V_1 + 2DV_1 = xD^2V_1 + (D^2)' V_1, \text{ etc.}$$

In general,

$$D^r(xV_1) = xD^rV_1 + rD^{r-1}V_1 = xD^rV_1 + (D^r)' V_1.$$

$$\therefore \quad f(D) xV_1 = (D^n + a_1 D^{n-1} + a_2 D^{n-2} + \dots + a_r D^{n-r} + \dots$$

$$+ a_{n-1}D + a_n) xV_1$$

$$= x f(D) V_1 + f(D) V_1. \qquad \qquad ...(1)$$

We, now, determine V_1 such that

$$f(D) V_1 = V \Rightarrow V_1 = \frac{1}{f(D)} V. \qquad \qquad ...(2)$$

From (1) and (2), we have

$$f(D) \, x \, \frac{1}{f(D)} \, V = xV + f'(D) \, \frac{1}{f(D)} \, V.$$

Operating with $1/f(D)$, we obtain

$$x \, \frac{1}{f(D)} \, V = \frac{1}{f(D)} \, xV + \frac{1}{f(D)} \, f'(D) \, \frac{1}{f(D)} \, V.$$

$$\therefore \quad \frac{1}{f(D)} \, xV = x \, \frac{1}{f(D)} \, V - \frac{1}{f(D)} \, f'(D) \, \frac{1}{f(D)} \, V$$

$$= \left[x - \frac{1}{f(D)} \, f'(D) \right] \frac{1}{f(D)} \, V.$$

EXAMPLES

1. *Solve* $\dfrac{d^2 y}{dx^2} + 4y = x \sin x.$

(Ravishankar, 1996; Bilaspur, 1996; Vikram, 1997)

We have

$$(D^2 + 4) \, y = x \sin x.$$

Since the roots of $D^2 + 4 = 0$ are $\pm 2i$, we have

C.F. $= c_1 \cos 2x + c_2 \sin 2x.$

$$\text{P.I.} = \frac{1}{D^2 + 4} \, x \sin 2x$$

$$= \left(x - \frac{1}{D^2 + 4} \, 2D \right) \frac{1}{D^2 + 4} \sin x$$

$$= \left(x - \frac{1}{D^2 + 4} \, 2D \right) \frac{1}{3} \sin x$$

$$= \frac{x}{3} \sin x - \frac{2}{3} \cdot \frac{1}{D^2 + 4} \cos x$$

$$= \frac{x}{3} \sin x - \frac{2}{9} \cos x$$

$$\therefore \quad y = c_1 \cos 2x + c_2 \sin 2x + \frac{1}{3} \, x \sin x - \frac{2}{9} \cos x.$$

2. *Solve* $\dfrac{d^4 y}{dx^4} - y = x^2 \sin x.$

We have

$$(D^4 - 1) \, y = x^2 \sin x.$$

The C.F., as may easily be seen, is

$$c_1 e^x + c_2 e^{-x} + c_3 \cos x + c_4 \sin x.$$

Again

$$\text{P.I.} = \frac{1}{D^4 - 1} x^2 \sin x$$

$$x^2 \sin x = x (x \sin x),$$

and apply the result obtained above by taking $V = x \sin x$. This process, however, becomes very tedious. The following process is comparatively shorter.

We have

$$\text{P.I.} = \text{Imaginary part of } \frac{1}{D^4 - 1} x^2 e^{ix}.$$

Now

$$\frac{1}{D^4 - 1} x^2 e^{ix} = e^{ix} \frac{1}{(D + i)^4 - 1} x^2$$

$$= e^{ix} \frac{1}{D^4 + 4D^3 i - 6D^2 - 4Di} x^2$$

$$= e^{ix} \frac{1}{-4Di} \left[1 + \frac{-6D + 4D^2 i + D^3}{4i} \right]^{-1} x^2$$

$$= -\frac{e^{ix}}{4i} \frac{1}{D} \left[1 + \frac{-6D + 4D^2 i + D^3}{4i} \right.$$

$$\left. + \left(\frac{-6D + ...}{4i} \right)^2 \right] x^2$$

$$= i \frac{e^{ix}}{4} \frac{1}{D} \left[1 - \frac{3D}{2i} - \frac{5}{4} D^2 ..... \right] x^2$$

$$= \frac{i}{4} e^{ix} \frac{1}{D} \left[x^2 + 3ix - \frac{5}{2} \right]$$

$$= \frac{i}{4} e^{ix} \left[\frac{x^3}{3} + \frac{3i}{2} x^2 - \frac{5}{2} x \right]$$

$$= \frac{i \cos x - \sin x}{4} \left(\frac{x^3}{3} + \frac{3i}{2} x^2 - \frac{5}{2} x \right)$$

whose imaginary part is

$$\frac{\cos x}{4} \left(\frac{x^3}{3} - \frac{5}{2} x \right) - \frac{3}{8} x^2 \sin x.$$

$$\therefore \quad y = c_1 e^x + c_2 e^{-x} + c_3 \cos x + c_4 \sin x$$

$$+ \frac{\cos x}{4}\left(\frac{x^3}{\lfloor 3} - \frac{5}{2}x\right) - \frac{3}{8}x^2 \sin x$$

3. *Solve* : $\dfrac{d^2 y}{dx^2} + 2\dfrac{dy}{dx} + y = x \cos x.$

(*Rohilkhand, 2000; Jiwaji, 1998; Bilaspur, 2000*)

Auxiliary equation is $m^2 + 2m + 1 = 0$ or $m = -1, -1.$

$\therefore \qquad$ C.F. $= (c_1 + c_2 x)\, e^{-x}.$

Now, $\quad$ P.I. $= \dfrac{1}{D^2 + 2D + 1}\, x \cos x$

$$= x \cdot \frac{1}{D^2 + 2D + 1}\cos x - \frac{2D + 2}{(D^2 + 2D + 1)^2}\cos x$$

$$= x \cdot \frac{1}{2D}\cdot \cos x - \frac{2D + 2}{4D^2}\cos x$$

$$= \frac{x}{2}\sin x + \frac{(D+1)}{2}\cos x$$

$$= \frac{x}{2}\sin x + \frac{\cos x}{2} - \frac{\sin x}{2}.$$

Therefore the complete solution is

$$y = (c_1 + c_2 x)\, e^{-x} + \frac{1}{2}x \sin \cdot + \frac{1}{2}\cos x - \frac{1}{2}\sin x.$$

4. *Solve* : $(D^4 + 2D^2 + 1)\, y = x^2 \cos x.$

(*Lucknow, 1995; Ravishankar, 1998; Gorakhpur, 2000*)

Auxiliary equation is $(m^2 + 1)^2 = 0 \; \therefore \; m = \pm i, \pm i.$

$\therefore \quad$ C.F. $= (c_1 + c_2 x)\cos x + (c_3 + c_4 x)\sin x.$

P.I. of $x^2 \cos x$ is real part of

$$\frac{1}{(D^2 + 1)^2}\, x^2 e^{ix}$$

$$= e^{ix}\frac{1}{[(D+i)^2 + 1]^2}\, x^2 = e^{ix}\frac{1}{(D^2 + 2Di)^2}\, x^2$$

$$= \frac{e^{ix}}{4D^2 i^2}\left(1 + \frac{D}{2i}\right)^{-2} x^2$$

$$= -\frac{e^{ix}}{4D^2}\left(1 - \frac{D}{2}i\right)^{-2} x^2$$

$$= -\frac{e^{ix}}{4D^2}\left(1 + 2\cdot\frac{D}{2}i + \frac{3}{4}D^2 i^2 + \dots\right) x^2$$

$$= -\frac{e^{ix}}{4D^2}\left[\left(x^2 - \frac{3}{2}\right) + 2x \cdot i\right]$$

$$= -\frac{e^{ix}}{4D}\left[\left(\frac{x^3}{3} - \frac{3}{2}x\right) + x^2 \cdot i\right]$$

$$= -\frac{\cos x + i \sin x}{4}\cdot\left[\left(\frac{x^4}{12} - \frac{3}{4}x^2\right) + \frac{x^3}{3}i\right].$$

Taking the real part, we get

$$\text{P.I.} = -\frac{1}{4}\left[\left(\frac{x^4 - 9x^2}{12}\right)\cos x - \frac{x^3}{3}\sin x\right].$$

$\therefore$ General solution is

$$y = (c_1 + c_2 x)\cos x + (c_3 + c_4 x)\sin x$$

$$-\frac{1}{4}\left[\frac{1}{12}(x^4 - 9x^2)\cos x - \frac{1}{3}x^3 \sin x\right].$$

5. *Solve* : $(D^2 - 4D + 4)\,y = 8x^2 e^{2x} \sin 2x.$

(Lucknow, 1993, 97; Bhopal, 1996, 98;
Ravishankar, 1995, 97; Sagar, 1998; Garhwal, 2000)

We have

$$\text{C.F.} = (c_1 + c_2 x)\,e^{2x}$$

$$\text{P.I.} = 8\cdot\frac{1}{(D-2)^2}\,e^{2x}\,(x^2 \sin 2x)$$

$$= 8e^{2x}\,\frac{1}{(D + 2 - 2)^2}\,x^2 \sin 2x$$

$$= 8e^{2x}\cdot\frac{1}{D^2}\,(x^2 \sin 2x)$$

$$= 8e^{2x}\cdot\text{I}$$

where $\quad \text{I} = \dfrac{1}{D^2}\,x^2 \sin 2x$

$$= \text{Imaginary part of } \frac{1}{D^2}\,x^2 e^{2ix}$$

$$= \text{I.P. of } e^{2ix}\,\frac{1}{(D + 2i)^2}\,x^2$$

$$= \text{I.P. of } \frac{e^{2ix}}{4i^2}\left(1 + \frac{D}{2i}\right)^{-2} x^2$$

$$= \text{I.P. of } \frac{e^{2ix}}{-4}\left(1 - \frac{iD}{2}\right)^{-2} x^2$$

$$= \text{I.P. of } \frac{e^{2ix}}{-4}\left[1 + 2\cdot\left(\frac{iD}{2}\right) + 3\cdot\left(\frac{iD}{2}\right)^3 + \dots\right] x^2$$

$$= \text{I.P. of } \frac{e^{2ix}}{-4}\left[1 + Di - \frac{3}{4}D^2 + \dots\right] x^2$$

$$= \text{I.P. of } \frac{e^{2ix}}{-4}\left[x^2 + 2xi - \frac{3}{2}\right]$$

$$= \text{I.P. of } -\frac{1}{4}(\cos 2x + i \sin 2x)\left(x^2 + 2xi - \frac{3}{2}\right)$$

$$= -\frac{1}{4}\left[\left(x^2 - \frac{3}{2}\right)\sin 2x + 2x \cos 2x\right]$$

$$= -\frac{1}{8}[(2x^2 - 3)\sin 2x + 4x \cos 2x].$$

$$\therefore \quad \text{P.I.} = 8e^{2x}\cdot I = 8e^{2x}\left[-\frac{1}{8}\{(2x^2 - 3)\sin 2x + 4x \cos 2x\}\right]$$

$$= -e^{2x}[(2x^2 - 3)\sin 2x + 4x \cos 2x].$$

Hence general solution is

$$y = e^{2x}(c_1 + c_2 x + 3 \sin 2x - 2x^2 \sin 2x - 4x \cos 2x).$$

EXERCISES

Solve

1. $(D^2 + 2D + 1)\, y = x \sin x.$

2. $(D^2 + 1)\, y = x^2 \sin 2x.$ *(Vikram, 1996)*

3. $(D - 1)^2\, y = x \sin x.$ *(Vikram, 1996; Sagar, 2000; Kanpur, 2000; Jabalpur, 1998; Agra, 2000)*

4. $(D^2 + D)\, y = x \cos x.$

5. $(D^2 + a^2)\, y = x \cos ax.$

6. $\dfrac{d^2 y}{dx^2} - y = xe^x \sin x.$

7. $\dfrac{d^2 y}{dx^2} - 2\dfrac{dy}{dx} + y = xe^x \sin x.$

(Vikram, 1998; Indore, 1999; Rewa, 1998, 2000; Gorakhpur, 2001; Jiwaji, 1999; Jabalpur, 2000; Rohilkhand, 1999, 2001)

8. $(D^2 - 1)\, y = x \sin x + (1 + x^2)\, e^x.$

ANSWERS

1. $y = (a + bx) e^{-x} + \dfrac{1}{2}(1 - x)\cos x + \dfrac{1}{2}\sin x.$

2. $y = a\cos x + b\sin x - \dfrac{1}{3}\left(x^2 - \dfrac{26}{9}\right)\sin 2x - \dfrac{8}{9}x\cos 2x.$

3. $y = (a + bx) e^{x} + \dfrac{x}{2}\cos x + \dfrac{1}{3}(\cos x - \sin x).$

4. $y = a + be^{-x} + \dfrac{x}{2}(\sin x - \cos x) + \cos x + \dfrac{1}{2}\sin x.$

5. $y = C_1\cos ax + C_2\sin ax + \dfrac{1}{4a^2}(ax^2\sin ax + x\cos ax).$

6. $y = ae^{x} + be^{-x} + \dfrac{1}{25}e^{x}\left[(14 - 5x)\sin x - 2(5x + 1)\cos x\right].$

7. $y = (a + bx - x\sin x - 2\cos x)\,e^{x}.$

8. $y = ae^{x} + be^{-x} - \dfrac{1}{2}(x\sin x + \cos x).$

18.10. Homogeneous Linear Equations. *To solve*

$$x^n \frac{d^n y}{dx^n} + a_1 x^{n-1}\frac{d^{n-1}y}{dx^{n-1}} + a_2 x^{n-2}\frac{d^{n-2}y}{dx^{n-2}} + \ldots\ldots$$

$$+ \ldots\ldots + a_{n-1}x\frac{dy}{dx} + a_n y = X,$$

where a_1, a_2, *etc., are constants and* X *is a function of* x.

The transformation

$$z = \log x \Rightarrow x = e^z,$$

will convert the equation into one with constant coefficients.

We have

$$\frac{dy}{dx} = \frac{dy}{dz}\frac{dz}{dx} = \frac{1}{x}\frac{dy}{dz},$$

$$\frac{d^2y}{dx^2} = \frac{d^2y}{dz^2}\cdot\frac{1}{x^2} - \frac{1}{x^2}\cdot\frac{dy}{dz} = \frac{1}{x^2}\left(\frac{d^2y}{dz^2} - \frac{dy}{dz}\right).$$

Similarly

$$\frac{d^3y}{dx^3} = \left(\frac{d^3y}{dz^3} - 3\frac{d^2y}{dz^2} + 2\frac{dy}{dz}\right)\frac{1}{x^3}.$$

We, now, write

$$D = \frac{d}{dz},$$

so that the above results can be re-written as

$$x \frac{dy}{dx} = Dy,$$

$$x^2 \frac{d^2y}{dx^2} = D(D-1)y,$$

$$x^3 \frac{d^3y}{dx^3} = (D^3 - 3D^2 + 2D)y = D(D-1)(D-2)y.$$

By mathematical induction, we will obtain

$$x^n \frac{d^n y}{dx^n} = D(D-1)(D-2)\ ..... \ (D-n+1) = y.$$

Thus the given differential equation becomes

$$[D(D-1)(D-2)\ .....\ (D-n+1)$$
$$+ a_1 D(D-1)\ .....\ (D-n+2) + \ .....\ + a_n]\, y = Z;$$

or $\qquad\qquad \varphi(D)\, y = Z,$

where Z is a function of z obtained from X by the substitution

$$z = \log x.$$

Here z is the independent variable.

The equation may now be solved by the methods already given.

EXAMPLES

1. Solve : $x^3 \dfrac{d^3y}{dx^3} + 2x^2 \dfrac{d^2y}{dx^2} + 2y = 10\left(x + \dfrac{1}{x}\right).$ *(Garhwal, 2003)*

By means of the transformation $z = \log x$, the equation becomes

$$[D(D-1)(D-2) + 2D(D+1) + 2]\, y = 10\,(e^z + e^{-z});\ D = d/dz$$
$$\Rightarrow \quad (D^3 - D^2 + 2)\, y = 10\,(e^z + e^{-z}).$$

Here z is the independent and y the dependent variable.

Now, by trial, -1, is a root of the equation

$$D^3 - D^2 + 2 = 0,$$

so that $D + 1$ is a factor of $D^3 - D^2 + 2$.

In fact, we have

$$D^3 - D^2 + 2 = D^3 + D^2 - 2D^2 + 2$$
$$= D^2(D+1) - 2(D^2 - 1)$$
$$= (D+1)(D^2 - 2D + 2).$$

Now the roots of $D^2 - 2D + 2 = 0$ are $1 \pm i$.

Thus the roots of $D^3 - D^2 + 2 = 0$ are $-1, 1+i, 1-i$.

$$\therefore \quad \text{C.F.} = c_1 e^{-z} + e^z (c_2 \cos z + c_3 \sin z)$$
$$= c_1 x^{-1} + x\,(c_2 \cos \log x + c_3 \sin \log x).$$

Also   P.I. $= \dfrac{1}{D^3 - D^2 + 2} 10\,(e^z + e^{-z})$

$\qquad = 10\,\dfrac{1}{D^3 - D^2 + 2}\,e^z + 10\,\dfrac{1}{D^3 - D^2 + 2}\,e^{-z}$

$\qquad = 10\,\dfrac{1}{1^3 - 1^2 + 2}\,e^z + 10\,\dfrac{1}{(D+1)\,(D^2 - 2D + 2)}\,e^{-z}$

$\qquad = 5e^z + 2ze^{-z} = 5x + 2x^{-1}\,\log x.$

$\therefore \qquad y = c_1 x^{-1} + x\,(c_2 \cos \log x + c_3 \sin \log x) + 5x + 2x^{-1}\,\log x.$

2. Solve : $x^2 \dfrac{d^2 y}{dx^2} - 3x\,\dfrac{dy}{dx} + 4y = 2x^2.$

This is homogeneous linear differential equation. To solve it

Put $x = e^z \therefore z = \log x$ and $\dfrac{d}{dz} \equiv D;$

then $\{D\,(D-1) - 3D + 4\}\,y = 2e^{2z}$

or $(D^2 - 4D + 4)\,y = 2e^{2z}.$

Auxiliary equation is

$\qquad m^2 - 4m + 4 = 0$ or $(m-2)^2 = 0;\ m = 2, 2.$

Hence   C.F. $= (c_1 + c_2 z)\,e^{2z}.$

$\qquad$ P.I. $= \dfrac{1}{(D-2)^2}\cdot 2e^{2z} = 2e^{2z}\cdot\dfrac{1}{(D+2-2)^2}\cdot 1$

$\qquad = 2e^{2z}\cdot\dfrac{1}{D^2}\cdot 1 = 2e^{2z}\cdot\dfrac{z^2}{2} = z^2 e^{2z}.$

Hence the general solution of the given equation is

$\qquad y = (c_1 + c_2 z)\,e^{2z} + z^2 e^{2z}$

or $y = (c_1 + c_2 \log x)\,x^2 + x^2\,(\log x)^2.$

3. Solve : $(x^4 D^3 + 2x^3 D^2 - x^2 D + x)\,y = 1,$

where $D \equiv \dfrac{d}{dx}.$

The given equation can be written as

$\qquad (x^3 D^3 + 2x^2 D^2 - xD + 1)\,y = \dfrac{1}{x}.$

Put $x = e^z$ and $z = \log x$ and let $D' \equiv \dfrac{d}{dz},$

then $x^3 D^3 = D'\,(D' - 1)\,(D' - 2),\ x^2 D^2 = D'\,(D' - 1)$

and $xD = D'$, the given differential equation becomes

$$[D'(D'-1)(D'-2) + 2D'(D'-1) - D' + 1]y = \frac{1}{e^z}$$

or $(D'^3 - D'^2 - D' + 1)x = e^{-z}.$

Auxiliary equation is

$$m^3 - m^2 - m + 1 = 0$$

or $m^2(m-1) - (m-1) = 0$ or $(m-1)^2(m+1) = 0$

∴ $m = 1, 1, -1.$

∴   C.F. $= (c_1 + c_2 z)e^z + c_3 e^{-z}$

$$\text{P.I.} = \frac{e^{-z}}{(D'-1)^2(D'+1)} = \frac{e^{-z} \cdot 1}{(-1-1)^2(D'+1)}$$

$$= \frac{e^{-z}}{4} \cdot \frac{1}{(D'-1+1)} 1 = \frac{ze^{-z}}{4}.$$

Hence general solution is

$$y = (c_1 + c_2 z)e^z + c_3 e^{-z} + \frac{1}{4}ze^{-z}$$

or $y = (c_1 + c_2 \log x)x + \frac{c_3}{x} + \frac{1}{4}\frac{\log x}{x}.$

4. Solve : $x^2 \dfrac{d^2 y}{dx^2} - x\dfrac{dy}{dx} - 3y = x^2 \log x.$

(Kumaon, 1999, 2003; Rohilkhand, 2002)

Put $x = e^z$ or $\log x = z$ and $\dfrac{d}{dz} \equiv D$. The given equation reduces to

$$[D(D-1) - D - 3]y = ze^{2z}.$$

Auxiliary equation is

$$m^2 - 2m - 3 = 0 \therefore m = 3, -1.$$

∴   C.F. $= c_1 e^{3z} + c_2 e^{-z} = c_1 x^3 + \dfrac{c_2}{x}$

$$\text{P.I.} = \frac{1}{(D-3)(D+1)} \cdot ze^{2z}$$

$$= e^{2z} \cdot \frac{1}{(D+2-3)(D+2+1)} \cdot z$$

$$= e^{2z} \cdot \frac{1}{(D-1)(D+3)} \cdot z$$

$$= -\frac{1}{3}e^{2z}(1-D)^{-1}\left(1 + \frac{D}{3}\right)^{-1} \cdot z$$

$$= -\frac{1}{3} e^{2z} (1 + D + ...)\left(1 - \frac{D}{3} + ...\right)z$$

$$= -\frac{1}{3} e^{2z} \left(1 + \frac{2D}{3} + ...\right)z$$

$$= -\frac{1}{3} e^{2z} \left(z + \frac{2}{3}\right)$$

$$= -\frac{1}{9} x^2 (3 \log x + 2).$$

$\therefore \quad y = \text{C.F.} + \text{P.I.}$

i.e., $\qquad y = c_1 x^3 + \dfrac{c_2}{x} - \dfrac{1}{9} x^2 (3 \log x + 2).$

5. *Solve* : $(x^2 D^2 + 3xD + 1) y = \dfrac{1}{(1-x)^2}.$ $\qquad$ *(Rewa, 1999)*

Put $x = e^z$, so that $z = \log x$ and if $\dfrac{d}{dz} \equiv D'$ (say), then the given equation reduces to

$$[D'(D'-1) + 3D' + 1] y = \frac{1}{(1-e^z)^2}$$

or $\qquad\qquad (D'+1)^2 = \dfrac{1}{(1-e^z)^2}.$

Auxiliary equation is

$$(m+1)^2 = 0, \; i.e., \; m = -1, -1.$$

$\therefore \quad$ C.F. $= (c_1 + c_2 z) e^{-z} = (c_1 + c_2 \log x) \dfrac{1}{x}$

$$\text{P.I.} = \frac{1}{(D'+1)^2} \cdot \frac{1}{(1-e^z)^2} \qquad\qquad ...(i)$$

Let us put $\qquad \dfrac{1}{(D'+1)} \cdot \dfrac{1}{(1-e^z)^2} = u$

$\therefore \qquad\qquad \dfrac{du}{dz} + u = \dfrac{1}{(1-e^z)^2}$ because $D' \equiv \dfrac{d}{dz}.$

This equation is linear and I.F. $= e^{\int 1 \cdot dz} = e^z.$

Hence solution of this equation will be

$$u \cdot e^z = \int \frac{e^z}{(1-e^z)^2} dz = \frac{1}{(1-e^z)}$$

$\therefore \quad u = \dfrac{1}{e^z (1-e^z)}$

$$\therefore \quad \text{P.I.} = \frac{1}{(D'+1)}\left[\frac{1}{(D'+1)}\cdot\frac{1}{(1-e^z)^2}\right] \qquad \text{[From } (i)\text{]}$$

$$= \frac{1}{(D'+1)}\,u = \frac{1}{(D+1)}\cdot\frac{1}{e^z(1-e^z)}$$

$$= v \text{ (say)}$$

$$\therefore \quad \frac{dv}{dz} + v = \frac{1}{e^z(1-e^z)}.$$

Proceeding as above,

$$u \cdot e^z = \int e^z \cdot \frac{1}{e^z(1-e^z)}\,dz.$$

Put $e^z = t$ $\therefore$ $e^z\,dz = dt$

$$= \int \frac{dt}{t(1-t)} = \int\left(\frac{1}{t}+\frac{1}{1-t}\right)dt$$

$$= \log t - \log(1-t)$$

$$\therefore \qquad v = \frac{1}{e^z}[\log e^z - \log(1-e^z)]$$

$$= \frac{1}{x}[\log x - \log(1-x)]$$

$$= \frac{1}{x}\log\frac{x}{1-x}.$$

Hence the general solution is

$$y = (c_1 + c_2 \log x)\frac{1}{x} + \frac{1}{x}\log\frac{x}{1-x}.$$

6. *Solve* : $x^2\dfrac{d^2y}{dx^2} + 4x\dfrac{dy}{dx} + 2y = e^x.$

Putting $x = e^z$, $z = \log x$ and $\dfrac{d}{dz} \equiv D$, we get

$$\{D(D-1) + 4D + 2\}\,y = e^{e^z}$$

or $\qquad (D^2 + 3D + 2)\,y = e^{e^z}.$

Auxiliary equation is

$$m^2 + 3m + 2 = 0 \quad \therefore \quad m = -1, -2.$$

$$\therefore \quad \text{C.F.} = c_1 e^{-z} + c_2 e^{-2z} = c_1 x^{-1} + c_2 x^{-2}.$$

$$\text{P.I.} = \frac{1}{(D+2)}\left(\frac{1}{D+1}e^{e^z}\right).$$

Let $\dfrac{1}{D+1} e^{e^z} = u$

$\therefore \quad \dfrac{du}{dz} + u = e^{e^z}.$

This is linear equation whose I.F. $= e^z$.

$\therefore \quad u \cdot e^z = \displaystyle\int e^{e^z} \cdot e^z \, dz = e^{e^z}$

$\therefore \quad u = e^{e^z} \cdot e^{-z}$

$\therefore \quad \text{P.I.} = \dfrac{1}{D+2} \cdot (e^{e^z} \cdot e^{-z}) = v \text{ say}$

$\therefore \quad \dfrac{dv}{dz} + 2v = e^{e^z} \cdot e^{-z}.$

This is again a linear equation where I.F. $= e^{2z}$.

$\therefore \quad v \cdot e^{2z} = \displaystyle\int e^{e^z} \cdot e^{-z} \cdot e^{2z} \, dz$

$\qquad\qquad = \displaystyle\int e^{e^z} \cdot e^z \, dz = e^{e^z}$

or $\qquad v = e^{e^z} \cdot e^{-2z} = \dfrac{e^x}{x^2}.$

$\therefore$ General solution of the equation is

$$y = c_1 x^{-1} + c_2 x^{-2} + \dfrac{e^x}{x^2}.$$

7. Solve : $x^2 \dfrac{d^2 y}{dx^2} + 7x \dfrac{dy}{dx} + 13y = \log x.$

(Bilaspur, 1997; Jabalpur, 1997;
Ravishankar, 1999S, 2001; Bhoj, 1999; Garhwal, 2001)

Given differential equation is

$$x^2 \dfrac{d^2 y}{dx^2} + 7x \dfrac{dy}{dx} + 13y = \log x \qquad\qquad ...(i)$$

which is a linear homogeneous differential equation of second order.

Hence, putting $x = e^z$, i.e., $z = \log x$, we get

$$x \dfrac{d}{dx} = D, \quad x^2 \dfrac{d^2}{dx^2} = D(D-1).$$

Hence (i) reduces in the form

$$[D(D-1) + 7D + 13] y = z$$

or $\qquad (D^2 + 6D + 13) y = z \qquad\qquad ...(ii)$

which is a linear differential equation, with constant coefficient, whose independent variable is y.

$$D \equiv \frac{d}{dz}.$$

Hence its auxiliary equation is

$$m^2 + 6m + 13 = 0$$

$$\Rightarrow \quad m = \frac{-6 \pm \sqrt{36-52}}{2} = \frac{-6 \pm 4i}{2} = -3 \pm 2i.$$

Hence, its C.F. $= e^{-3z}(c_1 \cos 2z + c_2 \sin 2z)$

and $\quad$ P.I. $= \dfrac{1}{D^2 + 6D + 13} \cdot z$

$$= \frac{1}{13}\left(1 + \frac{D^2 + 6D}{13}\right)^{-1} z = \frac{1}{13}\left(1 - \frac{6}{13}D\right)z$$

$$= \frac{1}{13}\left(z - \frac{6}{13}\right).$$

Hence, general solution of (ii) becomes

$$y = \text{C.F.} + \text{P.I.}$$

$$\Rightarrow \quad y = e^{-3z}(c_1 \cos 2z + c_2 \sin 2z) + \frac{1}{13}z - \frac{6}{169}.$$

Putting back the value of $z = \log x$ and simplifying, we get the general solution of (i) as

$$y = x^{-3}[c_1 \cos(2 \log x) + c_2 \sin(2 \log x)] + \frac{1}{13}\log x - \frac{6}{169}.$$

8. Solve : $x^2 \dfrac{d^2 y}{dx^2} + x \dfrac{dy}{dx} - y = x^2 e^x.$

(Bhopal, 2000; Indore, 2000; Jiwaji, 1999)

Given differential equation is :

$$x^2 \frac{d^2 y}{dx^2} + x \frac{dy}{dx} - y = x^2 e^x \qquad \qquad ...(i)$$

Putting $x = e^z$ or $z = \log_e x$, we get

$$[D(D-1) + D - 1]y = e^{2z} \cdot e^{e^z}$$

or $\quad (D^2 - 1)y = e^{2z} \cdot e^{e^z} \qquad \qquad ...(ii)$

where $\quad D \equiv \dfrac{d}{dz}.$

Auxiliary equation is $m^2 - 1 = 0 \Rightarrow m = \pm 1.$

$\therefore \quad$ C.F. $= c_1 e^z + c_2 e^{-z} = c_1 x + c_2 x^{-1}$

and $\quad$ P.I. $= \dfrac{1}{D^2-1} e^{2z} \cdot e^{e^z} = \dfrac{1}{(D-1)(D+1)} e^{2z} e^{e^z}$

$\qquad = \dfrac{1}{2}\left[\dfrac{1}{D-1} - \dfrac{1}{D+1}\right] e^{2z} e^{e^z}$

$\qquad = \dfrac{1}{2}\left[\dfrac{1}{D-1} e^{2z} e^{e^z} - \dfrac{1}{D+1} e^{2z} e^{e^z}\right]$

$\qquad = \dfrac{1}{2}\left[e^z \int e^{-z}(e^{2z} e^{e^z})\,dz - e^{-z} \int e^z (e^{2z} e^{e^z})\,dz\right]$

$\qquad = \dfrac{1}{2}\left[e^z \int e^z e^{e^z}\,dz - e^{-z} \int (e^z)^2\, e^{e^z} \cdot e^z\,dz\right]$

$$\left[\because\ z = \log x\ \therefore\ dz = \dfrac{1}{x}\,dx\right]$$

$\qquad = \dfrac{1}{2}\left[x \int xe^x \cdot \dfrac{1}{x}\,dx - x^{-1} \int x^2 e^x \cdot x \cdot \dfrac{1}{x}\,dx\right]$

$\qquad = \dfrac{1}{2}\left[xe^x - x^{-1} \int x^2 e^x\,dx\right]$

$\qquad = \dfrac{1}{2}\left[xe^x - x^{-1}\left(x^2 e^x - \int 2xe^x\,dx\right)\right]$

$\qquad = \dfrac{1}{2}\left[xe^x - x^{-1} x^2 e^x - 2\int xe^x\,dx\right]$

$\qquad = \dfrac{1}{2}\left[xe^x - xe^x + 2x^{-1}\left(xe^x - \int 1 \cdot e^x\,dx\right)\right]$

$\qquad = \dfrac{1}{2}[xe^x - xe^x + 2x^{-1}(xe^x - e^x)]$

$\qquad = e^x(x^{-1}x - x^{-1})$

$\qquad = e^x(1 - x^{-1}).$

Hence the general solution of the equation (i) is

$$y = \text{C.F.} + \text{P.I.} = c_1 x + c_2 x^{-1} + e^x(1-x)^{-1}.$$

EXERCISES

Solve

1. $x^2 \dfrac{d^2 y}{dx^2} + 7x \dfrac{dy}{dx} + 5y = 2x^6.$

2. $x^2 \dfrac{d^2 y}{dx^2} + x \dfrac{dy}{dx} - 4y = x^3.$

3. $x^2 \dfrac{d^2 y}{dx^2} + 3x \dfrac{dy}{dx} + y = (1-x)^2.$

4. $x^2 \dfrac{d^2y}{dx^2} - 2x \dfrac{dy}{dx} + 2y = x + x^2 \log x + x^3$.

5. $x^2 \dfrac{d^2y}{dx^2} + 2x \dfrac{dy}{dx} - 20y = (x+1)^2$.

6. $x^2 \dfrac{d^2y}{dx^2} + x \dfrac{dy}{dx} - y = x^m$.

7. $(x^3D^3 + 3x^2D^2 - 2xD + 2)\, y = 0$.   *(Kumaon, 2000)*

8. $x^2 \dfrac{d^2y}{dx^2} + 7x \dfrac{dy}{dx} + 5y = x^5$.

9. $x^2 \dfrac{d^2y}{dx^2} - 2x \dfrac{dy}{dx} - 4y = x^2$.

10. $x^2 \dfrac{d^2y}{dx^2} - 5x \dfrac{dy}{dx} + 4y = x^4$.

11. $x^2 \dfrac{d^2y}{dx^2} + 2x \dfrac{dy}{dx} = \log x$.

12. $x^2 \dfrac{d^2y}{dx^2} - 2x \dfrac{dy}{dx} + 2y = x^{-1}$.   *(Jabalpur, 1999)*

13. $x^2 \dfrac{d^2y}{dx^2} - x \dfrac{dy}{dx} + y = 2 \log x$.

14. $x^3 \dfrac{d^3y}{dx^3} + 2x^2 \dfrac{d^2y}{dx^2} + x \dfrac{dy}{dx} - y = \cos(\log x)$.

15. $x^2 \dfrac{d^2y}{dx^2} + 6x \dfrac{dy}{dx} + 6y = (\log x)^2$.

16. $x^2 \dfrac{d^2y}{dx^2} + 5x \dfrac{dy}{dx} + 4y = x \log x$.

         (Agra, 2000; Bhopal, 1997; Ravishankar, 2000)

17. $x^2 \dfrac{d^2y}{dx^2} - x \dfrac{dy}{dx} + 2y = x \log x$.

         (Bundelkhand, 1995; Lucknow, 1997)

18. $(x^4D^4 + 6x^3D^3 + 9x^2D^2 + 3xD + 1)\, y = (1 + \log x)^2$.

19. $x^3 \dfrac{d^3y}{dx^3} + 3x^2 \dfrac{d^2y}{dx^2} + x \dfrac{dy}{dx} + y = x + \log x$.   *(Indore, 1998)*

20. $x^2 \dfrac{d^2y}{dx^2} + 4x \dfrac{dy}{dx} + 2y = x + \log x$.   *(Rewa, 1999)*

ANSWERS

1. $y = ax^{-5} - bx^{-2} + \dfrac{2}{77}x^6$.   **2.** $y = ax^2 + bx^{-2} + \dfrac{1}{5}x^3$.

3. $y = (a + b \log x) x^{-1} + 1 - \dfrac{1}{2}x + \dfrac{1}{9}x^2$.

4. $y = ax^2 + bx + \dfrac{1}{2}x^3 - x \log x + x^2 \left[\dfrac{1}{2}(\log x)^2 - \log x \right]$.

5. $y = c_1 x^4 + c_2 x^{-5} - \dfrac{1}{14}x^2 - \dfrac{1}{9}x - \dfrac{1}{20}$.

6. $y = ax + bx^{-1} + \dfrac{x^m}{(m^2 - 1)}$.   **7.** $y = x (c_1 + c_2 \log x) + c_3 x^{-2}$.

8. $y = c_1 x^{-3} + c_2 x^{-2} + \dfrac{x^5}{20}$.   **9.** $y = (a + b \log x) x^{-2} + \dfrac{x^4}{36}$.

10. $y = c_1 x^4 + \dfrac{c_2}{x} + \dfrac{x^4 \log x}{5}$.   **11.** $y = c_1 + \dfrac{c_2}{x} + \dfrac{(\log x)^2}{2} - \log x$.

12. $y = ax + bx^2 - \dfrac{1}{6}x^{-1}$.   **13.** $y = x (a + b \log x) + 2 \log x + 4$.

14. $y = c_1 x + c_2 \cos (\log x) + c_3 \sin (\log x)$

$$+ \dfrac{1}{4} \log x \{\cos (\log x) - \sin (\log x)\}.$$

15. $y = c_1 e^{-2x} + c_2 e^{-3x} + \dfrac{1}{108}\{18 (\log x)^2 - 30 (\log x) + 19\}$.

16. $y = (a + b \log x) x^{-2} + \dfrac{x}{3}(\log x - 2/3)$.

17. $y = \{a \cos (\log x) + b \sin (\log x)\} + x \log x$.

18. $y = (c_1 + c_2 \log x) \cos (\log x) + (c_3 + c_4 \log x) \sin (\log x)$

$$+ (\log x)^3 + 2 (\log x) - 3.$$

19. $y = ax^{-1} + b \sqrt{x}\left\{\cos \dfrac{\sqrt{3}}{2}(\log x) + c\right\}$.

20. $y = ax^{-1} + bx^{-2} + \dfrac{1}{6}x + \dfrac{1}{2}\log x - \dfrac{3}{2}$.

18.11. Equations Reducible to Homogeneous Form.

Any equation of the form

$$(a + bx)^n \dfrac{d^n y}{dx^n} + P_1 (a + bx)^{n-1} \dfrac{d^{n-1}y}{dx^{n-1}} + \dots + P_{n-1} (a + bx) \dfrac{dy}{dx} + P_n y$$

$$= F(x) \qquad \qquad \dots(i)$$

where the coefficients P_1, P_2, ..., P_n are constants, can be transformed into homogeneous linear equation with constant coefficient by changing independent variable from x to z, by the substitution $a + bx = z$. For, on letting $a + bx = z$, we have

$$\frac{dy}{dx} = \frac{dy}{dz} \cdot \frac{dz}{dx} = b \frac{dy}{dz}$$

$$\frac{d^2 y}{dx^2} = \frac{d}{dx}\left(\frac{dy}{dx}\right) = \frac{d}{dz}\left(b \frac{dy}{dz}\right)\frac{dz}{dx}$$

$$= b^2 \frac{d^2 y}{dz^2}$$

$$\cdots\cdots = \cdots\cdots$$

$$\frac{d^n y}{dx^n} = b^n \frac{d^n y}{dz^n}.$$

Substituting these in (i) and dividing throughout by b^n, we obtain

$$z^n \frac{d^n y}{dz^n} + \frac{P_1}{b} z^{n-1} \frac{d^{n-1} y}{dz^{n-1}} + \frac{P_2}{b^2} z^{n-2} \frac{d^{n-2} y}{dz^{n-2}} + \dots + \frac{P_{n-1}}{b^{n-1}} z \frac{dy}{dz} + \frac{P_n}{b^n} y$$

$$= \frac{1}{b^n} F \cdot \left(\frac{z-a}{b}\right) \qquad\qquad \dots(ii)$$

This equation can be solved by the method of § 18.10

EXAMPLES

1. *Solve* : $(x + a)^2 \dfrac{d^2 y}{dx^2} - 4(x + a)\dfrac{dy}{dx} + 6y = x.$ (*Lucknow, 1996*)

Put $x + a = e^z$ so that $z = \log(x + a)$ and if D stands for $\dfrac{d}{dz}$, then b being equal to unity the above equation reduces to

$$[1^2 D (D-1) - 4 \cdot 1 \cdot D + 6] y = e^x - a$$

or $(D^2 - 5D + 6) y = e^z - ae^{0 \cdot z}.$

Auxiliary equation is $m^2 - 5m + 6 = 0$ or $m = 2, 3$.

∴   C.F. $= c_1 e^{2z} + c_2 e^{3z}$

$$= c_1 (x + a)^2 + c_2 (x + a)^3.$$

P.I. $= \dfrac{1}{D^2 - 5D + 6} e^z - ae^{0 \cdot z}$

$$= \frac{1}{1 - 5 + 6} e^z - \frac{a}{6}$$

$$= \frac{1}{2} e^z - \frac{a}{6} = \frac{1}{2}(x + a) - \frac{1}{6} a.$$

$$\therefore \quad y = c_1 (x+a)^2 + c_2 (x+a)^3 + \frac{1}{2}(x+a) - \frac{1}{6}a.$$

2. Solve : $(3x+2)^2 \dfrac{d^2 y}{dx^2} + 3(3x+2)\dfrac{dy}{dx} - 36y = 3x^2 + 4x + I.$

(Kanpur, 2000)

Put $3x + 2 = e^z$, $\dfrac{d}{dz} \equiv D$ and $x = \dfrac{1}{3}(e^z - 2)$, we get

$$[3^2 \, D(D-1) + 3(3D) - 36]\, y = 3\left(\frac{e^z - 2}{3}\right)^2 + \frac{4}{3}(e^z - 2) + 1$$

or
$$(D^2 - 4) = \frac{1}{27}(e^{2z} - 1).$$

Auxiliary equation is $m^2 - 4 = 0$ or $m = \pm 2$.

$$\therefore \quad \text{C.F.} = c_1 e^{2z} + c_2 e^{-2z} = c_1 (3x+2)^2 + c_2 (3x+2)^{-2}.$$

$$\text{P.I.} = \frac{1}{(D^2 - 4)} \frac{1}{27}(e^{2z} - 1) = \frac{1}{27}\left[z \cdot \frac{1}{2D} e^{2z} - \frac{1}{-4} \cdot 1 \right]$$

$$= \frac{1}{27}\left[\frac{1}{4} z e^{2z} + \frac{1}{4}\right] = \frac{1}{108}[(3x+2)^2 \log(3x+2) + 1].$$

$$\therefore \quad y = c_1 (3x+2)^2 + c_2 (3x+2)^{-2}$$

$$+ \frac{1}{108}[(3x+2)^2 \log(3x+2) + 1].$$

EXERCISES

Solve the following differential equations :

1. $(5+2x)^2 \dfrac{d^2 y}{dx^2} - 6(5+2x)\dfrac{dy}{dx} + 8y = 0.$

2. $(1+2x)^2 \dfrac{d^2 y}{dx^2} - 6(1+2x)\dfrac{dy}{dx} + 16y = 8(1+2x)^2.$

3. $16(x+1)^4 \dfrac{d^4 y}{dx^4} + 96(x+1)^3 \dfrac{d^3 y}{dx^3} + 104(x+1)^2 \dfrac{d^2 y}{dx^2}$

$$+ 8(x+1)\frac{dy}{dx} + y = x^2 + 4x + 3.$$

4. $(1+x)^2 \dfrac{d^2 y}{dx^2} + (1+x)\dfrac{dy}{dx} + x = 4 \cos \log (1+x).$

(Ravishankar, 1997)

5. $(3x+2)^2 \dfrac{d^2 y}{dx^2} + 5(3x+2)\dfrac{dy}{dx} - 3y = x^2 + x + 1.$

ANSWERS

1. $y = (5 + 2x)^2 [c_1 (5 + 2x)^{\sqrt{2}} + c_2 (5 + 2x)^{-\sqrt{2}}]$.

2. $y = \{c_1 + c_2 \log (1 + 2x)\} (1 + 2x)^2 + (1 + 2x)^2 \{\log (1 + 2x)\}^2$.

3. $y = (c_1 + c_2 z) e^{z/2} + (c_3 + c_4 z) e^{-z/2} + \dfrac{e^{2z}}{225} + \dfrac{2}{9} e^z$,

where $z = \log (1 + x)$.

4. $y = c_1 \cos \log (1 + x) + c_2 \sin \log (1 + x)$

$$+ 2 \log (1 + x) \sin \log (1 + x).$$

5. $y = c_1 (3x + 2)^{1/3} + c_2 (3x + 2)^{-1} + \dfrac{(3x + 2)^2}{405} - \dfrac{(3x + 2)}{108} - \dfrac{7}{27}$.

EXERCISES OF CHAPTER 18

Solve :

1. $\dfrac{d^2 y}{dx^2} - 2m \dfrac{dy}{dx} + m^2 y = \sin nx.$

2. $\dfrac{d^2 y}{dx^2} + 4y = \sin 3x \cos x.$

3. $\dfrac{d^2 y}{dx^2} - 6 \dfrac{dy}{dx} + 8y = (e^{2x} - 1)^2.$

4. Find the solution of the equation

$$\dfrac{d^2 y}{dx^2} - y = 1,$$

which vanishes when $x = 0$ and tends to a finite limit as $x \to -\infty$.

5. $4 \dfrac{d^2 y}{dx^2} - y = 2 \sin \left(x + \dfrac{1}{3} \pi \right).$

6. $\dfrac{d^2 y}{dx^2} - 4 \dfrac{dy}{dx} - 13y = e^{x/2} - \sin \dfrac{1}{3} x.$

7. $4 \dfrac{d^2 y}{dx^2} - 4 \dfrac{dy}{dx} + 2y = \cos^2 \left(x + \dfrac{1}{6} \pi \right).$

8. $\dfrac{d^2 y}{dx^2} - 4 \dfrac{dy}{dx} + y = e^{2x} \sin 2x.$

9. $\dfrac{d^4 y}{dx^4} - y = e^x \cos x.$

10. $\dfrac{d^4 y}{dx^4} + 2 \dfrac{d^2 y}{dx^2} + y = x^2 \cos x.$

11. $(D^3 - 1) y = xe^x + \cos^2 x$.

12. $\dfrac{d^2 y}{dx^2} + \dfrac{dy}{dx} + y = \cos 2x + x^2$.

13. $\dfrac{d^2 y}{dx^2} + y = xe^{2x}$.

14. $(D^2 + 4) y = x \cos 2x$.

15. $(D^2 + 3D + 2) y = x^2 \cos x$.

16. $(D^2 - 4D - 5) y = xe^{-x}$.

17. $(D^2 + 9) y = \cos^2 \dfrac{3x}{2}$.

18. $(D^5 + D^4 + 4D^3 + 4D^2 + 4D + 4) y = \cos 3x \cos x$.

19. $(x^2 D^2 + xD - 4) y = x^2$.

20. $(x^3 D^3 + 3x^2 D^2 + xD + 1) y = x \log x$.

21. $x \dfrac{d^3 y}{dx^3} + \dfrac{d^2 y}{dx^2} = \dfrac{1}{x}$.

22. $\dfrac{d^2 y}{dx^2} - \dfrac{6}{x^2} y = x \log x$.

23. $(x + 1)^2 \dfrac{d^2 y}{dx^2} - 3(x + 1) \dfrac{dy}{dx} + 4y = x^2$.

24. $x^2 D^2 y - 3xDy + 5y = x^2 \sin(\log x)$.

25. $(x + 3)^2 \dfrac{d^2 y}{dx^2} - 4(x + 3) \dfrac{dy}{dx} + 6y = x$.

26. $(D^4 + D^2 + 1) y = e^{(-x/2)} \cos \dfrac{x \sqrt{3}}{2}$.

ANSWERS

1. $y = (a + bx) e^{mx} + \dfrac{(m^2 - n^2) \sin nx + 2mn \cos nx}{(m^2 + n^2)^2}$.

2. $y = a \cos 2x + b \sin 2x - \dfrac{1}{24} \sin 4x - \dfrac{1}{8} x \cos 2x$.

3. $y = ae^{4x} + be^{2x} + \dfrac{1}{8} + \dfrac{1}{2} xe^{4x} + xe^{2x}$.

4. $y = e^x - 1$.

5. $y = ae^{-x/2} + be^{-x/2} - \dfrac{1}{5} (\sin x + \sqrt{3} \cos x)$.

6. $y = ae^{(2+\sqrt{17})x} + be^{(2-\sqrt{17})x} - \dfrac{4}{59} e^{\frac{1}{2}x}$

$$- \dfrac{9}{7034}\left(-59 \sin \dfrac{1}{3}x + 6 \cos \dfrac{1}{3}x\right).$$

7. $y = \left(a \cos \dfrac{x}{2} + b \sin \dfrac{x}{2}\right) e^{\frac{1}{2}x} + \dfrac{1}{4} - \dfrac{1}{520}[(7 + 4\sqrt{3}) \cos 2x$

$$+ (4 - 7\sqrt{3}) \sin 2x].$$

8. $y = ae^{(2+\sqrt{3})x} + be^{(2-\sqrt{3})x} - \dfrac{1}{7} e^{2x} \sin 2x.$

9. $y = ae^{-x} + be^{x} + c \cos x + d \sin x - \dfrac{e^{x}}{5} \cos x.$

10. $y = (a + bx) \cos x + (c + dx) \sin x - \dfrac{1}{48}(9x^2 - x^4) \cos x$

$$+ \dfrac{1}{12} x^3 \sin x.$$

11. $y = ae^{x} + \left(b \cos \dfrac{\sqrt{3}}{2}x + c \sin \dfrac{\sqrt{3}}{2}x\right) e^{-\frac{1}{2}x} - \dfrac{1}{2}$

$$+ \dfrac{1}{3}\left(\dfrac{1}{2}x^2 - x\right) e^{x} - \dfrac{1}{130}(8 \sin 2x + \cos 2x).$$

12. $y = \left(a \cos \dfrac{\sqrt{3}}{2}x + b \sin \dfrac{\sqrt{3}}{2}x\right) e^{-\frac{1}{2}x} - \dfrac{1}{13}(3 \cos 2x - 2 \sin 2x)$

$$+ (x^2 - 2x).$$

13. $y = (a \cos x + b \sin x) + \dfrac{1}{5}\left(x - \dfrac{4}{5}\right) e^{2x}.$

14. $y = (a \cos 2x + b \sin 2x) + \dfrac{1}{16} x \cos 2x + \dfrac{1}{8} x^2 \sin 2x.$

15. $y = ae^{-2x} + be^{-2x} + \dfrac{1}{10}(\cos x + 3 \sin x) x^2$

$$- \dfrac{1}{25}(17 \sin x - 6 \cos x) + \dfrac{1}{250}(81 \sin x - 133 \cos x).$$

16. $y = ae^{5x} + be^{-x} - \dfrac{1}{36} x (1 + 3x) e^{-x}.$

17. $y = a \cos 3x + b \sin 3x + \dfrac{1}{36}(3x \sin 3x + 2).$

18. $y = ae^{-x} + (bx + c) \cos \sqrt{2}\, x + (dx + e) \sin \sqrt{2}\, x$

$$+ \frac{1}{6664} (\cos 4x + 4 \sin 4x) + \frac{1}{40} (\cos 2x + 2 \sin 2x).$$

19. $y = ax^2 + bx^{-2} + \frac{1}{4} x^2 \log x.$

20. $y = ax^{-1} + \sqrt{x} \left[b \cos \left(\frac{1}{2} \sqrt{3} \log x \right) + c \sin \left(\frac{1}{2} \sqrt{3} \log x \right) \right]$

$$+ \frac{1}{2} x \log x - \frac{3x}{4}.$$

21. $y = a + (b \log x + c) x + \frac{1}{2} x (\log x)^2.$

22. $y = ax^3 + bx^{-2} + \frac{1}{50} (5 \log x - 2) x^3 \log x.$

23. $y = (x + 1)^2 [a \log (x + 1) + b]$

$$+ \frac{1}{4} [2 (x + 1)^2 \{\log (x + 1)\}^2 - 8x - 7].$$

24. $y = x^2 [a \cos (\log x) + b \sin (\log x)] - \frac{1}{2} x^2 \log x \cos (\log x).$

25. $y = a (x + 3)^2 + b (x + 3)^3 + \frac{1}{2} (x + 2).$

26. $y = e^{-\frac{1}{2}x} \left\{ \left(\frac{1}{4} x + a \right) \cos \frac{x \sqrt{3}}{2} + \left(b + \frac{x}{4\sqrt{3}} \right) \sin \frac{x \sqrt{3}}{2} \right\}$

$$+ ce^{\frac{1}{2}x} \cos \left(\frac{x \sqrt{3}}{2} + d \right).$$

OBJECTIVE QUESTIONS

To each of the following questions, four alternatives are given for the answer. Only one of them is correct. Choose the correct alternative.

1. A differential equation in which the dependent variable and its derivatives occur only in the first degree and no products of them occur is called a .... differential equation :

   (a) homogeneous   (b) exact

   (c) linear   (d) non-linear.

2. If $f(D)\, y = 0$ be a linear differential equation with constant coefficient, then its auxiliary equation is :

   (a) $f(D - m) = 0$ (b) $f(m) = 8$

   (c) $f(e^m) = 0$ (d) $f(x) = 0.$

3. If m_1 and m_2 are two different real roots of the auxiliary equation, then the corresponding part in the complementary function is :

   (a) $c_1 x^{m_1} + c_2 x^{m_2}$
   (b) $c_1 e^{m_1 x} + c_2 e^{m_2 x}$
   (c) $(c_1 + c_2 x) e^{m_1 x}$
   (d) $c_1 e^{m_1 x} + c_2 x e^{m_2 x}$.

4. If $\alpha \pm i\beta$ are complex roots of the auxiliary equation, then the corresponding part in the C.F. is :

   (a) $c_1 e^{\alpha x} (\beta x + c_2)$
   (b) $c_1 e^{\beta x} \cos(\alpha x + c_2)$
   (c) $c_1 e^{\alpha x} \sin(\beta x + c_2)$
   (d) $c_1 e^{\beta x} \sin(\alpha x + c_2)$.

   (Kanpur, 2001)

5. The general solution of $(D^2 - m^2) y = 0$ is :

   (a) $y = (c_1 + c_2 x) e^{mx}$
   (b) $y = c_1 \sin mx + c_2 \cos mx$
   (c) $c_1 e^{mx} + c_2 e^{-mx}$
   (d) None of these.

6. The general solution of $\dfrac{d^2 y}{dx^2} + n^2 y = 0$ is :

   (a) $y = c_1 \sqrt{\cos nx} + c_2 \sqrt{\sin nx}$
   (b) $y = c_1 \cos nx + c_2 \sin nx$
   (c) $y = c_1 \cos^2 nx + c_2 \sin^2 nx$
   (d) $y = c_1 e^{nx} + c_2 e^{-nx}$.

7. $\dfrac{1}{D - m} Q$ is equal to :

   (a) $e^{mx} \displaystyle\int Q \, dx$
   (b) $e^{-mx} \displaystyle\int Q e^{mx} \, dx$
   (c) $e^{-mx} \displaystyle\int Q \, dx$
   (d) $e^{mx} \displaystyle\int Q e^{-mx} \, dx$.

8. The solution of the differential equation $\dfrac{d^2 y}{dx^2} - 4\dfrac{dy}{dx} + 4y = 0$ is :

   (a) $y = (A_1 + A_2 x) e^{2x}$
   (b) $y = (A_1 + A_2 x) e^{-2x}$
   (c) $y = A_1 e^{2x} + A_2 e^{-2x}$
   (d) $y = (A_1 - A_2 x) e^{-2x}$.

   (Garhwal, 2003)

9. The solution of the differential equation $\dfrac{d^2 y}{dx^2} - 7\dfrac{dy}{dx} - 44y = 0$ is :

   (a) $y = c_1 e^{-11x} + c_2 e^{-4x}$
   (b) $y = c_1 e^{11x} + c_2 e^{-4x}$
   (c) $y = c_1 e^{11x} + c_2 e^{4x}$
   (d) $y = c_1 e^{-11x} + c_2 e^{4x}$.

10. The solution of the differential equation $\dfrac{d^2 y}{dx^2} + 4y = 0$ is :

    (a) $y = c_1 e^{2x} + c_2 e^{-2x}$
    (b) $y = c_1 e^{-2x} - c_2 e^{2x}$
    (c) $y = c_1 \cos 2x + c_2 \sin 2x$
    (d) $y = c_1 \cosh 2x + c_2 \sinh 2x$.

    (Avadh, 2002)

11. P.I. of the differential equation $(D^2 - 3D + 2) y = e^{5x}$ is :

    (a) e^{5x} (b) $\dfrac{1}{12} e^{5x}$ (c) $\dfrac{1}{6} e^{5x}$ (d) $\dfrac{1}{4} e^{5x}$.

12. P.I. of the differential equation $\dfrac{d^2 y}{dx^2} + \dfrac{dy}{dx} + y = e^{-x}$ is :

    (a) e^{-x} (b) $- e^{-x}$ (c) $3e^{-x}$ (d) $\dfrac{1}{3} e^{-x}$.

13. P.I. of the differential equation $(D^2 + D + 1) y = \sin 2x$ is :

    (a) $\dfrac{1}{13} \sin 2x$ (b) $-\dfrac{1}{13} \cos 2x$

    (c) $-\dfrac{1}{13} (2 \cos 2x + 3 \sin 2x)$ (d) $\dfrac{1}{13} (2 \cos 2x - 3 \sin 2x)$.

14. C.F. of the differential equation $(D^2 + 1) y = e^x$ is :

    (a) $(c_1 \cos x + c_2 \sin x)$ (b) $c_1 \cos x - c_2 \sin x$

    (c) $c_1 \cosh x + c_2 \sinh x$ (d) $c_1 \cosh x - c_2 \sinh x$.

15. C.F. of the differential equation $2\dfrac{d^2 y}{dx^2} + 5\dfrac{dy}{dx} + 2y = 5 + 2x$ is :

    (a) $c_1 e^{2x} + c_2 e^{x/2}$ (b) $c_1 e^{-2x} + c_2 e^{-x/2}$

    (c) $c_1 e^{2x} + c_2 e^{-x/2}$ (d) $c_1 e^{-2x} + c_2 e^{x/2}$.

16. To solve homogeneous linear differential equations, we put :

    (a) $x = X + h, \; y = Y + k$ (b) $y = vx$

    (c) $z = \log x$ (d) None of these.

17. Solution of the homogeneous linear differential equation

$x^2 \dfrac{d^2 y}{dx^2} - 3x \dfrac{dy}{dx} + 4y = 0$ is :

    (a) $y = (c_1 + c_2 x) \, e^x$ (b) $y = (c_1 + c_2 \log x) \, x^2$

    (c) $y = c_1 e^{\frac{3}{2} x} \cos\left(\dfrac{\sqrt{7}}{2} x + c_2\right)$ (d) None of these.

18. Solution of the homogeneous differential equation

$x^2 \dfrac{d^2 y}{dx^2} - x \dfrac{dy}{dx} - 3y = 0$ is :

    (a) $c_1 x^3 + \dfrac{c_2}{x}$ (b) $c_1 x^3 + c_2 x$

    (c) $c_1 e^{3x} + c_2 e^{-x}$ (d) $c_1 e^{-3x} + c_2 e^x$.

19. When we put $z = \log x$ in a homogeneous linear differential equation, the value of $x^2 \dfrac{d^2 y}{dx^2}$ is :

(a) $z^2 \dfrac{d^2 y}{dz^2}$

(b) $z^2 \dfrac{d^2 y}{dz^2} - z \dfrac{dy}{dz}$

(c) $\dfrac{d^2 y}{dz^2} - \dfrac{dy}{dz}$

(d) $\dfrac{d^2 y}{dz^2} + \dfrac{dy}{dz}$.

20. While solving homogeneous differential equations, we put
$$x^n \dfrac{d^n y}{dx^n} = D'(D' - 1)(D' - 2) \ldots (D' - n + 1) \text{ after the substitution}$$
$z = \log x$. Here D' denotes :

(a) $\dfrac{d}{dx}$

(b) $\dfrac{d}{dz}$

(c) $\dfrac{d^2}{dx^2}$

(d) $\dfrac{d^2}{dz^2}$.

ANSWERS

1. (c)	2. (b)	3. (b)	4. (a)	5. (c)
6. (b)	7. (d)	8. (a)	9. (b)	10. (c)
11. (b)	12. (a)	13. (c)	14. (a)	15. (b)
16. (c)	17. (b)	18. (a)	19. (c)	20. (b)

MISCELLANEOUS EXERCISES IV

Solve the following differential equations :

1. $\dfrac{dy}{dx} - \dfrac{\tan y}{1 + x} = (1 + x) e^x \sec y$.

2. $(y \sin x - 1) dx + \cos x \, dy = 0$.

3. $(x + y)^2 \, dx = xy \, dy$.

4. $(x + y)^2 \, dx = dy$.

5. $2xy^2 \, dx = e^x (dy - y \, dx)$.

6. $\dfrac{x + y - a}{x + y - b} \dfrac{dy}{dx} = \dfrac{x + y + a}{x + y + b}$.

7. $\dfrac{dy}{dx} + y \cot x = \sin x$.

8. $x \dfrac{dy}{dx} - 2y = x^2 + \sin \dfrac{1}{x^2}$.

9. $x \dfrac{dy}{dx} - y = 2x^2 \operatorname{cosec} 2x$.

10. $2 \cos x \dfrac{dy}{dx} + 4y \sin x = \sin 2x$, given that $y = 0$, when $x = \pi / 3$.

11. $x \dfrac{dy}{dx} + 3y = x^4 y^3 e^{1/x^2}$.

12. $xy - \dfrac{dy}{dx} = y^3 e^{-x^2}$.

13. $\dfrac{dy}{dx} = \dfrac{y(x + y)}{x(x - y)}$.

14. $\dfrac{dy}{dx} = \dfrac{6x - 4y + 3}{3x - 2y + 1}$.

15. $\dfrac{dy}{dx} = \dfrac{2x - y + 1}{x + 2y - 3}.$ **16.** $x^2 y \dfrac{dy}{dx} = xy^2 - e^{-1/x^3}.$

17. $3e^x \tan y + (1 - e^x) \sec^2 y \dfrac{dy}{dx} = 0.$

18. $(x + y + 1)\, dy = dx.$ **19.** $x \dfrac{dy}{dx} + y \log y = xye^x.$

20. $(3x - 2y + 1)\, dx + (2x - 3y + 4)\, dy = 0.$

21. $(2xy + y - \tan y)\, dx + (x^2 - x \tan^2 y + \sec^2 y)\, dy = 0.$

22. $x \dfrac{dy}{dx} - 2y = x^2 + \tan \dfrac{1}{x^2}.$

23. Solve the equation $\dfrac{dy}{dx} + 2y \tan x = \sin x$ and find the minimum value of y if $y = 2$, when $x = 0$.

24. $(x^2 + 3x + 2) \dfrac{dy}{dx} + (2x + 1) y = (xy + 2y)^2.$

25. $(x + 2y^3) \dfrac{dy}{dx} = y.$

26. Prove that the orthogonal trajectories to

$$y = \tan x + c$$

are the curves

$$4y + 2x + \sin 2x + c = 0.$$

27. Show that each curve of the system $x^2 - y^2 = c$; cuts at right angle each curve of the system $xy = a$.

28. Show that the orthogonal trajectories of the curves

$$r \sin^2 \theta = A,$$

are the curves

$$r^2 \cos \theta = A.$$

29. Prove that

$$(r^2 - 1) \sin \theta = cr,$$

are the orthogonal trajectories of the curve

$$(r^2 + 1) \cos \theta = cr.$$

30. Find the curves in which the polar sub-tangent at any point is proportional to the radius vector at that point.

31. Find the curves in which the angle between the tangent at any point and the radius vector to that point is equal to m times the vectorial angle.

32. Find the orthogonal trajectories of the system of curves

$$\left(\frac{dy}{dx}\right)^2 = \frac{a}{x}.$$

33. Prove that the differential equation of all parabolas lying in a plane is

$$\frac{d^2}{dx^2}\left(\frac{d^2y}{dx^2}\right)^{-2/3} = 0.$$

34. Find the cartesian equation of the curve in which the perpendicular from the origin to the tangent is equal to the abscissa of the point of contact.

35. Find a curve such that the area comprised between the curve, the axis of x and any two ordinates is proportional to the arc between those ordinates.

36. Find the solution of

$$\frac{d^2y}{dx^2} + 3\frac{dy}{dx} + 2y = e^{-x},$$

that satisfies the conditions $y = 0$, $dy/dx = 0$ at $x = 0$.

37. Solve

$$x^2\frac{d^2y}{dx^2} - 3x\frac{dy}{dx} + 4y = x^2,$$

given that $y = 0$, when $x = 1$ and that $y = e^2$, when $x = e$.

38. Find the solution of

$$4xy\frac{dy}{dx} = 4y^2 - x^2,$$

for which $y = 0$ when $x = 1$.

39. Solve

$$\left(\frac{dy}{dx}\right)^2 + (\sin x + \cos x)\, y\frac{dy}{dx} + \frac{1}{2}y^2\sin 2x = 0.$$

40. Solve the equation

$$(D^3 + D^2 - 2)\, y = x^3 e^x,$$

subject to the conditions that

$$y = 0 \text{ at } x = 0 \text{ and } y \to 0 \text{ as } x \to -\infty.$$

41. Solve

$$(D^4 + 2D^2 + 1)\, y = 24x\sin x.$$

42. Solve

$$(D-1)^2\, (D^2+1)^2\, y = \sin^2\frac{1}{2}x + e^x.$$

ANSWERS

1. $(1 + x)(e^x + c) = \sin y$.

2. $y = c \cos x + \sin x$.

3. $cx^3(x + 2y) = e^{2y/x}$.

4. $x + y = \tan(x + c)$.

5. $e^x + (c + x^2)y = 0$.

6. $2(x - y + c) = (b - a)\log[(x + y)^2 - ab]$.

7. $(2y + \cos x)\sin x = c + x$.

8. $2y = cx^2 + 2x^2 \log x + x^2 \cos(x^{-2})$.

9. $y = cx + x \log \tan x$.

10. $y \sec^2 x = \sec x - 2$.

11. $y^2 x^6 (c + e^{1/x^2}) = 1$.

12. $y^2(c + 2x) = e^{x^2}$.

13. $xy^{-1} + \log xy = c$.

14. $4x - 2y - 2 \log(3x - 2y + 3) = c$.

15. $xy + y^2 - 3y = x^2 + x + c$.

16. $3y^2 + 2x^2 e^{-1/x^3} = cx^2$.

17. $\sqrt[3]{\tan y} = c(1 - e^x)$.

18. $x + y + 2 = ce^y$.

19. $x \log y = (x - 1) e^x + c$.

20. $(y - x - 1)(y + x - 3)^5 = c$.

21. $x^2 y + xy - x \tan y + \tan y = c$.

22. $xy^{-2} = \log x + \dfrac{1}{2} \cos x^{-2} + c$.

23. $y = \cos x + c \cos^2 x; \ -\dfrac{1}{4}$.

24. $x + 1 = y(x + 2)^2 + cy(x + 2)^3$.

25. $x = y^3 + cy$.

30. Equiangular spirals.

31. $r^m = a^m \sin m\theta$.

32. $(x^{3/2} + c^{3/2})^2 = \dfrac{9}{4} ay^2$.

34. $x^2 + y^2 = 2cx$.

35. The system of catenaries $y = k \cosh \dfrac{x + c}{k}$; k being the given constant of proportionality.

36. $y = (x - 1) e^{-x} + e^{-2x}$.

37. $x^2 \log x \log(ex) = 2y$.

38. $xe^{2y^2/x^2} = 1$.

39. $(cy - e^{-\sin x})(cy - e^{\cos x}) = 0$.

40. $y = e^x \left(\dfrac{x^4}{20} - \dfrac{4x^3}{25} + \dfrac{33x^2}{125} - \dfrac{144x}{625} \right)$.

41. $y = (c_1 x + c_2) \cos x + (c_3 x + c_4) \sin x - (3 \cos x + x \sin x) x^2$.

42. $y = (c_1 + c_2 x) \cos x + (c_3 + c_4 x) \sin x + \left(c_5 + c_6 x + \dfrac{1}{8} x^2 \right) e^x$

$$- \dfrac{1}{32} x^2 \sin x + \dfrac{1}{2}.$$